Florida
Life Science

interactive SCIENCE

PEARSON

Boston, Massachusetts
Chandler, Arizona
Glenview, Illinois
Upper Saddle River, New Jersey

AUTHORS

You're an author!

As you write in this science book, your answers and personal discoveries will be recorded for you to keep, making this book unique to you. That is why you are one of the primary authors of this book.

✎ **In the space below, print your name, school, town, and state. Then write a short autobiography that includes your interests and accomplishments.**

YOUR NAME

SCHOOL

TOWN, STATE

AUTOBIOGRAPHY

Your Photo

Acknowledgments appear on pages 567–571, which constitute an extension of this copyright page.

ISBN-13:   978-0-13-253400-0
ISBN-10:   0-13-253400-2
1 2 3 4 5 6 7 8 9 10 V063 14 13 12 11 10

ON THE COVER
Diving Anhingas
Anhingas are large birds—measuring almost a meter from beak to tail. They fish in warm, shallow waters. Despite their size they leave hardly a ripple on the surface when they dive deep underwater. Anhingas are considered the best fresh water diver. Unlike most water birds they lack oil glands, so they can't waterproof their feathers. This helps anhingas swim better, but it also means they have to spread their wings to dry in the sun.

Program Authors

DON BUCKLEY, M.Sc.
*Information and Communications Technology Director,
The School at Columbia University, New York, New York*
Mr. Buckley has been at the forefront of K–12 educational
technology for nearly two decades. A founder of New York City
Independent School Technologists (NYCIST) and long-time chair
of New York Association of Independent Schools' annual IT
conference, he has taught students on two continents and
created multimedia and Internet-based instructional systems
for schools worldwide.

ZIPPORAH MILLER, M.A.Ed.
*Associate Executive Director for Professional Programs
and Conferences, National Science Teachers Association,
Arlington, Virginia*
Associate executive director for professional programs and
conferences at NSTA, Ms. Zipporah Miller is a former K–12 science
supervisor and STEM coordinator for the Prince George's County
Public School District in Maryland. She is a science education
consultant who has overseen curriculum development and staff
training for more than 150 district science coordinators.

MICHAEL J. PADILLA, Ph.D.
*Associate Dean and Director, Eugene P. Moore School of
Education, Clemson University, Clemson, South Carolina*
A former middle school teacher and a leader in middle school
science education, Dr. Michael Padilla has served as president of
the National Science Teachers Association and as a writer of the
National Science Education Standards. He is professor of science
education at Clemson University. As lead author of the *Science
Explorer* series, Dr. Padilla has inspired the team in developing a
program that promotes student inquiry and meets the needs of
today's students.

KATHRYN THORNTON, Ph.D.
*Professor and Associate Dean, School of Engineering
and Applied Science, University of Virginia,
Charlottesville, Virginia*
Selected by NASA in May 1984, Dr. Kathryn Thornton is a veteran
of four space flights. She has logged over 975 hours in space,
including more than 21 hours of extravehicular activity. As an
author on the *Scott Foresman Science* series, Dr. Thornton's
enthusiasm for science has inspired teachers around the globe.

MICHAEL E. WYSESSION, Ph.D.
*Associate Professor of Earth and Planetary Science,
Washington University, St. Louis, Missouri*
An author on more than 50 scientific publications, Dr. Wysession
was awarded the prestigious Packard Foundation Fellowship and
Presidential Faculty Fellowship for his research in geophysics. Dr.
Wysession is an expert on Earth's inner structure and has mapped
various regions of Earth using seismic tomography. He is known
internationally for his work in geoscience education and outreach.

Understanding by Design Author

GRANT WIGGINS, Ed.D.
*President, Authentic Education,
Hopewell, New Jersey*
Dr. Wiggins is coauthor of *Understanding
by Design*® (UbD), a philosophy of
instructional design. UbD is a disciplined
way of thinking about curriculum design,
assessment, and instruction that moves
teaching from covering the content to
ensuring understanding. Dr. Wiggins is
one of today's most influential educational
reformers, and consults with schools,
districts, and state education departments.

Planet Diary Author

JACK HANKIN
*Science/Mathematics Teacher,
The Hilldale School, Daly City, California
Founder, Planet Diary Web site*
Mr. Hankin is the creator and writer of
Planet Diary, a science current events
Web site. Mr. Hankin is passionate about
bringing science news and environmental
awareness into classrooms. He's offered
numerous Planet Diary workshops at NSTA
and other events to train middle school
and high school teachers.

ELL Consultant

JIM CUMMINS, Ph.D.
*Professor and Canada Research Chair,
Curriculum, Teaching and Learning
department at the University of Toronto*
Dr. Cummins's research focuses on literacy
development in multilingual schools
and the role of technology in promoting
student learning across the curriculum. The
Interactive Science program incorporates
essential research-based principles for
integrating language with the teaching of
academic content based on Dr. Cummins's
instructional framework.

Reading Consultant

HARVEY DANIELS, Ph.D.
*Professor of Secondary Education,
University of New Mexico,
Albuquerque, New Mexico*
Dr. Daniels serves as an international
consultant to schools, districts, and
educational agencies. Dr. Daniels has
authored or coauthored 13 books on
language, literacy, and education. His most
recent works include *Comprehension and
Collaboration: Inquiry Circles in Action* and
*Subjects Matter: Every Teacher's Guide to
Content-Area Reading.*

Contributing Writers

Edward Aguado, Ph.D.
Professor, Department of Geography
San Diego State University
San Diego, California

Elizabeth Coolidge-Stolz, M.D.
Medical Writer
North Reading, Massachusetts

Donald L. Cronkite, Ph.D.
Professor of Biology
Hope College
Holland, Michigan

Jan Jenner, Ph.D.
Science Writer
Talladega, Alabama

Linda Cronin Jones, Ph.D.
Associate Professor of Science and Environmental Education
University of Florida
Gainesville, Florida

T. Griffith Jones, Ph.D.
Clinical Associate Professor of Science Education
College of Education
University of Florida
Gainesville, Florida

Andrew C. Kemp, Ph.D.
Teacher
Jefferson County Public Schools
Louisville, Kentucky

Matthew Stoneking, Ph.D.
Associate Professor of Physics
Lawrence University
Appleton, Wisconsin

R. Bruce Ward, Ed.D.
Senior Research Associate
Science Education Department
Harvard-Smithsonian Center for Astrophysics
Cambridge, Massachusetts

Content Reviewers

Paul D. Beale, Ph.D.
Department of Physics
University of Colorado at Boulder
Boulder, Colorado

Jeff R. Bodart, Ph.D.
Professor of Physical Sciences
Chipola College
Marianna, Florida

Joy Branlund, Ph.D.
Department of Earth Science
Southwestern Illinois College
Granite City, Illinois

Marguerite Brickman, Ph.D.
Division of Biological Sciences
University of Georgia
Athens, Georgia

Bonnie J. Brunkhorst, Ph.D.
Science Education and Geological Sciences
California State University
San Bernardino, California

Michael Castellani, Ph.D.
Department of Chemistry
Marshall University
Huntington, West Virginia

Charles C. Curtis, Ph.D.
Research Associate Professor of Physics
University of Arizona
Tucson, Arizona

Diane I. Doser, Ph.D.
Department of Geological Sciences
University of Texas
El Paso, Texas

Rick Duhrkopf, Ph.D.
Department of Biology
Baylor University
Waco, Texas

Alice K. Hankla, Ph.D.
The Galloway School
Atlanta, Georgia

Mark Henriksen, Ph.D.
Physics Department
University of Maryland
Baltimore, Maryland

Chad Hershock, Ph.D.
Center for Research on Learning and Teaching
University of Michigan
Ann Arbor, Michigan

Jeremiah N. Jarrett, Ph.D.
Department of Biology
Central Connecticut State University
New Britain, Connecticut

Scott L. Kight, Ph.D.
Department of Biology
Montclair State University
Montclair, New Jersey

Jennifer O. Liang, Ph.D.
Department of Biology
University of Minnesota–Duluth
Duluth, Minnesota

Candace Lutzow-Felling, Ph.D.
Director of Education
The State Arboretum of Virginia
University of Virginia
Boyce, Virginia

Cortney V. Martin, Ph.D.
Virginia Polytechnic Institute
Blacksburg, Virginia

Joseph F. McCullough, Ph.D.
Physics Program Chair
Cabrillo College
Aptos, California

Heather Mernitz, Ph.D.
Department of Physical Science
Alverno College
Milwaukee, Wisconsin

Sadredin C. Moosavi, Ph.D.
Department of Earth and Environmental Sciences
Tulane University
New Orleans, Louisiana

David L. Reid, Ph.D.
Department of Biology
Blackburn College
Carlinville, Illinois

Scott M. Rochette, Ph.D.
Department of the Earth Sciences
SUNY College at Brockport
Brockport, New York

Karyn L. Rogers, Ph.D.
Department of Geological Sciences
University of Missouri
Columbia, Missouri

Laurence Rosenhein, Ph.D.
Department of Chemistry
Indiana State University
Terre Haute, Indiana

Sara Seager, Ph.D.
Department of Planetary Sciences and Physics
Massachusetts Institute of Technology
Cambridge, Massachusetts

Tom Shoberg, Ph.D.
Missouri University of Science and Technology
Rolla, Missouri

Patricia Simmons, Ph.D.
North Carolina State University
Raleigh, North Carolina

William H. Steinecker, Ph.D.
Research Scholar
Miami University
Oxford, Ohio

Paul R. Stoddard, Ph.D.
Department of Geology and Environmental Geosciences
Northern Illinois University
DeKalb, Illinois

John R. Villarreal, Ph.D.
Department of Chemistry
The University of Texas–Pan American
Edinburg, Texas

John R. Wagner, Ph.D.
Department of Geology
Clemson University
Clemson, South Carolina

Jerry Waldvogel, Ph.D.
Department of Biological Sciences
Clemson University
Clemson, South Carolina

Donna L. Witter, Ph.D.
Department of Geology
Kent State University
Kent, Ohio

Edward J. Zalisko, Ph.D.
Department of Biology
Blackburn College
Carlinville, Illinois

REVIEWERS

Florida Content Reviewers

Phillip Allman, Ph.D.
Department of Biological Sciences
Florida Gulf Coast University
Fort Myers, Florida

Jeff R. Bodart, Ph.D.
Professor of Physical Sciences
Chipola College
Marianna, Florida

Joshua Cohn, Ph.D.
Department of Physics
University of Miami
Coral Gables, Florida

Fred Hamann, Ph.D.
Department of Astronomy
University of Florida
Gainesville, Florida

Linda Cronin Jones, Ph.D.
Associate Professor of Science
and Environmental Education
University of Florida
Gainesville, Florida

T. Griffin Jones, Ph.D.
Clinical Associate Professor of
Science Education
College of Education
University of Florida
Gainesville, Florida

Thomas Juster, Ph.D.
Department of Geology
University of South Florida
Tampa, Florida

Stephen Kucera, Ph.D.
Department of Biology
University of Tampa
Tampa, Florida

Margaret Lowman, Ph.D.
Division of Natural Sciences
New College of Florida
Sarasota, Florida

Kurt Winkelmann, Ph.D.
Department of Chemistry
Florida Institute of Technology
Melbourne, Florida

Ping Zhu, Ph.D.
Department of Earth Sciences
Florida International University
Miami, Florida

Built especially for
Florida

Florida *Interactive Science* covers 100 percent of the Next Generation Sunshine State Standards with no extraneous content. Built on feedback from Florida educators, *Interactive Science* focuses on what's important to Florida, creating a personal, relevant, and engaging classroom experience.

Florida Middle Grades
Teacher Advisory Board

Roy Bernstein
Polo Park Middle School
Wellington, Florida

Marla Blair
Deerlake Middle School
West Tallahassee, Florida

Tracey Kumm
Lakeside Junior High School
Orange Park, Florida

Jan Plym
C.H. Price Middle School
Interlachen, Florida

Denise Skinner
Buddy Taylor Middle School
Palm Coast, Florida

Guytri Still
McNair Magnet School
Rockledge, Florida

Tania Studer
Bridgewater Middle School
Winter Garden, Florida

Gina Triboletti
Creekside Middle School
Port Orange, Florida

CONTENTS

 Enter the Lab zone for hands-on inquiry.

△ **Chapter Lab Investigations:**
• Directed Inquiry: Density Graphs • Keeping Flowers Fresh
• Open Inquiry: Density Graphs • Keeping Flowers Fresh

△ **Inquiry Warm-Ups:** • Is It Really True?
• How Keen Are Your Senses? • History of Measurement • How Many Marbles Are There? • What's in a Picture? • What's Happening?

△ **Quick Labs:** • Classifying Objects • Thinking Like a Scientist • Using Scientific Thinking • How Many Shoes? • Measuring Length in Metric • For Good Measure • How Close Is It? • What's a Line Graph? • Scientific Inquiry • Theories and Laws

my science ONLINE.com

Go to MyScienceOnline.com to interact with this chapter's content. Keyword: What Is Science?

▶ **UNTAMED SCIENCE**
• What Is Science, Anyway?

▶ **PLANET DIARY**
• What Is Science?

▶ **INTERACTIVE ART**
• Scientific Stumbling Blocks • The Need for Numbers • Plotting a Line Graph • Inquiry Diagram

▶ **VIRTUAL LAB**
• Introduction to Virtual Lab

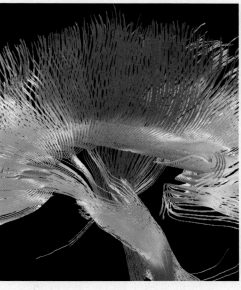
 Enter the Lab zone for hands-on inquiry.

Chapter Lab Investigations:
• Directed Inquiry: Piecing Information Together
• Open Inquiry: Piecing Information Together

Inquiry Warm-Ups: • Doing Science • What Do Scientists Do? • Changing Science • Scale Models

Quick Labs: • Scientific Explanation • Light Sources • Scientific Knowledge • Theories and Laws • Making Models • Systems • Models in Nature

my science ONLINE .com

Go to MyScienceOnline.com to interact with this chapter's content.
Keyword: The World of Science

▶ **UNTAMED SCIENCE**
• DNA Crop Dusters

▶ **PLANET DIARY**
• The World of Science

▶ **INTERACTIVE ART**
• Super Scientists • Building a Theory
• Modeling a System

▶ **REAL-WORLD INQUIRY**
• Where's the Evidence?

CONTENTS

 Lab zone® Enter the Lab zone for hands-on inquiry.

△ **Chapter Lab Investigation:**
  • Directed Inquiry: Design and Build a Microscope
  • Open Inquiry: Design and Build a Microscope

△ **Inquiry Warm-Ups:** • What Is a Compound? • What Can You See? • Homeostasis • How Large Are Cells? • What Are the Yeast Cells Doing?

△ **Quick Labs:** • Tissues, Organs, and Systems • Comparing Cells • Observing Cells • Effect of Concentration on Diffusion • Gelatin Cell Model • Observing Mitosis • Modeling Mitosis

my science online.com

Go to MyScienceOnline.com to interact with this chapter's content. **Keyword: Cells and Life Processes**

▷ **UNTAMED SCIENCE**
• Touring Hooke's Crib!

▷ **PLANET DIARY**
• Cells and Life Processes

▷ **INTERACTIVE ART**
• Specialized Cells • Plant and Animal Cells
• Cell Growth and Division

▷ **VIRTUAL LAB**
• How Can You Observe Cells?

CHAPTER 4

Introduction to the Human Body

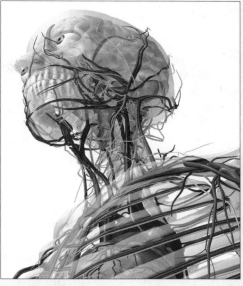

 Enter the Lab zone for hands-on inquiry.

Chapter Lab Investigation:
• Directed Inquiry: A Look Beneath the Skin
• Open Inquiry: A Look Beneath the Skin

Inquiry Warm-Ups: • How Is Your Body Organized? • How Does Your Body Respond? • Out of Balance • Hard as a Rock? • How Do Muscles Work? • What Can You Observe About Skin?

Quick Labs: • Observing Cells and Tissues • Working Together, Act I • Working Together, Act II • Working to Maintain Balance • The Skeleton • Observing Joints • Soft Bones? • Observing Muscle Tissue • Modeling How Skeletal Muscles Work • Sweaty Skin

my science online.com

Go to MyScienceOnline.com to interact with this chapter's content. Keyword: Introduction to the Human Body

› UNTAMED SCIENCE
• Keeping Cool and Staying Warm

› PLANET DIARY
• Introduction to the Human Body

› ART IN MOTION
• Body Systems in Action • Muscle Motion

› INTERACTIVE ART
• Build a Skeleton • The Skeletal and Muscular Systems

› REAL-WORLD INQUIRY
• A Wrench in the System

CONTENTS

 Enter the Lab zone for hands-on inquiry.

Chapter Lab Investigation: • As the Stomach Churns, A Breath of Fresh Air • Open Inquiry: As the Stomach Churns, A Breath of Fresh Air

Inquiry Warm-Ups: • Food Claims • Observing a Heart • How Big Can You Blow Up a Balloon? • How Does Filtering a Liquid Change the Liquid?

Quick Labs: • Predicting Starch Content • Direction of Blood Flow • Do You Know Your A-B-Os? • Modeling Respiration • Kidney Function • Perspiration

my science online.com

Go to MyScienceOnline.com to interact with this chapter's content.
Keyword: Managing Materials in the Body

▶ **PLANET DIARY**
• Managing Materials in the Body

▶ **ART IN MOTION**
• Gas Exchange

▶ **INTERACTIVE ART**
• Nutrients at Work • The Heart
• The Respiratory System

▶ **VIRTUAL LAB**
• Up Close: Components of Blood

▶ **REAL-WORLD INQUIRY**
• A Digestive Journey

Enter the Lab zone for hands-on inquiry.

Chapter Lab Investigation:
• Directed Inquiry: Ready or Not!
• Open Inquiry: Ready or Not!

Inquiry Warm-Ups: • How Simple Is a Simple Task? • What's the Signal? • What's the Big Difference? • Prenatal Growth

Quick Labs: • How Does Your Knee React? • Working Together • Making Models • Modeling Negative Feedback • Reproductive Systems • Looking at Hormone Levels • Way to Grow! • Egg-cellent Protection • Labor and Delivery

my science online.com

Go to MyScienceOnline.com to interact with this chapter's content.
Keyword: Controlling Body Processes

› UNTAMED SCIENCE
• Think Fast!

› PLANET DIARY
• Controlling Body Processes

› ART IN MOTION
• How a Nerve Impulse Travels • Stages of Prenatal Development

› INTERACTIVE ART
• The Nervous System • Negative Feedback in the Endocrine System • Reproductive Anatomy

› REAL-WORLD INQUIRY
• Sensing the World

CONTENTS

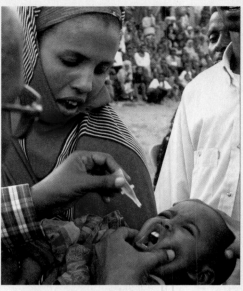

**Enter the Lab zone
for hands-on inquiry.**

Chapter Lab Investigation:
• Directed Inquiry: The Skin as a Barrier
• Open Inquiry: The Skin as a Barrier

Inquiry Warm-Ups: • The Agents of
Disease • Which Pieces Fit Together? • Types
of Immunity • Causes of Death, Then and Now
• How Does HIV Spread?

Quick Labs: • How Do Pathogens Cause
Disease? • How Does a Disease Spread?
• Stuck Together • Modeling Active and
Passive Immunity • What Substances Can Kill
Pathogens? • What Happens When Air Flow
Is Restricted? • What Does Sunlight Do to the
Beads? • How Does HIV Attack? • What Will
Spread HIV?

my science online.com

**Go to MyScienceOnline.com to
interact with this chapter's content.
Keyword: Fighting Disease**

> **PLANET DIARY**
• Fighting Disease

> **ART IN MOTION**
• How Do Vaccines Work?

> **INTERACTIVE ART**
• Immune Response

> **VIRTUAL LAB**
• Up Close: Pathogens

> **REAL-WORLD INQUIRY**
• Diagnosis Please, Doctor

CHAPTER 8

Diversity of Life

 The Essential Question 312
How are living things alike yet different?

Lab zone® Enter the Lab zone for hands-on inquiry.

Chapter Lab Investigation:
• Directed Inquiry: Please Pass the Bread
• Open Inquiry: Please Pass the Bread

Inquiry Warm-Ups: • Is It Living or Nonliving? • Can You Organize a Junk Drawer? • What Organism Goes Where? • Observing Similarities

Quick Labs: • React! • Compare Broth Samples • Classifying Seeds • Make a Classification Chart • Living Mysteries • Staining Leaves • Common Ancestors

my science online.com

Go to MyScienceOnline.com to interact with this chapter's content.
Keyword: **Diversity of Life**

> **UNTAMED SCIENCE**
• What Can You Explore in a Swamp?

> **PLANET DIARY**
• Diversity of Life

> **ART IN MOTION**
• Finding a Common Ancestor

> **INTERACTIVE ART**
• Redi's and Pasteur's Experiments
• Taxonomic Key

> **VIRTUAL LAB**
• Classifying Life

CONTENTS

Lab zone ® Enter the Lab zone for hands-on inquiry.

Chapter Lab Investigations:
• Directed Inquiry: Nature at Work
• Open Inquiry: Nature at Work

Inquiry Warm-Ups: • How Can You Classify a Species? • How Do Living Things Vary?
• How Much Variety Is There?

Quick Labs: • Understanding Evolution
• Finding Proof • Bird Beak Adaptations
• Large Scale Isolation • Grocery Gene Pool
• Disappearing Act

my science online.com

Go to MyScienceOnline.com to interact with this chapter's content. Keyword: **Change Over Time**

> **UNTAMED SCIENCE**
• Why Would a Fish Have Red Lips?

> **PLANET DIARY**
• Change Over Time

> **INTERACTIVE ART**
• Homologous Structures • What Is It Adapted To?

> **REAL-WORLD INQUIRY**
• What Affects Natural Selection?

> **VIRTUAL LAB**
• Is Variety the Spice of Live?

 Enter the Lab zone for hands-on inquiry.

Chapter Lab Investigations:
- Directed Inquiry: Guilty or Innocent?
- Open Inquiry: Guilty or Innocent?

Inquiry Warm-Ups: • Can You Crack the Code? • What Does the Father Look Like? • What's the Chance? • Which Chromosome Is Which?

Quick Labs: • Modeling the Genetic Code • Observing Pistols and Stamens • Inferring the Parent Generation • Coin Crosses • Make the Right Call • Chromosomes and Inheritance • Modeling Meiosis • Types of Reproduction

my science online

Go to MyScienceOnline.com to interact with this chapter's content.
Keyword: Genetics and DNA: The Science of Heredity

> UNTAMED SCIENCE
• Where'd You Get Those Genes?

> PLANET DIARY
• Genetics and DNA: The Science of Heredity

> ART IN MOTION
• Understanding DNA • Meiosis

> INTERACTIVE ART
• Copying DNA • Punnett Squares

> VIRTUAL LAB
• Mendel's Experiments 101

CONTENTS

 Enter the Lab zone
for hands-on inquiry.

Chapter Lab Investigations:
• Directed Inquiry: How Are Genes on Sex
Chromosomes Inherited?
• Open Inquiry: How Are Genes on Sex
Chromosomes Inherited?

Inquiry Warm-Ups: • How Tall Is Tall?
• How Many Chromosomes? • What Do
Fingerprints Reveal? • Using Genetic
Information

Quick Labs: • The Eyes Have It • What Went
Wrong? • Family Puzzle • Selective Breeding
• Impact of Biotechnology • Extraction in
Action

my science online.com

**Go to MyScienceOnline.com to
interact with this chapter's content.
Keyword: Human Genetics and Genetic
Technology**

> **UNTAMED SCIENCE**
• The Case of the X-Linked Gene

> **PLANET DIARY**
• Human Genetics and Genetic Technology

> **ART IN MOTION**
• Understanding Genetic Engineering

> **INTERACTIVE ART**
• DNA Fingerprinting • Pedigree

> **VIRTUAL LAB**
• Why Does My Brother Have It and I Don't?

 Enter the Lab zone for hands-on inquiry.

Chapter Lab Investigations:
  • Directed Inquiry: World in a Bottle
  • Open Inquiry: World in a Bottle

Inquiry Warm-Ups: • What's in the Scene?
• Where Did Your Dinner Come From? • Can You Hide a Butterfly? • Populations

Quick Labs: • Organisms and Their Habitats
• Organizing an Ecosystem • Observing Decomposition • Adaptations for Survival • Competition and Predation • Type of Symbiosis • Growing and Shrinking • Elbow Room

my science online.com

Go to MyScienceOnline.com to interact with this chapter's content.
Keyword: Populations and Communities

> **UNTAMED SCIENCE**
• Clown(fish)ing Around

> **PLANET DIARY**
• Populations and Communities

> **INTERACTIVE ART**
• Ocean Food Web • Animal Defense Strategies • Changes in Population

> **REAL-WORLD INQUIRY**
• An Ecological Mystery

> **VIRTUAL LAB**
• Where's All the Food?

CONTENTS

Lab zone® Enter the Lab zone for hands-on inquiry.

△ **Chapter Lab Investigations:**
• Directed Inquiry: Exhaling Carbon Dioxide
• Open Inquiry: Exhaling Carbon Dioxide

△ **Inquiry Warm-Ups:** • Where Does the Energy Come From? • Cellular Respiration • Are You Part of a Cycle?

△ **Quick Labs:** • Energy From the Sun • Looking at Pigments • Observing Fermentation • Following Water • Modeling the Carbon Cycle • Conservation in Living Systems

MY SCIENCE online.com

Go to MyScienceOnline.com to interact with this chapter's content.
Keyword: Energy, Matter, and Living Things

▶ **UNTAMED SCIENCE**
• Tracking Your Carbon Atoms

▶ **PLANET DIARY**
• Energy, Matter, and Living Things

▶ **INTERACTIVE ART**
• Photosynthesis • Cellular Respiration • Water Cycle

▶ **ART IN MOTION**
• Opposite Processes

▶ **REAL-WORLD INQUIRY**
• Alert: Matter Disruption!

Video Series: Chapter Adventures

Untamed Science created this captivating video series for interactive SCIENCE featuring a unique segment for every chapter of the program.

Featuring

FLORIDA interactive SCIENCE

This is your book. You can write in it!

ESSENTIAL ?

Get Engaged!

At the start of each chapter, you will see two questions: an Engaging Question and the Essential Question. Each chapter's Essential Question will help you start thinking about the Big Ideas of Science. Look for the Essential Q symbol throughout the chapter!

HOW CAN AN ELEPHANT FLOAT, BUT A PENNY SINK?

 How do scientists investigate the natural world?

Scientists are constantly asking questions about elephants, oceans, planets—you name it! They're curious about the world around them, and they're looking for answers. Every scientist has their own interests that lead to different observations and investigations about the natural world. **Pose Questions** What question do you have about this elephant that you would like to investigate?

How long can this elephant swim?

> **UNTAMED SCIENCE** Watch the **Untamed Science** video to learn more about scientific inquiry.

2   Practicing Science

 **Untamed Science**™

Follow the Untamed Science video crew as they travel the globe exploring the Big Ideas of Science.

Interact with your textbook.   Interact with inquiry.   Interact online.

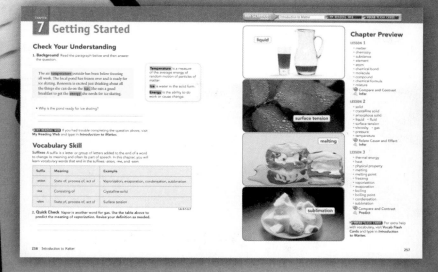

Build Reading, Inquiry, and Vocabulary Skills

In every lesson you will learn new 🔄 Reading and △ Inquiry skills. These skills will help you read and think like a scientist. Vocabulary skills will help you communicate effectively and uncover the meaning of words.

Go Online!

Look for the MyScienceOnline.com technology options. At MyScienceOnline.com you can immerse yourself in amazing virtual environments, get extra practice, and even blog about current events in science.

Florida Standards!

Look for your Next Generation Sunshine State Standards throughout every chapter to see the interesting concepts you will be exploring.

Explore the Key Concepts.

Each lesson begins with a series of Key Concept questions. The interactivities in each lesson will help you understand these concepts and Unlock the Essential Question.

my PLANET DiARY *for Florida*

At the start of each lesson, My Planet Diary will introduce you to amazing events, significant people, and important discoveries in science or help you to overcome common misconceptions about science concepts.

Desertification If the soil
of moisture and nutrients, th
advance of desertlike conditi
fertile is called **desertificatio**

One cause of desertificati
is a period when less rain tha
droughts, crops fail. Without
blows away. Overgrazing of g
cutting down trees for firewo

Desertification is a seriou
and graze livestock where de
people may face famine and
central Africa. Millions of ru
cities because they can no lo

apply it!

Desertification affects many
areas around the world.

1 Name Which continent h
the most existing desert?

2 Interpret Maps Where in
United States is the greatest
desertification?

3 Infer Is desertification a
is existing desert? Explain. C
your answer.

4 CHALLENGE If an area is fa
things people could do to po

256 Land, Air, and Water R

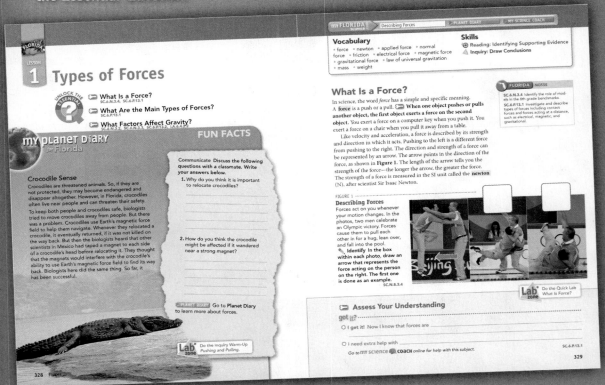

Explain what you know.

Look for the pencil. When you see it, it's time to interact with your book and demonstrate what you have learned.

apply it!

Elaborate further with the Apply It activities. This is your opportunity to take what you've learned and apply it to new situations.

Lab Zone

Look for the Lab zone triangle. This means it's time to do a hands-on inquiry lab. In every lesson, you'll have the opportunity to do many hands-on inquiry activities that will help reinforce your understanding of the lesson topic.

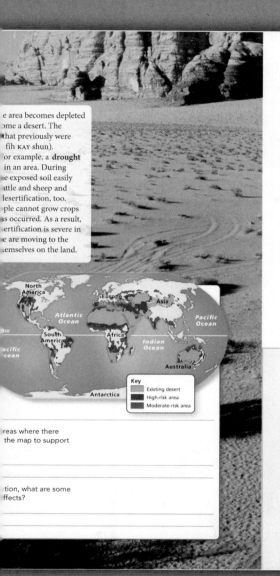

e area becomes depleted
ome a desert. The
that previously were
fih KAY shun).
or example, a **drought**
in an area. During
e exposed soil easily
attle and sheep and
esertification, too.
ple cannot grow crops
s occurred. As a result,
ertification is severe in
e are moving to the
emselves on the land.

Key
■ Existing desert
■ High-risk area
■ Moderate-risk area

reas where there
the map to support

tion, what are some
ffects?

Land Reclamation   Fortunately, it is possible to replace land damaged by erosion or mining. The process of restoring an area of land to a more productive state is called **land reclamation.** In addition to restoring land for agriculture, land reclamation can restore habitats for wildlife. Many different types of land reclamation projects are currently underway all over the world. But it is generally more difficult and expensive to restore damaged land and soil than it is to protect those resources in the first place. In some cases, the land may not return to its original state.

FIGURE 4 ·······························
Land Reclamation
These pictures show land before and after it was mined.
✎ **Communicate** Below the pictures, write a story about what happened to the land.

Lab zone   Do the Quick Lab
Modeling Soil Conserv...

📖 Assess Your Understanding

1a. Review Subsoil has (less/more) plant and
animal matter than topsoil.
                                    SC.7.E.6.6

b. Explain What can happen to soil if plants are
removed?

_____

_____
                                    SC.7.E.6.6

c. Apply Concepts W...
that could preve...
land reclama...

got it? ··

○ **I get it!** Now I know that soil management is important beca...

_____

○ **I need extra help with** _____

Go to **my science COACH** online for help with this subject.

got it?

Evaluate Your Progress.

After answering the Got It question, think about how you're doing. Did you get it or do you need a little help? Remember, my SCIENCE Ⓢ COACH is there for you if you need extra help.

Explore the Essential Question.

At one point in the chapter, you'll have the opportunity to take all that you've learned to further explore the Essential Question.

Pollution and Solutions

How do people use Earth's resources?

FIGURE 4 ....

REAL-WORLD INQUIRY All living things depend on land, air, and water. Conserving these resources for the future is important. Part of resource conservation is identifying and limiting sources of pollution.

Identify On the photograph, write the letter from the key into the circle that best identifies the source of pollution. Then fill out each box.

Land
Identify one impact humans have had on land. Then describe one way to reduce pollution on land.

Air
Identify one impact humans have had on the air. Then describe one way to reduce air pollution.

Water
Identify one impact humans have had on water. Then describe one way to reduce water pollution.

Key of Pollution Sources
A. Sediments
B. Runoff from development
C. Emissions

Lab zone

Assess Your Unde

1a. Define What are sediment

b. Explain How can bacteria spill in the ocean?

c. ANSWER THE ESSENTIAL How do people u resources?

d. CHALLENGE Why might a to recycle the waste they would reduce water poll

got it? ....
O I get it! Now I know tha
can be reduced by

O I need extra help with

Go to MY SCIENCE c
with this subject.

Answer the Essential Question.

Now it's time to show what you know and answer the Essential Question.

Review What You've Learned.

Use the Chapter Study Guide to review the
Essential Question and prepare for the test.

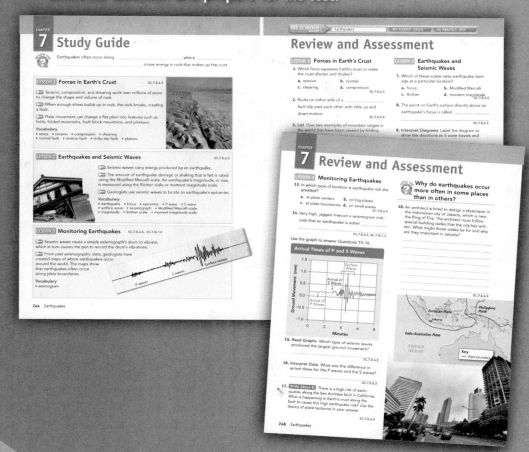

Practice Taking Tests.

Apply the Essential Question
and take a practice test in
standardized test format.

INTERACT ... WITH YOUR TEXTBOOK...

Go to **MyScienceOnline.com** and immerse yourself in amazing virtual environments.

ESSENTIAL QUESTION

Each online chapter starts with an Essential Question. Your mission is to unlock the meaning of this Essential Question as each science lesson unfolds.

Unit 4 > Chapter 1 > Lesson 1

Ask | Unlock | Explore | Answer | Apply
Essential Question | Untamed Science | Check Your Understanding | Vocabulary Skill | Vocabulary Flashcards

How do living things affect one another?

Unit 2 > Chapter 4 > Lesson 1

Engage & Explore | Expla
Planet Diary

my planet diary

VOCAB FLASH CARDS

Practice chapter vocabulary with interactive flash cards. Each card has an image, definitions in English and Spanish, and space for your own notes.

Unit 4 > Chapter 1 > Lesson 1

Ask | Unlock | Explore | Answer | Apply
Essential Question | Untamed Science | Check Your Understanding | Vocabulary Skill | Vocabulary Flashcards

Vocabulary Flashcards

Card List | Create-a-Card | 10 Cards Left | Test Me
Lesson Cards | My Cards

Birth Rate
Carrying Capacity
Commensalism
Community
Competition
Death Rate
Ecology
Ecosystem
Emigration
Habitat
Host
Immigration
Limiting Factor

Science Vocabulary

Term: **Community**

Definition: **All the different populations that live together in a particular area.**

Add Notes

View Spanis

Card 5 of

Unit 6 > Chapter 1 > Les

Engage & Explore
Apply It | Directed Virtua

Color in Light

Unit 6 > Chapter 1 > Lesson 1

Engage & Explore | Explain | Elaborate | Evaluate
Apply It | Do the Math | Art in Motion | Interactive Art | Real World Inquiry

The Nebraska Plains

▶ Bald Eagle
Information | Media

Haliaeetus leucocephalus
Bald Eagles are 80-95 cm tall with a wingspan of 180-230 cm. These birds are born with all brown feathers but grow white feathers on their head, neck, and tail.

Layers List | ▲ Show

Next
22 of 22
Back

INTERACTIVE ART

At MyScienceOnline.com, many of the beautiful visuals in your book become interactive so you can extend your learning.

interactive SCIENCE
GO ONLINE

my science online.com > Populations and Communities > **PLANET DIARY** > **LAB ZONE** > **VIRTUAL LAB**

> PLANET DIARY

My Planet Diary online is the place to find more information and activities related to lesson topics.

Elaborate | Evaluate

Everest

Still Growing! Mount Everest in the Himalayas is the highest mountain on Earth. Climbers who reach the peak stand 8,850 meters above sea level. You might think that mountains never change. But forces inside Earth push Mount Everest at least several millimeters higher each year. Over time, Earth's forces slowly but constantly lift, stretch, bend, and break Earth's crust in dramatic ways!

> Planet Diary Go to Planet Diary to learn more about forces in the Earth's crust.

Tools

Next
22 of 22
Back

> VIRTUAL LAB

Get more practice with realistic virtual labs. Manipulate the variables on-screen and test your hypothesis.

http://www.myscienceonline.com/

Find Your Chapter

1 Go to www.myscienceonline.com.

2 Log in with username and password.

3 Click on your program and select your chapter.

Keyword Search

1 Go to www.myscienceonline.com.

2 Log in with username and password.

3 Click on your program and select Search.

4 Enter the keyword (from your book) in the search box.

Other Content Available Online

> UNTAMED SCIENCE Follow these young scientists through their amazing online video blogs as they travel the globe in search of answers to the Essential Questions of Science.

> MY SCIENCE COACH Need extra help? My Science Coach is your personal online study partner. My Science Coach is a chance for you to get more practice on key science concepts. There you can choose from a variety of tools that will help guide you through each science lesson.

> MY READING WEB Need extra reading help on a particular science topic? At My Reading Web you will find a choice of reading selections targeted to your specific reading level.

As you study this unit, look for answers to these questions.

What types of **OBSERVATIONS** could these scientists make?

How could scientific knowledge change as a result of this **INVESTIGATION**?

Student scientists survey a section of the ocean floor near Palm Harbor, Florida.

Introducing

 Big Ideas and Essential Questions

Nature of Science

 Florida Big Idea 1

The Practice of Science

A: Scientific inquiry is a multifaceted activity; the processes of science include the formulation of scientifically investigable questions, construction of investigations into those questions, the collection of appropriate data, the evaluation of the meaning of those data, and the communication of this evaluation.

B: The processes of science frequently do not correspond to the traditional portrayal of "the scientific method."

C: Scientific argumentation is a necessary part of scientific inquiry and plays an important role in the generation and validation of scientific knowledge.

D: Scientific knowledge is based on observation and inference; it is important to recognize that these are very different things. Not only does science require creativity in its methods and processes, but also in its questions and explanations.

 How do scientists investigate the natural world?

 How does scientific knowledge develop?

 Florida Big Idea 2

The Characteristics of Scientific Knowledge

A: Scientific knowledge is based on empirical evidence, and is appropriate for understanding the natural world, but it provides only a limited understanding of the supernatural, aesthetic, or other ways of knowing, such as art, philosophy, or religion.

B: Scientific knowledge is durable and robust, but open to change.

C: Because science is based on empirical evidence it strives for objectivity, but as it is a human endeavor, the processes, methods, and knowledge of science include subjectivity, as well as creativity and discovery.

 How does scientific knowledge develop?

 Florida Big Idea 3

The Role of Theories, Laws, Hypotheses, and Models

The terms that describe examples of scientific knowledge, for example; "theory," "law," "hypothesis," and "model" have very specific meanings and functions within science.

 How does scientific knowledge develop?

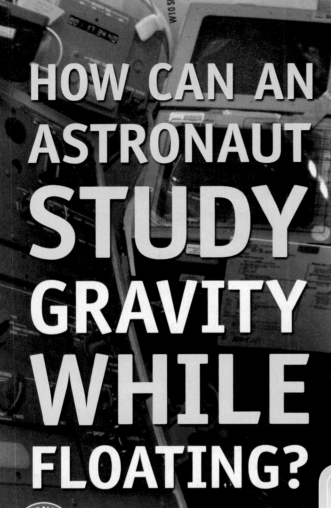

HOW CAN AN ASTRONAUT STUDY GRAVITY WHILE FLOATING?

How do scientists investigate the natural world?

> UNTAMED SCIENCE Watch the **Untamed Science** video to learn more about science.

NASA studies how microgravity, or very little gravity, affects humans, plants, crystals, and liquids. For example, NASA has found that the muscles and bones of astronauts weaken during space missions. Plants grow in different directions and crystals grow larger. Water does not pour as it would on Earth, but falls out in spheres.

Infer **What other ideas might NASA study in space?**

_____

_____

_____

_____

_____

What Is Science?

🔲 **FLORIDA** Next Generation Sunshine State Standards

Big Idea 1: SC.7.N.1.1, SC.7.N.1.2, SC.7.N.1.3, SC.7.N.1.4

Language Arts: LA.7.2.2.3, LA.7.4.2.2
Mathematics: MA.6.A.3.6, MA.6.S.6.2

Check Your Understanding

1. **Background** Read the paragraph below and then answer the question.

> Miki is in the **process** of preparing a stew for dinner at her campsite. After it is cooked, she sets the pot aside to cool. When she returns, the pot is empty. Immediately, she **poses** questions: Who ate the stew? What animals are active in the evening? She soon finds **evidence:** the pot cover, greasy spills, and a stinky smell. The thief is a skunk.

> A **process** is a series of actions or events.
>
> To **pose** is to put forward a question or a problem.
>
> Facts, figures, or signs that help prove a statement are all pieces of **evidence.**

- How does the process of posing questions and looking for evidence help Miki solve the mystery of the missing stew?

_____

_____

> MY READING WEB If you had trouble completing the question above, visit **My Reading Web** and type in *What Is Science?*

Vocabulary Skill

Identify Related Word Forms Learn related forms of words to increase your vocabulary. The table below lists forms of words related to vocabulary terms.

Verb	Noun	Adjective
observe, *v.* to gather information using the senses	observation, *n.* facts learned by gathering information using the senses	observable, *adj.* able to be heard, seen, touched, tasted, or smelled
predict, *v.* to state or claim what will happen in the future	prediction, *n.* a statement or claim of what will happen in the future	predictable, *adj.* able to be predicted; behaving in a way that is expected

LA.7.1.6.1

2. **Quick Check** Complete the sentence with the correct form of the word.

- It is difficult to _____ how much rain will fall.

observing

subjective

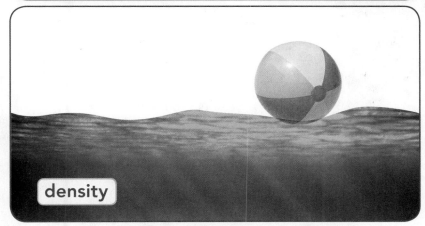

density

accuracy

Chapter Preview

LESSON 1
- science • observing • inferring
- predicting • classifying
- evaluating • making models
- variable • independent variable
- dependent variable

Ask Questions

Predict

LESSON 2
- skepticism • ethics
- personal bias • cultural bias
- experimental bias • objective
- subjective • deductive reasoning
- inductive reasoning

Relate Cause and Effect

Classify

LESSON 3
- metric system
- International System of Units (SI)
- mass • weight • volume
- meniscus • density

Compare and Contrast

Measure

LESSON 4
- estimate • accuracy • precision
- significant figures • percent error
- mean • median • mode
- range • anomalous data

Relate Cause and Effect

Calculate

LESSON 5
- graph • linear graph
- nonlinear graph

Relate Text and Visuals

Predict

LESSON 6
- scientific inquiry • hypothesis
- controlled experiment • data
- repeated trials • replication

Sequence

Control Variables

Science and the Natural World

UNLOCK THE ESSENTIAL

🔑 **What Skills Do Scientists Use?**
SC.7.N.1.1, SC.7.N.1.4, LA.7.4.2.2, MA.6.A.3.6

my planeT DiaRY

BIOGRAPHY

The Wild Chimpanzees of Gombe

The following words are from the writings of Jane Goodall, a scientist who studied wild chimpanzees in Africa for many years.

"Once, as I walked through thick forest in a downpour, I suddenly saw a chimp hunched in front of me. Quickly I stopped. Then I heard a sound from above. I looked up and there was a big chimp there, too. When he saw me he gave a loud, clear wailing *wraaaaah*— a spine-chilling call that is used to threaten a dangerous animal. To my right I saw a large black hand shaking a branch and bright eyes glaring threateningly through the foliage. Then came another savage *wraaaah* from behind...I was surrounded." Because Jane stood still, the chimps no longer felt threatened, so they went away.

Answer the question.

What is one advantage and one disadvantage of studying wild animals in their natural environment?

_____

_____

_____

_____

_____

_____

> PLANET DIARY Go to **Planet Diary** to learn more about science and the natural world.

Lab zone Do the Inquiry Warm-Up
Is It Really True?

Vocabulary

- science • observing • inferring • predicting
- classifying • evaluating • making models • variable
- independent variable • dependent variable

Skills

⟳ Reading: Ask Questions

△ Inquiry: Predict

What Skills Do Scientists Use?

Jane Goodall trained herself to become a scientist, or a person who does science. **Science** is a way of learning about the natural world. Science also includes all the knowledge gained by exploring the natural world. 🔑 **Scientists use skills such as observing, inferring, predicting, classifying, evaluating, and making models to study the world.**

Observing **Observing** means using one or more of your senses to gather information. It also means using tools, such as a microscope, to help your senses. By observing chimps like the one in **Figure 1,** Jane Goodall learned what they eat. She also learned what sounds chimps make and even what games they play.

Observations can be either quantitative or qualitative. A quantitative observation deals with numbers, or amounts. For example, seeing that you have 11 new e-mails is a quantitative observation. A qualitative observation deals with descriptions that cannot be expressed in numbers. Noticing that a bike is blue or that a lemon tastes sour is a qualitative observation.

FLORIDA NGSSS

SC.7.N.1.1 Define a problem from the seventh grade curriculum, plan and carry out scientific investigation of various types, identify variables, collect and organize data, interpret data, analyze information, make predictions, and defend conclusions.

SC.7.N.1.4 Identify test variables (independent variables) and outcome variables (dependent variables) in an experiment.

LA.7.4.2.2 The student will record information related to a topic.

MA.6.A.3.6 Construct and analyze tables, graphs, and equations.

⟳ **Ask Questions** In the graphic organizer ask a *what, how,* or *why* question based on the text under Observing. As you read, write an answer to your question.

FIGURE 1 ⋯⋯⋯⋯⋯⋯⋯⋯⋯⋯⋯⋯⋯⋯

Observing

A chimpanzee uses a rock as a tool to crack open a nut.

✎ **Observe** Write one quantitative observation and one qualitative observation about this chimp.

_____
_____
_____
_____
_____
_____
_____
_____

Thinking Like a Scientist

Question

_____
_____
_____
_____

Answer

_____
_____
_____
_____

7

Inferring One day, Jane watched as a chimp peered into a tree hollow. The chimp picked up a handful of leaves and chewed on them. Then, it took the leaves out of its mouth and pushed them into the hollow. When the chimp pulled the leaves out, Jane saw the gleam of water. The chimp then put the wet leaves back into its mouth. Jane reasoned that there was water in the tree. Jane made three observations. She saw the chimp pick up dry leaves, put them in the hollow, and then pull them out wet. But, Jane was not observing when she reasoned that there was water inside the tree. She was inferring. When you explain or interpret the things you observe, you are **inferring,** or making an inference. Inferring is not guessing. Inferences are based on reasoning from what you already know. They could also be based on assumptions you make about your observations. See what inferences you can make about the chimps in **Figure 2**.

FIGURE 2 ···

Inferring
What can you infer about the chimps and the termite mound?

✎ **Complete the activities below.**

1. **Observe** In the chart below, write two observations about the chimp on the left.

2. **Infer** Use the observations you wrote to make two related inferences.   LA.7.4.2.2

Observation	Inference

Predicting Jane's understanding of chimp behavior grew over time. Sometimes, she could predict what a chimp would do next. **Predicting** means making a statement or a claim about what will happen in the future based on past experience or evidence.

By observing, Jane learned that when a chimp was frightened or angry its hairs stood on end. This response was sometimes followed by threatening gestures such as charging, throwing rocks, and shaking trees. Therefore, when Jane saw a chimp with its hair on end, she was able to predict that there was danger.

Predictions and inferences are closely related. While inferences are attempts to explain what is happening or *has* happened, predictions are statements of claims about what *will* happen. If you see a broken egg on the floor by a table, you might infer that the egg had rolled off the table. If, however, you see an egg rolling toward the edge of a table, you can predict that it's about to create a mess.

FIGURE 3 ·······························
Predicting
Predictions are forecasts of what will happen next.

✏️ **Predict** Write a prediction about what this angry chimp might do next.

_____

_____

_____

_____

do the
math!

Like all animals, chimps prefer to eat certain foods when they are available.

❶ **Graph** Use the information in the table to create a bar graph.

❷ **Label** the *x*-axis and the *y*-axis. Then write a title for the graph.

❸ **Interpret Data** Did chimps feed more on seeds or leaves during May?

_____

_____

❹ **Infer** What might chimps eat more of if fruits are not available in June?

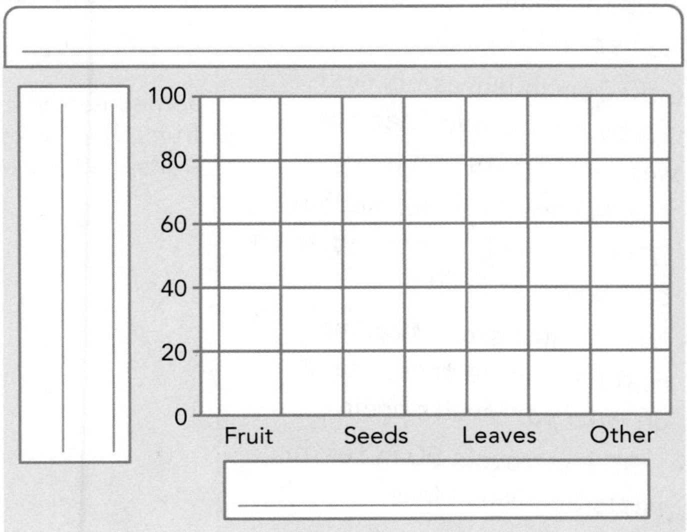

_____

_____

_____

_____

Chimp Diet in May	
Fruits	52%
Seeds	30%
Leaves	12%
Other foods	6%

100
80
60
40
20
0
Fruit   Seeds   Leaves   Other

MA.6.A.3.6, MA.7.S.6.2

9

Classifying

What did chimps do all day? To find out, Jane's research team followed the chimps through the forest. They took detailed field notes about the chimps' behaviors. **Figure 4** shows some notes about Jomeo, an adult male chimp.

Suppose Jane had wanted to know how much time Jomeo spent feeding or resting that morning. She could have found out by classifying Jomeo's actions. **Classifying** is the grouping together of items that are alike in some way. Jane could have grouped together all the information about Jomeo's feeding habits or his resting behavior.

Evaluating

Suppose Jane had found that Jomeo spent most of his time resting. What would this observation have told her about chimp behavior? Before Jane could have reached a conclusion, she would have needed to evaluate her observations. **Evaluating** involves comparing observations and data to reach a conclusion about them. For example, Jane would have needed to compare all of Jomeo's behaviors with those of other chimps to reach a conclusion. She would also need to have evaluated the resulting behavior data of Jomeo and the other chimps.

FIGURE 4 ·······························
Classifying

By classifying the information related to a chimp's resting, climbing, or feeding, a scientist can better understand chimp behavior.

✎ **Classify** Use the chart to classify the details from the field notes.   LA.7.4.2.2

- 6:45 A.M. Jomeo rests in his nest. He lies on his back.

- 6:50 Jomeo leaves his nest, climbs a tree, and feeds on *viazi pori* fruits and leaves.

- 7:16 He wanders along about 175 m from his nest feeding on *budyankende* fruits.

- 8:08 Jomeo stops feeding, rests in a large tree, feeds on *viazi pori* fruits again.

- 8:35 He travels 50 m further, rests by a small lake.

Feeding	Resting	Changing Location
Jomeo eats *viazi pori* fruits, *budyankende* fruits, and leaves.		

Making Models How far do chimps travel? Where do they go? Sometimes, Jane's research team followed a particular chimp for many days at a time. To show the chimp's movements, they might have made a model like the one shown in **Figure 5.** The model shows Jomeo's movements and behaviors during one day. **Making models** involves creating representations of complex objects or processes. Some models can be touched, such as a map. Others are in the form of mathematical equations or computer programs. Models help people study things that can't be observed directly. By using models, Jane and her team shared information that would otherwise be difficult to explain.

FIGURE 5 ···

Making Models
This model shows Jomeo's movements and behaviors during one day.

✏️ **Use the map to answer the questions.**

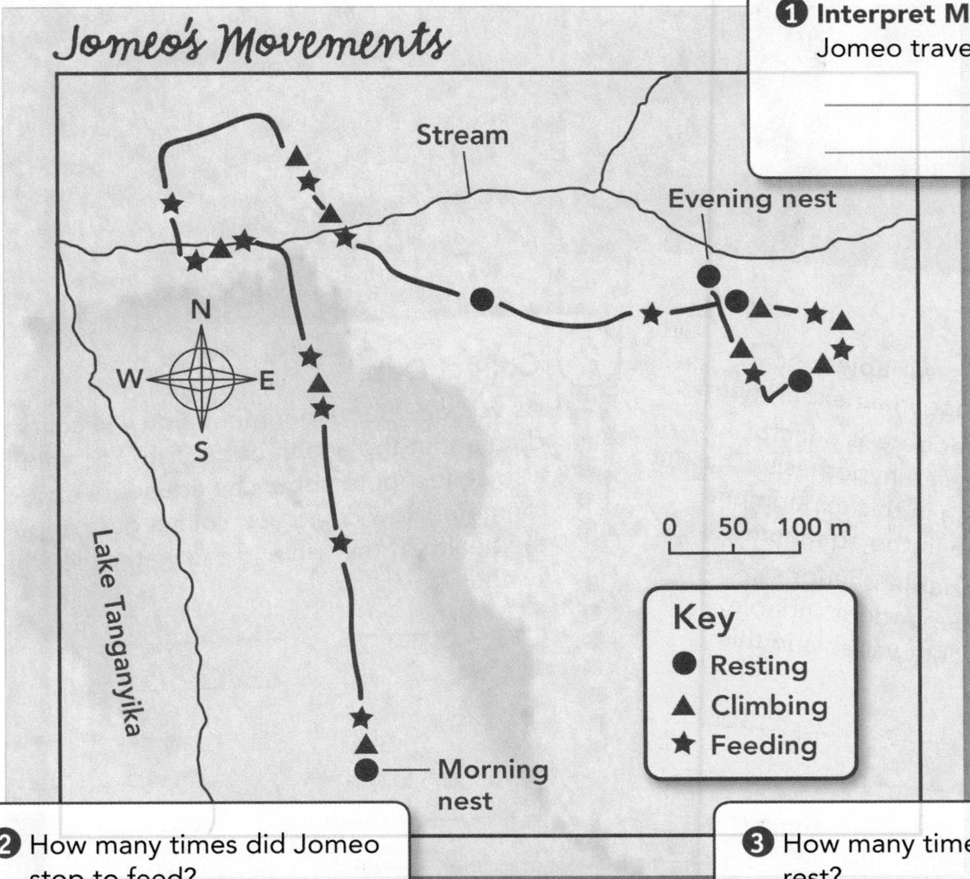

Jomeo's Movements

Stream

Evening nest

N
W · E
S

Lake Tanganyika

0   50   100 m

Key
● Resting
▲ Climbing
★ Feeding

Morning nest

① Interpret Maps How far did Jomeo travel during this day?

_____

_____

② How many times did Jomeo stop to feed?

_____

_____

③ How many times did Jomeo rest?

_____

_____

Plan and Carry Out an Investigation

There are many types of scientific investigations. Some involve observing, while others use experiments to find out more about the natural world.

Imagine that you and your classmates have an aquarium in your classroom. You want to know if the number of fish in the aquarium affects the health of the fish. As you do your experiment, you will need to make observations and collect data about the health of the fish. You might also look for other factors that are affecting the health of the fish, such as the quality of the water. Once you collect your data, you will need to organize your data. Finally, form a conclusion about your data and defend it to your classmates.

FIGURE 6 ·····························

▶ VIRTUAL LAB **Too Crowded?**
You predict that as more fish are added to the aquarium, the health of the fish will get worse.

✎ **Explain Read the text in each box about each step of your experiment. Then answer the question in the space provided.**

1 Identify Variables

Every experiment has **variables,** or factors that can change in an experiment. The **independent variable** is a factor that is changed to test a hypothesis. The independent variable in this experiment is the number of fish in the aquarium. The **dependent variable** changes in response to the independent variable. What is the dependent variable in this experiment?

_____

_____

_____

_____

2 Collect Data

As you do your experiment, you will collect data about the health of the fish. You should also collect data about the aquarium environment. How could you collect data about the health of the fish and the water they are living in?

_____

_____

_____

_____

_____

_____

_____

3 Organize Data

How would you organize the data you collected? Would you show it in a chart or graph? Would you make a table?

_____
_____
_____
_____
_____
_____
_____
_____
_____
_____

4 Defend Your Conclusions

At the end of your experiment, how would you present your data and defend your conclusions to your classmates?

_____
_____
_____
_____
_____
_____
_____

Lab ® Do the Quick Lab
zone *Classifying Objects.*

🔑 Assess Your Understanding

1a. Identify You are studying how the amount of sunlight a plant gets affects its height. What are the independent and dependent variables?

_____
_____
_____

SC.7.N.1.4

b. Compare and Contrast How do observations differ from inferences?

_____
_____
_____
_____

SC.7.N.1.1

got it? ....

O **I get it!** Now I know that scientists use skills

such as _____

_____

_____

_____

O **I need extra help with** _____

Go to **MY SCIENCE** ⑤ **COACH** *online for help with this subject.* **SC.7.N.1.1, SC.7.N.1.4**

13

Thinking Like a Scientist

🔑 **What Attitudes Help You Think Scientifically?**
SC.7.N.1.1, LA.7.2.2.3

🔑 **What Is Scientific Reasoning?**
SC.7.N.1.1

my planet diary

Incredible Inventions

Most scientific inventions are purposely created and result from curiosity, persistence, and years of hard work. However, some inventions have been accidentally discovered when their inventors were in the process of creating something else. While developing wallpaper cleaner, a type of clay was invented. A coil-shaped toy was originally designed as a spring to be used on ships. Instead of developing a substitute for synthetic rubber, toy putty was created. Self-stick notes, potato chips, and the hook and loop fasteners used on items such as clothing, shoes, and toys are also inventions that were discovered by accident. Like the inventors of these items, your curiosity may help you invent the next "big thing"!

DISCOVERY

Communicate Discuss the following questions with a partner. Write your answers below.

1. Why do you think it is important for scientists to be curious?

_____

_____

2. What might you want to invent? Why?

_____

_____

_____

_____

> **PLANET DIARY** Go to **Planet Diary** to learn more about thinking like a scientist.

Lab zone® Do the Inquiry Warm-Up *How Keen Are Your Senses?*

Vocabulary

- skepticism • ethics • personal bias • cultural bias
- experimental bias • objective • subjective
- deductive reasoning • inductive reasoning

Skills

⟳ **Reading:** Relate Cause and Effect
△ **Inquiry:** Classify

What Attitudes Help You Think Scientifically?

Perhaps someone has told you that you have a good attitude. What does that mean? An attitude is a state of mind. Your actions say a lot about your attitude. **Scientists possess certain important attitudes, including curiosity, honesty, creativity, open-mindedness, skepticism, good ethics, and awareness of bias.**

Curiosity One attitude that drives scientists is curiosity. Scientists want to learn more about the topics they study. **Figure 1** shows some things that may spark the interest of scientists.

Honesty Good scientists always report their observations and results truthfully. Honesty is especially important when a scientist's results go against previous ideas or predictions.

Creativity Whatever they study, scientists may experience problems. Sometimes, it takes creativity to find a solution. Creativity means coming up with inventive ways to solve problems or produce new things.

FLORIDA NGSSS

SC.7.N.1.1 Define a problem from the seventh grade curriculum, use appropriate reference materials to support scientific understanding, plan and carry out scientific investigation of various types, such as systematic observations or experiments, identify variables, collect and organize data, interpret data in charts, tables, and graphics, analyze information, make predictions, and defend conclusions.

LA.7.2.2.3 The student will organize information to show understanding.

FIGURE 1 ·································

Curiosity

Wherever you go in Florida, there are plenty of things to be curious about!

✎ **Ask Questions** For each image, write a question you are curious about in the boxes.

15

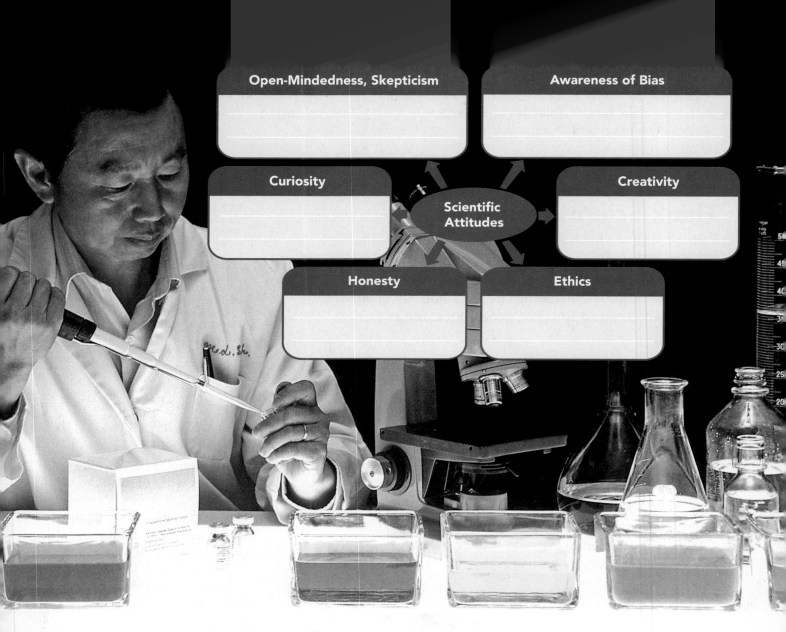

Open-Mindedness, Skepticism

Awareness of Bias

Curiosity

Scientific Attitudes

Creativity

Honesty

Ethics

FIGURE 2 ·······························

Attitudes of Scientists
This scientist is carefully conducting an experiment.

✎ **Summarize** After you have read the section What Attitudes Help You Think Scientifically?, write a summary of each scientific attitude in the graphic organizer.   LA.7.2.2.3

Open-Mindedness and Skepticism Scientists need to be open-minded, or capable of accepting new and different ideas. However, open-mindedness should always be balanced by **skepticism,** which is having an attitude of doubt. Skepticism keeps a scientist from accepting ideas that may be untrue.

Ethics Because scientists work with the natural world, they must be careful not to damage it. Scientists need a strong sense of **ethics,** which refers to the rules that enable people to know right from wrong. Scientists must consider all the effects their research may have on people and the environment. They make decisions only after considering the risks and benefits to living things or the environment. For example, scientists test medicine they have developed before the medicine is sold to the public. Scientists inform volunteers of the new medicine's risks before allowing them to take part in the tests. Look at **Figure 2** to review scientific attitudes.

Awareness of Bias What scientists expect to find can influence, or bias, what they observe and how they interpret observations. For example, a scientist might misinterpret the behavior of an animal because of what she already knows about animals.

There are different kinds of bias. **Personal bias** comes from a person's likes and dislikes. For instance, if you like the taste of a cereal, you might think everyone else should, too. **Cultural bias** stems from the culture in which a person grows up. For example, a culture that regards snakes as bad might overlook how well snakes control pests. **Experimental bias** is a mistake in the design of an experiment that makes a particular result more likely. For example, suppose you wanted to determine the boiling point of pure water. If your experiment uses water that has some salt in it, your results would be biased.

➲ Relate Cause and Effect
In the first paragraph, underline an example of bias. Then circle its effect.

$1.00

$1.25

Salted Peanuts

RAISINS

$0.75 cheese CRACKERS

NET WT. 1 ½ OZ (42.5 g)

apply it!

Matt likes cheese crackers best and thinks that most other students do too. So he observed what students bought at the vending machine during one lunch. Seven bought crackers, three bought nuts, and none bought raisins.

❶ Circle the evidence of personal bias.

❷ CHALLENGE Describe the experimental bias.

_____

_____

_____

Lab zone® Do the Quick Lab
Thinking Like a Scientist.

🔖 Assess Your Understanding

1a. Explain What can bias a scientist's observations?

_____

_____
SC.7.N.1.1

b. Apply Concepts Debbie discovered a new way to make pizza. What scientific attitude is this an example of?

_____

_____
SC.7.N.1.1

got it?

○ **I get it!** Now I know that attitudes that help you think scientifically are _____

_____

_____

_____

○ **I need extra help with** _____

Go to MY SCIENCE COACH *online for help with this subject.*
SC.7.N.1.1

FLORIDA NGSSS

SC.7.N.1.1 Define a problem from the seventh grade curriculum, use appropriate reference materials to support scientific understanding, plan and carry out scientific investigation of various types, such as systematic observations or experiments, identify variables, collect and organize data, interpret data in charts, tables, and graphics, analyze information, make predictions, and defend conclusions.

What Is Scientific Reasoning?

You use reasoning, or a logical way of thinking, when you solve word problems. Scientists use reasoning in their work, too. **Scientific reasoning requires a logical way of thinking based on gathering and evaluating evidence.** There are two types of scientific reasoning. Scientific reasoning can be deductive or inductive.

Because scientific reasoning relies on gathering and evaluating evidence, it is objective reasoning. Being **objective** means that you make decisions and draw conclusions based on available evidence. For example, scientists used to think chimps ate only plants. However, Jane Goodall observed chimps eating meat. Based on this evidence, she concluded that chimps ate meat and plants.

In contrast, being **subjective** means that personal feelings have entered into a decision or conclusion. Personal opinions, values, and tastes are subjective because they are based on your feelings about something. For example, if you see a clear stream in the woods, you might take a drink because you think clear water is clean. However, you have not objectively tested the water's quality. The water might contain microorganisms you cannot see and be unsafe to drink.

apply it!

Classify Read the sentences below. Then decide if each example uses objective reasoning or subjective reasoning to reach a conclusion. Place a check mark in the corresponding column.

	Objective	Subjective
Jane Goodall saw a chimp chewing on wet leaves. She reasoned that chimps sometimes used leaves to drink water.		
I like to run. I must be the fastest person in the class.		
Emily is 1.7 m tall. No one else in class is taller than 1.6 m. So Emily is the tallest person in class.		
I dislike dogs. Dogs must be the least friendly animals.		

Deductive Reasoning

Explaining things by starting with a general idea and then applying the idea to a specific observation is called **deductive reasoning**. For example, you could use deductive reasoning to help you conclude why there are earthquakes in California. You would start with a general idea: the theory of plate tectonics. The theory states that earthquakes happen mostly where large pieces of Earth's crust, called plates, meet. Then you would apply this idea to a specific observation: There are many earthquakes in California. This leads you to a conclusion, called a deduction: California has earthquakes because it is a place where plates meet. Practice using this process in **Figure 3.**

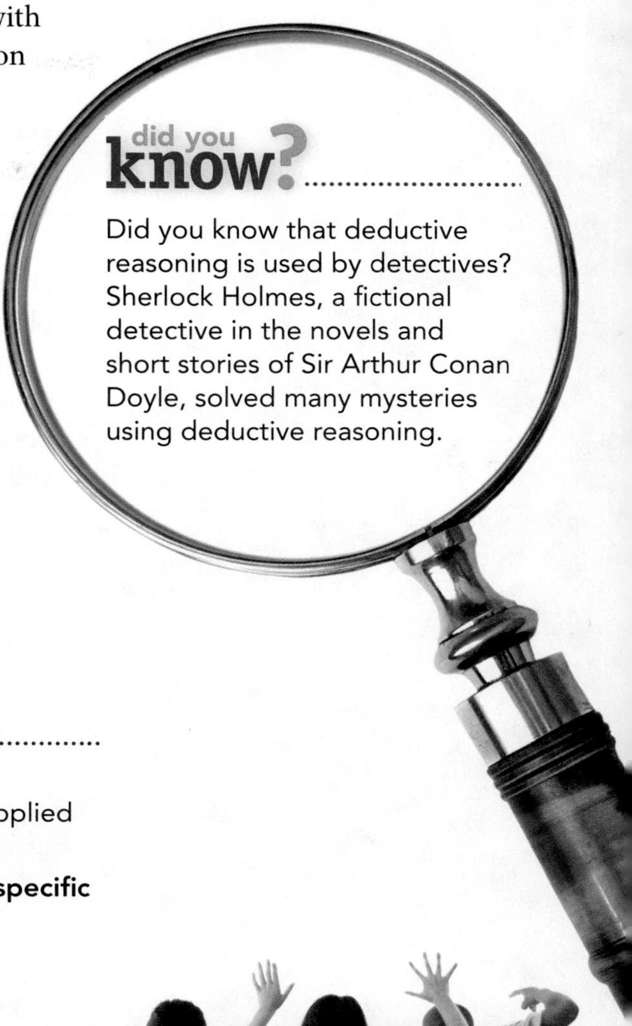

did you **know?**

Did you know that deductive reasoning is used by detectives? Sherlock Holmes, a fictional detective in the novels and short stories of Sir Arthur Conan Doyle, solved many mysteries using deductive reasoning.

FIGURE 3

Deductive Reasoning

Deductive reasoning occurs when a general idea is applied to a specific example and a conclusion is reached.

Apply Concepts Apply each general idea to a specific example and then draw a conclusion.

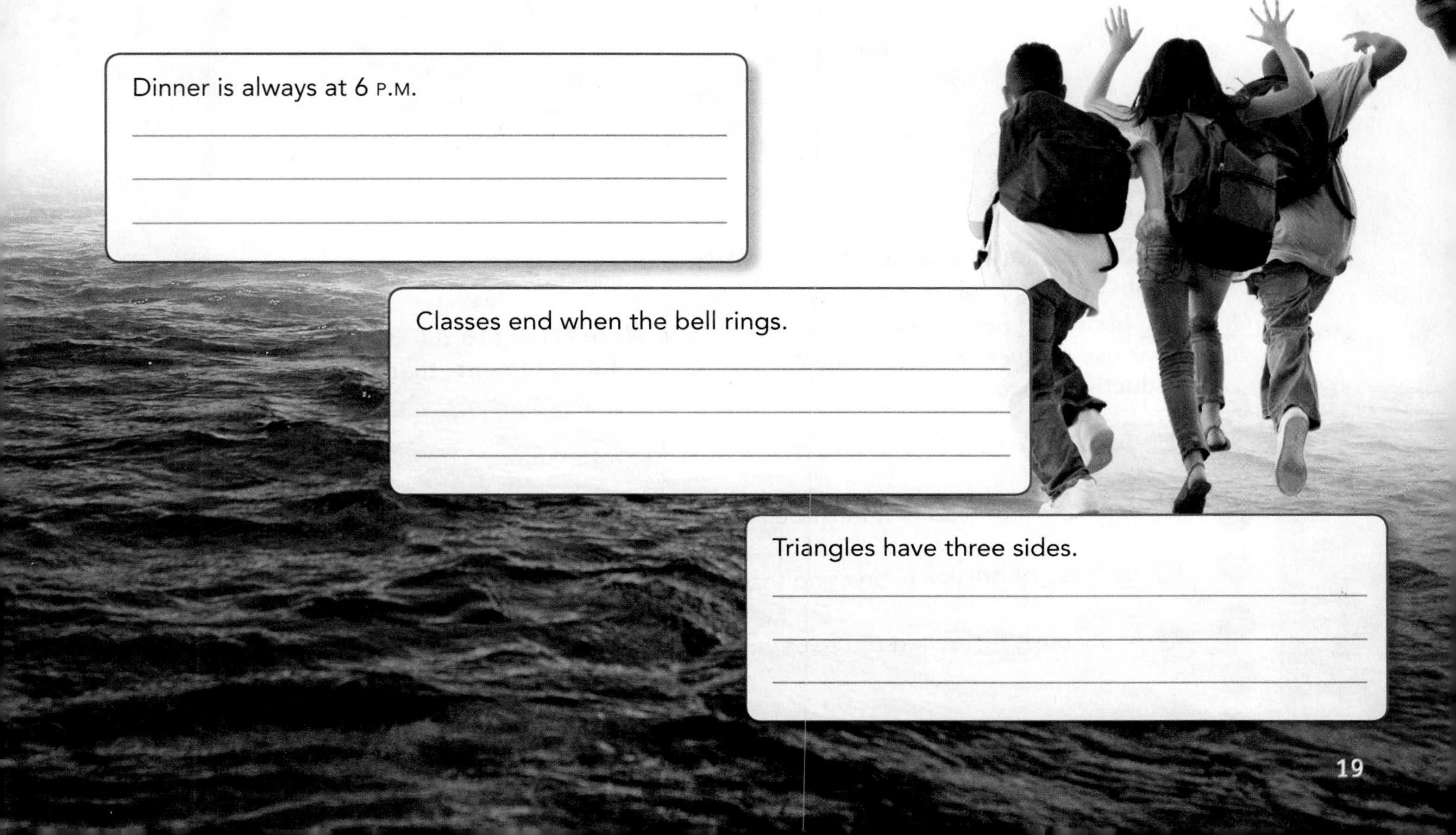

Dinner is always at 6 P.M.

Classes end when the bell rings.

Triangles have three sides.

Inductive Reasoning Scientists also use inductive reasoning, which can be considered the opposite of deductive reasoning. **Inductive reasoning** uses specific observations to make generalizations. For example, suppose you notice that leaf-cutter ants appear to follow other ants along specific paths, as shown in **Figure 4**. The ants follow the paths to sources of food, water, and nest material. Then they return to their nests. These observations about the leaf-cutter ants are specific. From these specific observations you conclude that these ants must communicate to be able to always follow the same path. This conclusion is a generalization about the behavior of leaf-cutter ants based on your observations. Scientists frequently use inductive reasoning. They collect data and then reach a conclusion based on that data.

FIGURE 4 ···

> INTERACTIVE ART **Scientific Reasoning**
Leaf-cutter ants follow a chemical trail to find and harvest leaves.

✎ **Identify Look at the statements below. Write *D* next to the statements that use deductive reasoning. Write *I* next to the statements that use inductive reasoning.**

❶ Turtles have shells. They must use shells for protection. _____

❷ A puddle has frozen. It must be below 0°C outside. _____

❸ Because of gravity, everything that goes up must come down. _____

❹ Many birds fly toward the equator in fall. Birds prefer warm weather. _____

Faulty Reasoning Scientists must be careful not to use faulty reasoning, because it can lead to faulty conclusions. If you draw a conclusion based on too little data, your reasoning might lead you to the wrong general idea. For example, to conclude accurately that all ants communicate with each other, you would have to observe leaf-cutter ants and many other kinds of ants many times. In addition, based on observations of how leaf-cutter ants follow paths, you cannot conclude how they communicated. For example, you cannot say they follow the tiny footprints of the ants ahead of them. Such a conclusion would be a guess not based on observation.

apply it!

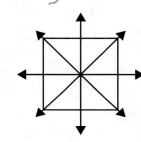

Joy drew lines of symmetry on a square. She saw that a rectangle has four straight sides and four right angles, so she drew the same lines of symmetry on a rectangle.

1 Make Models Fold a piece of rectangular notebook paper according to the lines of symmetry Joy drew on the rectangle. Are her lines of symmetry correct? Explain how you know.

_____

_____

2 Identify Faulty Reasoning Underline Joy's reasoning for drawing the lines of symmetry on the rectangle. What other characteristic should Joy have considered?

_____

_____

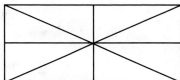 Do the Quick Lab
Using Scientific Thinking.

🔑 Assess Your Understanding

2a. Define _____ reasoning uses a general idea to make a specific observation.
SC.7.N.1.1

b. Relate Cause and Effect What is a cause of faulty reasoning?

_____

_____

SC.7.N.1.1

got it?

○ **I get it!** Now I know that scientific reasoning includes _____

_____

○ **I need extra help with** _____

Go to MY SCIENCE ⓢ COACH *online for help with this subject.*
SC.7.N.1.1

Measurement— A Common Language

🔑 **Why Do Scientists Use a Standard Measurement System?**
SC.7.N.1.1

🔑 **What Are Some SI Units of Measure?**
SC.7.N.1.1, LA.7.2.2.3

MY PLANET DiARY

Extreme Measurements

Here are some fascinating animal measurements.

- The Queen Alexandra's Birdwing butterfly has a wingspan of 30 centimeters.

- A newborn giraffe stands 1.8 meters tall.

- When a blue whale exhales, the spray from its blowhole can reach up to 9 meters into the air.

- A colossal squid's eye measures about 28 centimeters across.

- With a mass of only 20 grams, the rhinoceros beetle can lift 850 times its own mass.

- A hummingbird's egg has a mass of about half a gram while an ostrich egg has a mass of about 1,500 grams.

Ostrich egg

FUN FACTS

Read the following questions. Write your answers below.

1. What problems could arise if some scientists measured length in inches and others measured length in centimeters?

_____

_____

_____

2. What units of measurement would you use to measure your height and mass?

_____

_____

_____

_____

> PLANET DIARY Go to **Planet Diary** to learn more about measurement.

 Do the Inquiry Warm-Up *History of Measurement.*

Hummingbird eggs

Vocabulary

- metric system • International System of Units (SI) • mass • weight
- volume • meniscus • density

Skills

Reading: Compare and Contrast

Inquiry: Measure

Why Do Scientists Use a Standard Measurement System?

Standard measurement is important. Without it, cooks would use handfuls and pinches instead of cups and tablespoons.

Scientists also use standard measurements. This allows scientists everywhere to repeat experiments. In the 1790s, scientists in France developed the metric system of measurement. The **metric system** is a measurement system based on the number 10. Modern scientists use a version of the metric system called the **International System of Units**, or SI (from the French, *Système International d'Unités*). **Using SI as the standard system of measurement allows scientists to compare data and communicate with each other about their results.** The prefixes used in the SI system are shown in **Figure 1.**

FLORIDA NGSSS

SC.7.N.1.1 Define a problem from the seventh grade curriculum, use appropriate reference materials to support scientific understanding, plan and carry out scientific investigation of various types, such as systematic observations or experiments, identify variables, collect and organize data, interpret data in charts, tables, and graphics, analyze information, make predictions, and defend conclusions.

FIGURE 1 ·······································

SI Prefixes

SI units are similar to our money units, in which a dime is ten times more than a penny.

 Complete the tasks below.

1. **Name** In the table at the right, finish filling in the Example column.

2. **Calculate** How many times larger is a *kilo-* than a *deka-*?

_____

_____

Common SI Prefixes

Prefix	Meaning	Example
kilo- (k)	1,000	_____
hecto- (h)	100	_____
deka- (da)	10	dekameter
no prefix	1	meter
deci- (d)	0.1 (one tenth)	_____
centi- (c)	0.01 (one hundredth)	_____
milli- (m)	0.001 (one thousandth)	_____

Lab zone® Do the Quick Lab *How Many Shoes?*

Assess Your Understanding

got it? ··

○ **I get it!** Now I know that scientists use a standard measurement system to _____

_____

○ **I need extra help with** _____

Go to my science **coach** *online for help with this subject.*

SC.7.N.1.1

23

Conversions for Length

1 km	=	1,000 m
1 m	=	100 cm
1 m	=	1,000 mm
1 cm	=	10 mm

What Are Some SI Units of Measure?

Scientists regularly measure attributes such as length, mass, volume, density, temperature, and time. Each attribute is measured in an SI unit.

Length Length is the distance from one point to another. 🔑 **In SI, the basic unit for measuring length is the meter (m).** Many distances can be measured in meters. For example, you can measure a softball throw or your height in meters. One meter is about the distance from the floor to a doorknob. A tool used to measure length is a metric ruler.

For measuring lengths smaller than a meter, you use the centimeter (cm) and millimeter (mm). For example, the length of this page is about 28 centimeters. For measuring a long distance, such as the distance between cities, you use the unit called a kilometer (km). The table at the left shows you how to convert between different metric length units. Try measuring the turtle's shell in **Figure 2**.

FIGURE 2 ··

Measuring Length
To use a metric ruler, line up one end of an object with the zero mark. Then read the number at the object's other end.

✏️ **Use the ruler to measure the length of the turtle's shell and record it above the arrow. Then, working in small groups, complete the activity below.**

1. ⚠️ **Measure** Measure the width of a penny and a dime in millimeters.

_____

_____

2. **Calculate** Convert the width of each coin in millimeters into centimeters.

_____

_____

_____

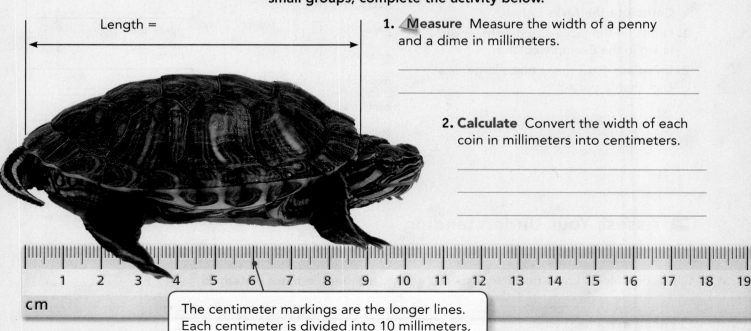

Length =

The centimeter markings are the longer lines. Each centimeter is divided into 10 millimeters, which are marked by the shorter lines.

cm

Mass

A balance, such as the one shown in **Figure 3**, is used to measure mass. **Mass** is a measure of the amount of matter in an object. A balance compares the mass of an object to a known mass. 🔑 **In SI, the basic unit for measuring mass is the kilogram (kg).** The mass of cars, bicycles, and people is measured in kilograms. If you want to measure much smaller masses, you would use grams (g) or milligrams (mg). The table at the right shows how to convert between kilograms, grams, and milligrams.

Unlike mass, **weight** is a measure of the force of gravity acting on an object. A scale is used to measure weight. When you stand on a scale on Earth, gravity pulls you downward. This compresses springs inside the scale. The more you weigh, the more the springs compress. On the moon, the force of gravity is weaker than it is on Earth. So the scale's springs would not compress as much on the moon as on Earth. Unlike weight, your mass on the moon is the same as your mass on Earth.

Conversions for Mass

1 kg	=	1,000 g
1 g	=	1,000 mg

✏️

Compare and Contrast
Use the chart to compare and contrast mass and weight.
LA.7.2.2.3

Alike	Different
_____	_____
_____	_____
_____	_____
_____	_____
_____	_____
_____	_____
_____	_____
_____	_____
_____	_____
_____	_____

FIGURE 3 ·······················

Measuring Mass
A triple-beam balance can be used to measure mass.

✏️ **Measure** Read the balance to find the mass of the turtle. Record your answer in grams and then in milligrams.

_____

_____

1 Place an object on the pan.

2 Shift the riders on the beams until they balance the object and the pointer hits 0.

3 Add up the grams shown on all three beams to find the mass.

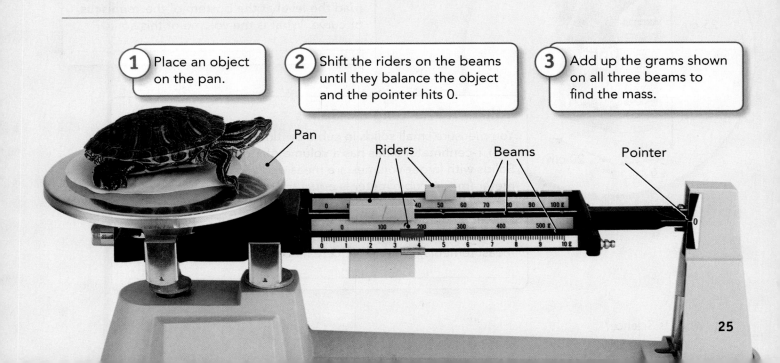

Pan   Riders   Beams   Pointer

Conversions for Volume

1 m³	=	1,000,000 cm³
1 cm³	=	1 mL
1 L	=	1,000 mL
1 L	=	1,000 cm³

Volume Instead of measuring your juice, you just look to see how much of the glass you have filled up. **Volume** is the amount of space an object or substance takes up. 🔑 **In SI, the basic unit for measuring volume is the cubic meter (m³).** Other units include the liter (L) and the cubic centimeter (cm³). Cubic meters or centimeters are used to measure the volume of solids. The liter is commonly used for measuring the volume of liquids. The green table shows how to convert between these units.

FIGURE 4 ·······································

Volume of Liquids, Rectangular Solids, and Irregular Solids

Measuring the volume of liquids and rectangular solids requires different methods.

✏️ **Complete the activity on this page. Then follow the steps to measure the volume of an irregular solid on the next page.**

Explain In the boxes, find the volume of the liquid and the cereal box. Below, explain which has a greater volume.

_____

_____

_____

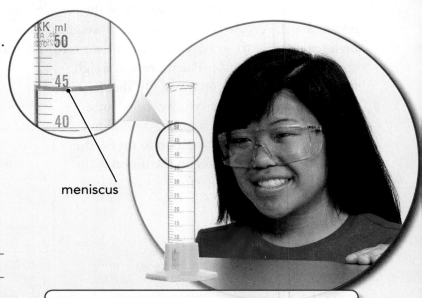

meniscus

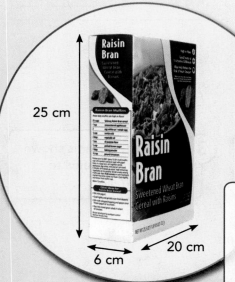

25 cm

6 cm

20 cm

Volume of Liquids

You are probably familiar with the liter from seeing 1-liter and 2-liter bottles. You can measure smaller liquid volumes by using milliliters (mL). There are 1,000 milliliters in one liter. To measure the volume of a liquid, read the level at the bottom of the **meniscus,** or curve. What is the volume of this liquid?

_____

Volume of Rectangular Solids

You measure small solids in cubic centimeters (cm³). A cube with 1-centimeter sides has a volume of 1 cubic centimeter. Solids with larger volumes are measured with the cubic meter (m³). A cubic meter is equal to the volume of a cube with 1-meter sides. To calculate a rectangular solid's volume, multiply length times width times height. When you use this formula, you must use the same units for all measurements. What is the cereal box's volume?

_____

Volume of Irregular Solids

Suppose you wanted to measure the volume of a rock. Because of its irregular shape, you cannot measure a rock's length, width, or height. However, you can use the displacement method shown on this page. To use this method, you immerse the object in water and measure how much the water level rises.

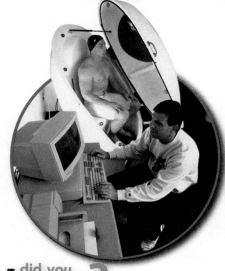

did you know?

Athletes may have their body volume measured to calculate their density, which can be used to determine their body fat percentage. One method for measuring an athlete's volume involves displacement of air by the athlete in an airtight device.

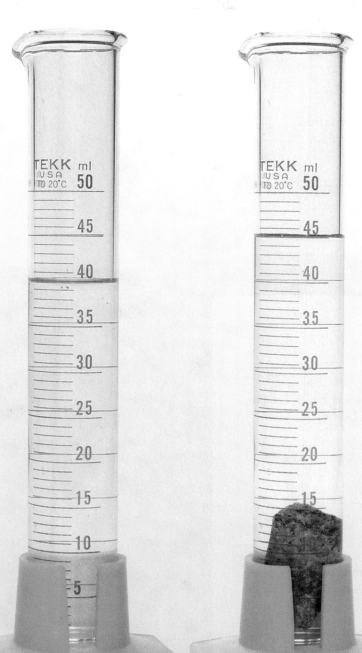

1 Fill a graduated cylinder about two thirds full of water.

What is the volume of water in the graduated cylinder?

_____

2 Place the object into the water.

What is the volume of the water plus the object?

_____

3 Find the volume of the object by subtracting the volume of the water alone from the volume of the water plus the object.

What is the volume of the object?

_____

Density Look at **Figure 5.** Two objects of the same size can have different masses. This is because different materials have different densities. **Density** is a measure of how much mass is contained in a given volume.

Units of Density Because density is made up of two measurements, mass and volume, an object's density is expressed as a relationship between two units. 🗝 **In SI, the basic unit for measuring density is kilograms per cubic meter (kg/m³).** Other units of density are grams per cubic centimeter (g/cm³) and grams per milliliter (g/mL).

FIGURE 5 ··

Comparing Densities

The bowling ball and the beach ball have the same volume but not the same mass.

✏️ **Form Operational Definitions** Use this information to decide which object has a greater density. Explain your answer in terms of volume and mass.

_____

_____

_____

do the math!

Calculating Density

The density of an object is the object's mass divided by its volume. To find the density of an object, use the formula below.

$$\text{Density} = \frac{\text{mass}}{\text{volume}}$$

1 Calculate Find the density of a piece of metal that has a mass of 68 g and a volume of 6 cm³.

_____

2 Predict Suppose a piece of metal has the same mass as the metal in Question 1 but a greater volume. How would its density compare to the metal in Question 1?

_____

_____

_____

MA.7.A.3.2

Density of Substances The table in **Figure 6** lists the densities of some common substances. The density of a pure substance is the same for all samples of that substance. For example, all samples of pure gold, no matter how large or small, have a density of 19.3 g/cm³.

Once you know an object's density, you can determine whether the object will float in a given liquid. An object will float if it is less dense than the surrounding liquid. For example, the density of water is 1 g/cm³. A piece of wood with a density of 0.8 g/cm³ will float in water. A ring made of pure silver, which has a density of 10.5 g/cm³, will sink.

FIGURE 6 ···

A Density Experiment
Knowing the density of an object helps you predict how it will float and identify what it is made of.

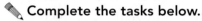 **Complete the tasks below.**

1. **Infer** An object has a density of 0.7 g/cm³. Do you think it floats or sinks in water? Explain.

_____

_____

2. **Design Experiments** Use what you know about density and measuring tools to describe the steps you might use to determine if a bar of metal is gold. Write your procedure in the notebook.

Densities of Some Common Substances	
Substance	**Density (g/cm³)**
Air	0.001
Ice	0.9
Water	1.0
Aluminum	2.7
Gold	19.3

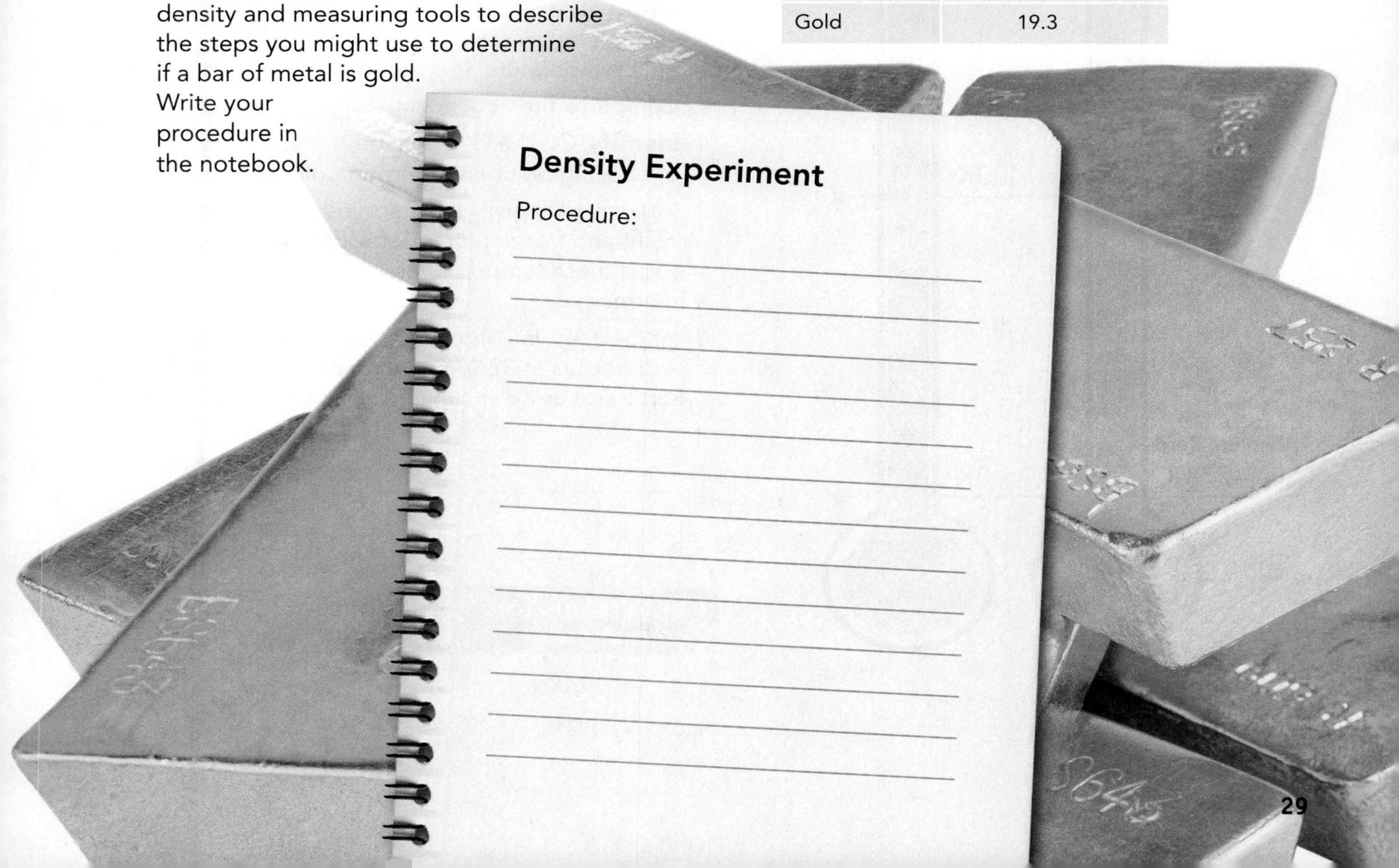

Density Experiment

Procedure:

_____

_____

_____

_____

_____

_____

_____

_____

_____

_____

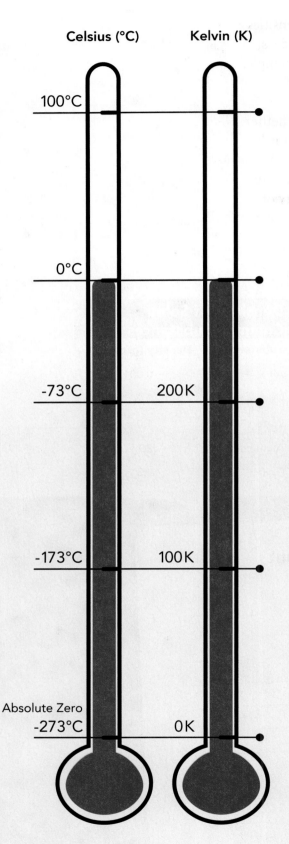

Celsius (°C)   Kelvin (K)

100°C

0°C

-73°C   200K

-173°C   100K

Absolute Zero
-273°C   0K

Temperature

Is it cold out this morning? How high will the temperature rise? You probably use temperature measurements often in your everyday life. So do scientists.

Scientists commonly use the Celsius temperature scale to measure temperature. On the Celsius scale, water freezes at 0°C and boils at 100°C. 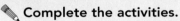 **In addition to the Celsius scale, scientists sometimes use another temperature scale, called the Kelvin scale. In fact, the kelvin (K) is the official SI unit for temperature.** Kelvin is useful in science because there are no negative numbers. Units on the Kelvin scale are the same size as those on the Celsius scale, as shown in **Figure 7.** The table below shows how to convert between Celsius and Kelvin.

A thermometer is used to measure temperature. When you place a liquid thermometer in a substance, the liquid inside the thermometer will increase or decrease in volume. This makes the level rise or fall. Wait until the level stops changing. Then read the number next to the top of the liquid in the thermometer.

FIGURE 7 ···

Temperature Scales
Zero on the Kelvin scale (0 K) is the coldest possible temperature. It is called absolute zero.

✎ **Complete the activities.**

1. **Identify** On the Celsius thermometer, label the boiling point and freezing point of water.

2. **Interpret Diagrams** Determine the boiling point and freezing point of water in Kelvins. Label these temperatures on the Kelvin thermometer.

3. **CHALLENGE** In Fahrenheit, water boils at 212° and freezes at 32°. Are Fahrenheit units the same size as Kelvin units? Explain.

_____

_____

_____

Conversions for Temperature

0°C	=	273 K
100°C	=	373 K

Time You push to run even faster with the finish line in sight. But an opponent is catching up. Just one second can mean the difference between winning and losing. What is a second?

🔑 **The second (s) is the SI unit used to measure time.** Just like all the SI units, the second is divided into smaller units based on the number 10. For example, a millisecond (ms) is one thousandth of a second. You use minutes or hours for longer periods of time. There are 60 seconds in a minute, and 60 minutes in an hour.

Clocks and watches are used to measure time. Some clocks are more accurate than others. Most digital stopwatches measure time accurately to one hundredth of a second, as shown in **Figure 8.** Devices used for timing Olympic events measure time to a thousandth of a second or even closer.

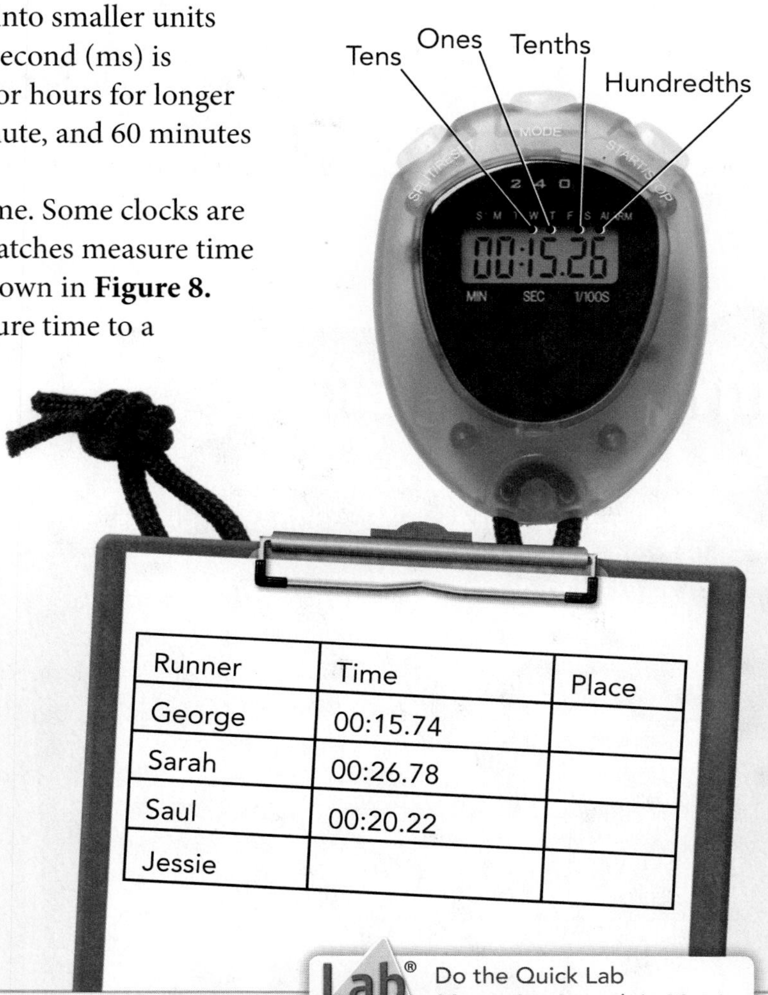

Tens   Ones   Tenths   Hundredths

00:15.26

MIN   SEC   1/100S

FIGURE 8 ···

It's About Time

This stopwatch measured Jessie's best time in a school race.

✏️ **Write Jessie's time in the chart and then complete the activity.**

Interpret Tables In the last column, write the order that the runners finished.

Runner	Time	Place
George	00:15.74	
Sarah	00:26.78	
Saul	00:20.22	
Jessie		

Lab zone® Do the Quick Lab *Measuring Length in Metric.*

🔑 **Assess Your Understanding**

1a. Identify What tool would you use to measure the mass of a baseball?

_____

_____

SC.7.N.1.1

b. Sequence What steps would you take to determine the density of a baseball?

_____

_____

_____

_____

_____

SC.7.N.1.1

got it?

○ **I get it!** Now I know that basic SI units of measurement are _____

_____

_____

_____

_____

○ **I need extra help with** _____

Go to **MY SCIENCE** ⓢ **COACH** *online for help with this subject.*

SC.7.N.1.1

Mathematics and Science

🔑 **What Math Skills Do Scientists Use?**
SC.7.N.1.1

🔑 **What Math Tools Do Scientists Use?**
SC.7.N.1.1, MA.6.S.6.2, MA.6.A.3.6

my planeт DiaRY

Measuring Earthquakes

The ground shakes, windows shatter, debris falls from above, and the streets are crowded with screaming people. This is how earthquakes are often depicted in the media. However, not all earthquakes cause such chaos and destruction. Some are so small they aren't even felt.

Since earthquakes occur all over the world, scientists must use a universal system of measurement to compare them. For large earthquakes, scientists use a measurement known as the moment magnitude scale. As the number on the scale increases, so does the size of the earthquake. So far, the largest earthquake on record occurred in Chile in 1960 and measured 9.5 on the moment magnitude scale.

DISCOVERY

Communicate Discuss the following questions with a partner. Write your answers below.

What do you know about earthquakes? How can you stay safe during one?

_____

_____

_____

_____

_____

_____

_____

> PLANET DIARY Go to **Planet Diary** to learn more about mathematics and science.

Lab zone Do the Inquiry Warm-Up
How Many Marbles Are There?

Vocabulary

- estimate • accuracy • precision
- significant figures • percent error • mean
- median • mode • range • anomalous data

Skills

⟳ Reading: Relate Cause and Effect

△ Inquiry: Calculate

What Math Skills Do Scientists Use?

From measuring to collecting data, scientists use math every day. 🔑 **Math skills that scientists use to collect data include estimation, accuracy and precision, and significant figures.**

Estimation An **estimate** is an approximation of a number based on reasonable assumptions. An estimate is not a guess. It is always based on known information. Scientists often rely on estimates when they cannot obtain exact numbers. Their estimates might be based on indirect measurements, calculations, and models. For example, they may estimate the distance between stars based on indirect measurements because they can't measure the distance directly. Other estimates might be based on a sample.

FLORIDA NGSSS

SC.7.N.1.1 Define a problem from the seventh grade curriculum, use appropriate reference materials to support scientific understanding, plan and carry out scientific investigation of various types, such as systematic observations or experiments, identify variables, collect and organize data, interpret data in charts, tables, and graphics, analyze information, make predictions, and defend conclusions.

do the math!

Estimation

Estimating from a sample is a quick way to determine the large number of birds in this photo.

❶ Interpret Photos How many birds are in the yellow square? This number is your sample.

_____

❷ Explain By what number should you multiply the sample to find an estimate for the total number of birds in the total area? Explain your answer.

_____

_____

_____

❸ Estimate Calculate your estimate for the total number of birds. Show your work.

_____

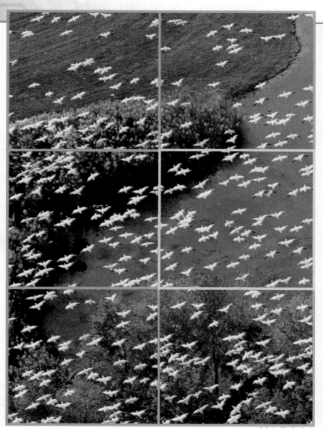

MA.7.S.6.1

FIGURE 1 ·····································

Accuracy and Precision

In a game of darts, accurate throws land close to the bull's eye. Precise throws land close to one another.

✎ **Apply Concepts** Draw dots on boards C and D to show the situations described.

Accuracy and Precision

People often use the words *accuracy* and *precision* to describe the same idea. In science, these words have different meanings. **Accuracy** refers to how close a measurement is to the true or accepted value. **Precision** refers to how close a group of measurements are to each other.

How can you be sure that a measurement is both accurate and precise? First, use a high-quality measurement tool. Second, measure carefully. Finally, repeat the measurement a few times. If your measurement is the same each time, you can assume that it is reliable. A reliable measurement is both accurate and precise. Look at **Figure 1**.

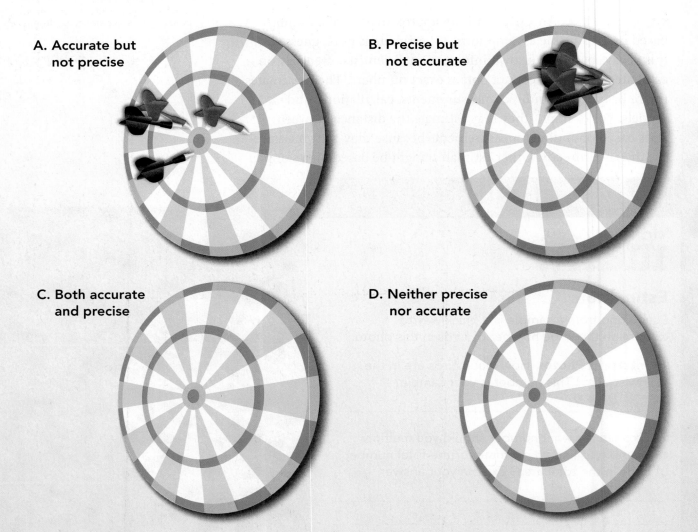

A. Accurate but not precise

B. Precise but not accurate

C. Both accurate and precise

D. Neither precise nor accurate

Significant Figures

Significant figures communicate how precise measurements are. The **significant figures** in a measurement include all digits measured exactly, plus one estimated digit. If the measurement has only one digit, you must assume it is estimated. Use **Figure 2** to learn more about significant figures.

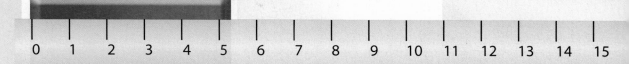

| | | | | | | | | | | | | | | | |
|0|1|2|3|4|5|6|7|8|9|10|11|12|13|14|15|

Adding or Subtracting Measurements

When you add or subtract measurements, your answer can only have as many places after the decimal point as the measurement with the fewest places after the decimal point. For example, suppose you add a tile that is 5.3 centimeters long to a row of tiles that is 21.94 centimeters long. Find the new length of the row.

21.9**4** cm (2 places after the decimal)
+ **5.3** cm (1 place after the decimal)
27.2**4** cm → 27.**2** cm (1 place after the decimal)

If you remove a tile that is 5.3 centimeters long from a row of tiles that is 21.94 centimeters long, what is the new length of the row? How many significant figures are in this measurement?

_____

_____

FIGURE 2 ·······································

Significant Figures

Suppose you are tiling a bathroom. You might estimate that the tile is 5.3 cm long. The measurement 5.3 cm has two significant figures, or sig figs. You are certain of the 5, but you have estimated the 3.

✎ **Calculate** **Read about adding, subtracting, and multiplying measurements. Then complete the activities in the boxes.**

Multiplying Measurements

When you multiply measurements, the answer should only have the same number of significant figures as the measurement with the fewest significant figures. For example, suppose you need to find the area of a space that measures 2.25 meters by 3 meters.

2.25 m (3 sig figs)
× 3 m (1 sig fig)
6.75 m² → 7 m² (1 sig fig)

Find the area of a space that measures 4.4 meters by 2 meters. How many significant figures are in this measurement?

_____

_____

Lab zone Do the Quick Lab
For Good Measure.

🔑 Assess Your Understanding

1a. Review What math skill do scientists rely on when they cannot obtain exact numbers?

_____

SC.7.N.1.1

b. Interpret Data Lia measures a wall of her room to be 3.7 meters by 2.45 meters. How many significant figures are in the measurement of its area? Explain.

_____

_____

SC.7.N.1.1

got it?

○ **I get it!** Now I know that the math skills scientists use to collect data include _____

_____

_____

○ **I need extra help with** _____

Go to **MY SCIENCE ⑤ COACH** *online for help with this subject.* SC.7.N.1.1

35

SC.7.N.1.1 Define a problem from the seventh grade curriculum, use appropriate reference materials to support scientific understanding, plan and carry out scientific investigation of various types, such as systematic observations or experiments, identify variables, collect and organize data, interpret data in charts, tables, and graphics, analyze information, make predictions, and defend conclusions.

MA.6.S.6.2 Select and analyze measures of central tendency.

MA.6.A.3.6 Construct and analyze tables, graphs, and equations.

What Math Tools Do Scientists Use?

Mathematics is just as powerful a tool for analyzing data as it is for collecting it. **Scientists use certain math tools to analyze data. These tools include calculating percent error; finding the mean, median, mode, and range; and checking the reasonableness of data.**

Percent Error Often, scientists must make measurements that already have accepted values. For example, an accepted, or true, value for the density of the metal copper is 8.92 g/cm³. Suppose you measure the mass and volume of a sample of the metal copper, and calculate a density of 9.37 g/cm³. You know your calculation is not accurate, but by how much? **Percent error** calculations are a way to determine how accurate an experimental value is. A low percent error means that the result you obtained was accurate. A high percent error means that your result was not accurate. It may not be accurate because you did not measure carefully or something was wrong with your measurement tool.

✎

↪ Relate Cause and Effect
Underline the causes of a high percent error.

do the math! Sample Problem

Percent Error

The experimental density of copper is 9.37 g/cm³. The true value is 8.92 g/cm³. To calculate the percent error, use the following formula and substitute.

$$\text{Percent error} = \frac{\text{Difference between experimental value and true value}}{\text{true value}} \times 100\%$$

$$\%E = \frac{9.37 \text{ g/cm}^3 - 8.92 \text{ g/cm}^3}{8.92 \text{ g/cm}^3} \times 100\%$$

The percent error in the calculation of the density of copper was 5.04%.

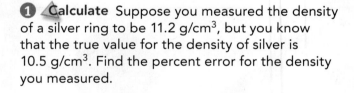

❶ Calculate Suppose you measured the density of a silver ring to be 11.2 g/cm³, but you know that the true value for the density of silver is 10.5 g/cm³. Find the percent error for the density you measured.

_____

_____

_____

❷ CHALLENGE What are two possible sources of error when measuring a sample's mass and volume?

_____

_____

_____

MA.6.A.3.6, MA.7.A.3.2

Mean, Median, Mode, and Range

Walking in the forest one day, you see a nest of eastern hognose snake eggs on the ground. You start to wonder about snake eggs. What is the average number of eggs in a nest? What is the range of eggs in a group of nests? Scientists ask questions like these, too. Their answers come from analyzing data. Use **Figure 3** to analyze hognose snake egg data yourself.

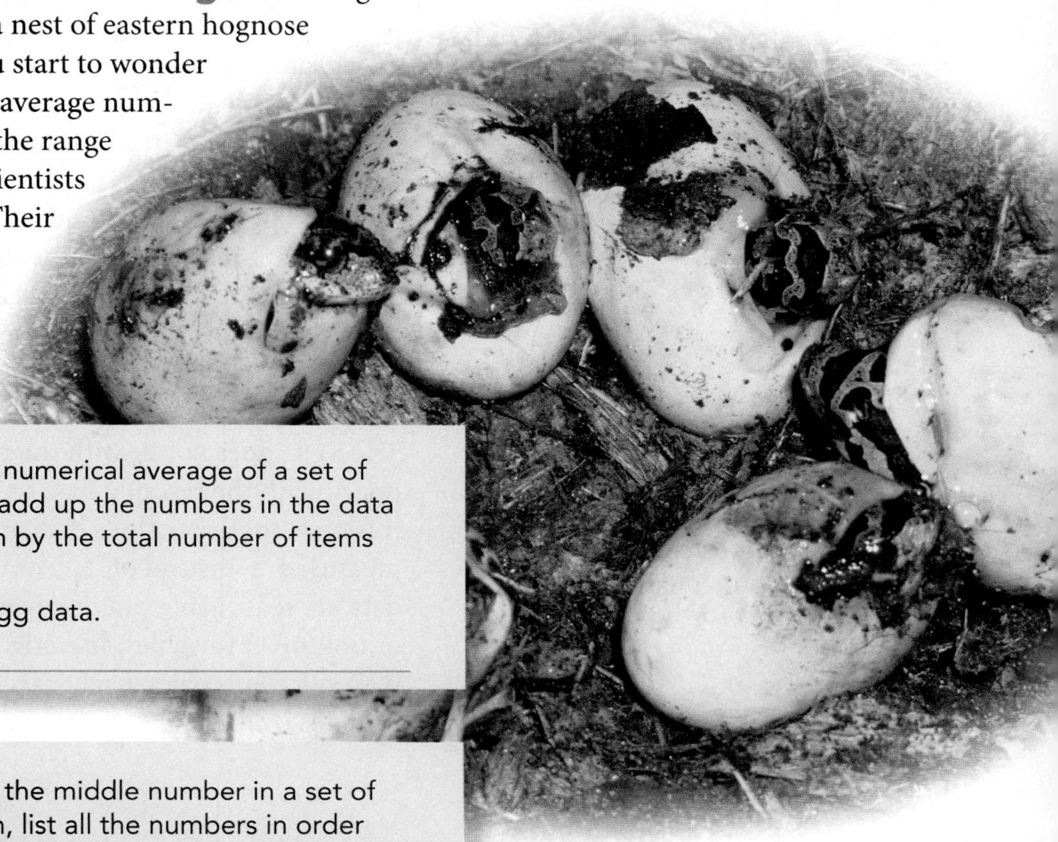

Mean The **mean** is the numerical average of a set of data. To find the mean, add up the numbers in the data set. Then divide the sum by the total number of items you added.

Find the mean for the egg data.

_____

Median The **median** is the middle number in a set of data. To find the median, list all the numbers in order from least to greatest. The median is the middle entry. If a list has an even number of entries, add the two middle numbers together and divide by two to find the median.

Find the median for the egg data.

_____

_____

Mode The **mode** is the number that appears most often in a list of numbers.

Find the mode for the egg data.

_____

Range The **range** of a set of data is the difference between the greatest value and the least value in the set.

Find the range for the egg data.

_____

FIGURE 3 ·····································

Hognose Snake Egg Data
You can use math to analyze the data in the table below about the number of hognose snake eggs in seven nests.

✏ **Calculate** Fill in the boxes with the mean, median, mode, and range of the hognose snake egg data. MA.6.S.6.2

Nest	Number of Eggs
A	21
B	33
C	18
D	54
E	42
F	33
G	27

Sea Turtles at Nesting Beach

Day	Turtles
Day 1	7
Day 2	7
Day 3	8
Day 4	7
Day 5	2

FIGURE 4 ·····················

Collected Data

On Day 5, only two turtles are at the beach.

✎ **Analyze Experimental Results**
Describe an unknown variable that could have affected the data.

_____

_____

_____

_____

Reasonable and Anomalous Data

An important part of analyzing any set of data is to ask, "Are these data reasonable? Do they make sense?" For example, suppose a scientist who studies sea turtles measures the ocean water temperature each night for five nights. His data for the first four nights are 26°C, 23°C, 25°C, and 24°C. On the last night, he asks a student to make the measurement. The student records 81 in the data book.

Are the data reasonable? The reading on Day 5 is very different. Some variation in ocean temperature makes sense within a small range. But it doesn't make sense for ocean temperature to rise 57°C in one day, from 24°C to 81°C. The 81°C does not fit with the rest of the data. Data that do not fit with the rest of a data set are **anomalous data.** In this case, the anomalous data are explainable. The student measured °F instead of °C. Sometimes asking whether data are reasonable can uncover sources of error or unknown variables. Investigating the reason for anomalous data can lead to new discoveries.

The pale green coloring on the map shows areas where green sea turtles commonly nest in Florida.

FIGURE 5 ··

> INTERACTIVE ART Scientists use mathematics to help answer the question, "How and why are the number of sea turtle nests in Florida changing?"

✎ **Design Experiments Answer the questions in the boxes below.**

1 **How would you collect accurate and precise turtle nest data?**

2 **What properties of the nests could you measure?**

3 **How might a hurricane in Florida cause anomalous nest data?**

4 **How could you estimate the total number of nests in Florida?**

Do the Quick Lab
How Close Is It?

🔑 Assess Your Understanding

2a. Describe Why is it important for scientists to calculate percent error?

_____

_____

SC.7.N.1.1

b. Apply Concepts You rush through a lab activity and get a percent error of 50 percent. Why might the percent error be so high?

_____

_____

_____

SC.7.N.1.1

got it? ··

○ **I get it!** Now I know that math tools scientists use to analyze data include _____

_____

_____

_____

○ **I need extra help with** _____

Go to **MY SCIENCE** Ⓢ **COACH** *online for help with this subject.* SC.7.N.1.1

LESSON 5

Graphs in Science

UNLOCK THE ESSENTIAL ?

🔑 **What Kinds of Data Do Line Graphs Display?**
SC.7.N.1.1, MA.6.A.3.6

🔑 **Why Are Line Graphs Powerful Tools?**
SC.7.N.1.1, LA.7.2.2.3

MY PLANET DIARY

Waste and Recycling Data

The information below shows the amount of waste generated and recovered for recycling per person per day for each year listed.

- 1980: Generated waste was about 1.68 kg and recovered waste was about 0.16 kg.
- 1990: Generated waste was about 2.04 kg and recovered waste was about 0.33 kg.
- 2000: Generated waste was 2.09 kg and recovered waste was about 0.51 kg.
- 2002: Generated waste was about 2.09 kg and recovered waste was about 0.61 kg.
- 2007: Generated waste was about 2.09 kg and recovered waste was about 0.70 kg.

SCIENCE STATS

Communicate Discuss the following question with a partner. Write your answer below.

How do you think society's view on recycling has changed over the years?

_____

_____

_____

_____

_____

▶ PLANET DIARY Go to **Planet Diary** to learn more about graphs in science.

Lab zone® Do the Inquiry Warm-Up
What's in a Picture?

🔲 **FLORIDA** NGSSS

SC.7.N.1.1 Plan and carry out scientific investigation of various types, such as systematic observations or experiments, identify variables, collect and organize data, interpret data in charts, tables, and graphics, analyze information, make predictions, and defend conclusions.

MA.6.A.3.6 Construct and analyze tables, graphs, and equations.

What Kinds of Data Do Line Graphs Display?

Could the saying "A watched pot never boils" really be true? Or does it take longer to boil water when there is more water in the pot? You could do an experiment to find out. The table in **Figure 1** shows data from such an experiment. But what do the data mean? Does it take longer to boil a larger volume of water?

Vocabulary
- graph
- linear graph
- nonlinear graph

Skills
- Reading: Relate Text and Visuals
- Inquiry: Predict

Line Graphs To help see what the data mean, you can use a graph. A **graph** is a "picture" of your data. One kind of graph is a line graph. **Line graphs display data that show how one variable (the dependent variable) changes in response to another variable (the independent variable).**

Using Line Graphs Scientists control changes in the independent variable. Then they collect data about how the dependent variable changes. A line graph is used when a independent variable is continuous, which means there are other points between the tested ones. For example, in the water-boiling experiment, many volumes are possible between 500 mL and 2,000 mL.

FIGURE 1 ·······························

> INTERACTIVE ART **A Line Graph**

This line graph plots the data from the table at the left.

Identify Identify the independent variable and the dependent variable in the experiment.

_____

_____

_____

_____

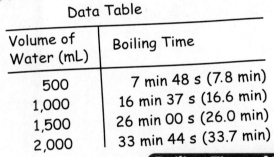

Data Table

Volume of Water (mL)	Boiling Time
500	7 min 48 s (7.8 min)
1,000	16 min 37 s (16.6 min)
1,500	26 min 00 s (26.0 min)
2,000	33 min 44 s (33.7 min)

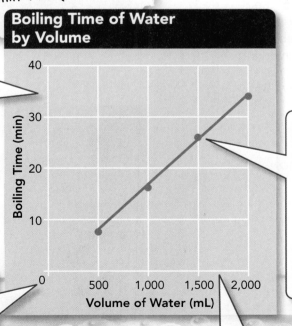

Boiling Time of Water by Volume

The vertical axis, or y-axis, runs up and down. It's labeled with the dependent variable.

A coordinate gives the location of a point on a graph. This point has the coordinates of

(1,500, 27)

x-coordinate
(horizontal units from origin)

y-coordinate
(vertical units from origin)

The point where the two axes cross is called the origin of the graph.

The horizontal axis, or x-axis, runs left to right. It's labeled with the independent variable.

How to Make a Line Graph When should you plot a line graph? The answer is, when your independent variable is continuous—that is, when there are other points between the ones that you tested. In the water-boiling experiment, volumes of 501 mL, 502 mL, and so on exist between 500 mL and 2,000 mL. Time and mass are other continuous variables. Use the steps in **Figure 2** to practice plotting a line graph.

FIGURE 2 ························

Panda Growth

Panda cubs grow quickly in their first few months of life. ✎ **Graph Follow the instructions in Steps 1, 2, and 3. Draw your graphs in the space provided.**

MA.6.A.3.6

Weight of a Panda	
Age (months)	Weight (lbs)
1	2.5
2	7.6
3	12.5
4	17.1
6	24.3

2 **Plot the data.**

Plot a point for each piece of data. Follow an imaginary vertical line extending up from the horizontal axis at the 1 mark. Then follow an imaginary horizontal line extending across from the vertical axis where the value 2.5 would be. Draw a point where these two lines cross, or intersect. The point showing the location of that intersection is called a data point.

1 Draw and label the axes. Then create a scale.

Draw the horizontal and vertical axes. Label the horizontal axis with the name of the independent variable. Label the vertical axis with the name of the dependent variable. Be sure to include units of measurement in each label. On each axis, create a scale by marking off equally spaced intervals that cover the range of values you will show. Both scales should begin at zero.

3 Draw a "line of best fit."

A line of best fit is a smooth line that shows the general pattern of a graph. Look at the points you plotted to find a trend in the data. Then draw a smooth line between the points to reflect that pattern. Make sure there are about as many points above your line as there are below it. Last, add a title that describes the variables or relationship shown in the graph.

Lab zone® Do the Quick Lab
What's a Line Graph?

🔑 Assess Your Understanding

1a. Identify The location of a point on a graph is called the (*y-axis/x-axis/coordinate*).

SC.7.N.1.1

b. Describe What is a line of best fit?

_____

_____

SC.7.N.1.1

c. Apply Concepts You want to measure how tall your friends grow over one year. What is the independent and the dependent variable?

_____

_____

_____

SC.7.N.1.1

got it? ·······································

○ **I get it!** Now I know that line graphs display data that show_____

_____

○ **I need extra help with** _____

Go to **MY SCIENCE** 🅢 **COACH** *online for help with this subject.*

SC.7.N.1.1

43

Relate Text and Visuals

Underline statements in the text that describe the graphs in Figure 2.

Why Are Line Graphs Powerful Tools?

A line graph in which the data points yield a straight line is a **linear graph.** The kind of graph in which the data points do not fall along a straight line is called a **nonlinear graph.** As shown in **Figure 2,** both kinds of line graphs are useful. 🔑 **Line graphs are powerful tools in science because they allow you to identify trends, make predictions, and recognize anomalous data.**

For example, the graph of experimental data in **Figure 3** on the next page shows that the trend is linear, even though most points do not fall exactly on the line. One point is clearly not part of the trend. It is an anomalous data point. Graphs make it easy to see anomalous data points like this one. When a graph does not have any clear trends, it probably means that the variables are not related.

FIGURE 2 ···

Linear Trends

Data plotted in a line graph may show a trend.

✏️ **Read Graphs** In the boxes, tell whether the graph is linear or nonlinear, and describe the graph's trend.

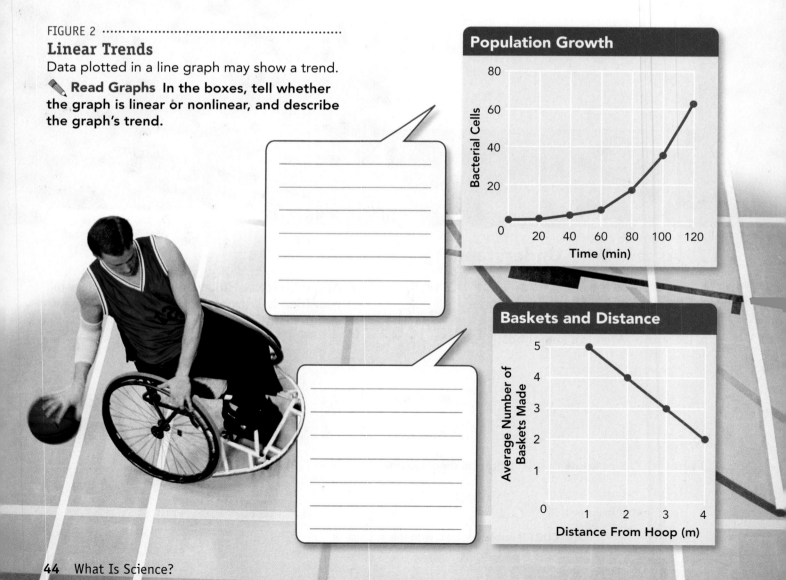

Population Growth

Baskets and Distance

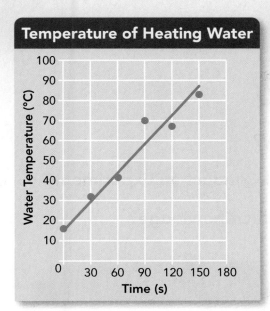

Temperature of Heating Water

Water Temperature (°C) vs Time (s)

FIGURE 3 ···

Data Variation

Even though some points do not fall on the line, this graph shows a trend.

✎ **Complete the following tasks.**

1. **Identify** Label the anomalous data point.

2. **Predict** Use the graph to predict the temperature of the water after 180 seconds.

_____

apply it!

This graph shows the distance two friends biked in one hour.

❶ **Interpret Data** What is the relationship between the variables distance and time?

_____

❷ [CHALLENGE] During which time interval were the friends biking fastest? Explain.

_____

_____

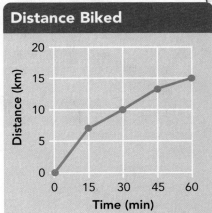

Distance Biked

Distance (km) vs Time (min)

Lab zone ® Do the Lab Investigation *Density Graphs.*

🔑 Assess Your Understanding

2a. Review What does a graph with no trend show about the variables?

_____

_____
SC.7.N.1.1

b. Compare and Contrast How does a graph with no trend differ from a graph with anomalous data points?

_____

_____

_____

SC.7.N.1.1, LA.7.2.2.3

got it?

○ **I get it!** Now I know that line graphs are powerful tools because _____

_____

_____

_____

○ **I need extra help with** _____

Go to **my science** ⑤ **coach** *online for help with this subject.*
SC.7.N.1.1

my planeT DiaRY

The Law of Falling Objects

Misconception: Heavier objects fall faster than lighter ones. This assumption is not true. They actually fall at the same rate, or with the same acceleration. The misconception was introduced by a philosopher named Aristotle and accepted for more than 2,000 years. But in the late 1500s, Galileo Galilei discovered something different—all free-falling objects fall with the same acceleration. To prove this, Galileo performed a number of experiments. Galileo's experiments involved rolling balls with different masses down a ramp called an inclined plane and making careful measurements.

Galileo and one of his acceleration experiments

MISCONCEPTION

Communicate Discuss the following questions with a partner. Write your answers below.

1. Why did Galileo perform experiments to see if all objects fall with the same acceleration?

_____

_____

2. Do you think a feather and a book that are dropped from the same height at the same time will hit the ground at the same time? Explain your answer in terms of Galileo's discovery.

_____

_____

_____

_____

_____

_____

_____

> **PLANET DIARY** Go to **Planet Diary** to learn more about scientific inquiry.

 Lab zone Do the Inquiry Warm-Up *What's Happening?*

Vocabulary
- scientific inquiry • hypothesis • controlled experiment • data • repeated trials • replication

Skills
↻ Reading: Sequence
△ Inquiry: Control Variables

What Is Scientific Inquiry?

Chirp, chirp, chirp. It is one of the hottest nights of summer and your bedroom windows are wide open. On most nights, the quiet chirping of crickets gently lulls you to sleep, but not tonight. The noise from the crickets is almost deafening. Why do all the crickets in your neighborhood seem determined to keep you awake tonight? Your thinking and questioning is the start of the **scientific inquiry** process. ⬤ **Scientific inquiry refers to the diverse ways in which scientists study the natural world and propose explanations based on the evidence they gather.**

Posing Questions and Defining a Problem

Scientific inquiry often begins with a question about an observation. Your observation about the loud and frequent chirping may lead you to ask a question: Why are the crickets chirping so much tonight? Questions come from your experiences, observations, and inferences. Curiosity plays a role, too. Use your question to help you define a problem to research. Look at **Figure 1** to pose a scientific question about an observation.

Using Reference Materials
Other people may have asked a question similar to yours. You should do research to find out what information is already known about this topic. Be sure to use a variety of sources such as encyclopedia entries, the Internet, or books in your school library. Use reference material that you trust, and remember to be skeptical of the source of information. See **Appendix A** for more information about reference materials.

FLORIDA NGSSS

SC.7.N.1.1 Define a problem from the seventh grade curriculum, use appropriate reference materials to support scientific understanding, plan and carry out scientific investigation of various types, such as systematic observations or experiments, identify variables, collect and organize data, interpret data in charts, tables, and graphics, analyze information, make predictions, and defend conclusions.

LA.7.4.2.2 The student will record information related to a topic.

FIGURE 1 ·············
Posing Questions
The photo at the right is of a Roesel's bush cricket from England.

✎ **Pose Questions** Make an observation about this cricket. Then pose a question about this observation that you can study.

_____

_____

_____

Why has my digital music player stopped working?

Developing a Hypothesis How could you answer your question about cricket chirping? In trying to answer the question, you are in fact developing a hypothesis. A **hypothesis** (plural: *hypotheses*) is a possible answer to a scientific question. In this case, you may suspect that the hot temperatures affected the chirping. Your hypothesis would be that cricket chirping increases as a result of warmer air temperatures. Use **Figure 2** to practice developing a hypothesis.

A hypothesis is *not* a fact. In science, a fact is an observation that has been confirmed repeatedly. For example, that a cricket rubs its forelegs together to make the chirping noise is a fact. A hypothesis, on the other hand, is one possible answer to a question. For example, perhaps the crickets only seemed to be chirping more that night because there were fewer other sounds than usual.

In science, a hypothesis must be testable. Researchers must be able to carry out investigations and gather evidence that will either support or disprove the hypothesis.

FIGURE 2 ⋯⋯⋯⋯⋯⋯⋯⋯⋯⋯⋯⋯⋯⋯⋯⋯⋯
Developing a Hypothesis
✎ **Develop Hypotheses** Write two hypotheses that might answer this student's question. LA.7.4.2.2

Hypothesis A	Hypothesis B

 Do the Quick Lab
Scientific Inquiry.

🔑 Assess Your Understanding

1a. Explain Can you test a hypothesis that crickets chirp more when they hide under logs? Explain.

_____

_____

_____

SC.7.N.1.1

b. Develop Hypotheses What other hypothesis might explain why crickets chirp more frequently on some nights?

_____

_____

_____

SC.7.N.1.1

got it? ⋯⋯⋯⋯⋯⋯⋯⋯⋯⋯⋯⋯⋯⋯⋯⋯⋯⋯⋯⋯⋯⋯

○ **I get it!** Now I know that scientific inquiry is _____

_____

○ **I need extra help with** _____

Go to MY SCIENCE 🔊 COACH *online for help with this subject.*　　　SC.7.N.1.1

How Do You Design and Conduct an Experiment?

After developing your hypothesis, you are ready to test it by designing an experiment. 🔑 **An experiment must follow sound scientific principles for its results to be valid.** You know your experiment will involve counting cricket chirps at warm temperatures. But, how will you know how often a cricket would chirp at a low temperature? You cannot know unless you count other cricket chirps at low temperatures for comparison.

Controlling Variables To test your hypothesis, you will observe crickets at different air temperatures. All other variables, or factors that can change in an experiment, must be the same. This includes variables such as food and hours of daylight. By keeping these variables the same, you will know that any difference in cricket chirping is due to temperature alone.

Recall that the variable that is purposely changed to test a hypothesis is the independent variable. The independent variable here is air temperature. The factor that may change in response to the independent variable is the dependent variable. The dependent variable here is the number of cricket chirps.

FLORIDA NGSSS

SC.7.N.1.1 Define a problem from the seventh grade curriculum, use appropriate reference materials to support scientific understanding, plan and carry out scientific investigation of various types, such as systematic observations or experiments, identify variables, collect and organize data, interpret data in charts, tables, and graphics, analyze information, make predictions, and defend conclusions.

SC.7.N.1.2 Distinguish replication (by others) from repetition (multiple trials).

MA.6.A.3.6 Construct and analyze tables, graphs, and equations.

apply it!

A student performs an experiment to determine whether 1 g of sugar or 1 g of salt dissolves more quickly in water.

❶ **Control Variables** Identify the independent variable and the dependent variable.

_____

_____

❷ **Identify** What are two other variables in this experiment?

_____

_____

_____

❸ **Draw Conclusions** Write a hypothesis for this experiment.

_____

_____

_____

Water

Water

Salt

Sugar

Setting Up a Controlled Experiment
An experiment in which only one variable is manipulated at a time is called a **controlled experiment.** You decide to test the crickets at three different temperatures: 15°C, 20°C, and 25°C, as shown in **Figure 3.** All other variables are kept the same. Otherwise, your experiment would have more than one independent variable. Then there would be no way to tell which variable influenced your results.

Experimental Bias
In any experiment there is a risk of introducing bias. For example, if you expect crickets to chirp more at 25°C, you may run experiments at just that temperature. Or, without meaning to, you might bias your results by selecting only the crickets to test that chirp the most often. Having a good sample size, or the number of crickets tested, is also important. Having too few crickets may bias your results because individual differences exist from cricket to cricket.

FIGURE 3 ···

A Controlled Experiment
The independent variable in the experiment below is temperature.

✎ **Design Experiments** In the boxes, write the number of crickets you would test for this controlled experiment. On the lines below, write three other variables that must be kept the same.

_____

_____

_____

Temperature 15°C

Crickets _____

Temperature 20°C

Crickets _____

Temperature 25°C

Crickets _____

Collecting and Interpreting Data

You are almost ready to begin your experiment. You decide to test five crickets, one at a time, at each temperature. You also decide to run multiple trials for each cricket. This is because a cricket may behave differently from one trial to the next. Before you begin your experiment, decide what observations you will make and what data you will collect. **Data** are the facts, figures, and other evidence gathered through qualitative and quantitative observations. To organize your data, you may want to make a data table. A data table provides you with an organized way to collect and record your observations. Decide what your table will look like. Then you can start to collect your data.

After your data have been collected, they need to be interpreted. One tool that can help you interpret data is a graph. Graphs can reveal patterns or trends in data. Sometimes, there is more than one interpretation for a set of data. For example, scientists all agree that global temperatures have gone up over the past 100 years. What they do not agree on is how much they are likely to go up over the next 100 years.

Sequence Underline and number the steps involved in collecting and interpreting data.

do the math!

A data table helps you organize the information you collect in an experiment. Graphing the data may reveal any patterns in your data.

❶ Read Graphs Identify the independent variable and the dependent variable.

_____

_____

_____

❷ Read Graphs As the temperature increases from 15°C to 25°C, what happens to the number of chirps per minute?

_____

_____

❸ Predict How many chirps per minute would you expect when the temperature is 10°C?

_____

_____

Number of Chirps per Minute

Cricket	15°C	20°C	25°C
1	91	135	180
2	80	124	169
3	89	130	176
4	78	125	158
5	77	121	157
Average	83	127	168

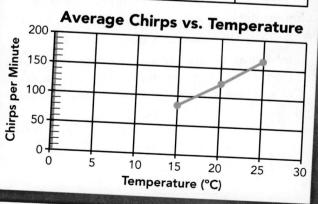

Average Chirps vs. Temperature

(Graph: Chirps per Minute (y-axis, 0 to 200) vs. Temperature (°C) (x-axis, 0 to 30))

MA.6.A.3.6, MA.7.A.1.5

Drawing Conclusions Now you should draw conclusions about your hypothesis. A conclusion is a summary of what you have learned from an experiment. To draw a conclusion, examine your data to see if they support or do not support your hypothesis. You should also consider whether you collected enough data.

Repetition and Repeated Trials You may decide that the data support your hypothesis. You conclude that the frequency of cricket chirping increases with temperature. Your next step should be to repeat your experiment. **Repeated trials** are a repetition of an experiment. Repeating your experiment helps you to be sure that your results were not due to chance. Many trials are needed before a hypothesis can be accepted as true.

Good scientists also use **replication,** meaning another scientist repeats your experiment. If that scientist gets the same results and comes to the same conclusion, then it is more likely that your conclusion is correct.

Examining Your Experiment After you finish your experiment, check your procedure for mistakes you may have made. Try to make improvements to your procedure. If your hypothesis was proved wrong but your experiment was done correctly, try to come up with a new hypothesis to test. Scientific inquiry usually doesn't end once an experiment is done. Often, one experiment leads to another.

Number of Chirps per Minute			
Cricket	15°C	20°C	25°C
1	98	100	120
2	92	95	105
3	101	93	99
4	102	85	97
5	91	89	98
Average	96	92	103

FIGURE 4 ....

Drawing Conclusions

Sometimes the same experiment can have very different data.

✎ **Answer the questions below.**

1. Interpret Tables Look at the data in the table. Do the data support the hypothesis that crickets chirp more in warmer temperatures? Explain.

_____

_____

_____

_____

2. Analyze Sources of Error If the data in this table were yours, what might you do next? Explain.

_____

_____

_____

_____

3. CHALLENGE Can you draw a conclusion from these data? Why or why not?

_____

_____

_____

Communicating Communicating is the sharing of ideas and results with others through writing and speaking. Scientists communicate by giving talks at scientific meetings, exchanging information on the Internet, or publishing articles in scientific journals.

When scientists share the results of their research, they describe their procedures so that others can replicate their experiments. It is important for scientists to wait until an experiment has been repeated many times before accepting a result. Therefore, scientists must keep accurate records of their methods and results. This way, scientists know that the result is accurate. Before the results are published, other scientists review the experiment for sources of error, such as bias, data interpretation, and faulty conclusions.

Sometimes, a scientific inquiry can be part of a huge project in which many scientists are working together around the world. For example, the Human Genome Project involved scientists from 18 different countries. The scientists' goal was to create a map of the information in your cells that makes you who you are. On such a large project, scientists must share their ideas and results regularly. Come up with ideas for communicating the results of your cricket experiment in **Figure 5**.

Vocabulary Identify Related Word Forms *Communication* is the noun form of the verb *communicate*. Write a sentence using the noun *communication*.

_____

_____

_____

_____

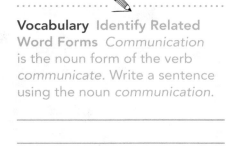

The Human Genome Project logo

FIGURE 5 ·······················

Communicating Results
Since the Human Genome Project touched upon many areas of science, communication was important.

✎ **Communicate** Get together as a group and write three ways to share the results of your cricket experiment with other students.

53

In a Scientist's Shoes

How do scientists investigate the natural world?

Design an Experiment

QUESTION _____

SCIENTIFIC ATTITUDES INVOLVED _____

HYPOTHESIS _____

VARIABLES
Independent Variables _____
Dependent Variables _____
Factors to Consider _____

COLLECT DATA
Number of Trials _____
Units of Measure _____
SCIENTIFIC SKILLS USED _____

NEXT STEPS _____

FIGURE 6 ••••••••••••••••••••••

▶ **INTERACTIVE ART** When you think like a scientist, you develop hypotheses and design experiments to test them.

✏️ **Design Experiments** Think like a scientist to find out which falls fastest: an unfolded sheet of paper, a sheet of paper folded in fourths, or a crumpled sheet of paper.

 Lab zone Do the Lab Investigation *Keeping Flowers Fresh.*

🔑 Assess Your Understanding

2a. Explain How are repeated trials different from replication?

_____
_____
_____
_____

SC.7.N.1.2

b. ANSWER THE ESSENTIAL ? How do scientists investigate the natural world?

_____
_____
_____
_____

SC.7.N.1.1

got it? ••

○ **I get it!** Now I know that an experimental design must _____
_____

○ **I need extra help with** _____

Go to **MY SCIENCE** ⑤ **COACH** *online for help with this subject.*

SC.7.N.1.1

How Do We Gain Scientific Knowledge?

Scientists often use experiments to study the natural world. Experiments involve identifying and controlling variables, and designing ways to test those variables. But sometimes it isn't practical to do an experiment. **Observations and modeling are two other ways of gaining scientific knowledge.** Observations are useful when you cannot do an experiment about what you want to study. For example, you can't set up an experiment involving a distant star, but you can use a telescope to observe that star and find out more about it. Modeling is useful when you are studying something that is too complex to observe, or when it is unsafe to experiment directly.

For instance, suppose that you are a scientist who has found some dinosaur bones. You want to know what this dinosaur's body looked like, but you cannot go back in time to find out. Instead, you observe the bones to help you figure out what the dinosaur looked like. The size and shape of the bones might help you infer what the size and shape of the dinosaur was. Using the information from the bones, you can make a model of what the dinosaur may have looked like, like the one shown in **Figure 7.**

FLORIDA NGSSS

SC.7.N.1.3 Distinguish between an experiment (which must involve the identification and control of variables) and other forms of scientific investigation and explain that not all scientific knowledge is derived from experimentation.

FIGURE 7 ················

Use the Clues
Fossilized bones can provide clues about extinct organisms.

✎ **Observe** Look at the dinosaur skeleton below. Then, describe how the skeleton might reveal how this dinosaur looked or acted.

_____

_____

_____

Lab zone® Do the Quick Lab
Observing and Modeling.

⚷ Assess Your Understanding

got it? ·····················

○ **I get it!** Now I know that other ways of gaining scientific knowledge are _____

_____

_____

○ **I need extra help with** _____

Go to my science ⑤ coach *online for help with this subject.*

SC.7.N.1.3

1 Study Guide

To think like a scientist, you must use _____, _____,
and _____ to observe the world.

LESSON 1 Science and the Natural World
SC.7.N.1.1, SC.7.N.1.4

🔑 Scientists use skills such as observing, inferring, predicting, classifying, evaluating, and making models to study the world.

Vocabulary
• science • observing • inferring
• predicting • classifying • evaluating
• making models • variable
• independent variable • dependent variable

LESSON 2 Thinking Like a Scientist
SC.7.N.1.1

🔑 Scientists possess certain important attitudes, including curiosity, honesty, creativity, open-mindedness, skepticism, good ethics, and awareness of bias.

🔑 Scientific reasoning requires logical thinking based on gathering and evaluating evidence.

Vocabulary
• skepticism • ethics • personal bias • cultural bias
• experimental bias • objective • subjective
• deductive reasoning • inductive reasoning

LESSON 3 Measurement—A Common Language
SC.7.N.1.1

🔑 Using SI as the standard system of measurement allows scientists to compare data and communicate with each other.

🔑 SI units of measurement include meter (m), kilogram (kg), cubic meter (m³), kilograms per cubic meter (kg/m³), kelvin (K), and second (s).

Vocabulary
• metric system • International System of Units (SI)
• mass • weight • volume • meniscus • density

LESSON 4 Mathematics and Science
SC.7.N.1.1

🔑 Math skills that scientists use to collect data include estimation, accuracy and precision, and significant figures.

🔑 Scientists calculate percent error; find the mean, median, mode, and range; and check reasonableness to analyze data.

Vocabulary
• estimate • accuracy • precision
• significant figures • percent error • mean
• median • mode • range • anomalous data

LESSON 5 Graphs in Science
SC.7.N.1.1

🔑 Line graphs display data that show how the dependent variable changes in response to the independent variable.

🔑 Line graphs are powerful tools in science because they allow you to identify trends, make predictions, and recognize anomalous data.

Vocabulary
• graph • linear graph
• nonlinear graph

LESSON 6 Scientific Inquiry
SC.7.N.1.1, SC.7.N.1.2, SC.7.N.1.3

🔑 Scientific inquiry refers to the diverse ways in which scientists study the natural world.

🔑 An experiment must follow sound scientific principles for its results to be valid.

🔑 Observations and modeling are two other ways of gaining scientific knowledge.

Vocabulary
• scientific inquiry • hypothesis
• controlled experiment • data • repeated trials
• replication

Review and Assessment

LESSON 1 Science and the Natural World

1. When you explain or interpret an observation, you are

   a. making models.   **b.** classifying.

   c. inferring.   **d.** predicting.

                              SC.7.N.1.1

2. A variable that is changed to test a hypothesis is an _____.

                              SC.7.N.1.4

3. Predict How do scientists use observations to make predictions?

_____

_____

_____

                              SC.7.N.1.1

LESSON 2 Thinking Like a Scientist

4. The scientific attitude of having doubt is called

   a. open-mindedness.   **b.** curiosity.

   c. honesty.   **d.** skepticism.

                              SC.7.N.1.1

5. When a person allows personal opinions, values, or tastes to influence a conclusion, that person is using _____ reasoning.

                              SC.7.N.1.1

6. Compare and Contrast Describe the three types of bias that can influence a science experiment.

_____

_____

_____

_____

_____

_____

                              SC.7.N.1.1

LESSON 3 Measurement— A Common Language

7. The amount of matter an object contains is its

   a. length.   **b.** mass.

   c. weight.   **d.** volume.

                              SC.7.N.1.1

8. The basic SI unit of length is the

_____

                              SC.7.N.1.1

9. Write About It You are a sports reporter interviewing an Olympic swimmer who lost the silver medal by a few hundredths of a second. Write a one page interview in which you discuss the meaning of time and the advanced instruments used to measure time.

                              SC.7.N.1.1

LESSON 4 Mathematics and Science

10. The significant figures in a measurement

   a. include only the first two digits.

   b. include only the estimated digits.

   c. include only the digits that have been measured exactly.

   d. include all of the digits that have been measured exactly, plus one estimated digit.

                              SC.7.N.1.1

11. _____ refers to how close a measurement is to the true or accepted value.

                              SC.7.N.1.1

12. Apply Concepts What is the median of 7, 31, 86, 6, 20, 85, and 12?

_____

                              SC.7.N.1.1

LESSON 5 Graphs in Science

13. A line graph is used when an independent variable is

   a. responsive.   **b.** linear.

   c. continuous.   **d.** anomalous.

                     SC.7.N.1.1

14. A _____ is a graph in which the data points do not fall along a straight line.

                     SC.7.N.1.1

15. Make Generalizations What do line graphs help you see about your data?

_____

_____

_____

_____

                     SC.7.N.1.1

LESSON 6 Scientific Inquiry

16. The facts, figures, and other evidence gathered through observations are called

   a. conclusions.

   b. data.

   c. predictions.

   d. hypotheses.

                     SC.7.N.1.1

17. Scientists use _____ to make sure that experimental results are not due to chance.

                     SC.7.N.1.2

18. **Write About It** You are a scientist and would like to study the planet Venus. You cannot go to Venus to carry out an experiment. What other ways could you gain scientific knowledge about the planet?

                     SC.7.N.1.3

 APPLY THE ESSENTIAL ? **How do scientists investigate the natural world?**

19. Central Middle School is having problems with attendance during the winter. Many students get sick and miss school. The principal wants to fix the problem, but she is not sure what to do. One idea is to install hand sanitizer dispensers in the classrooms.

Think about this problem scientifically. What is a possible hypothesis in this situation? What experiment could you design to test it? Mention at least three attitudes or skills that will be important in finding the answer.

_____

_____

_____

_____

_____

_____

_____

_____

_____

_____

_____

_____

_____

                     SC.7.N.1.1

Florida Benchmarks Review

Circle the letter of the best answer.

① Sophia noticed that many birds pick through the seeds in her bird feeder until they get a sunflower seed. What is an inference she could make from this observation?

  A Birds are attracted to white objects.
  B Sunflower seeds are crunchy.
  C Birds do not like seeds.
  D Birds prefer sunflower seeds.

SC.7.N.1.1

② Another scientist conducts your experiment. This is an example of what process?

  A repeated trials
  B replication
  C scientific inquiry
  D deductive reasoning

SC.7.N.1.2

③ Marie observed people at a store. Which is a qualitative observation she may have made?

  A Twenty people walked into the store.
  B The store sells clothes.
  C It was 1:00 P.M.
  D all of the above

SC.7.N.1.1

④ Ellis measured the mass of five samples of quartz. His results were 39.75 g, 38.91 g, 37.66 g, 39.75 g, and 39.55 g. What was the mean mass of the samples?

  A 39.55 g
  B 39.75 g
  C 39.12 g
  D 38.91 g

SC.7.N.1.1

⑤ A student grows tomatoes for an experiment. Which piece of equipment will be needed to determine the mass of each tomato?

  A graduated cylinder
  B meter stick
  C stopwatch
  D triple-beam balance

SC.7.N.1.1

Use the graph below to answer Question 6.

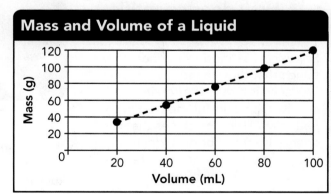

⑥ What is the general trend in the data?

  A linear   **B** no trend
  C nonlinear   **D** linear at first and then nonlinear

SC.7.N.1.1

HOW DO SCIENTISTS "SEE" YOUR BRAIN?

How does scientific knowledge develop?

Scientists use models to understand things that they cannot see directly. This scan is a model of brain activity. The colorful lines are nerve pathways. Using machines that read energy from our bodies, doctors can see how and when different areas of the brain are active.

When your brain performs a task, such as remembering a phone number, blood circulation to that part of our brain increases. The scan recognizes that activity.

Infer What might the colors of this brain scan mean?

_____

_____

_____

_____

> **UNTAMED SCIENCE** Watch the **Untamed Science** video to learn more about how scientific knowledge develops.

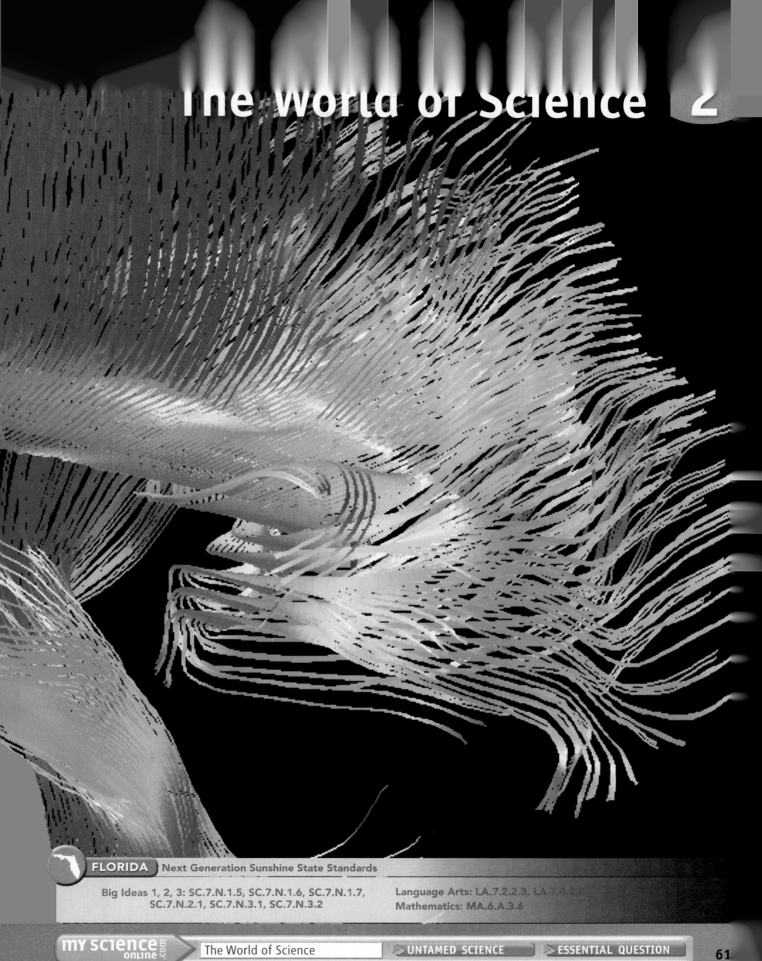

The World of Science 2

FLORIDA | Next Generation Sunshine State Standards

Big Ideas 1, 2, 3: SC.7.N.1.5, SC.7.N.1.6, SC.7.N.1.7, SC.7.N.2.1, SC.7.N.3.1, SC.7.N.3.2

Language Arts: LA.7.2.2.3, LA.7.4.2.2
Mathematics: MA.6.A.3.6

2 Getting Started

Check Your Understanding

1. Background Read the paragraph below and then answer the question.

> Jodi enjoys doing science investigations. She especially likes to go outside to make observations. In one investigation, she learned how to create an image of the sun on a piece of paper without looking directly at the sun. Then she observed the number of sunspots that she saw each day. She made a table to record her data.

Science is a way of learning about the natural world.

Observation is the act of using one or more of your senses to gather information.

Data are facts, figures, and other evidence gathered through observation.

• What data do you think that Jodi recorded in her table?

> **MY READING WEB** If you had trouble completing the question above, visit **My Reading Web** and type in *The World of Science.*

Vocabulary Skill

Use Context to Determine Meaning Science texts often contain unfamiliar words. Look for context clues in surrounding words and phrases to figure out the meaning of a new word. In the paragraph below, look for clues to the meaning of *controversial.*

Sometimes a scientist's work is in conflict with the beliefs of society. As a result, the work is *controversial.* A controversy is a public disagreement between groups with different views. For instance, Galileo's model of Earth revolving around the sun was *controversial* because it conflicted with society's beliefs in the 1600s.

2. Quick Check In the paragraph above, circle a phrase that helps you understand the meaning of the word *controversial.*

Introduction to Vocabulary	A scientist's work is in conflict with the beliefs of society.
Word	controversial, *adj.*
Definition	of, subject to, or stirring up controversy
Example	Galileo's model of Earth revolving around the sun

LA.7.1.6.3

scientific explanation

controversy

scientific law

An Afternoon Sea Breeze

system

1 Warm air rises

2 Cooler air moves to take warm air's place

Warm land

Cool water

Chapter Preview

LESSON 1
- scientific explanation
- empirical evidence
- opinion
  - ↺ Relate Cause and Effect
  - △ Classify

LESSON 2
- controversy
  - ↺ Sequence
  - △ Predict

LESSON 3
- scientific theory
- scientific law
  - ↺ Identify Supporting Evidence
  - △ Draw Conclusions

LESSON 4
- model
- system
- input
- process
- output
- feedback
  - ↺ Identify the Main Idea
  - △ Make Models

> **VOCAB FLASH CARDS** For extra help with vocabulary type in the *The World of Science.*

Scientific Explanation

🔑 **How Do Scientists Form Scientific Explanations?**
SC.7.N.1.5

🔑 **What Is the Basis for Scientific Explanations?**
SC.7.N.1.6, MA.6.A.3.6

MY PLANET DIARY for Florida

DISASTER

On Jan. 28, 1986, the Challenger Space Shuttle launched from Kennedy Space Center. Seventy-three seconds later, the Challenger exploded. All seven crew members died in the explosion. Scientists and engineers reviewed all the data and records. They carried out many tests and experiments. They concluded that the joint between the two lower segments of the right Solid Rocket Booster did not work correctly. The rubber seal, or O-ring, hardened overnight in freezing weather. When the boosters ignited at launch, hot gas from within the solid rocket motor leaked out through the seal and ignited. Since that time, many changes in the Solid Rocket Booster and shuttle design were made to improve safety.

Write your answer to the question below.

A number of television stations had cameras focused on the Challenger. How could viewing video of the accident help scientists explain what had happened?

_____

_____

_____

_____

_____

_____

▶ **PLANET DIARY** Go to **Planet Diary** to learn more about scientific explanations.

 Lab zone Do the Inquiry Warm-up *Doing Science*

Solid Rocket Booster

Vocabulary
- scientific explanation • empirical evidence
- opinion

Skills
- ↪ Reading: Relate Cause and Effect
- △ Inquiry: Classify

How Do Scientists Form Scientific Explanations?

Consider the following statements.

- The shape of the Florida coastline is changing due to erosion.
- Adult flamingos are pink because of the food they eat.

What do these statements have in common? They are scientific explanations. A **scientific explanation** describes how something works or why something happens. ⚷ **Scientists use methods such as researching information, designing experiments, and making models to form a scientific explanation.**

Scientists from different fields use these methods in their work. For example, geologists research information about an area of land before allowing a company to drill for oil or natural gas. Physicists design experiments to understand how matter behaves on a tiny scale. Biologists make models of cell division to understand how cells divide. Often scientists have to use more than one method.

FLORIDA NGSSS

SC.7.N.1.5 Describe the methods used in pursuit of scientific explanations as seen in different fields of science such as biology, geology, and physics.

FIGURE 1 ·························○
Scientific Explanation
This photo is of the Dead Lakes region in Florida.

✎ **Pose Questions** Write a question that a scientist might want an explanation for based on this photo.

_____

_____

_____

_____

_____

Lab ® Do the Quick Lab *Form a Scientific Explanation.*
zone

⚷ Assess Your Understanding

got it? ···

○ **I get it!** Now I know the methods scientists use to form scientific explanations are _____

_____

○ **I need extra help with** _____

Go to MY SCIENCE ⓢ COACH *online for help with this subject.* SC.7.N.1.5

FLORIDA NGSSS

SC.7.N.1.6 Explain that empirical evidence is the cumulative body of observations of a natural phenomenon on which scientific explanations are based.

MA.6.A.3.6 Construct and analyze graphs to describe simple relations.

What Is the Basis for Scientific Explanations?

Scientists cannot state that Florida's coastline is changing due to erosion unless they have some evidence to support this claim. In science, **empirical evidence** is the data and observations that have been collected through scientific processes. **Scientific explanations are always based on empirical evidence.**

Collecting and Analyzing Evidence To answer a question, scientists begin by collecting evidence. Then they analyze the evidence and form a scientific explanation. For example, to figure out what is causing the erosion, or the wearing away, of Florida's coastline, scientists use computers that map the coastline. They also take photographs of the beaches. Scientists look for patterns when they analyze the evidence. For example, they might see a pattern of erosion near inlets and conclude that the construction of inlets is causing the erosion.

Sometimes scientists need to change their explanations based on new evidence. For example, new evidence might show that changes in the sea level are also causing the erosion. The scientists would need to include both causes in their explanation.

do the math!

Scientists often use graphs to analyze the evidence collected during an experiment. This graph shows how many radish seeds sprouted over time at two different temperatures. Scientists planted one hundred radish seeds in two identical trays of soil. One tray was kept at 10°C. The other tray was kept at 20°C. The trays received equal amounts of sun and water.

❶ **Read Graphs** On Day 13, _____ seeds sprouted in the 20°C tray.

❷ **Analyze Experimental Results** Based on the graph, what can you conclude about the relationship between the two temperatures and the sprouted seeds?

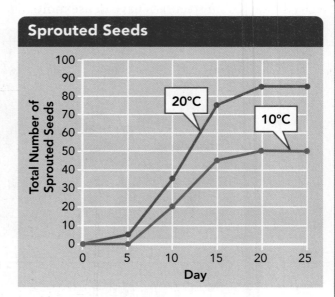

Sprouted Seeds

❸ **Relate Evidence and Explanation** After the experiment, another scientist claims that more seeds will always sprout at higher temperatures. Does the evidence support this claim? Why or why not?

_____

_____

MA.6.A.3.6, MA.7.A.1.5

Evaluating Different scientists might interpret the same evidence differently. For example, some scientists might conclude that coastal storms are causing the erosion in Florida, while others might have another explanation. For this reason, scientists must evaluate, or determine the quality of, each other's scientific explanations. To do this, they start by studying all of the evidence and other scientists' conclusions. Then they point out any errors in the analysis. Finally, they may challenge each other's conclusions.

Sometimes explanations are based on opinions. An **opinion** is an idea that may be formed from evidence but has not been confirmed by evidence. For example, you might conclude that there is no global warming because the past summer was unusually cool. But evidence shows that the temperature of Earth's atmosphere has been gradually rising for over 120 years. This evidence supports global warming. Explanations that are based on opinion rather than evidence are not scientific.

Relate Cause and Effect
Underline three possible causes of the coastal erosion in Florida.

FIGURE 2 ....
> **REAL-WORLD INQUIRY**

Scientific Explanation and Opinion
This wildlife refuge contains a variety of wildlife including some endangered species.

Classify Suggest both a scientific explanation and an opinion about the refuge.

_____
_____
_____
_____
_____
_____

Lab zone Do the Lab Investigation
Piecing Information Together.

🔑 Assess Your Understanding

1a. Define What is empirical evidence?

_____
_____
_____
_____
_____

SC.7.N.1.6

b. Explain Why do scientists need to evaluate scientific explanations?

_____
_____
_____
_____
_____

SC.7.N.1.6

got it? ....

○ **I get it!** Now I know that scientific explanations are always based on _____

○ **I need extra help with** _____

Go to my science ⓢ coach *online for help with this subject.*

SC.7.N.1.6

Scientists and Society

How Do Scientists Affect Society?
SC.7.N.1.7, LA.7.2.2.3

my planet diary
for Florida

CAREERS

Marine Scientist

Why are marine scientists in Sarasota Bay, Florida, spying on dolphins? Dolphins send out a series of high-frequency clicks to navigate and find food. They whistle to communicate with each other. The scientists are recording underwater sounds in the bay. They are also noting dolphin sightings. They will use the data to determine how boat noise in the bay affects dolphin behavior.

Boat noise, underwater drilling, and sonar devices used by the military have all been shown to affect dolphins, porpoises, and whales. For this reason, it is a rich area of research for marine scientists.

Make Judgments Write your answers to the questions below.

1. How do you think boat noise could affect the dolphins in the bay?

_____

_____

_____

_____

2. How could the work of the marine scientists affect the boating community and the millitary?

_____

_____

_____

_____

_____

_____

> **PLANET DIARY** Go to **Planet Diary** to learn more about scientists and society.

 Lab zone® Do the Inquiry Warm-Up *What Do Scientists Do?*

Vocabulary
- controversy

Skills
- ⟳ Reading: Sequence
- △ Inquiry: Predict

How Do Scientists Affect Society?

Scientists are constantly trying to make new discoveries. When they do discover something new, other scientists thoroughly check their work. They review any experiments, data, and results. They can also debate the conclusions of any experiments. Only after a thorough review process will a new discovery be published.

Just because the scientific community confirms a discovery, it does not mean that society will accept it, though. Sometimes a discovery conflicts with the beliefs of a society or its leaders. When this happens, a scientist's work can cause a **controversy,** or a public disagreement between groups. ⟳ **Scientists can change society by defending their work in the face of controversy.** By doing so, scientists have helped people better understand the world.

Galileo Galilei For many years, Galileo Galilei observed the night sky with a telescope. In 1610, he published his discoveries, which supported the heliocentric model, a model of the universe in which Earth moves around the sun. The heliocentric model, shown at the right, conflicted with the beliefs of society's leaders at the time. In 1616, all books that supported this model were banned. In 1632, Galileo published another book that supported this model. As a result, he was tried, found guilty, and lived the rest of his life under house arrest. In time, though, Galileo's work led to an acceptance of science as a way of explaining the natural world.

FLORIDA NGSSS

SC.7.N.1.7 Explain that scientific knowledge is the result of a great deal of debate and confirmation within the scientific community.

LA.7.2.2.3 The student will organize information to show understanding (e.g., representing main ideas within text through charting and mapping)

Galileo's diagram of the heliocentric model

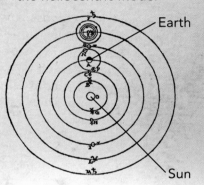

Earth

Sun

⟳ **Sequence** Write in your own words the order of events that led to Galileo's house arrest.

LA.7.2.2.3

Event 1	Event 2	Event 3
_____	_____	_____

Event 4	Event 5	Event 6
_____	_____	Galileo was placed under house arrest.

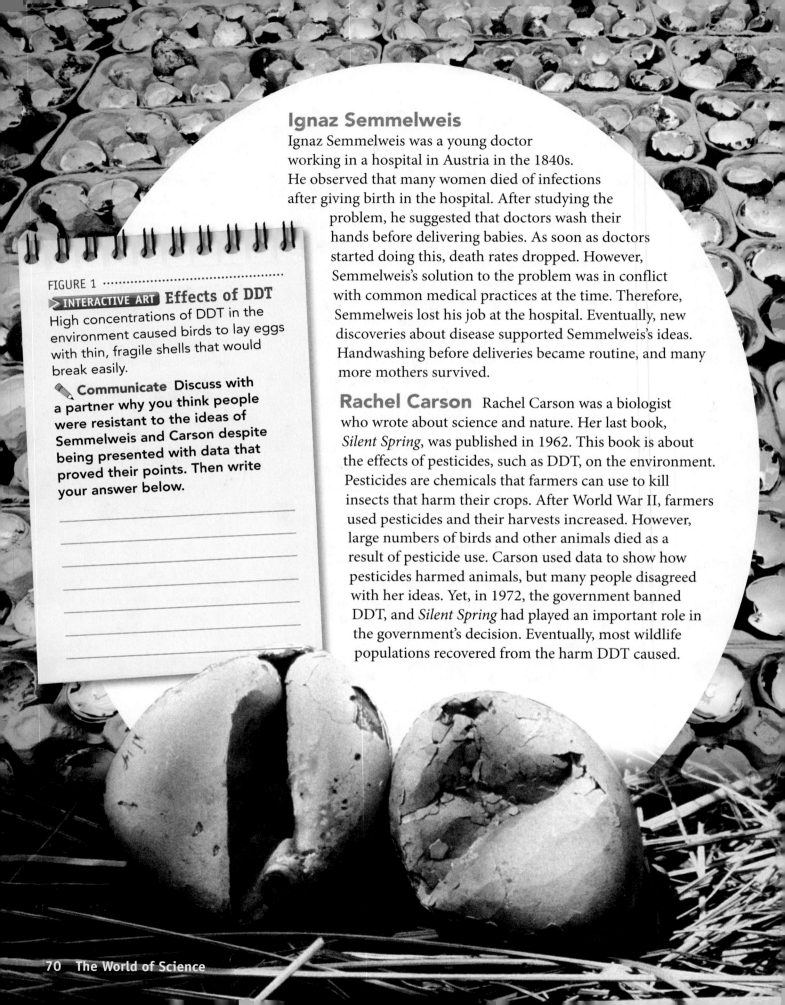

Ignaz Semmelweis

Ignaz Semmelweis was a young doctor working in a hospital in Austria in the 1840s. He observed that many women died of infections after giving birth in the hospital. After studying the problem, he suggested that doctors wash their hands before delivering babies. As soon as doctors started doing this, death rates dropped. However, Semmelweis's solution to the problem was in conflict with common medical practices at the time. Therefore, Semmelweis lost his job at the hospital. Eventually, new discoveries about disease supported Semmelweis's ideas. Handwashing before deliveries became routine, and many more mothers survived.

Rachel Carson Rachel Carson was a biologist who wrote about science and nature. Her last book, *Silent Spring*, was published in 1962. This book is about the effects of pesticides, such as DDT, on the environment. Pesticides are chemicals that farmers can use to kill insects that harm their crops. After World War II, farmers used pesticides and their harvests increased. However, large numbers of birds and other animals died as a result of pesticide use. Carson used data to show how pesticides harmed animals, but many people disagreed with her ideas. Yet, in 1972, the government banned DDT, and *Silent Spring* had played an important role in the government's decision. Eventually, most wildlife populations recovered from the harm DDT caused.

FIGURE 1 ·······
> INTERACTIVE ART **Effects of DDT**
High concentrations of DDT in the environment caused birds to lay eggs with thin, fragile shells that would break easily.

✎ **Communicate** Discuss with a partner why you think people were resistant to the ideas of Semmelweis and Carson despite being presented with data that proved their points. Then write your answer below.

_____
_____
_____
_____
_____
_____
_____

apply it!

Suppose that fish in your town's river are dying. Scientists conclude that polluted water from a nearby factory is killing the fish. If it costs too much to fix the problem, the factory will have to close. Many people in town work in the factory. Many others work in fishing camps that attract tourists who come for the great fishing.

1 **Predict** Do you think each group below will reject or agree with the conclusion about why the fish are dying? Explain each answer.

Factory workers

_____

_____

_____

Fishing camp owners

_____

_____

_____

2 **CHALLENGE** What would be a cost and a benefit if the town offered to fix the problem for the factory?

_____

_____

_____

_____

Lab zone® Do the Quick Lab *Light Sources.*

🔑 Assess Your Understanding

1a. Define What is a scientific controversy?

_____

_____

_____

SC.7.N.1.7

b. Explain Why was there controversy over Semmelweis's ideas?

_____

_____

_____

_____

SC.7.N.1.7

got it? ....

○ **I get it!** Now I know that scientists can change society by _____

_____

○ **I need extra help with** _____

   Go to MY SCIENCE ⓢ COACH *online for help with this subject.*

SC.7.N.1.7

LESSON

3 How Science Changes

UNLOCK THE ESSENTIAL

🗝 **How Does Scientific Knowledge Change?**
SC.7.N.2.1

🗝 **How Is a Scientific Law Different From a Theory?**
SC.7.N.3.1, LA.7.2.2.3

mY pLaNeT DiaRY

VOICES FROM HISTORY

Albert Einstein

Born in 1879 in Germany, Albert Einstein is recognized as one of history's most brilliant scientists. He is best known for his physics equation $E = mc^2$, which describes his theory of relativity. E stands for energy, m stands for mass, and c stands for the speed of light. This equation describes the relationship between mass and energy. Here are two of Einstein's quotations.

"No amount of experimentation can ever prove me right; a single experiment can prove me wrong."

"Intellectual growth should commence at birth and cease only at death."

Read the following question. Write your answer below.

What do you think Einstein was saying about science in the first quotation?

_____

_____

_____

_____

_____

_____

▶ PLANET DIARY Go to **Planet Diary** to learn more about scientists and society.

Lab® zone   Do the Inquiry Warm-Up *Changing Science.*

$$f(x,y,z) = \frac{1}{\partial x} + \frac{1}{\partial y} + \frac{1}{\partial z}$$

$$E = mc^2$$

$$y = \int f(x)$$

Vocabulary
- scientific theory
- scientific law

Skills
- Reading: Identify Supporting Evidence
- Draw Conclusions

How Does Scientific Knowledge Change?

During the early part of the twentieth century, Marie Curie observed that 30 grams of radium gave off 970 Joules of thermal energy every hour. Scientists could not explain why. That is until Albert Einstein.

At the time, Einstein was working as a clerk in a German patent office. But he was also studying the relationship between mass and energy. In a 1905 paper, Einstein stated that mass could be converted to energy. And that energy could be converted to mass. According to Einstein, some of the radium's mass was being converted to thermal energy. A similar reaction happens in the sun and other stars. For example, every second, about 4.5 million tons of the sun's mass is converted to energy. Other scientists could not explain Curie's experiment because they thought of mass and energy as separate quantities.

Einstein's work demonstrates one of two ways in which scientific knowledge can change. ⌐ **Scientific knowledge changes as a result of new evidence or new interpretations of existing evidence.** Einstein's interpretation of why radium gave off thermal energy changed scientific knowledge about mass and energy.

FLORIDA NGSSS

SC.7.N.2.1 Identify an instance from the history of science in which scientific knowledge has changed when new evidence or new interpretations are encountered.

FIGURE 1 ···

Scientific Knowledge
Einstein's work contributed to scientific knowledge about the sun and other stars.

✎ **Identify** Describe another instance of how scientific knowledge has changed. (*Hint:* Review Lesson 2 if you can not think of an example.)

_____

_____

_____

_____

_____

_____

_____

Lab zone | Do the Quick Lab
Scientific Knowledge.

⌐ Assess Your Understanding

got it?··

○ **I get it!** Now I know that scientific knowledge changes as a result of _____

_____

_____

○ **I need extra help with** _____

Go to my science ⓢ **coach** *online for help with this subject.*

SC.7.N.2.1

FLORIDA NGSSS

SC.7.N.3.1 Recognize and explain the difference between theories and laws and give several examples of scientific theories and the evidence that supports them.

LA.7.2.2.3 The student will organize information to show understanding (e.g., comparing/contrasting)

Identify Supporting Evidence Underline three or four sentences in the text that support the statement, "Scientific knowledge is built up cautiously."

How Is a Scientific Law Different From a Theory?

Scientific knowledge is built up cautiously. Scientists do not accept a new explanation after just one successful experiment. Rather, an explanation is tested repeatedly as many different scientists try to apply it to their own work.

Scientific Theories Sometimes, a large set of related observations can be connected by a single explanation. This can lead to the development of a scientific theory. A **scientific theory** is a well-tested explanation for a wide range of observations or experimental results. For example, according to the atomic theory, all substances are composed of tiny particles called atoms. The atomic theory helps to explain many observations, such as why ice melts at a particular temperature and why iron nails rust.

Scientists accept a theory only when there is a large body of evidence that supports it. However, future testing can still prove an accepted theory to be incorrect. If that happens, scientists may modify the theory, or discard it altogether. This illustrates the ever growing—and exciting—nature of scientific knowledge.

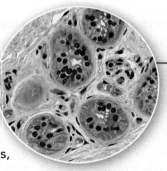

Animal cells

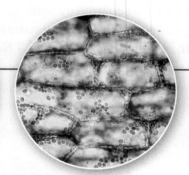

Plant cells

apply it!

Cell theory is a widely accepted explanation of the relationship between cells and living things. According to cell theory, cells are the basic units of structure and function in living things, and all cells are produced from other cells.

1 Explain It took almost 200 years after cells were discovered for cell theory to be developed. Why do you think that it took so long?

_____

_____

2 Compare and Contrast Create an analogy in which you compare the structure of a building to the structure of living things.

_____

_____

_____

3 Draw Conclusions Why do you suppose cell theory is important for scientists?

_____

LA.7.2.2.3

Scientific Laws

Have you ever heard someone say, "What goes up must come down"? When scientists repeatedly observe the same result in specific circumstances, they may arrive at a scientific law. A **scientific law** is a statement that describes what scientists expect to happen every time under a particular set of conditions.

🔑 **Unlike a theory, a scientific law describes an observed pattern in nature without attempting to explain it.** For example, the law of gravity states that all objects in the universe attract each other. This law has been verified over and over again. However, the law of gravity does not explain why all objects attract each other.

FIGURE 2 ....

▶ **INTERACTIVE ART** **A Scientific Law**

According to the law of gravity, this parachutist will eventually land on Earth.

✏️ **Apply Concepts** List two more examples of scientific laws.

_____

_____

_____

_____

_____

_____

Lab zone ® Do the Quick Lab *Theories and Laws.*

🔑 **Assess Your Understanding**

1a. Define A scientific (theory/law) is a well-tested explanation for a wide range of observations or experimental results.

SC.7.N.3.1

b. Compare and Contrast Describe one way that laws passed by state legislatures differ from scientific laws.

_____

_____

_____

SC.7.N.3.1

c. Classify Suppose the results of one experiment supported a scientist's hypothesis. Could the supported hypothesis be called a theory? Why or why not?

_____

_____

_____

SC.7.N.3.1

**got it? ** ....

○ **I get it!** Now I know that the difference between a scientific theory and a law is that _____

○ **I need extra help with** _____

Go to my science ⑤ coach *online for help with this subject.*

SC.7.N.3.1

LESSON 4

Models as Tools in Science

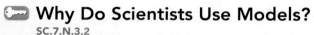

UNLOCK THE ESSENTIAL ?

🔑 **Why Do Scientists Use Models?**
SC.7.N.3.2

🔑 **What Is a System?**
SC.7.N.3.2, LA.7.4.2.2

🔑 **How Are Models of Systems Used?**
SC.7.N.3.2

my pLaneT DiaRY

Flying Through Space

You don't have to be an astronaut to experience what it's like to fly in space. Thanks to technological advances, space flight simulation software programs have been created. These programs range from simple and straightforward to detailed and complicated. Depending on which one you use, you can experience what it might feel like to fly to the moon, command a mission to Mars, and even explore other solar systems. If you've ever wondered what it's like to be an astronaut, now you have the chance to find out!

FUN FACTS

Read the following questions. Write your answers below.

1. Why would a flight simulation software program created today be more realistic than one that was created ten years ago?

_____

_____

_____

_____

2. Would you be able to really fly in space if you knew how to use a space flight simulation software program? Explain.

_____

_____

_____

> PLANET DIARY Go to **Planet Diary** to learn more about models as tools in science.

Lab zone® Do the Inquiry Warm-Up *Scale Models.*

Inside a flight simulator

Vocabulary
- model
- system
- input
- process
- output
- feedback

Skills
- Reading: Identify the Main Idea
- Inquiry: Make Models

Why Do Scientists Use Models?

"Who is that model on the cover?" "I still have that model car I built." The word *model* has many meanings. But, as with many words, *model* has a specific meaning in science. In science, a **model** is any representation of an object or process. Pictures, diagrams, computer programs, and mathematical equations are all examples of scientific models.

FLORIDA NGSSS

SC.7.N.3.2 Identify the benefits and limitations of the use of scientific models.

Scientists use models to understand things they cannot observe directly. For example, scientists use models as reasonable representations of things that are either very large, such as Earth's core, or very small, such as an atom. These kinds of models are physical models—drawings or three-dimensional objects. Other models, such as mathematical equations or word descriptions, are models of processes. Look at the models in **Figure 1**.

FIGURE 1 ··

Two Science Models
Models may be three-dimensional objects or equations.

✏️ **Explain** Tell whether each of these models represents an object or a process and why each is useful.

Photosynthesis

_____
_____
_____
_____

sunlight
Carbon dioxide + Water ———⟶ Food + Oxygen

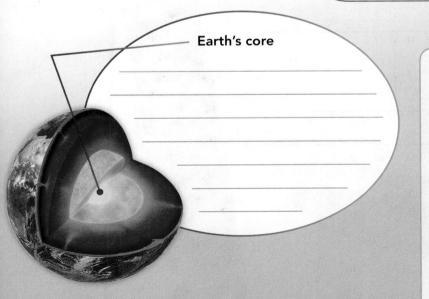

Earth's core

_____
_____
_____
_____

Lab zone® Do the Quick Lab *Making Models.*

🔑 Assess Your Understanding

got it? ···

○ **I get it!** Now I know that scientists use models to _____
_____

○ **I need extra help with** _____

Go to **MY SCIENCE COACH** online for help with this subject.

SC.7.N.3.2

77

FLORIDA NGSSS

SC.7.N.3.2 Identify the benefits and limitations of the use of scientific models.

LA.7.4.2.2 The student will record information (e.g., observations, notes, lists, charts, legends) related to a topic, including visual aids to organize and record information.

Identify the Main Idea
Circle the main idea in the second paragraph. Underline the details.

What Is a System?

Many things you see and use are systems. For example, a toaster oven, your town's water pipes, and your bicycle are all systems. **A system is a group of parts that work together to perform a function or produce a result.**

Systems have common properties. All systems have input, process, and output. **Input** is the material or energy that goes into a system. **Process** is what happens in a system. **Output** is the material or energy that comes out of a system. In addition, some systems have feedback. **Feedback** is output that changes the system in some way. For example, the heating and cooling system in most homes has feedback. A sensor in the thermostat recognizes when the desired temperature has been reached. The sensor provides feedback that turns the system off temporarily. Look at **Figure 2** to see another example of a system.

FIGURE 2 ···

An Everyday System

In a flashlight, many parts work together as a system.

Apply Concepts Look at the flashlight and use what you know to fill in the chart. LA.7.4.2.2

	Flashlight
Parts of System	
Input	
Process	
Output	

apply it!

Sun, air, land, and water are the parts of a system that produce a sea breeze. During the day, the sun's energy heats both the land and the water. The land and water, in turn, heat the air above them. Air over the land becomes much warmer than the air over water. As the warmer air rises, the cooler air from over the water rushes in to replace it. A sea breeze is the result.

An Afternoon Sea Breeze

1 Warm air rises

2 Cooler air moves to take warm air's place

Warm land   Cool water

❶ **Identify** Identify the input, output, and process of the sea breeze system.

_____

_____

_____

_____

❷ CHALLENGE Which part(s) of this system will change after the sun sets? How will the system change?

_____

_____

 Do the Quick Lab *Systems.*

🔑 Assess Your Understanding

1a. List What are the properties of a system?

_____

_____

_____

_____

SC.7.N.3.2

b. Apply Concepts A student uses a calculator to solve a math problem. Is this an example of a system? Explain your answer.

_____

_____

_____

_____

SC.7.N.3.2

got it? ●

○ **I get it!** Now I know that a system is _____

_____

○ **I need extra help with** _____

Go to MY SCIENCE ⓢ COACH *online for help with this subject.*

SC.7.N.3.2

FLORIDA NGSSS

SC7.N.3.2 Identify the benefits and limitations of the use of scientific models.

How Are Models of Systems Used?

It's easy to identify the materials and energy that make up the inputs and outputs of a system. It's not easy to observe a system's process. 🗝 **Scientists use models to understand how systems work. They also use models to predict changes in a system as a result of feedback or input changes.** However, they keep in mind that predictions based on models are uncertain.

When scientists construct a model of a system, they begin with certain assumptions. These assumptions allow them to make a basic model that accurately reflects the parts of the system and their relationships. For example, a scientist who wants to study how energy moves through living things in an environment might use a model called a food chain. A food chain is a series that shows who eats whom to obtain energy in an environment. The food chain shown in **Figure 3** assumes that largemouth bass only eat flagfish. Largemouth bass actually eat many kinds of animals. However, the model still accurately reflects the relationships between the parts of a system.

Anhinga

Largemouth bass

Flagfish

Algae

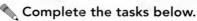

FIGURE 3 ·······················⊙
A Basic Model
In this model of a food chain in the Florida Everglades, the algae make food using the sun's energy. Algae are tiny living things that make their own food.

✏️ **Complete the tasks below.**

1. ⚠️ **Make Models** On the blank line next to each living thing in this system, write who eats it.

2. CHALLENGE What is the energy source for this system?

_____

The arrows show the direction in which energy moves. You can "read" an arrow as saying "are eaten by."

Flagfish: _____

Bass: _____

Algae: _____

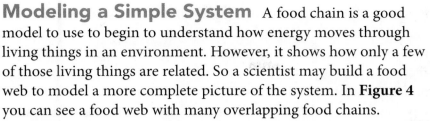

Modeling a Simple System

A food chain is a good model to use to begin to understand how energy moves through living things in an environment. However, it shows how only a few of those living things are related. So a scientist may build a food web to model a more complete picture of the system. In **Figure 4** you can see a food web with many overlapping food chains. The food web is more detailed than one food chain. But it does not provide information about other factors, such as weather, that affect energy flow in the system.

FIGURE 4 ·····················

A Model of a Simple System

This model of an Everglades food web contains overlapping food chains.

✎ **Interpret Diagrams** Study the food web model. On the notebook page, write two things you learned from this complex model.

Alligator

Anhinga

Pig frog

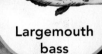
Largemouth bass

Raccoon

Everglades crayfish

Flagfish

Plants, leaves, seeds, and fruits

Algae

Vocabulary Use Context to Determine Meaning Underline the sentence in the text that helps you understand the word *complex.*

Modeling a Complex System Some systems that scientists study are complex. Many parts and many variables interact in these systems. So scientists may use a computer to keep track of all the variables. Because such systems are difficult to model, scientists may model only the specific parts of the system they want to study. Their model may be used to show the processes in the system or to make predictions. For example, the system that involves the melting of sea ice in the Arctic is a complex system. **Figure 5** shows how some parts of that system affect other parts.

FIGURE 5

How Arctic Sea Ice Melts

The Arctic sea-ice system can be modeled by a diagram.

Identify List some of the variables in the Arctic sea-ice system. Then identify the input, process, and output in this model and fill in the boxes.

____

____

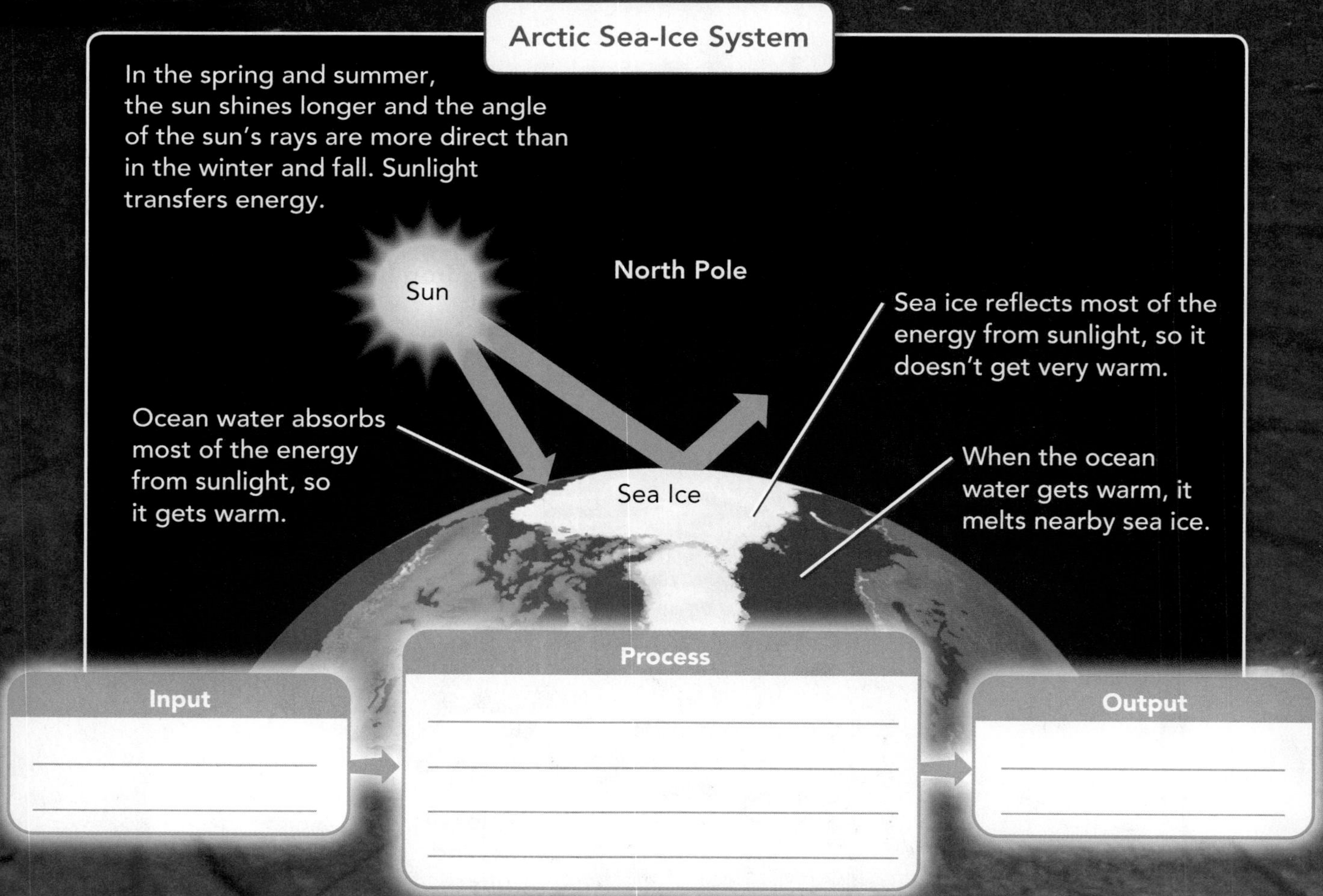

Arctic Sea-Ice System
In the spring and summer, the sun shines longer and the angle of the sun's rays are more direct than in the winter and fall. Sunlight transfers energy.
Sun
North Pole
Sea ice reflects most of the energy from sunlight, so it doesn't get very warm.
Ocean water absorbs most of the energy from sunlight, so it gets warm.
Sea Ice
When the ocean water gets warm, it melts nearby sea ice.
Input
Process
Output

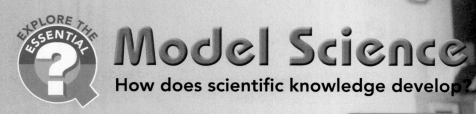

Model Science

How does scientific knowledge develop?

Input

_____

_____

Feedback

_____

_____

Process (Methods)

1. _____

   _____

2. _____

   _____

3. _____

   _____

Output

1. _____

2. _____

FIGURE 6 ··

A Model of the Scientific Community

> **INTERACTIVE ART** The work of scientists can be modeled in a diagram.

✎ **Make Models** Use the terms below to complete the diagram above showing how scientific knowledge develops.

new evidence	design an experiment	make a model	ask questions
research information	explanations	theories and laws	

 Do the Quick Lab
Models in Nature.

🔑 Assess Your Understanding

2a. Identify What is a benefit and a limitation of using models to explain how things work?

_____

_____

_____

_____

SC.7.N.3.2

b. ANSWER THE ESSENTIAL ? How does scientific knowledge develop?

_____

_____

_____

_____

SC.7.N.3.2

got it? ···

○ **I get it!** Now I know that scientists use models of systems to _____

_____

○ **I need extra help with** _____

    Go to **MY SCIENCE** 🔵 **COACH** *online for help with this subject.*

SC.7.N.3.2

REVIEW THE ESSENTIAL ? The pursuit of scientific knowledge begins with a _____ and ends with a(n) _____, a(n)_____, or a law.

LESSON 1 Scientific Explanation
SC.7.N.1.5, SC.7.N.1.6

🗝 Scientists use methods such as researching information, designing experiments, and making models to form a scientific explanation.

🗝 Scientific explanations are always based on empirical evidence.

Vocabulary
• scientific explanation
• empirical evidence
• opinion

LESSON 2 Scientists and Society
SC.7.N.1.7

🗝 Scientists can change society by defending their work in the face of controversy.

Vocabulary
• controversy

LESSON 3 How Science Changes
SC.7.N.2.1, SC.7.N.3.1

🗝 Scientific knowledge changes as a result of new evidence or new interpretations of existing evidence.

🗝 Unlike a theory, a scientific law describes an observed pattern in nature without attempting to explain it.

Vocabulary
• scientific theory
• scientific law

LESSON 4 Models as Tools in Science
SC.7.N.3.2

🗝 Scientists use models to understand things they cannot observe directly.

🗝 A system is a group of parts that work together to perform a function or produce a result.

🗝 Scientists use models to understand how systems work. They also use models to predict changes in a system as a result of feedback or input changes.

Vocabulary
• model • system • input • process • output • feedback

Review and Assessment

LESSON 1 Scientific Explanation

1. Data and observations that have been collected through scientific porcesses are called

   a. empirical evidence.   **b.** opinions.

   c. facts.   **d.** scientific explanations

                                      SC.7.N.1.6

2. A biologist reads a scientific journal to learn more about how cancer cells multiply. Which method is the biologist using to form a scientific explanation?

_____

                                      SC.7.N.1.5

Use the graph below to answer Questions 3 and 4.

Effect of Body Mass on Calories Burned While Bicycling

3. Relate Evidence and Explanation Write a scientific explanation based on the empirical evidence shown in the graph.

_____

_____

_____

                                      SC.7.N.1.6

4. Infer Suppose your friend states that if you double the amount of time that you bike, you will double the calories burned. Can you infer this for certain from the graph? Explain.

_____

_____

_____

                                      SC.7.N.1.6

LESSON 2 Scientists and Society

5. The scientist who said that Earth moves around the sun is

   a. Rachel Carson.   **b.** Galileo Galilei.

   c. Albert Einstein.   **d.** Ignaz Semmelweis.

                                        SC.7.N.1.7

6. A public disagreement between groups with different views is called a(n)_____

                                      SC.7.N.1.7

7. Sequence What process must occur before a new scientific discovery is published?

_____

_____

_____

                                      SC.7.N.1.7

8. Evaluate Science in the Media Identify a scientific controversy that you have seen reported on television, in a newspaper or magazine, or on the Internet.

_____

_____

_____

                                      SC.7.N.1.7

9. Evaluate Science in the Media How do you think Ignaz Semmelweis's discovery in the 1840s affects modern medicine?

_____

_____

_____

_____

                                      SC.7.N.1.7

10. Write About It A company must clear the land of existing trees in order to erect a new building. Some people support the company because the expansion will provide new jobs. Other people are against it because they don't want the wildlife to be destroyed. On a separate sheet of paper, write which side of the controversy you would support and why.

                                      SC.7.N.1.7

LESSON 3 How Science Changes

11. What is a statement that describes what scientists expect to happen every time under a specific set of conditions?

a. law   **b.** theory

c. explanation   **d.** model

SC.7.N.3.1

12. Albert Einstein changed scientific knowledge about _____

SC.7.N.2.1

13. Infer For years, Pluto was considered a planet. Then, in 2006, it was recategorized as a dwarf planet. Why do you suppose scientists changed Pluto's status?

_____

_____

_____

_____

SC.7.N.2.1

14. Apply Concepts For years, scientists noticed that Earth's continents looked as though they could fit together into a single landmass. The theory of plate tectonics now explains this observation. Explain how this observation could lead to a theory.

_____

_____

_____

_____

_____

_____

SC.7.N.2.1

15. Compare and Contrast Why do you suppose plate tectonics is a theory and not a law?

_____

_____

_____

_____

SC.7.N.3.1

LESSON 4 Models as Tools in Science

16. A model of a system must show the relationship between the

a. input and predictions.

b. output and predictions.

c. process and variables.

d. input, process, and output.

SC.7.N.3.2

17. Make Models What are some forms that a scientific model could take?

_____

_____

SC.7.N.3.2

18. Analyze Models and Systems Choose one technology and explain why it is useful for modeling complex systems.

_____

_____

_____

SC.7.N.3.2

How does scientific knowledge develop?

19. Two geranium plants are located in a classroom. One day Morgan notices that one of the plants is turning yellow and losing leaves. She wonders why. Describe the methods that she could use to pursue a scientific explanation. Include any empirical evidence that she may need to collect.

_____

_____

_____

_____

_____

_____

_____

_____

SC.7.N.1.5, SC.7.N.1.6

Florida Benchmarks Review

Circle the letter of the best answer.

1 Galileo drew the following model of the solar system. What does this model show?

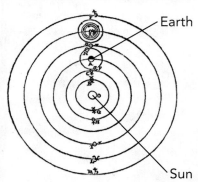

A The distance between Earth and the sun changes as Earth moves around the sun.

B Some, but not all, of the planets move around the sun.

C Earth is the center of the solar system.

D Earth and the other planets move around the sun.

SC.7.N.3.2

2 What is the basis for all scientific explanations?

A laws

B opinions

C controversy

D empirical evidence

SC.7.N.1.6

3 Why should scientists debate the results of a scientific experiment?

A They want to figure out who gets credit.

B They notice errors in the data.

C The results go against the thinking of society.

D Some of the scientists who worked on the experiment are relatively young and inexperienced.

SC.7.N.1.7

4 How did Rachel Carson change scientific knowledge?

A Her observations of the night sky supported the heliocentric model.

B She proved that doctors should wash their hands before delivering babies.

C She showed that the pesticide, DDT, harms animals.

D She proved that mass could be converted to energy.

SC.7.N.2.1

5 Why is the law of gravity not a theory?

A It describes an observed pattern in nature without attempting to explain it.

B It does not describe an observed pattern in nature.

C It describes a wide range of observations.

D Scientists think that it could one day be proved incorrect.

SC.7.N.3.1

6 The graph shows the amount of ultraviolet (UV) rays during a day. What is a scientific explanation for the trend shown in the graph?

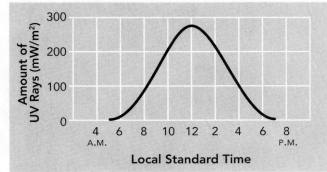

A UV rays are strongest when the sun is highest in the sky.

B UV rays are strongest when the sun rises and weakest when the sun sets.

C UV rays are dangerous to your health.

D The amount of UV rays does not depend on the angle of the sun in the sky.

SC.7.N.1.5

AN ABOMINABLE MYSTERY

chloranthaceae

eudicots

Flowering plants can be divided into five main groups. University of Florida researchers found evidence that monocots and eudicots are the two groups that are most closely related. ▶

magnoliids

You may have heard of the abominable snowman, but have you heard of the "abominable mystery?" That's what Darwin called the evolution of flowering plants. Before these plants there were ferns and other non-flowering plants. The fossil record shows that these were the main types of plants for hundreds of millions of years. Then, in a relatively short period of time, flowering plants took over. Now, the "abominable mystery" is starting to be solved—with the help of University of Florida (UF) researchers.

Working with other scientists, the UF researchers found evidence that the five main groups of flowering plants evolved in only five million years. In terms of evolution, five million years is very short. Of the five groups of plants, the researchers found that two groups are most closely related: monocots and eudicots. Monocots include grasses and irises. The eudicots include orange trees and sunflowers.

The UF researchers came to their conclusions after comparing genetic material, or DNA, from different groups of plants. The more similar the DNA, the more closely two groups are related. Scientists hope to use this research to learn more about what environmental factors led to the rapid evolution of angiosperms.

Research It Research the methods the scientists used in their investigation. Then find examples of monocots and eudicots that live in Florida. Make a list of at least five species for each group. Be sure to list your sources of information.

ceratophyllum

monocots

READY FOR A CLOSE-UP

Whether they are filming animal behavior in the wild or documenting new medical technologies, science filmmakers never know what's going to happen next. For one film, a filmmaker spent 16 weeks sitting hidden under an animal skin for 14 hours every day, just so he could film bird behavior. To film a lion attack, another film crew put themselves in danger by parking a few meters away from some very hungry lions in the middle of the night.

Making a good science film is about more than getting the perfect shot. Crews working in fragile ecosystems like the Arctic or in deserts take care not to wreck habitats. This means they travel light—sometimes using just one hand-held camera.

Writers and producers also try to avoid bias. If there is more than one theory about a topic, they try to find experts who can discuss each theory, and they present as many facts as possible. The makers of a film about the Jarkov woolly mammoth relied heavily on their scientific advisors to make sure scientific facts weren't sacrificed for a good story.

Patience, an adventurous spirit, and science knowledge are all part of being a great science filmmaker!

Research It Research one species of animal. Use facts about the animal to write a proposal for a documentary about that animal. Include a list of four or five questions you hope to answer with your film. Be sure to list the sources of information used in your research.

FLORIDA NGSSS

SC.7.N.1.6 Explain that empirical evidence is the accumulation of observations of natural phenomena.

SC.7.L.17.3 Describe limiting factors in ecosystems and their impact on populations.

LA.7.4.2.2 The student will record information related to a topic and include a list of sources used.

Student scientists survey a section of the ocean floor near Palm Harbor, Florida.

Summarizing

Nature of Science

In this Nature of Science unit, you learned about the skills scientists use in their work and how they design and conduct experiments. In addition, you learned about the processes of science and how scientific understanding changes and grows.

What types of observations could these scientists make?

_____

_____

_____

_____

_____

_____

_____

_____

How could scientific knowledge change as a result of this investigation?

_____

_____

_____

_____

_____

_____

_____

_____

How is this bird's body ORGANIZED?

How does the bird get ENERGY?

Limpkins, a type of bird, live year-round throughout Florida. Their long, curved bills probe freshwater marshes and swamps for animals to eat, such as snails, insects, and worms.

Introducing

Life Science

 Florida Big Idea 14

Organization and Development of Living Organisms

A. All living things share certain characteristics.

B. The scientific theory of cells, also called cell theory, is a fundamental organizing principle of life on Earth.

C. Life can be organized in a functional and structural hierarchy.

D. Life is maintained by various physiological functions essential for growth, reproduction, and homeostasis.

? What are cells made of?

? How does your body work?

? How do systems of the body move and manage materials?

? What systems regulate and control body processes?

? Why do you sometimes get sick?

Florida Big Idea 15

Diversity and Evolution of Living Organisms

A. The scientific theory of evolution is the organizing principle of life science.

B. The scientific theory of evolution is supported by multiple forms of evidence.

C. Natural Selection is a primary mechanism leading to change over time in organisms.

? How are living things alike yet different?

HOW ARE YOU LIKE THIS CREATURE?

What are cells made of?

You sure don't see this sight when you look in the mirror! This deep-sea animal does not have skin, a mouth, or hair like yours. It is a shrimplike animal, called a krill, that lives in the Atlantic Ocean. Yet you and this creature have more in common than you think.

Infer What might you have in common with this young sea animal?

_____

_____

_____

_____

_____

_____

> UNTAMED SCIENCE Watch the **Untamed Science** video to learn more about cells.

Cells and Life Processes

FLORIDA Next Generation Sunshine State Standards

Big Idea 3: SC.6.N.2.1, SC.6.N.3.1, SC.6.N.3.4
Big Idea 14: SC.6.L.14.1, SC.6.L.14.2, SC.6.L.14.3,
SC.6.L.14.4

Language Arts: LA.6.2.2.3,
LA.6.4.2.2
Mathematics: MA.6.A.3.6

3 Getting Started

Check Your Understanding

1. **Background** Read the paragraph below and then answer the question.

> You heard that a pinch of soil can contain millions of **organisms,** and you decide to check it out. Many organisms are too small to see with just your eyes, so you bring a hand **lens.** You see a few organisms, but you think you would see more with greater **magnification.**

An **organism** is a living thing.

A **lens** is a curved piece of glass or other transparent material that bends light.

Magnification is the condition of things appearing larger than they are.

- How does a hand lens help you see more objects in the soil than you can see with just your eyes?

_____

_____

> **MY READING WEB** If you had trouble answering the question above, visit **My Reading Web** and type in *Cells and Life Processes.*

Vocabulary Skill

Prefixes Some words can be divided into parts. A root is the part of the word that carries the basic meaning. A prefix is a word part that is placed in front of the root to change the word's meaning. The prefixes below will help you understand some of the vocabulary in this chapter.

Prefix	Meaning	Example
multi-	many	multicellular, *adj.* having many cells
chroma-	color	chromatin, *n.* the genetic material in the nucleus of a cell that can be colored with dyes

LA.6.1.6.7

2. **Quick Check** Circle the prefix in the boldface word below. What does the word tell you about the organisms?
- Fishes, insects, grasses, and trees are examples of **multicellular** organisms.

_____

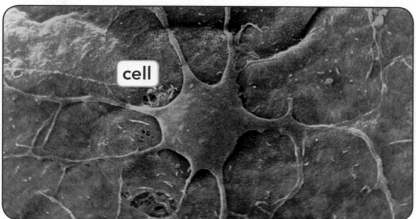

cell

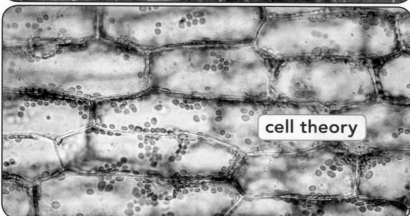

cell theory

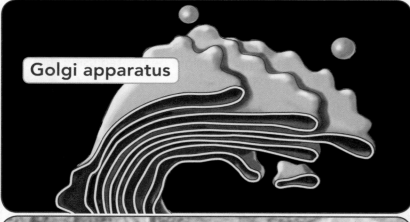

Golgi apparatus

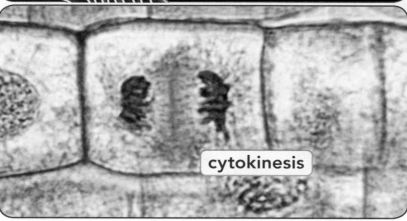

cytokinesis

Chapter Preview

LESSON 1
- element • atom
- compound • molecule • DNA
- cell • unicellular • multicellular
- tissue • organ • organ system

⟳ Identify the Main Idea
△ Draw Conclusions

LESSON 2
- microscope • cell theory

⟳ Sequence
△ Measure

LESSON 3
- homeostasis • cellular respiration
- photosynthesis • cell membrane
- diffusion • cell division

⟳ Compare and Contrast
△ Predict

LESSON 4
- cell wall • nucleus
- organelle • ribosome
- cytoplasm • mitochondria
- endoplasmic reticulum
- Golgi apparatus • vacuole
- chloroplast • lysosome

⟳ Compare and Contrast
△ Make Models

LESSON 5
- cell cycle
- interphase
- replication
- chromosome
- mitosis
- cytokinesis

⟳ Ask Questions
△ Interpret Data

> VOCAB FLASH CARDS For extra help with vocabulary, visit **Vocab Flash Cards** and type in *Cells and Life Processes.*

What Are the Levels of Organization in an Organism?

SC.6.L.14.1, LA.6.2.2.3, MA.6.A.3.6

my planet diary

TECHNOLOGY

Click Print for New Skin

You've probably seen text or images printed by an ink-jet printer. Imagine using the same technology to make skin. A research team, headed by Professor Brian Derby, has adapted ink-jet printers to print human cells. The research team hopes to use this technology to build tissues, such as skin to help treat burn victims. A small number of healthy cells are taken from the patient and used to grow many more cells. These cells are placed in a liquid that serves as the "ink." As the liquid goes through the printer, the cells are seeded onto a piece of plastic that provides a base for more cells to grow. The new tissue should fit the wound perfectly. This technology can print more than one type of cell at a time, just as printers can use more than one color ink. It can also be used to build three-dimensional objects. Researchers hope to be able to print not just skin, but bone, cartilage, and, someday, maybe entire organs!

Professor Brian Derby with three-dimesional objects made by ink-jet printing wax

Communicate **Discuss these questions with a classmate. Then write your answers.**

1. How is this technology similar to printing words on a page?

_____

_____

_____

2. What other medical conditions eventually might be treated using this technology?

_____

_____

_____

> PLANET DIARY Go to **Planet Diary** to learn more about the body's levels of organization.

 Do the Inquiry Warm-Up
What Is a Compound?

Vocabulary
- element • atom • compound • molecule • DNA
- cell • unicellular • multicellular • tissue • organ
- organ system

Skills
⊙ Reading: Identify the Main Idea
△ Inquiry: Draw Conclusions

What Are the Levels of Organization in an Organism?

Have you ever thought about what you are made of? You may say that you are made of blood, bones, muscles, and more. That would be correct. But what is each of those body parts made of? Organisms, or living things, are made of tiny particles that can join together, making larger structures. 🔑 **The levels of organization in an organism from smallest to largest are atoms, elements, molecules, compounds, cells, tissues, organs, and organ systems.**

Elements and Atoms Every living thing, and even every nonliving thing, is a type of matter. Matter is anything that has mass and takes up space. That means that you, and everything that surrounds you, are all forms of matter. Elements make up matter. An **element** is any substance that cannot be broken down into simpler substances. You have probably heard of carbon, hydrogen, oxygen, and nitrogen. All of these are examples of elements found in your body. Some other important elements in your body include sulfur, phosphorus, calcium, and sodium. The smallest unit of an element is a particle called an **atom.** Any single element is made up of only one kind of atom.

FLORIDA NGSSS

SC.6.L.14.1 Describe and identify patterns in the hierarchical organization of organisms from atoms to molecules and cells to tissues to organs to organ systems to organisms.

LA.6.2.2.3 The student will organize information to show understanding (e.g., representing main ideas within text through charting).

MA.6.A.3.6 Construct and analyze tables, graphs, and equations to describe simple relations.

FIGURE 1 ···

Elements
Sulfur is an element. In its pure form, it can form crystals like those shown in the photo.

✏ **Identify** The colored spheres represent atoms. Circle the examples that you think represent all the same element.

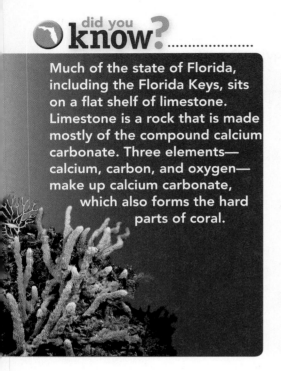
Compounds and Molecules Most elements in living things occur as compounds. **Compounds** form when two or more elements combine chemically. The smallest part, or unit, of many compounds is a **molecule.** For example, a molecule of carbon dioxide consists of one carbon atom and two oxygen atoms. **Figure 2,** illustrates a carbon dioxide molecule and a water molecule, which is made of hydrogen and oxygen atoms.

Carbohydrates, lipids, proteins, water, and nucleic acids are molecules that all living things need. Carbohydrates mainly provide cells with energy. Lipids have many functions, which include forming structures in cells and storing energy. Proteins form body structures, also. And they speed up the chemical reactions in living things. Water helps living things perform these chemical reactions. Water is essential for life and makes up about two thirds of your body.

Nucleic acids contain the instructions necessary to carry out all the functions of life. One important nucleic acid is **DNA,** the genetic material that carries information about an organism and is passed from parent to offspring.

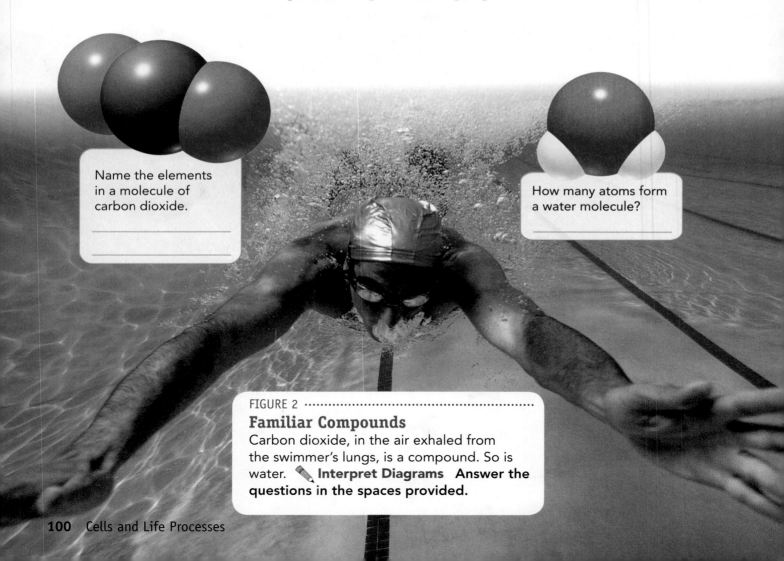

Name the elements in a molecule of carbon dioxide.

_____

_____

How many atoms form a water molecule?

_____

FIGURE 2 ·······················

Familiar Compounds
Carbon dioxide, in the air exhaled from the swimmer's lungs, is a compound. So is water. ✎ **Interpret Diagrams** Answer the questions in the spaces provided.

Cells Carbohydrates, lipids, proteins, nucleic acids, water, and other molecules make up cells. A **cell** is the basic unit of structure and function in living things. If a living thing has only one cell, it is called **unicellular.** Plants and animals (including you) are **multicellular,** which means "made of many cells." In a multicellular organism, the cells often look quite different from one another. They also perform different functions.

All cells in a multicellular organism must carry out key functions, such as using energy, to survive. However, cells also may be specialized. That is, they perform specific functions that benefit the entire organism. These specialized cells share what can be called a "division of labor." One type of cell does one kind of job. Other types of cells do other jobs. For example, red blood cells carry oxygen to other cells that may be busy digesting your food.

Just as specialized cells differ in function, they also differ in structure. **Figure 3** shows specialized cells from plants and animals. Each type of cell has a distinct shape. For example, a nerve cell has thin, fingerlike extensions that reach toward other cells. These structures help nerve cells send signals from one part of your body to another. The nerve cell's shape wouldn't be helpful for a red blood cell.

Identify the Main Idea
Reread the second and third paragraphs on this page. Then underline the phrases or sentences that describe the main ideas about specialized cells

FIGURE 3 ·······························
> INTERACTIVE ART The Right Cell for the Job
Many cells in plants and animals carry out specialized functions.

✎ **Infer** Write the number of each kind of cell in the circle of the matching function.

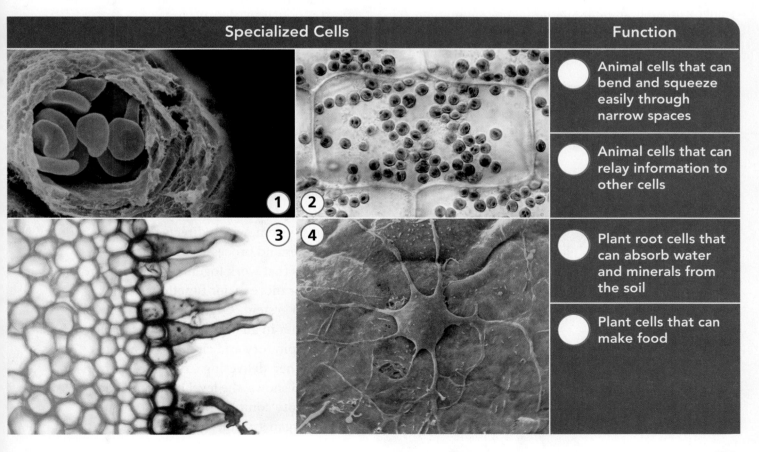

Specialized Cells	Function
① ② ③ ④	○ Animal cells that can bend and squeeze easily through narrow spaces
	○ Animal cells that can relay information to other cells
	○ Plant root cells that can absorb water and minerals from the soil
	○ Plant cells that can make food

do the math!

Most cells contain the same molecules. The graph compares the percentages of some molecules found in a bacterial cell and in an animal cell. Write a title for the graph and answer the questions below.

❶ Analyze Graphs Put a check mark above the bar that shows the percentage of water in an animal cell. How does this number compare to the percentage of water in a bacterial cell?

_____

_____

❷ Analyze Graphs (Lipids/Nucleic acids) make up a larger percentage of an animal cell.

❸ Draw Conclusions In general, how do you think a bacterial cell and an animal cell compare in their chemical composition?

_____

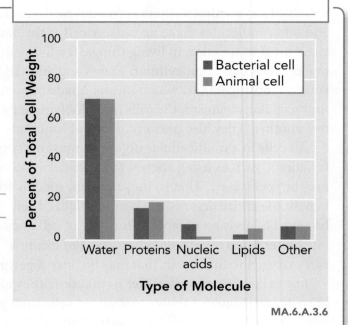

Legend: ■ Bacterial cell ■ Animal cell

Y-axis: Percent of Total Cell Weight (0, 20, 40, 60, 80, 100)

X-axis: Type of Molecule — Water, Proteins, Nucleic acids, Lipids, Other

MA.6.A.3.6

FIGURE 4 ···

Organs
Organs, like the liver, lungs, and intestines, each perform a specific job.

✎ **Compare and Contrast** How are the organs in this model of the human body the same and how are they different?

_____

_____

_____

_____

_____

_____

_____

_____

_____

_____

Tissues, Organs, and Organ Systems
In multicellular organisms, cells are organized into tissues, organs, and organ systems. A **tissue** is a group of similar cells that work together and perform a specific function.

For example, your brain is made mostly of nerve tissue, which consists of nerve cells that relay information to other parts of your body. An **organ,** such as your brain, is made of different kinds of tissues that function together. For example, the brain also has blood vessels that carry the blood that supplies oxygen to your brain cells. Your brain is part of your nervous system, which directs body activities and processes. A group of organs that work together and perform one or more major functions is an **organ system.** Organ systems work together in an organism. For example, your respiratory and circulatory systems work together, delivering oxygen to your cells. As **Figure 5** shows, the level of organization becomes more complex from cell, to tissue, to organ, to organ system.

FIGURE 5 ·······································

Levels of Organization

Living things are organized in levels of increasing complexity.

✎ **Use the flowchart to complete the following tasks.**

1. **Identify Patterns** Fill in the missing terms to show the patterns of organization of organisms from simple to complex.

2. **Chart** In the space, draw a flowchart of levels of organization for a nonliving example, such as a school building.

LA.6.2.2.3

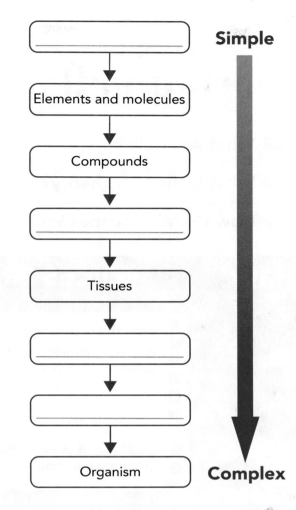

Simple

Elements and molecules

Compounds

Tissues

Organism

Complex

Lab zone® **Do the Quick Lab**
Tissues, Organs, and Systems.

🔑 Assess Your Understanding

1a. Describe How are atoms and molecules related?

_____

SC.6.L.14.1

b. ✎ **Infer** Would a tissue or an organ have more kinds of specialized cells? Explain your answer.

_____

_____

SC.6.L.14.1

c. CHALLENGE How are atoms, molecules, and cells similar? Explain.

_____

_____

_____

_____

_____

SC.6.L.14.1

got it? ··

○ **I get it!** Now I know that the levels of organization in a multicellular organism include_____

_____

○ **I need extra help with** _____

Go to **MY SCIENCE** 🔵 **COACH** *online for help with this subject.*

SC.6.L.14.1

Discovering Cells

What Are Cells?
SC.6.L.14.2

What Is the Cell Theory?
SC.6.N.3.1, SC.6.L.14.2

How Do Microscopes Work?
SC.6.L.14.2, LA.6.4.2.2

my planeт Diary

Life at First Sight

Anton van Leeuwenhoek was the first researcher to see bacteria under a microscope. In his journal, he described how he felt after discovering this new and unfamiliar form of life.

"For me . . . no more pleasant sight has met my eye than this of so many thousand of living creatures in one small drop of water."

VOICES FROM HISTORY

Read the quote, and answer the question below.

Why do you think Leeuwenhoek was so excited about what he saw?

_____

_____

> **PLANET DIARY** Go to **Planet Diary** to learn more about studying cells.

A modern view of bacteria similar to those seen by Leeuwenhoek

 Lab zone® Do the Inquiry Warm-Up *What Can You See?*

What Are Cells?

What do you think you have in common with a mushroom, a tree, a spider, and a bird? All are living things, or organisms. Like all organisms, they are made of cells. Cells form the parts of an organism and carry out all of its functions. **Cells are the basic units of structure and function in living things.**

Cells and Structure When you describe the structure of an object, you describe what it is made of and how its parts are put together. For example, the structure of a building depends on the way bricks, steel beams, or other materials are arranged. The structure of a living thing is determined by the amazing variety of ways its cells are put together.

FLORIDA NGSSS

SC.6.L.14.2 Investigate and explain the components of the scientific theory of cells (cell theory): all organisms are composed of cells (single-celled or multicellular), all cells come from pre-existing cells, and cells are the basic unit of life.

Vocabulary
- microscope
- cell theory

Skills
↻ Reading: Sequence
△ Inquiry: Measure

FIGURE 1 ....

Needs of Cells
A single cell has the same needs as an entire organism.

✎ **Classify** On each blank arrow, write the name of a material that moves in the direction shown.

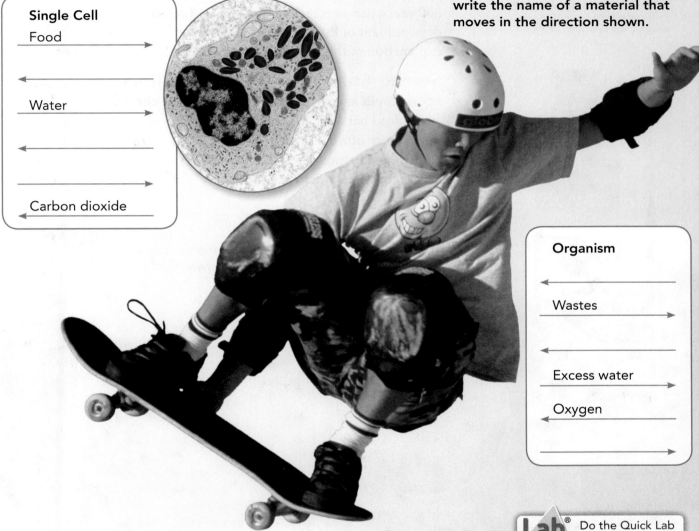

Single Cell

Food →

←

Water →

←

Carbon dioxide ←

Organism

←

Wastes →

←

Excess water →

Oxygen ←

Lab zone® Do the Quick Lab *Comparing Cells.*

Cells and Function An organism's functions are the processes that enable it to live, grow, and reproduce. Those functions include obtaining oxygen, food, and water and getting rid of wastes. Cells are involved in all of these functions. For example, cells in your digestive system absorb food. The food provides your body with energy and materials needed for growth. Cells in your lungs help you get oxygen. Your body's cells work together, keeping you alive. And for each cell to stay alive, it must carry out many of the same functions as the entire organism.

🔑 **Assess Your Understanding**

got it? ....

○ **I get it!** Now I know that a cell is the basic unit of _____

_____

○ **I need extra help with** _____

Go to **my science** ⑤ **coach** *online for help with this subject.*

SC.6.L.14.2

105

FLORIDA NGSSS

SC.6.N.3.1 Recognize and explain that a scientific theory is a well-supported and widely accepted explanation of nature.

SC.6.L.14.2 Investigate and explain the components of the cell theory: all organisms are composed of cells, all cells come from pre-existing cells, and cells are the basic unit of life.

What Is the Cell Theory?

Until the 1600s, no one knew cells existed because there was no way to see them. Around 1590, the invention of the first microscope allowed people to look at very small objects. A **microscope** is an instrument that makes small objects look larger. Over the next 200 years, this new technology revealed cells and led to the development of the cell theory. The **cell theory** is a widely accepted explanation of the relationship between cells and living things.

Seeing Cells English scientist Robert Hooke built his own microscopes and made drawings of what he saw when he looked at the dead bark of certain oak trees. Hooke never knew the importance of what he saw. A few years later, Dutch businessman Anton van Leeuwenhoek (LAY von hook) was the first to see living cells through his microscopes.

FIGURE 2

Growth of the Cell Theory

The cell theory describes how cells relate to the structure and function of living things. ✎ **Review** **Answer the questions in the spaces below.**

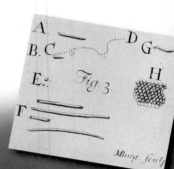

Drawing by Leeuwenhoek

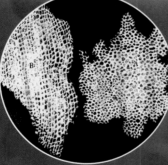

Hooke's drawing of cork

Hooke's Microscope

In 1663, Robert Hooke used his microscope to observe a thin slice of cork. Cork, the bark of the cork oak tree, is made up of cells that are no longer alive. To Hooke, the empty spaces in the cork looked like tiny rectangular rooms. Therefore, Hooke called the empty spaces cells, which means "small rooms."

What was important about Hooke's work?

_____

_____

Leeuwenhoek's Microscope

Leeuwenhoek built microscopes in his spare time. Around 1674, he looked at drops of lake water, scrapings from teeth and gums, and water from rain gutters. Leeuwenhoek was surprised to find a variety of one-celled organisms. He noted that many of them whirled, hopped, or shot through water like fast fish. He called these moving organisms animalcules, meaning "little animals."

What did Leeuwenhoek's observations reveal?

_____

_____

What the Cell Theory Says

Figure 2 highlights people who made key discoveries in the early study of cells. Their work and the work of many others led to the development of the cell theory. **The cell theory states the following:**

- **All living things are composed of cells.**
- **Cells are the basic units of structure and function in living things.**
- **All cells are produced from other cells.**

Living things differ greatly from one another, but all are made of cells. The cell theory holds true for unicellular and multicellular organisms. Because cells are common to all living things, cells can provide clues about the functions that living things perform. And because all cells come from other cells, scientists can study cells to learn about growth and reproduction.

Sequence Fill in the circle next to the name of the person who was the first to see living cells through a microscope.

- ◯ Matthias Schleiden
- ◯ Robert Hooke
- ◯ Anton van Leeuwenhoek
- ◯ Rudolf Virchow
- ◯ Theodor Schwann

Schleiden, Schwann, and Virchow

In 1838, using his own research and the research of others, Matthias Schleiden concluded that all plants are made of cells. A year later, Theodor Schwann reached the same conclusion about animals. In 1855, Rudolf Virchow proposed that new cells are formed only from cells that already exist. "All cells come from cells," wrote Virchow.

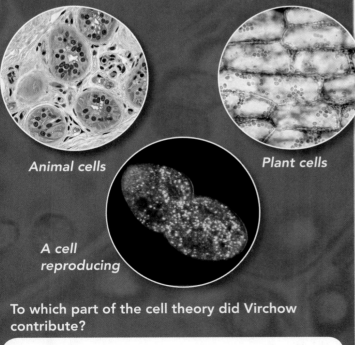

Animal cells

Plant cells

A cell reproducing

To which part of the cell theory did Virchow contribute?

_____
_____

Lab zone® Do the Quick Lab *Observing Cells.*

Assess Your Understanding

1a. Relate Cause and Effect Why would Hooke's discovery have been impossible without a microscope?

_____
_____
_____

SC.6.L.14.2

b. Recognize and Explain Use Virchow's ideas to explain why plastic plants and stuffed animals are not alive.

_____
_____
_____
_____

SC.6.N.3.1, SC.6.L.14.2

got it?

◯ **I get it!** Now I know that the cell theory describes _____

_____
_____

◯ **I need extra help with** _____

Go to **my science coach** *online for help with this subject.*   SC.6.N.3.1, SC.6.L.14.2

107

Vocabulary Prefixes The prefix magni- means "great" or "large." Underline all the words in the paragraph at the right that you can find with this prefix.

How Do Microscopes Work?

The cell theory could not have been developed without microscopes. **Some microscopes focus light through lenses to produce a magnified image, and other microscopes use beams of electrons.** Both light microscopes and electron microscopes do the same job in different ways. For a microscope to be useful, it must combine two important properties—magnification and resolution.

Magnification and Lenses Have you ever looked at something through spilled drops of water? If so, did the object appear larger? Something is magnified if it appears larger than it really is. Looking through a magnifying glass has the same result. A magnifying glass consists of a convex lens, which has a center that is thicker than its edge. When light passes through a convex lens and into your eye, the image you see is magnified. Magnification changes how you can see objects and reveals details you may not have known were there, as shown in **Figure 3.**

❶ Leaf; green color and veins

❷

❸

❹

FIGURE 3

Magnification

The images above have all been magnified, which makes them look unfamiliar. ✎ **Infer** On the lines, write what you think each photograph shows, and explain your reasoning. **(One answer is completed for you.)** LA.6.4.2.2

Magnification With a Compound Microscope

Figure 4 shows a microscope that is similar to one you may use in your classroom. This type of instrument, called a compound microscope, magnifies the image using two lenses at once. One lens is fixed in the eyepiece. A second lens is chosen from a group of two or three lenses on the revolving nosepiece. Each of these lenses has a different magnifying power. By turning the nosepiece, you can select the lens you want. A glass slide on the stage holds the object to be viewed.

A compound microscope can magnify an object more than a single lens can. Light from a lamp (or reflecting off a mirror) passes through the object on the slide, the lower lens, and then the lens in the eyepiece. The total magnification of the object equals the magnifications of the two lenses multiplied together. For example, suppose the lower lens magnifies the object 10 times, and the eyepiece lens also magnifies the object 10 times. The total magnification of the microscope is 10 × 10, or 100 times, which is written as "100×."

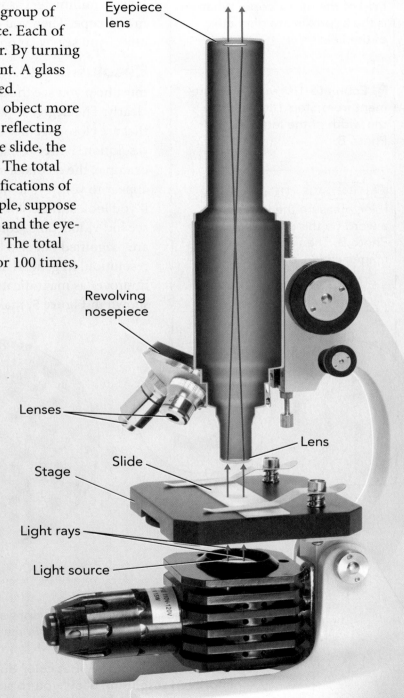

Eyepiece lens

Revolving nosepiece

Lenses

Stage

Slide

Lens

Light rays

Light source

FIGURE 4 ·······················

> VIRTUAL LAB **A Compound Microscope**

This microscope has a 10× lens in the eyepiece. The revolving nosepiece holds three different lenses: 4×, 10×, and 40×.

✎ **Complete the following tasks.**

1. **Calculate** Find the three total magnifications possible for this microscope.

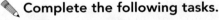

_____

_____

_____

2. **Predict** What would happen if the object on the slide were too thick for light to pass through it?

_____

_____

_____

_____

A   B

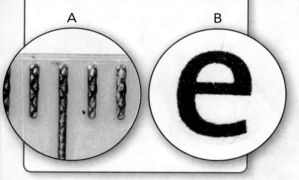

Measuring Microscopic Objects

When you see objects through a microscope, they look larger than they really are. How do you know their true size? One way is to use a metric ruler to measure the size of the circular field in millimeters as you see it through the microscope. Then you can estimate the size of the object you see by comparing it to the width of the field.

Resolution To create a useful image, a microscope must help you see the details of the object's structure clearly. The degree to which two separate structures that are close together can be distinguished is called resolution. Better resolution shows more details. For example, the colors of a newspaper photograph may appear to your eye to be solid patches of color. However, if you look at the colors through a microscope, you will see individual dots. You see the dots not only because they are magnified but also because the microscope improves resolution. In general, for light microscopes, resolution improves as magnification increases. Good resolution, as shown in **Figure 5,** makes it easier to study cells.

FIGURE 5 ··

Resolution

The images in colorful photographs actually consist of only a few ink colors in the form of dots.

✏ **Interpret Photos** What color dots does improved resolution allow you to see?

_____

_____

_____

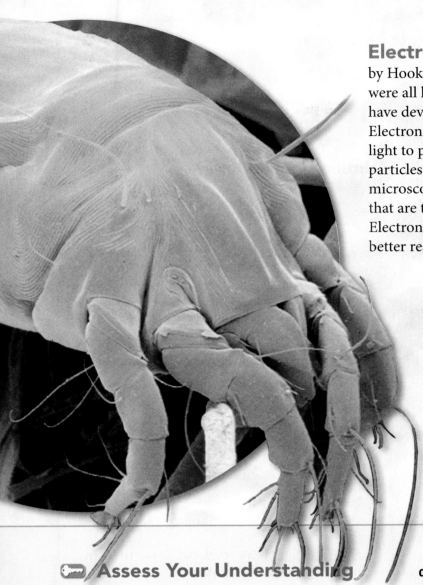

Electron Microscopes
The microscopes used by Hooke, Leeuwenhoek, and other early researchers were all light microscopes. Since the 1930s, scientists have developed several types of electron microscopes. Electron microscopes use a beam of electrons instead of light to produce a magnified image. (Electrons are tiny particles that are smaller than atoms.) By using electron microscopes, scientists can obtain pictures of objects that are too small to be seen with light microscopes. Electron microscopes allow higher magnification and better resolution than light microscopes.

FIGURE 6 ··
A Dust Mite
Dust mites live in everyone's homes. A colorized image made with an electron microscope reveals startling details of a mite's body.

✎ **Observe** List at least three details that you can see in the photo.

_____

_____

_____

 Do the Lab Investigation
Design and Build a Microscope.

🔑 Assess Your Understanding

2a. Define Magnification makes objects look (smaller/larger) than they really are.
SC.6.L.14.2

b. Estimate The diameter of a microscope's field of view is estimated to be 0.9 mm. About how wide is an object that fills two thirds of the field? Circle your answer.

1.8 mm   0.6 mm   0.3 mm
SC.6.L.14.2

c. Compare and Contrast How are magnification and resolution different?

_____

_____

_____

_____
SC.6.L.14.2

d. Explain How do the characteristics of electron microscopes make them useful for studying cells?

_____

_____

_____

_____

_____
SC.6.L.14.2

got**it**? ···

○ **I get it!** Now I know that light microscopes work by_____

_____

○ **I need extra help with** _____

Go to MY SCIENCE COACH *online for help with this subject*
SC.6.L.14.2

111

Cells and Homeostasis

UNLOCK THE ESSENTIAL **?**

🔑 **How Do Cells Maintain Homeostasis?**
SC.6.N.2.1, SC.6.L.14.3, LA.6.2.2.3

MY PLANET DIARY

Sleeping Away the Cobwebs

Has your thinking ever felt fuzzy from lack of sleep? New research suggests that brain cells function better when well rested. Tests conducted with fruit flies and rats showed that proteins build up in the brain during wakeful times and decrease during sleep. These proteins take up space between brain cells and use energy. Researchers think sleep helps "clean house," saving energy and space and restoring balance in the brain. In a way, sleep refreshes the brain and prepares it to learn more effectively during the day.

DISCOVERY

Communicate **Complete the tasks.** SC.6.N.2.1

1. On a separate paper, write a short, short story about not getting enough sleep.

2. How is writing a story different from researching the effects of sleep?

_____

_____

_____

▸ PLANET DIARY Go to **Planet Diary** to learn more about cellular processes.

Lab zone® Do the Inquiry Warm-Up *Homeostasis.*

FLORIDA NGSSS

SC.6.N.2.1 Distinguish science from other activities involving thought.

SC.6.L.14.3 Recognize and explore how cells of all organisms undergo similar processes to maintain homeostasis, including extracting energy from food, getting rid of waste, and reproducing.

LA.6.2.2.3 The student will organize information to show understanding (e.g., representing main ideas within text through comparing/contrasting).

How Do Cells Maintain Homeostasis?

Have you ever felt sweaty on a very warm day? The evaporation of sweat from your skin helps to cool your body. Keeping your internal body temperature about the same in spite of the temperature outside is just one example of how your body maintains homeostasis. **Homeostasis** (hoh mee oh STAY sis) is the maintenance of internal stable conditions that are necessary for life functions. Just as entire organisms maintain homeostasis, so do individual cells. 🔑 **In all cells, the processes that help maintain homeostasis include getting and using energy from food and removing wastes.**

Vocabulary

- homeostasis • cellular respiration • photosynthesis
- cell membrane • diffusion • cell division

Skills

↻ Reading: Compare and Contrast

△ Inquiry: Predict

Getting and Using Energy What foods did you eat for breakfast? Have you ever thought about why you should eat breakfast? Food provides the cells in your body with the energy you need to walk to the bus stop, listen in class, and write assignments.

Energy From Food Like you, most organisms get energy from cell processes that break down foods. The most common process involves a sugar called glucose. During **cellular respiration,** cells break down glucose molecules in the presence of oxygen, releasing energy. Waste products of this process include carbon dioxide and water. Animals and some other organisms get food for energy by eating other organisms. For example, a mouse eats fruits and grains from plants. An owl sometimes eats mice.

Making Food Unlike animals, plants and some other organisms can make their own food. The process by which cells capture the energy in sunlight and convert it to energy stored in food is called **photosynthesis** (foh toh SIN thuh sis). Often, the foods produced in photosynthesis are glucose or other sugars. Through cellular respiration, these compounds then supply the energy needed for a plant cell's activities. The raw materials for photosynthesis are carbon dioxide from the air and water. Oxygen leaves the cell as a waste product.

↻ **Compare and Contrast**
Underline the sentences that describe how energy processes in organisms are the same and different.

LA.6.2.2.3

FIGURE 1 ....
Energy From Food
Florida's orange crop comes from the energy captured in photosynthesis. The 2008–2009 crop totaled 162 million boxes.

✎ **Complete the following tasks.**

1. **Recognize** Check the box for each process that applies to the organism.

2. **Apply Concepts** How does energy from the sun become energy the boy can use?

_____
_____
_____
_____

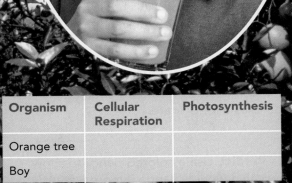

Organism	Cellular Respiration	Photosynthesis
Orange tree		
Boy		

113

FIGURE 2

Diffusion

Some materials move across the cell membrane by way of diffusion.

✏️ **Predict** Draw an arrow to show the overall direction that molecules will travel as a result of diffusion.

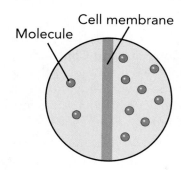

Molecule
Cell membrane

Removing Wastes To maintain homeostasis, materials such as food and oxygen must move into cells. At the same time, waste materials must exit. If waste materials build up, they act as poisons that can harm a cell and disrupt homeostasis.

Cell Membrane Wastes and other materials that move into or out of a cell must cross a structure called the cell membrane. The **cell membrane** surrounds a cell and separates it from the outside environment. It also controls which substances enter and leave. You can think of the cell membrane much like a gatekeeper who controls the flow of traffic into and out of a parking lot.

Diffusion One way materials move across the cell membrane involves collisions of molecules. Since molecules are always moving, they constantly bump into one another. If they are crowded, or concentrated, in a small space, they collide more often. These collisions push the molecules away from one another in a process called diffusion. During **diffusion** (dih FYOO zhun), molecules move from an area of *higher* concentration (a lot of molecules) to an area of *lower* concentration (fewer molecules). Eventually, the molecules spread evenly throughout a space. Look at **Figure 2.**

Molecules of gases and water move easily across the cell membrane. Other materials move in directions opposite to the way they would move during diffusion. In these cases, the cell uses energy—the energy it gets from cellular respiration!

apply it!

Without water a cell cannot live or function. *Osmosis* is the term used to describe the diffusion of water across a cell membrane. Osmosis happens constantly as water molecules move into and out of a cell. These photos show a plant cell that has been affected by osmosis. (The cell wall is a rigid structure that surrounds a plant cell.)

❶ **Interpret Photos** Which cell shows the effect of water loss? Explain your reasoning.

❷ **Relate Cause and Effect** How do you think homeostasis would be affected in a cell that loses a lot of water?

❸ ✏️ **Predict** Use a colored pencil to show how cell B would change if more water flowed into the cell.

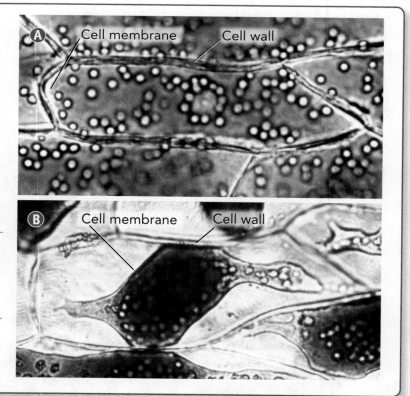

Reproduction of Cells Are you bigger now than when you were a baby? Of course, you are! Have you grown even in the last few months? All multicellular organisms grow during some part of their lifetimes. They also have structures that wear out or become injured and must be replaced. Think about a time when you may have gotten a skinned knee. In just a few days, new skin appeared, and your injury healed.

Growth and repair can occur because cells reproduce, or make more cells. **Cell division** is a process in which one cell splits into two new cells that are genetically identical to the original cell. You can see a cell dividing in **Figure 3**.

🔑 **Reproduction of cells is one of the processes that helps multicellular organisms maintain homeostasis.** Through cell division, your body can replace damaged skin cells and worn out blood cells. You grow as your body produces more muscle cells, bone cells, and other kinds of cells. Growth and repair help your body maintain homeostasis.

FIGURE 3 ··························
New Cells
This photo shows one cell that is becoming two as a result of cell division.

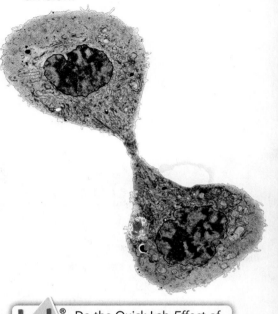

Lab zone Do the Quick Lab *Effect of Concentration on Diffusion.*

🔑 Assess Your Understanding

1a. Define What is homeostasis?

_____

_____

_____

_____

SC.6.L.14.3

b. Recognize How does photosynthesis help plants maintain homeostasis?

_____

_____

_____

_____

SC.6.L.14.3

c. Relate Cause and Effect Diffusion results in molecules moving from areas of (lower/higher) concentration to areas of (lower/higher) concentration.

SC.6.L.14.3

d. CHALLENGE What would happen to a cell if materials could not move across the cell membrane? Justify your answer.

_____

_____

_____

_____

SC.6.L.14.3

got it? ··

○ **I get it!** Now I know that maintaining homeostasis in cells and organisms involves _____

_____

○ **I need extra help with** _____

Go to MY SCIENCE Ⓢ COACH *online for help with this subject.*

SC.6.L.14.3

115

Looking Inside Cells

🔑 **How Do the Parts of a Cell Work?**
SC.6.N.3.4, SC.6.L.14.4, LA.6.2.2.3

MY PLANET DIARY

Glowing Globs

Do these cells look as if they're glowing? This photograph shows cells that have been stained with dyes that make cell structures easier to see. Scientists view such treated cells through a fluorescent microscope, which uses strong light to activate the dyes and make them glow. Here, each green area is a cell's nucleus, or control center. The yellow "fibers" form a kind of support structure for the cell.

Lab zone® Do the Inquiry Warm-Up *How Large Are Cells?*

TECHNOLOGY

Communicate Discuss these questions with a partner. Then write your answers below.

1. Why is staining useful when studying cells through a microscope?

_____

_____

2. If you had a microscope, what kinds of things would you like to look at? Why?

_____

_____

_____

▶ **PLANET DIARY** Go to **Planet Diary** to learn more about cell parts.

Vocabulary

- cell wall • nucleus • organelle
- ribosome • cytoplasm • mitochondria
- endoplasmic reticulum • Golgi apparatus • vacuole
- chloroplast • lysosome

Skills

↻ Reading: Compare and Contrast

△ Inquiry: Make Models

How Do the Parts of a Cell Work?

When you look at a cell through a microscope, you can usually see the outer edge of the cell. Sometimes you can also see smaller structures within the cell. ⊙ **Each kind of cell structure has a different function within a cell.** In this lesson, you will read about the structures that plant and animal cells have in common. You will also read about some differences between the cells.

Cell Wall The **cell wall** is a rigid layer that surrounds the cells of plants and some other organisms, such as mushrooms. The cells of animals, in contrast, do not have cell walls. A plant's cell wall helps protect and support the cell. The cell wall is made mostly of a strong material called cellulose. Still, many materials, including water and oxygen, can pass through the cell wall.

Cell Membrane Think about how a window screen allows air to enter and leave a room but keeps insects out. One of the functions of the cell membrane is something like that of a screen. The cell membrane controls which substances pass into and out of a cell. Everything a cell needs, such as food particles, water, and oxygen, enters through the cell membrane. Waste products leave the same way. In addition, the cell membrane prevents harmful materials from entering the cell.

All cells have cell membranes, which are made mostly of lipids. In plant cells, the cell membrane is just inside the cell wall. In cells without cell walls, the cell membrane forms the border between the cell and its environment.

FLORIDA NGSSS

SC.6.N.3.4 Identify the role of models in the context of the sixth grade science benchmarks.

SC.6.L.14.4 Compare and contrast the structure and function of major organelles of plant and animal cells, including cell wall, cell membrane, nucleus, cytoplasm, chloroplasts, mitochondria, and vacuoles.

LA.6.2.2.3 The student will organize information to show understanding (e.g., representing main ideas within text through comparing/constrasting).

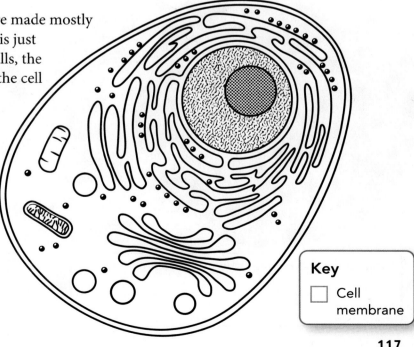

FIGURE 1 ·······························
A Typical Animal Cell
You will see this diagram of a cell again in this lesson.

✎ **Identify** Use a colored pencil to shade the cell membrane and fill in the box in the key.

Key
☐ Cell membrane

Nucleus

A cell doesn't have a brain, but it has something that functions in a similar way. A large oval structure called the **nucleus** (NOO klee us) acts as a cell's control center, directing all of the cell's activities. The nucleus is the largest of cell structures, called **organelles,** that carry out specific functions within a cell. Notice in **Figure 2** that the nucleus is surrounded by a membrane called the nuclear envelope. Molecules pass in and out of the nucleus through pores in the nuclear envelope.

Chromatin

You may wonder how the nucleus "knows" how to direct the cell. Chromatin, thin strands of DNA and proteins that fill the nucleus, contains information for directing a cell's functions. For example, the instructions in the chromatin ensure that leaf cells grow and divide to form more leaf cells.

Nucleolus

Notice the small, round structure in the nucleus. This structure, the nucleolus, is where ribosomes are made. **Ribosomes** are small, grain-shaped organelles that produce proteins. Proteins are important substances in cells.

FIGURE 2 ··

Organelles of a Cell

The structures of a cell look as different as their functions.

✏️ **Complete each task.**

1. **Review** Answer the questions in the boxes.

2. **Relate Text and Visuals** In the diagram on the facing page, use different-colored pencils to color each structure and its matching box in the color key.

Nucleus

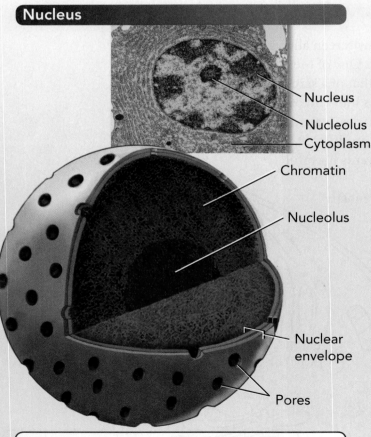

- Nucleus
- Nucleolus
- Cytoplasm
- Chromatin
- Nucleolus
- Nuclear envelope
- Pores

What does the nuclear envelope do?

_____

_____

Mitochondrion

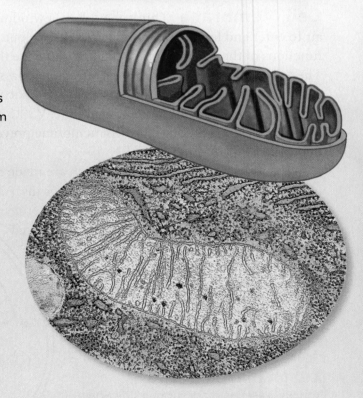

[CHALLENGE] **In what types of cells would you expect to find a lot of mitochondria?**

_____

Organelles in the Cytoplasm

Most of a cell consists of a thick, clear, watery, gel-like fluid. The **cytoplasm** fills the region between the cell membrane and the nucleus. The fluid of the cytoplasm moves constantly within a cell, carrying along the nucleus and other organelles that have specific jobs.

Mitochondria Floating in the cytoplasm are rod-shaped structures that are nicknamed the "powerhouses" of a cell. Look again at **Figure 2. Mitochondria** (myt oh KAHN dree uh; singular *mitochondrion*) carry out cellular respiration, releasing energy the cell can use to live and function.

Endoplasmic Reticulum and Ribosomes In **Figure 2,** you can see what looks something like a maze of passageways. The **endoplasmic reticulum** (en doh PLAZ mik rih TIK yuh lum), often called the ER, is an organelle with a network of membranes that produces many substances. Ribosomes dot some parts of the ER, while other ribosomes float in the cytoplasm. The ER helps the attached ribosomes make proteins. These newly made proteins and other substances leave the ER.

Vocabulary Prefixes The prefix *endo-* is Greek for "within." If the word part *plasm* refers to the "body" of the cell, what does the prefix *endo-* tell you about the endoplasmic reticulum?

_____

_____

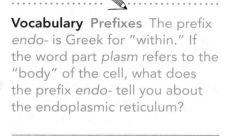

Endoplasmic Reticulum and Ribosomes

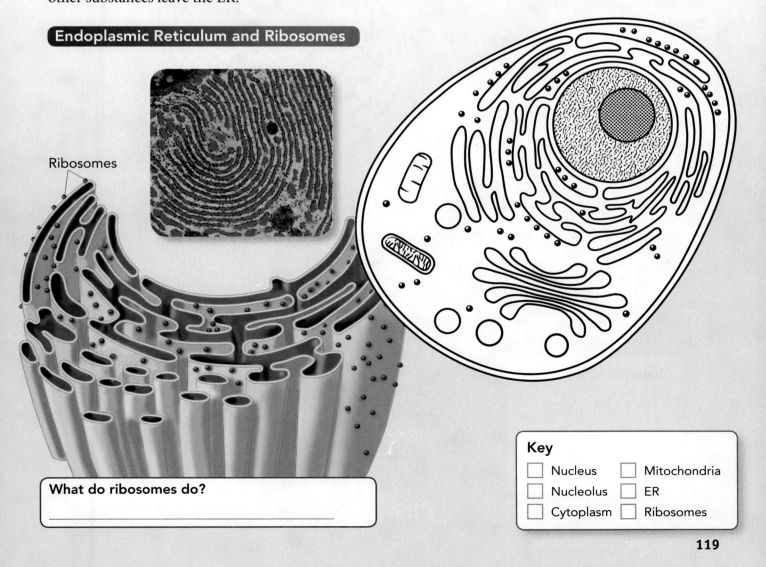

Ribosomes

What do ribosomes do?

_____

Key

- [ ] Nucleus
- [ ] Nucleolus
- [ ] Cytoplasm
- [ ] Mitochondria
- [ ] ER
- [ ] Ribosomes

CELLS IN LIVING THINGS

What are cells made of?

FIGURE 3 ···

▶**INTERACTIVE ART** These illustrations show typical structures found in plant and animal cells. The cells of other living things share many of these structures, too. ✎ **Describe** As you complete this lesson, describe the function of each structure in the boxes provided.

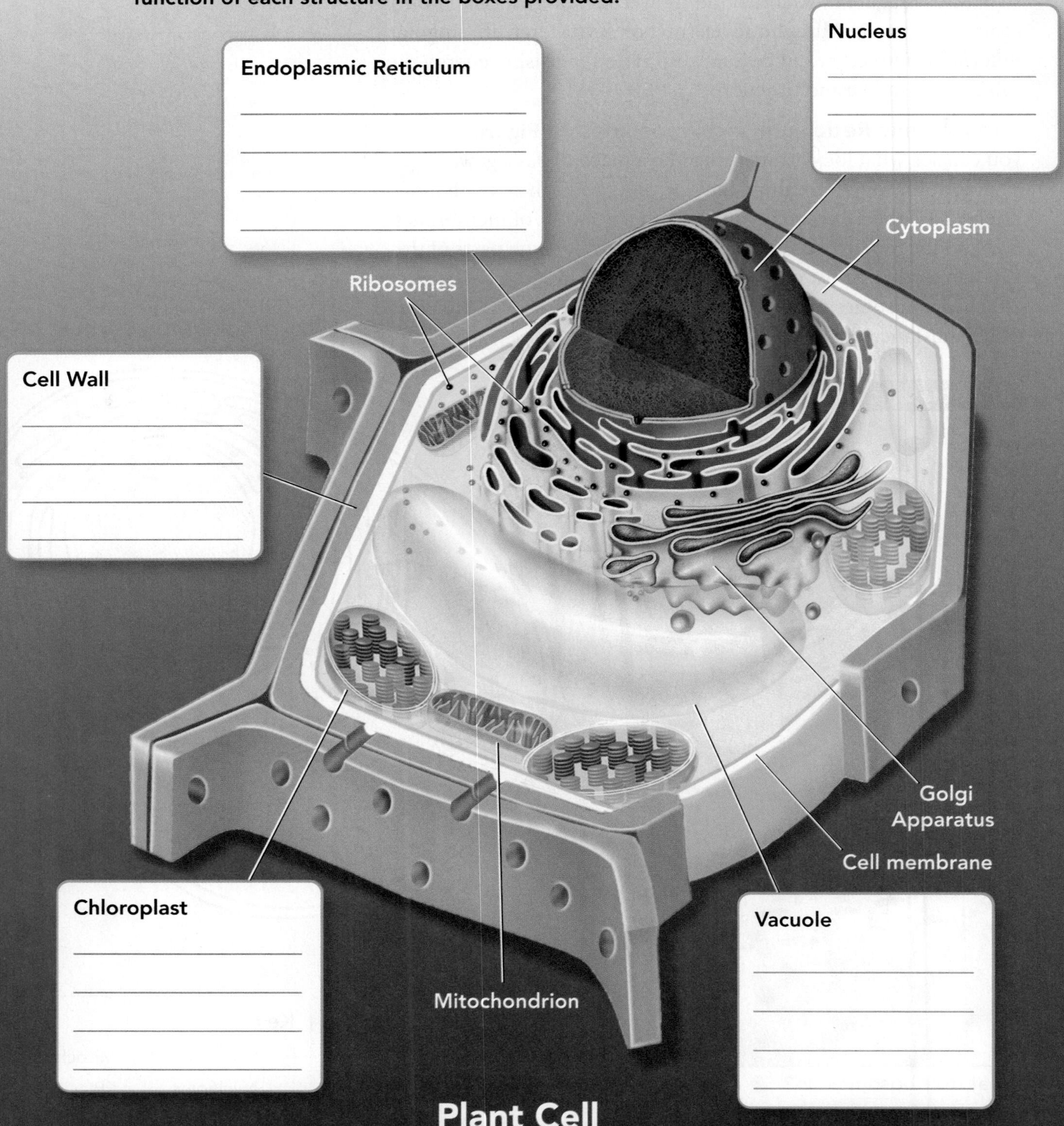

Nucleus
_____
_____
_____

Endoplasmic Reticulum
_____
_____
_____
_____

Cytoplasm

Ribosomes

Cell Wall
_____
_____
_____
_____

Golgi
Apparatus

Cell membrane

Chloroplast
_____
_____
_____
_____

Vacuole
_____
_____
_____
_____

Mitochondrion

Plant Cell

Structure	Cell wall	Cell membrane	Cytoplasm	Nucleus	Mitochondria	Chloroplasts	Ribosomes	Endoplasmic reticulum	Vacuoles	Golgi apparatus	Lysosomes
Plant cells											
Animal cells											

Compare and Contrast Check the box for each structure present in plant cells or animal cells.

Ribosomes
_____
_____

Cytoplasm
_____
_____
_____

Mitochondria
_____
_____
_____

Endoplasmic Reticulum

Golgi Apparatus
_____
_____
_____
_____

Lysosomes
_____
_____
_____
_____

Vacuole

Cell Membrane
_____
_____
_____
_____

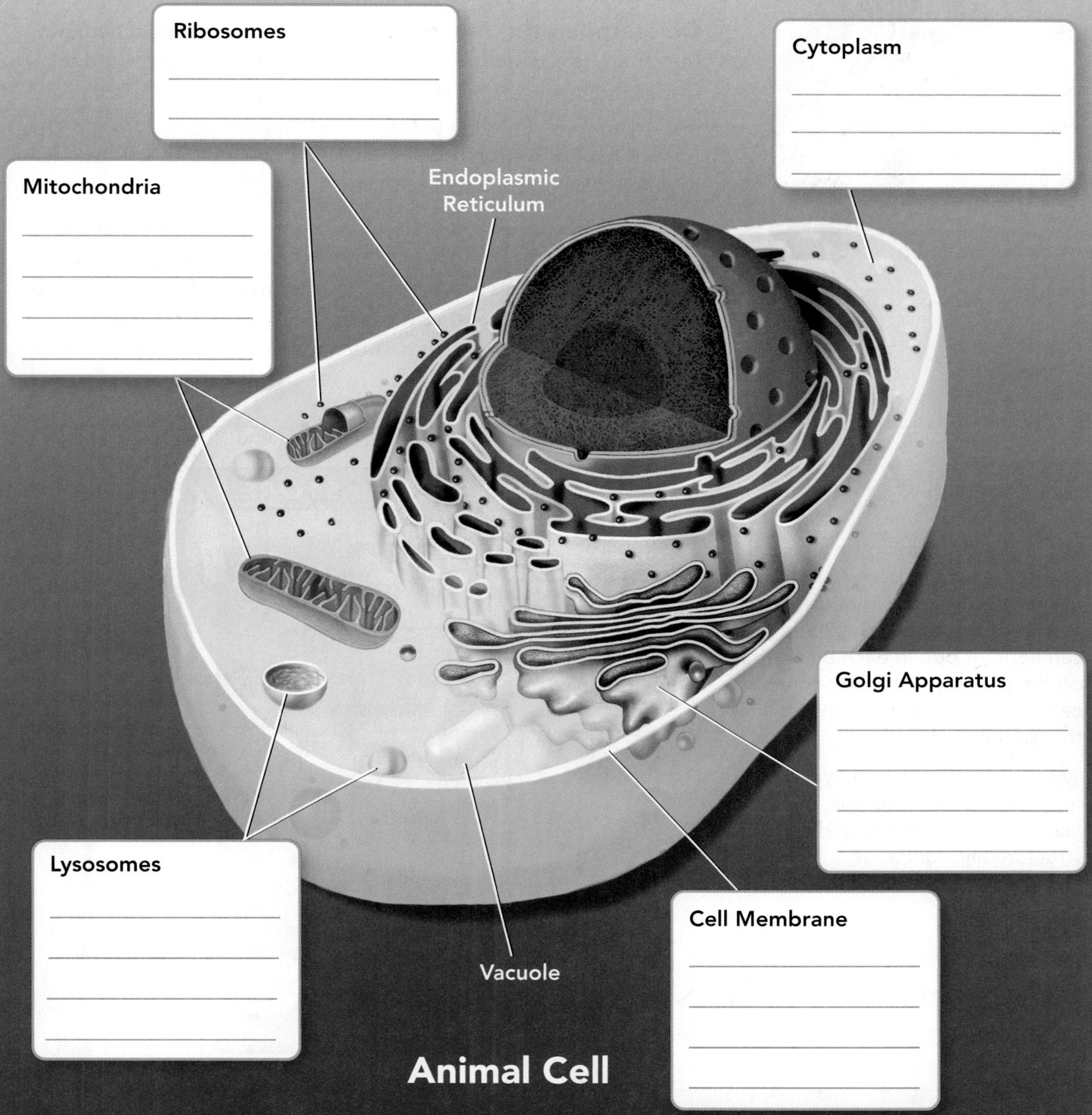

Animal Cell

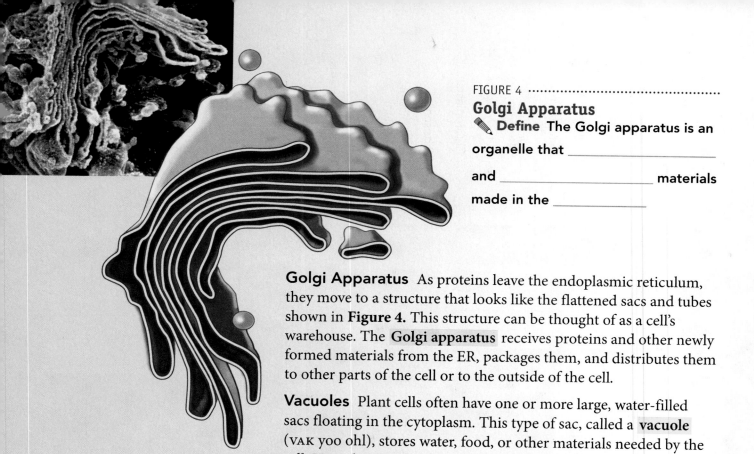

FIGURE 4 ·······························

Golgi Apparatus

✏️ **Define** The Golgi apparatus is an

organelle that _____

and _____ materials

made in the _____

Golgi Apparatus As proteins leave the endoplasmic reticulum, they move to a structure that looks like the flattened sacs and tubes shown in **Figure 4.** This structure can be thought of as a cell's warehouse. The **Golgi apparatus** receives proteins and other newly formed materials from the ER, packages them, and distributes them to other parts of the cell or to the outside of the cell.

Vacuoles Plant cells often have one or more large, water-filled sacs floating in the cytoplasm. This type of sac, called a **vacuole** (VAK yoo ohl), stores water, food, or other materials needed by the cell. Vacuoles can also store waste products until the wastes are removed. Some animal cells do not have vacuoles, while others do.

apply it!

Can a store's building be a model for a cell? If so, how do the parts of a cell function in ways that are similar to the parts of a building? See if you can figure it out. In each blank space on the picture, write the name of a cell structure that functions most like that part of the store.

⚠️ **Make Models** How do you think making real-world comparisons with cells helps you understand cell structure and function?

_____

_____

_____

_____

ELECTRONICS STORE

MANAGER

SC.N.6.3.4

Chloroplasts Recall from **Figure 3** that a typical plant cell contains green structures, called chloroplasts, in the cytoplasm. **Chloroplasts** carry out photosynthesis. They capture energy from sunlight and change it to a form of energy cells can use in making food. Animal cells don't have chloroplasts, but the cells of plants and some other organisms do. Chloroplasts make leaves green because leaf cells contain many chloroplasts.

Lysosomes Look again at the animal cell in **Figure 3**. Notice the saclike organelles, called **lysosomes** (LY suh sohmz), which contain substances that break down large food particles into smaller ones. Lysosomes also break down old cell parts and release the substances so they can be used again. You can think of lysosomes as a cell's recycling centers.

FIGURE 5 ·····································
A Chloroplast
✎ **Infer** In which part of a plant would you *not* expect to find cells with chloroplasts?

_____

_____

 Do the Quick Lab
Gelatin Cell Model.

🔑 Assess Your Understanding

1a. Compare and Contrast Summarize how the functions of organelles in animal cells and plant cells are the same and different.

_____

_____

_____

_____

_____

_____

_____

SC.6.L.14.4

b. CHALLENGE A solar panel collects sunlight and converts it to heat or electrical energy. How is a solar panel similar to chloroplasts?

_____

_____

_____

SC.6.N.3.4, SC.6.L.14.4

c. ANSWER THE ESSENTIAL **?** What are cells made of?

_____

_____

_____

SC.6.L.14.4

got it? ···

○ **I get it!** Now I know that different kinds of organelles in a cell _____

○ **I need extra help with** _____

Go to **MY SCIENCE** ⓢ **COACH** *online for help with this subject.*

SC.6.L.14.4

LESSON
5 | Cell Division

UNLOCK THE ESSENTIAL **?**

🗝 **What Are the Functions of Cell Division?**
SC.6.L.14.3, SC.6.L.14.4

🗝 **What Happens During the Cell Cycle?**
SC.6.L.14.3, SC.6.L.14.4, LA.6.4.2.2, MA.6.A.3.6

mY PLaneT DiaRY

Cycling On

How long do you think it takes a cell to grow and reproduce, that is, to complete one cell cycle? The answer depends on the type of cell and the organism. Some cells, such as the cells in frog eggs shown here, divide every 30 minutes, and others take as long as a year! The table below compares the length of different cell cycles.

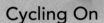

Comparing Cell Cycles			
Frog Egg Cells	**Yeast Cells**	**Fruit Fly Wing Cells**	**Human Liver Cells**
30 minutes	90 minutes	9–10 hours	Over 1 year

SCIENCE STATS

Interpret Data Use the table to help you answer the following questions.

1. Which type of cell completes a cell cycle the fastest?

_____

2. With each cell cycle, two cells form from one cell. In three hours, how many cells could form from one frog egg cell?

_____

▶ PLANET DIARY Go to **Planet Diary** to learn more about cell division.

 Lab zone Do the Inquiry Warm-Up *What Are the Yeast Cells Doing?*

 FLORIDA NGSSS

SC.6.L.14.3 Recognize and explore how cells of all organisms undergo similar processes to maintain homeostasis, including reproduction.

SC.6.L.14.4 Compare and contrast the function of major organelles of plant and animal cells.

What Are the Functions of Cell Division?

How do tiny frog eggs become big frogs? Cell division allows organisms to grow larger. One cell splits into two, two into four, and so on, until a single cell becomes a multicellular organism.

How does a broken bone heal? Cell division produces new healthy bone cells that replace the damaged cells. Similarly, cell division can replace aging cells and those that die from disease.

Vocabulary

- cell cycle
- replication
- mitosis
- interphase
- chromosome
- cytokinesis

Skills

- Reading: Ask Questions
- Inquiry: Interpret Data

Cell division allows organisms to grow, repair damaged structures, and reproduce. Growth and repair are two functions of cell division that help an organism maintain homeostasis. A third function is reproduction of the organism. Some organisms reproduce simply through cell division. Many single-celled organisms, such as amoebas, reproduce this way. Other organisms can reproduce when cell division leads to the growth of new structures. For example, a cactus can grow new stems and roots. These structures can then break away from the parent plant and become a separate plant.

Most multicellular organisms reproduce when specialized cells from two parents combine, forming a new cell. This cell undergoes many divisions and grows into a new organism.

FIGURE 1 ·····················

Cell Division

Each photo represents at least one function of cell division.

✎ **Answer these questions.**

1. **Identify** Label each photo as
   (A) growth,
   (B) repair, or
   (C) reproduction.

2. **CHALLENGE** Which photo(s) represent(s) more than one function and what are they?

_____

_____

Lab zone® Do the Quick Lab *Observing Mitosis.*

Assess Your Understanding

got it? ··

O **I get it!** Now I know the functions of cell division are _____

O **I need extra help with** _____

Go to my science ⓢ coach *online for help with this subject.*

SC.6.L.14.3, SC.6.L.14.4

FLORIDA NGSSS

SC.6.L.14.3 Recognize and explore how cells of all organisms undergo similar processes to maintain homeostasis, including reproduction.

SC.6.L.14.4 Compare and contrast the function of major organelles of plant and animal cells.

LA.6.4.2.2 The student will record information (e.g., lists) related to a topic, including visual aids to organize and record information.

MA.6.A.3.6 Construct and analyze tables, graphs, and equations to describe simple relations.

What Happens During the Cell Cycle?

The regular sequence of growth and division that cells undergo is known as the **cell cycle.** **During the cell cycle, a cell grows, prepares for division, and divides into two new cells, which are called "daughter cells."** Each of the daughter cells then begins the cell cycle again. The cell cycle consists of three main stages: interphase, mitosis, and cytokinesis.

Stage 1: Interphase

The first stage of the cell cycle is **interphase.** This stage is the period before cell division. During interphase, the cell grows, makes a copy of its DNA, and prepares to divide into two cells.

Growing Early during interphase, a cell grows to its full size and produces the organelles it needs. For example, plant cells make more chloroplasts. And all cells make more ribosomes and mitochondria. Cells also make more enzymes, substances that speed up chemical reactions in living things.

Copying DNA Next, the cell makes an exact copy of the DNA in its nucleus in a process called **replication.** You may know that DNA holds all the information that a cell needs to carry out its functions. Within the nucleus, DNA and proteins form threadlike structures called **chromosomes.** At the end of replication, the cell contains two identical sets of chromosomes.

Preparing for Division Once the DNA has replicated, preparation for cell division begins. The cell produces structures that will help it to divide into two new cells. In animal cells, but not plant cells, a pair of centrioles is duplicated. You can see the centrioles in the cell in **Figure 2.** At the end of interphase, the cell is ready to divide.

FIGURE 2 ·······················

Interphase: Preparing to Divide
The changes in a cell during interphase prepare the cell for mitosis.

✎ **List Make a list of the events that occur during interphase.** LA.6.4.2.2

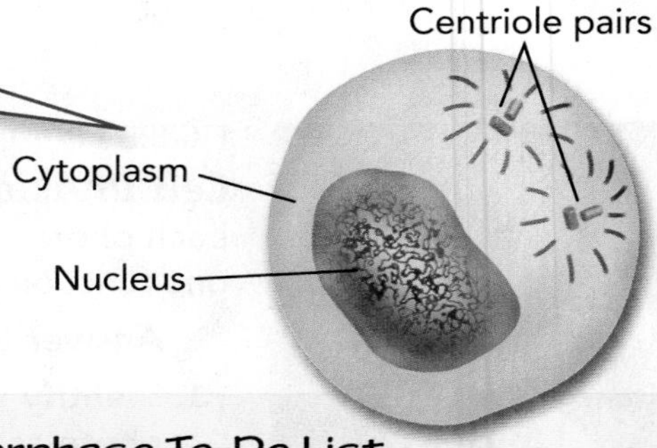

Centriole pairs

Cytoplasm

Nucleus

Interphase To-Do List

_____
_____
_____
_____
_____
_____
_____
_____
_____
_____
_____
_____
_____

apply it!

When one cell splits in half during cell division, the result is two new cells. Each of those two cells can divide into two more, and so on.

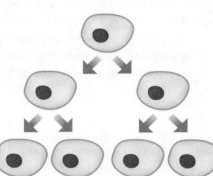

1 **Calculate** How many cell divisions would it take to produce at least 1,000 cells from one cell?

_____

2 **Describe** What happens to the number of cells after each division?

_____

3 [CHALLENGE] Do you think all human cells divide at the same rate throughout life? Justify your answer.

_____

_____

_____

Stage 2: Mitosis

Once interphase ends, the second stage of the cell cycle begins. During **mitosis** (my TOH sis), the cell's nucleus divides into two new nuclei and one set of DNA is distributed into each daughter cell.

Scientists divide mitosis into four parts, or phases: prophase, metaphase, anaphase, and telophase. During prophase, the replicated chromosomes condense into shapes that can be seen under a microscope. In **Figure 3** you can see that a replicated chromosome consists of two rodlike parts, called chromatids. Each chromatid is an exact copy of the other, containing identical DNA. A structure known as a centromere holds the chromatids together until they move apart later in mitosis. One of the two chromatids will move into each daughter cell during the final phases of mitosis. When the chromatids separate, they are called chromosomes again. Each cell then has a complete copy of DNA. **Figure 4** on the next page summarizes what happens during mitosis.

FIGURE 3 ··

Mitosis: Prophase

Mitosis begins with prophase, which involves further changes to the cell.

✎ **Compare and Contrast** How does prophase look different from interphase?

_____

_____

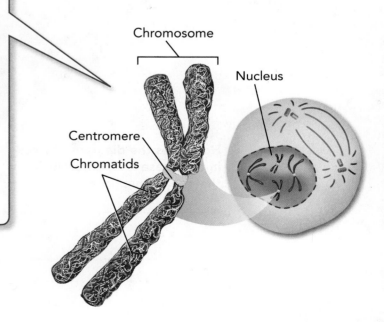

Chromosome

Nucleus

Centromere

Chromatids

FIGURE 4

> INTERACTIVE ART The Cell Cycle

Cells undergo an orderly sequence of events as they grow and divide. The photographs show cells of a developing whitefish.

✎ **Interpret Diagrams** Answer the questions and draw the missing parts of the stages in the spaces provided.

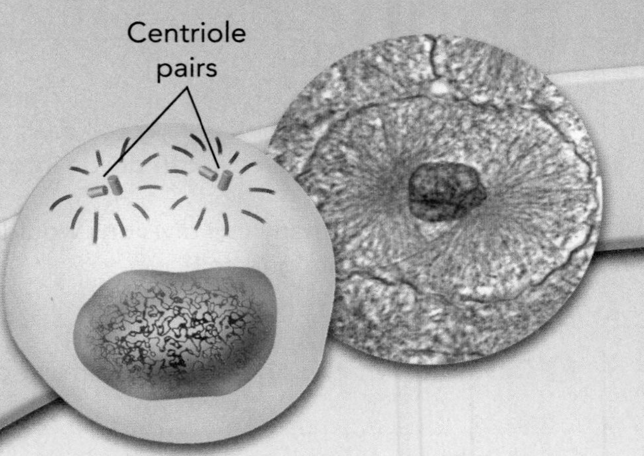

Centriole pairs

1 Interphase

Two cylindrical structures called centrioles are copied.
Identify two other changes that happen in interphase.

_____

_____

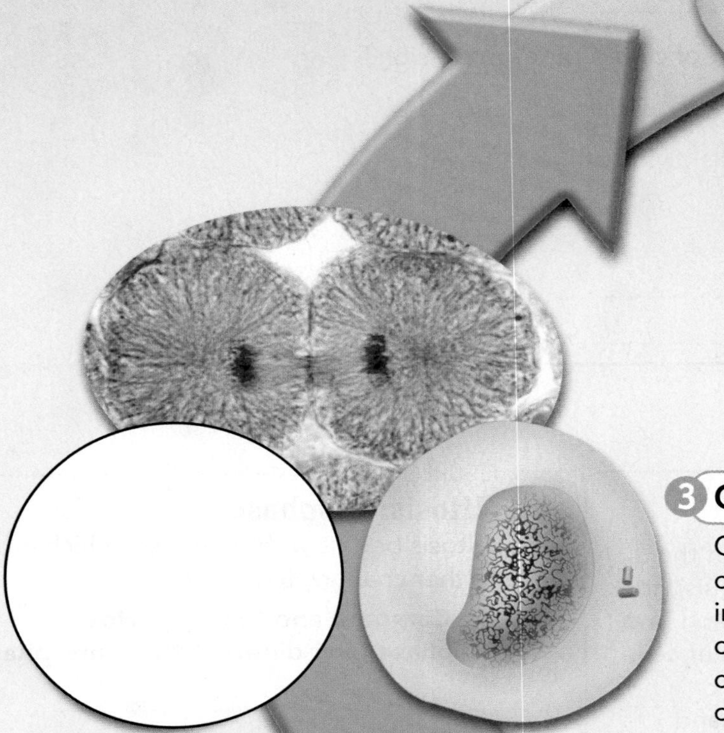

3 Cytokinesis

Cytokinesis begins during mitosis. As cytokinesis continues, the cell splits into two daughter cells. Each daughter cell ends up with an identical set of chromosomes and about half the organelles of the parent cell.

Draw this daughter cell.

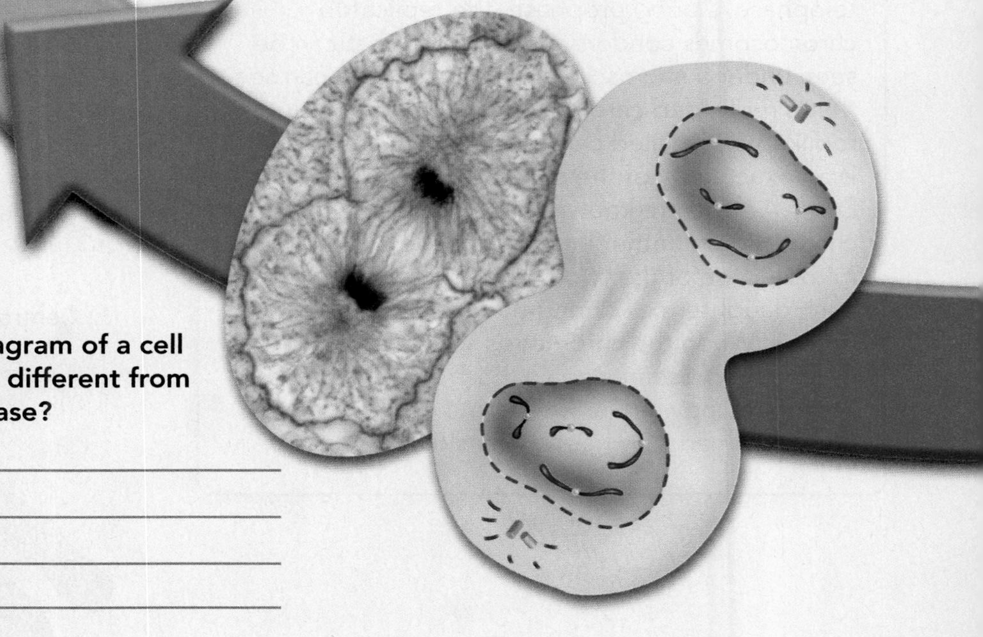

Telophase
How does the diagram of a cell in telophase look different from the one in anaphase?

_____

_____

_____

_____

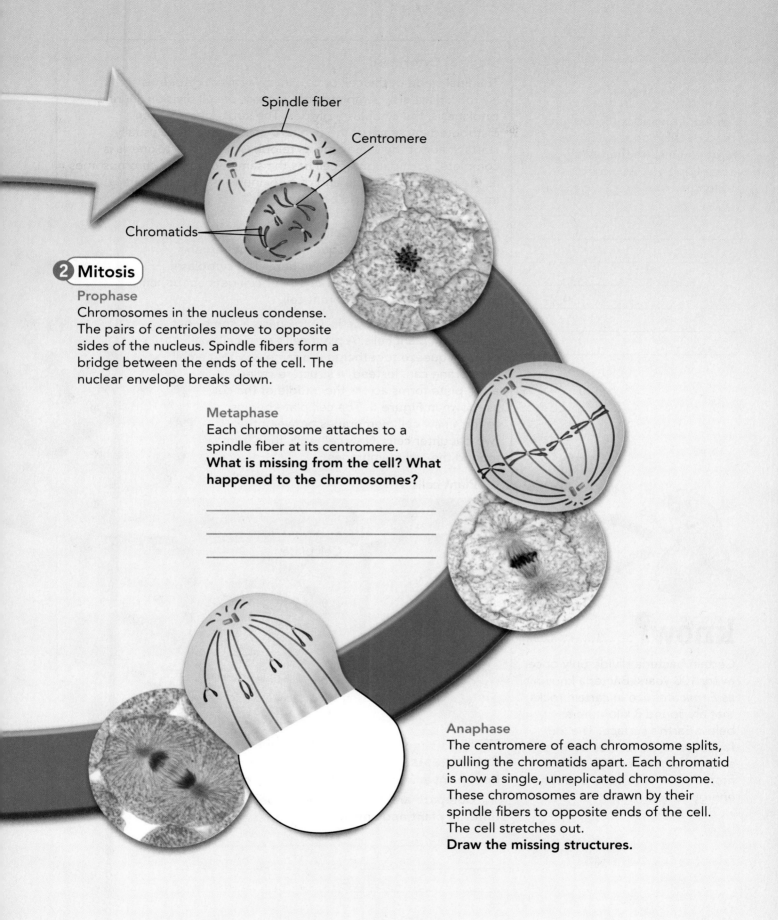

Spindle fiber

Centromere

Chromatids

2 Mitosis

Prophase

Chromosomes in the nucleus condense. The pairs of centrioles move to opposite sides of the nucleus. Spindle fibers form a bridge between the ends of the cell. The nuclear envelope breaks down.

Metaphase

Each chromosome attaches to a spindle fiber at its centromere. **What is missing from the cell? What happened to the chromosomes?**

_____

_____

_____

Anaphase

The centromere of each chromosome splits, pulling the chromatids apart. Each chromatid is now a single, unreplicated chromosome. These chromosomes are drawn by their spindle fibers to opposite ends of the cell. The cell stretches out.

Draw the missing structures.

The final stage of the cell cycle, which is called **cytokinesis** (sy toh kih NEE sis), completes the process of cell division. During cytokinesis, the cytoplasm divides. The structures are then distributed into each of the two new cells. Cytokinesis usually starts at about the same time as telophase. When cytokinesis is complete, each daughter cell has the same number of chromosomes as the parent cell. At the end of cytokinesis, each cell enters interphase, and the cycle begins again.

Cytokinesis in Animal Cells During cytokinesis in animal cells, the cell membrane squeezes together around the middle of the cell, as shown here. The cytoplasm pinches into two cells. Each daughter cell gets about half of the organelles of the parent cell.

Cytokinesis in Plant Cells Cytokinesis is somewhat different in plant cells. A plant cell's rigid cell wall cannot squeeze together in the same way that a cell membrane can. Instead, a structure called a cell plate forms across the middle of the cell, as shown in **Figure 5.** The cell plate begins to form new cell membranes between the two daughter cells. New cell walls then form around the cell membranes.

Plant cells ▼   **Animal cells ▶**

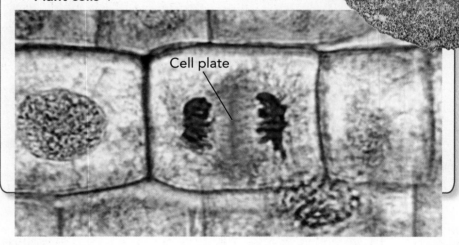

Cell plate

FIGURE 5 ·······················

Cytokinesis
Both plant and animal cells undergo cytokinesis.

✎ **Compare and Contrast** How does cytokinesis differ in plant and animal cells?

_____

_____

_____

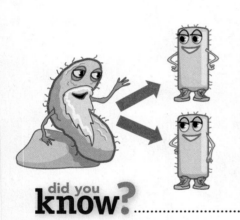

🔄 **Ask Questions** Before you read details about cytokinesis, write a question that asks something you would like to learn.

_____

_____

_____

_____

_____

_____

did you know?··················

Certain bacteria divide only once every 100 years! Bacteria known as *Firmicutes* live in certain rocks that are found 3 kilometers below Earth's surface. The life functions of *Firmicutes* occur so slowly that it takes 100 years or more for them to store enough energy to split in two.

do the math! Analyzing Data

Length of a Liver Cell Cycle

How long does one cell cycle take? It depends on the type of cell. Human liver cells generally divide less than once per year. But sometimes, they can complete one cell cycle in about 22 hours, as shown in the circle graph. Study the graph and answer the following questions.

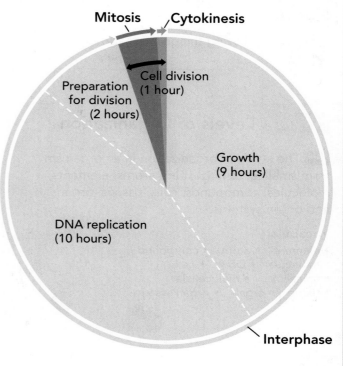

1 **Analyze Graphs** What do the three curved arrows outside of the circle represent?

_____

_____

2 **Analyze Graphs** In which stage of the cell cycle is the time when growth occurs?

_____

3 **Interpret Data** About what percentage of the cell cycle involves copying DNA?

_____

4 **Interpret Data** What stage in the cell cycle takes the shortest amount of time? How do you know?

_____

MA.6.A.3.6

Do the Quick Lab
Modeling Mitosis.

🔑 Assess Your Understanding

1a. List What are the three stages of the cell cycle?

_____

SC.6.L.14.3 , SC.6.L.14.4

b. Sequence Put the following terms in correct order: anaphase, cytokinesis, interphase, telophase, metaphase, prophase.

_____

_____

_____

SC.6.L.14.3 , SC.6.L.14.4

c. Predict What do you think would happen if a cell's DNA did not replicate correctly?

_____

_____

_____

_____

_____

SC.6.L.14.3 , SC.6.L.14.4

got it? •••

○ **I get it!** Now I know that during the cell cycle _____

_____

○ **I need extra help with** _____

Go to MY SCIENCE COACH *online for help with this subject.*

SC.6.L.14.3, SC.6.L.14.4

3 Study Guide

REVIEW THE ESSENTIAL

All living things are made of _____, which are the smallest units of _____ and _____

LESSON 1 Levels of Organization
SC.6.L.14.1

🔑 The levels of organization in an organism from smallest to largest are atoms, elements, molecules, compounds, cells, tissues, organs, and organ systems.

Vocabulary
• element • atom • compound
• molecule • DNA • cell
• unicellular • multicellular
• tissue • organ • organ system

LESSON 2 Discovering Cells
SC.6.N.3.1, SC.6.L.14.2

🔑 Cells are the basic units of structure and function in living things.

🔑 All living things are composed of cells, and all cells come from other cells.

🔑 Some microscopes focus light through lenses to produce a magnified image, and other microscopes use beams of electrons.

Vocabulary
• microscope • cell theory

LESSON 3 Cells and Homeostasis
SC.6.N.2.1. SC.6.L.14.3

🔑 In all cells, the processes that help maintain homeostasis include getting and using energy from food and removing wastes.

🔑 Reproduction of cells is one of the processes that helps organisms maintain homeostasis.

Vocabulary
• homeostasis • cellular respiration
• photosynthesis • cell membrane • diffusion
• cell division

LESSON 4 Looking Inside Cells
SC.6.N.3.4, SC.6.L.14.4

🔑 Each kind of cell structure has a different function within a cell.

🔑 In multicellular organisms, cells are organized into tissues, organs, and organ systems.

Vocabulary
• cell wall • nucleus • organelle
• ribosome • cytoplasm • mitochondria
• endoplasmic reticulum • Golgi apparatus
• vacuole • chloroplast • lysosome

LESSON 5 Cell Division
SC.6.L.14.3, SC.6.L.14.4

🔑 Cell division allows organisms to grow, repair damaged structures, and reproduce.

🔑 During the cell cycle, a cell grows, prepares for division, and divides into two new cells, which are called "daughter cells."

Vocabulary
• cell cycle • interphase • replication
• chromosome • mitosis • cytokinesis

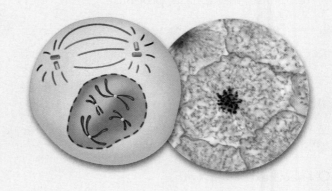

Review and Assessment

LESSON 1 Levels of Organization

1. The smallest unit of many compounds is a(n)

a. tissue. **b.** molecule.

c. element. **d.** cell.

SC.6.L.14.1

2. When different tissues work together, they form a(n) _____.

SC.6.L.14.1

3. Identify Patterns Arrange the following from smallest to largest level of organization: organ system, tissue, cell, organ, atom.

_____

_____

_____

SC.6.L.14.1

4. Compare and Contrast What is the difference between an element and a compound?

_____

_____

_____

SC.6.L.14.1

5. math! The graph below shows the amounts of different molecules that make up an animal cell. What percentage of the total cell weight is made up of lipids?

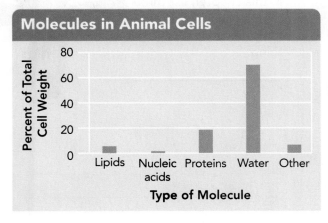

Molecules in Animal Cells

SC.6.L.14.1

LESSON 2 Discovering Cells

6. Which tool could help you see a plant cell?

a. a filter **b.** a microscope

c. a hand lens **d.** an electromagnet

SC.6.L.14.2

7. The _____ grew from the work of many scientists who studied cells, beginning in the 1600s.

SC. 6.N.3.1, SC.6.L.14.2

8. Explain What are the three parts of the cell theory?

_____

_____

_____

_____

_____

SC.6.N.3.1, SC.6.L.14.2

LESSON 3 Cells and Homeostasis

9. The process by which most cells use oxygen and get energy from food is

a. diffusion. **b.** homeostasis.

c. cellular respiration. **d.** photosynthesis.

SC.6.L.14.3

10. Replacement of damaged and worn-out cells in an organism can happen as a result of

_____

SC.6.L.14.3

11. Compare and Contrast How is cellular respiration different from photosynthesis?

_____

_____

_____

_____

_____

SC.6.L.14.3

12. Which cellular structures are found in plant cells but NOT in animal cells?

   a. chloroplast and cell wall

   b. Golgi apparatus and vacuole

   c. mitochondrion and ribosome

   d. endoplasmic reticulum and nucleus

                SC.6.L.14.4

13. Mitochondria and chloroplasts are two types of _____

                SC.6.L.14.4

14. Interpret Diagrams What is the name and function of the structure shown in purple in the cell at the right?

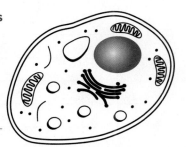

                SC.6.L.14.4

15. Infer A certain cell can no longer package and release materials out of the cell. Which of the cell's organelles is not working?

                SC.6.L.14.4

16. Compare and Contrast In a plant cell, how are the functions of the cell wall and the cell membrane alike? How are they different?

                SC.6.L.14.4

17. Write About It Imagine you are a tour guide. You and the tour group have shrunk to the size of water molecules to start your tour of the cell. Write a narrative of your tour that you could give a new tour guide to use.

                SC.6.L.14.4

18. During which phase of the cell cycle does DNA replication occur?

   a. mitosis   **b.** division

   c. interphase   **d.** cytokinesis

        SC.6.L.14.3, SC.6.L.14.4

19. During _____, a cell's chromosomes are divided into two new nuclei.

        SC.6.L.14.3, SC.6.L.14.4

20. Make Generalizations How does cell division help maintain homeostasis in living things?

        SC.6.L.14.3, SC.6.L.14.4

21. Relate Cause and Effect Why is replication a necessary step in cell division?

        SC.6.L.14.3, SC.6.L.14.4

 What are cells made of?

22. At right is a photograph of a multicellular plant called a primrose. Using what you have learned in this chapter, list three things you know about the primrose as a living thing.

    SC.6.L.14.1, SC.6.L.14.2, SC.6.L.14.3, SC.6.L.14.4

Florida Benchmarks Review

Circle the letter of the best answer.

❶ Choose the name and cellular process that match the organelle shown below.

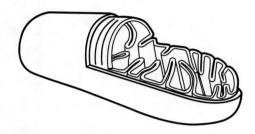

A chloroplast; cellular respiration
B mitochondrion; cellular respiration
C chloroplast; photosynthesis
D mitochondrion; photosynthesis

SC.6.L.14.4

❷ Which of the following is a correct sequence of levels of organization in the body?

A atoms, molecules, cells, tissues, organs
B atoms, organ systems, cells, organs, tissues
C molecules, organs, cells, tissues, organ systems
D atoms, cells, tissues, molecules, organ systems

SC.6.L.14.1

❸ The process in plant cells that converts energy from the sun into energy stored in food is

A photosynthesis.
B cellular respiration.
C homeostasis.
D cell division.

SC.6.L.14.3

❹ Which of the following is *not* part of the cell theory?

A Cells come from other cells.
B All living things are made of cells.
C Cells can be seen through a microscope.
D Cells are the units of structure and function in living things.

SC.6.N.3.1, SC.6.L.14.2

❺ What is the result of cell division?

A one daughter cell with double the DNA of the parent cell
B two daughter cells with double the DNA of the parent cell
C one daughter cell with half the DNA of the parent cell
D two daughter cells with the same DNA as the parent cell

SC.6.L.14.3

❻ The diagram below is useful as a scientific model because it shows

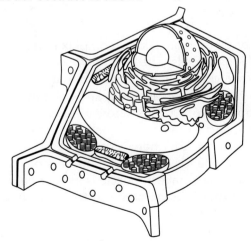

A an animal cell as it really looks.
B a plant cell as it really looks.
C the structures of a typical plant cell.
D how the structures of a cell function.

SC.6.N.3.4, SC.6.L.14.4

WHAT CAN THESE BODY PARTS DO?

 ESSENTIAL QUESTION

How does your body work?

Your body is an amazingly complex mass of trillions of cells. These cells work together, doing all the functions that keep you alive. On average, an adult has 206 bones, 96,500 kilometers of blood vessels, and a brain with a mass of 1.4 kilograms. Your nerves can send signals at speeds of up to 120 meters per second. Your smallest muscle is in your ear.

Infer What jobs do some of these body parts do?

_____

_____

_____

_____

_____

> UNTAMED SCIENCE Watch the **Untamed Science** video to learn more about body systems.

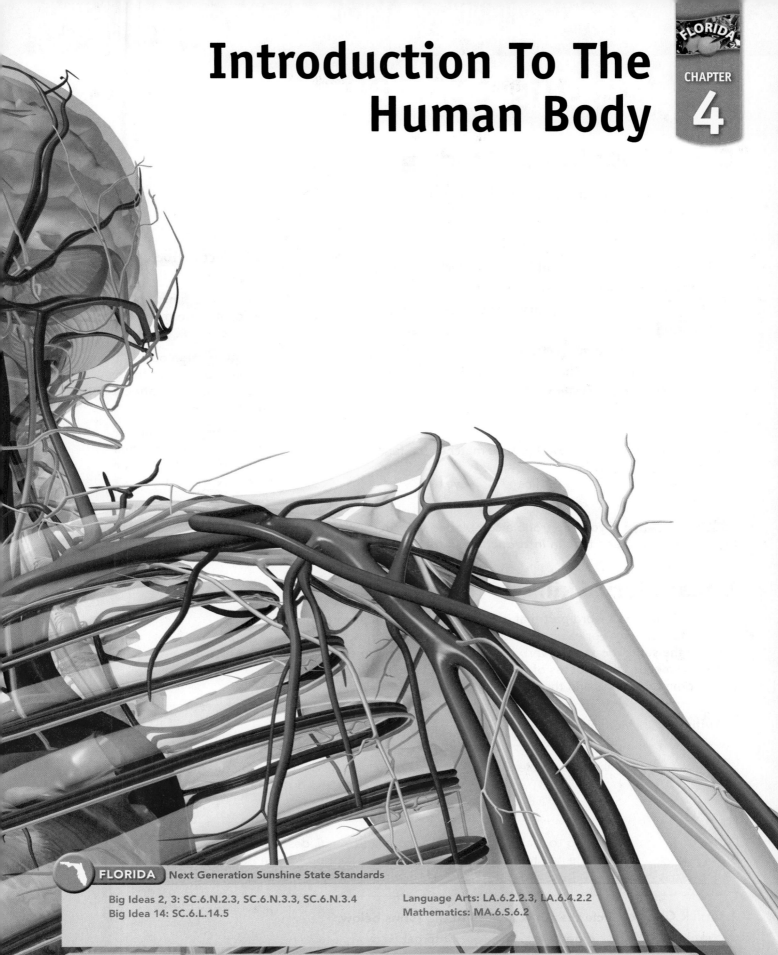

Introduction To The Human Body

FLORIDA Next Generation Sunshine State Standards

Big Ideas 2, 3: SC.6.N.2.3, SC.6.N.3.3, SC.6.N.3.4
Big Idea 14: SC.6.L.14.5

Language Arts: LA.6.2.2.3, LA.6.4.2.2
Mathematics: MA.6.S.6.2

4 Getting Started

Check Your Understanding

1. Background Read the paragraph below and then answer the question.

Fara is learning how to build and fix bicycles. First, she learned to change a tire using a tire lever. This tool's **structure**—a lever with a curved end—matches its **function**—to pry a tire off a metal rim. She's also learning about the **interactions** between the different bike parts—how the chain, gears, wheels, and brakes all work together as a **system.**

- Circle the structure below that best matches the function of helping a fish to swim.

  scales   gills   fins   eyes

An object's **structure** is its shape or form.

An object's **function** is the action it performs or the role it plays.

An **interaction** occurs when two or more things work together or affect one another.

A **system** is a group of parts that work together to perform a function or produce a result.

> **MY READING WEB** If you had trouble completing the question above, visit **My Reading Web** and type in *Introduction to the Human Body.*

Vocabulary Skill

Suffixes A suffix is a word part that is added to the end of a word to change its meaning. For example, the suffix *-tion* means "process of." If you add the suffix *-tion* to the verb *digest*, you get the noun *digestion*. *Digestion* means "the process of digesting." The table below lists some other common suffixes and their meanings.

Suffix	Meaning	Example
-al	of, like, or suitable for	epithelial, *adj.* describes a tissue that covers inner and outer surfaces of the body
-ive	of, relating to, belonging to, having the nature or quality of	connective, *adj.* describes a tissue that provides support for the body and connects all of its parts

LA.6.1.6.7

2. Quick Check Circle the suffix in each of the terms below.

skeletal   digestive   internal

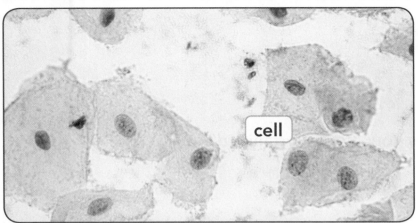

cell

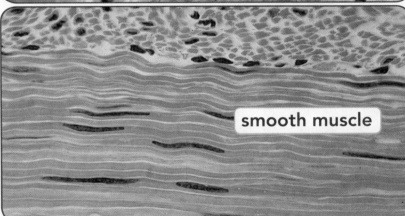

nervous tissue

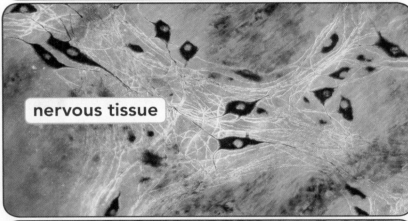

smooth muscle

epidermis

Chapter Preview

LESSON 1
- cell • cell membrane • nucleus
- cytoplasm • tissue
- muscle tissue • nervous tissue
- connective tissue
- epithelial tissue • organ
- organ system

↻ **Identify the Main Idea**
△ **Make Models**

LESSON 2
- skeleton • skeletal muscle • joint
- nutrient • absorption • gland
- stimulus • response • hormone

↻ **Summarize**
△ **Develop Hypotheses**

LESSON 3
- homeostasis • stress

↻ **Relate Cause and Effect**
△ **Communicate**

LESSON 4
- skeleton • vertebrae • joint
- ligament • compact bone
- spongy bone • marrow
- cartilage • osteoporosis

↻ **Summarize**
△ **Classify**

LESSON 5
- involuntary muscle
- voluntary muscle
- skeletal muscle • tendon
- smooth muscle • cardiac muscle
- striated muscle

↻ **Compare and Contrast**
△ **Infer**

LESSON 6
- epidermis • melanin • dermis
- pore • follicle

↻ **Relate Cause and Effect**
△ **Observe**

139

UNLOCK THE ESSENTIAL

🔑 **How Is Your Body Organized?**
SC.6.N.3.4, SC.6.L.14.5

MY PLANET DIARY

CAREER

Medical Illustrator

Who made the colorful drawings of human body structures in this book? The drawings are the work of specialized artists called medical illustrators. These artists use their drawing skills and knowledge of human biology to make detailed images of body structures. Many artists draw images, such as the one on this page, using 3-D computer graphics. The work of medical illustrators appears in textbooks, journals, magazines, videos, computer learning programs, and many other places.

Communicate Answer the question below. Then discuss your answer with a partner.

Why do you think medical illustrations are important to the study of human biology?

_____

_____

_____

_____

> PLANET DIARY Go to **Planet Diary** to learn more about body organization.

Lab zone Do the Inquiry Warm-Up *How Is Your Body Organized?*

FLORIDA NGSSS

SC.6.N.3.4 Identify the role of models in the context of the sixth grade science benchmarks.

SC.6.L.14.5 Identify and investigate the general functions of the major systems of the human body and describe ways these systems interact with each other to maintain homeostasis.

How Is Your Body Organized?

The bell rings—lunchtime! You hurry to the cafeteria, fill your tray, and pay the cashier. You look around the cafeteria for your friends. Then you walk to the table, sit down, and begin to eat.

Think about how many parts of your body were involved in the simple act of getting and eating your lunch. Every minute of the day, whether you are eating, studying, walking, or even sleeping, your body is busily at work. Each part of the body has a specific job to do. And all these different parts usually work together so smoothly that you don't even notice them.

Vocabulary

- cell • cell membrane • nucleus • cytoplasm • tissue
- muscle tissue • nervous tissue • connective tissue
- epithelial tissue • organ • organ system

Skills

○ Reading: Identify the Main Idea
△ Inquiry: Make Models

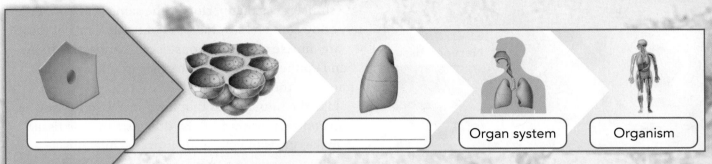

_____ _____ _____ Organ system Organism

FIGURE 1 ··

Body Organization

You will see this diagram three more times in this lesson. It will help you track the levels of organization in the body.

✎ **Name Fill in the missing terms in the diagram above.**

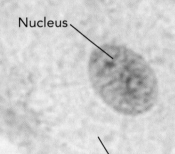

Cell membrane

Nucleus

Cytoplasm

FIGURE 2 ·····························

Cell Structure

A microscope reveals some of the parts of a human cheek cell.

The smooth functioning of your body is due partly to how the body is organized. 🔑 **The levels of organization in the human body consist of cells, tissues, organs, and organ systems.** The smallest unit of organization is a cell. The next largest unit is a tissue, then an organ. Finally, an organ system is the largest unit of organization in an organism. **Figure 1** shows body organization.

Cells A **cell** is the basic unit of structure and function in a living thing. Complex organisms are made up of many cells in the same way that your school is made up of many rooms. The human body contains about 100 trillion tiny cells. Most cells cannot be seen without a microscope.

Structures of Cells Almost all cells in the human body have the same basic parts, as shown in **Figure 2.** The **cell membrane** forms the outside border of a cell. The **nucleus** directs the cell's activities and holds information that controls a cell's function. The rest of the cell, called the **cytoplasm** (SYT oh plaz um), is made of a clear, jellylike substance that contains many cell structures. Each of these structures has a specific job, or function.

Functions of Cells Cells carry on the processes that keep organisms alive. Inside cells, for example, molecules from digested food undergo changes that release energy that the cells can use. Cells also grow, reproduce, and get rid of the waste products that result from these activities.

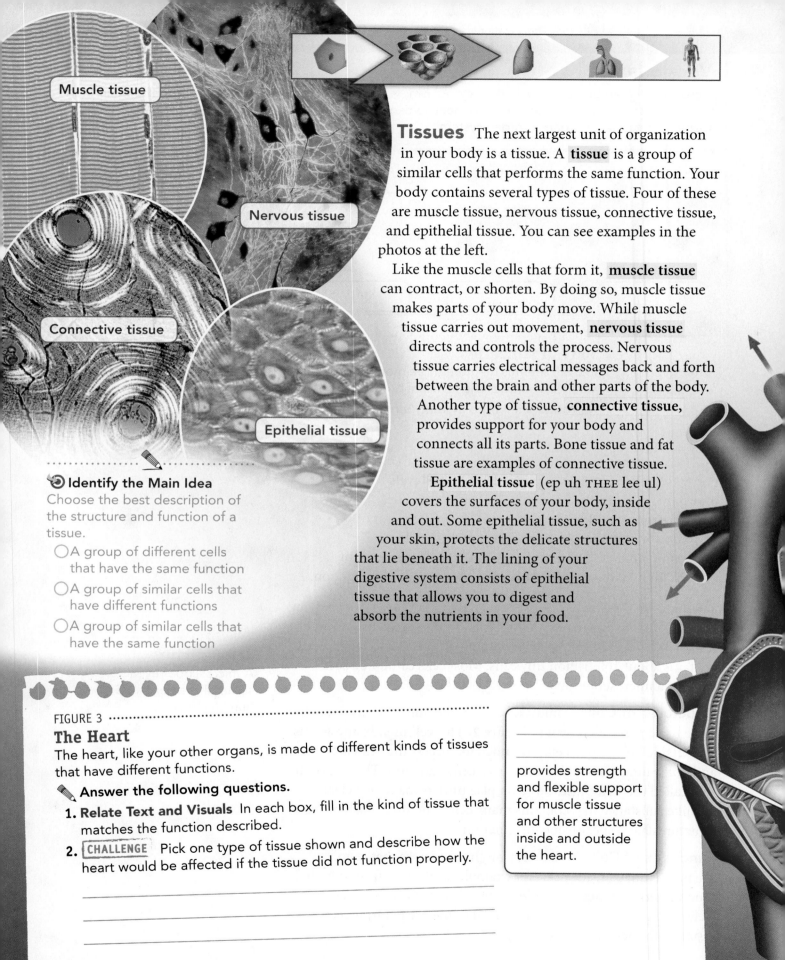

Muscle tissue

Nervous tissue

Connective tissue

Epithelial tissue

Tissues The next largest unit of organization in your body is a tissue. A **tissue** is a group of similar cells that performs the same function. Your body contains several types of tissue. Four of these are muscle tissue, nervous tissue, connective tissue, and epithelial tissue. You can see examples in the photos at the left.

Like the muscle cells that form it, **muscle tissue** can contract, or shorten. By doing so, muscle tissue makes parts of your body move. While muscle tissue carries out movement, **nervous tissue** directs and controls the process. Nervous tissue carries electrical messages back and forth between the brain and other parts of the body. Another type of tissue, **connective tissue**, provides support for your body and connects all its parts. Bone tissue and fat tissue are examples of connective tissue.

Epithelial tissue (ep uh THEE lee ul) covers the surfaces of your body, inside and out. Some epithelial tissue, such as your skin, protects the delicate structures that lie beneath it. The lining of your digestive system consists of epithelial tissue that allows you to digest and absorb the nutrients in your food.

✏️ **Identify the Main Idea**
Choose the best description of the structure and function of a tissue.

◯ A group of different cells that have the same function

◯ A group of similar cells that have different functions

◯ A group of similar cells that have the same function

FIGURE 3
The Heart
The heart, like your other organs, is made of different kinds of tissues that have different functions.

✏️ **Answer the following questions.**

1. **Relate Text and Visuals** In each box, fill in the kind of tissue that matches the function described.

2. **CHALLENGE** Pick one type of tissue shown and describe how the heart would be affected if the tissue did not function properly.

_____

_____

provides strength and flexible support for muscle tissue and other structures inside and outside the heart.

_____

_____

_____

Organs Your stomach, heart, brain, and lungs are all organs. An **organ** is a structure that is made up of different kinds of tissue. Like a tissue, an organ performs a specific job. The job of an organ, however, is usually more complex than that of a tissue. For example, the heart pumps blood through your body over and over again. The heart contains muscle, connective, and epithelial tissues. In addition, nervous tissue connects to the heart and helps control heart function. **Figure 3** shows a diagram of a human heart and describes how some of the heart's tissues work. Each type of tissue contributes in a different way to the organ's job of pumping blood.

covers the inside surfaces of the heart and of the blood vessels that lead into and out of the heart.

carries electrical messages from the brain to the heart but is not shown in this diagram.

contracts, squeezing the heart so blood moves through the heart's chambers and then into blood vessels that lead to the body.

apply it!

Books are a nonliving model of levels of organization. Find out how a book is organized.

STEP 1 **Observe** Examine this book to see how its chapters, lessons, and other parts are related.

STEP 2 **Make Models** Next, compare levels of organization in this book to those in the human body. Draw lines to show which part of this book best models a level in the body.

Organism   Lessons

Organ systems   Book

Organs   Words

Tissues   Chapters

Cells   Paragraphs

STEP 3 **Make Models** Where in the book model do you think this Apply It fits? What level of organization in the body does the Apply It represent?

_____

_____

_____

_____

_____

SC.6.N.3.4

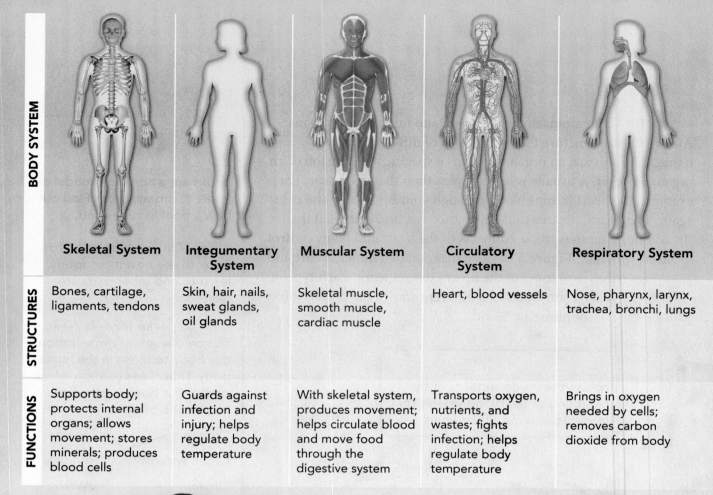

BODY SYSTEM	Skeletal System	Integumentary System	Muscular System	Circulatory System	Respiratory System
STRUCTURES	Bones, cartilage, ligaments, tendons	Skin, hair, nails, sweat glands, oil glands	Skeletal muscle, smooth muscle, cardiac muscle	Heart, blood vessels	Nose, pharynx, larynx, trachea, bronchi, lungs
FUNCTIONS	Supports body; protects internal organs; allows movement; stores minerals; produces blood cells	Guards against infection and injury; helps regulate body temperature	With skeletal system, produces movement; helps circulate blood and move food through the digestive system	Transports oxygen, nutrients, and wastes; fights infection; helps regulate body temperature	Brings in oxygen needed by cells; removes carbon dioxide from body

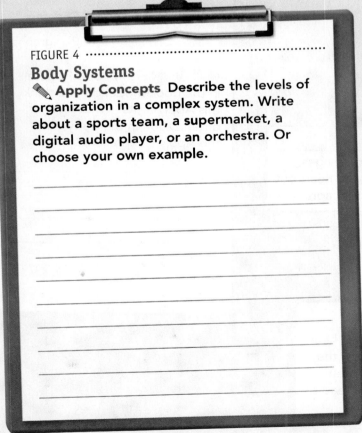

FIGURE 4 ·······························

Body Systems

✏ **Apply Concepts** Describe the levels of organization in a complex system. Write about a sports team, a supermarket, a digital audio player, or an orchestra. Or choose your own example.

_____

_____

_____

_____

_____

_____

_____

_____

_____

_____

Systems Each organ in your body is part of an **organ system,** which is a group of organs that work together, carrying out major functions. For example, your heart is part of your circulatory system, which carries oxygen and other materials throughout your body. The circulatory system also includes blood vessels and blood. **Figure 4** shows most of the organ systems in the human body.

Organisms Starting with cells, the levels of organization in an organism become more and more complex. A tissue is more complex than a cell, an organ is more complex than a tissue, and so on. You, as an organism, are the next level of organization. And all organisms are part of levels of organization within the environment.

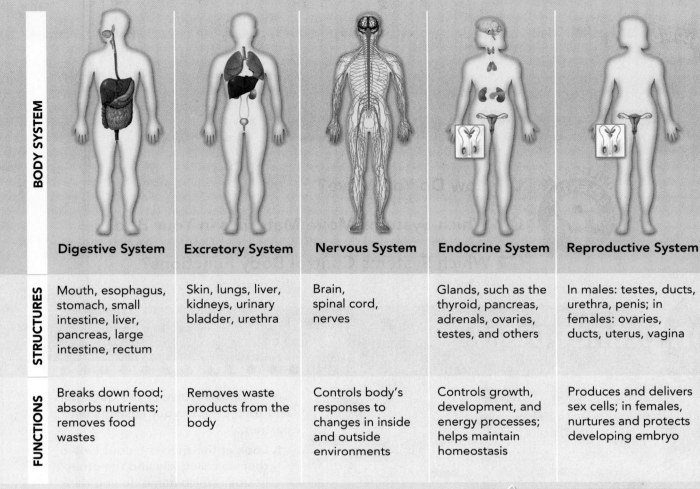

BODY SYSTEM	Digestive System	Excretory System	Nervous System	Endocrine System	Reproductive System
STRUCTURES	Mouth, esophagus, stomach, small intestine, liver, pancreas, large intestine, rectum	Skin, lungs, liver, kidneys, urinary bladder, urethra	Brain, spinal cord, nerves	Glands, such as the thyroid, pancreas, adrenals, ovaries, testes, and others	In males: testes, ducts, urethra, penis; in females: ovaries, ducts, uterus, vagina
FUNCTIONS	Breaks down food; absorbs nutrients; removes food wastes	Removes waste products from the body	Controls body's responses to changes in inside and outside environments	Controls growth, development, and energy processes; helps maintain homeostasis	Produces and delivers sex cells; in females, nurtures and protects developing embryo

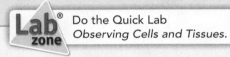 Do the Quick Lab
Observing Cells and Tissues.

🔑 Assess Your Understanding

1a. Review How are cells, tissues, and organs related?

_____

_____

_____
SC.6.L.14.5

b. Infer What systems of the body are involved in preparing and eating a sandwich?

_____

_____

_____
SC.6.L.14.5

c. Make Judgments How does learning about body systems help you make informed decisions about your health?

_____

_____

_____

_____

_____

_____

_____
SC.6.L.14.5

got it? ....

○ **I get it!** Now I know that the body's levels of organization, from least complex to most complex, are

_____

○ I need extra help with _____

Go to **MY SCIENCE COACH** online for help with this subject.
SC.6.L.14.5

System Interactions

UNLOCK THE ESSENTIAL ?

🔑 **How Do You Move?**
SC.6.L.14.5, LA.6.2.2.3

🔑 **Which Systems Move Materials in Your Body?**
SC.6.L.14.5

🔑 **Which Systems Control Body Functions?**
SC.6.N.2.3, SC.6.L.14.5

MY PLANET DIARY

FUN FACTS

Do you hear in color?

What color is the letter *b* or the roar of a tiger? You might not see colors when you hear sounds, but some people do. In people with synesthesia (sin us THEE zhuh), their senses overlap. Some people with synesthesia may taste a shape or hear music in colors. Others may hear a sound when they see motion. Even people without synesthesia experience some connections between their senses. You can explore how your own senses overlap in the first question on this page.

Communicate **Answer the questions and then discuss your answers with a partner.**

1. Look at the shapes below. One of them is called kiki and the other bouba. Which name do you think matches each shape?

A   B

_____

_____

2. Most people call the rounded shape bouba and the pointed shape kiki. Why do you think that is?

_____

_____

_____

▶ **PLANET DIARY** Go to **Planet Diary** to learn more about how body systems interact.

 Do the Inquiry Warm-Up
How Does Your Body Respond?

Vocabulary

- skeleton • skeletal muscle • joint • nutrient
- absorption • gland • stimulus • response • hormone

Skills

↻ **Reading: Summarize**

△ **Inquiry: Develop Hypotheses**

How Do You Move?

Carefully coordinated movements let you thread a needle, ride a bicycle, brush your teeth, and dance. These movements—and all of your body's other movements—happen as a result of the interactions between body systems. Your muscular system is made up of all the muscles in your body. Your skeletal system, or skeleton, includes all the bones in your body. 🗝 **Muscles and bones work together, making your body move. The nervous system tells your muscles when to act.**

FLORIDA   NGSSS

SC.6.L.14.5 Identify and investigate the general functions of the major systems of the human body and describe these systems interact with each other to maintain homeostasis.

LA.6.2.2.3 The student will organize information to show understanding.

Muscles and Bones

Skeletal muscles are attached to the bones of your skeleton and provide the force that moves your bones. Muscles contract and relax. When a muscle contracts, it shortens and pulls on the bones to which it is attached, as shown in **Figure 1.**

FIGURE 1 ....

Muscles Moving Bones

As this dancer's muscles pull on his leg bones, he can make rapid, skillful moves.

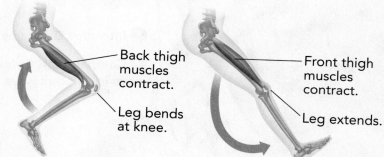

Back thigh muscles contract.

Leg bends at knee.

Front thigh muscles contract.

Leg extends.

△ **Develop Hypotheses** An octopus has no bones. Explain how you think it moves.

_____

_____

_____

147

Summarize In your own words, describe which of your systems work together when you write in this book.

_____
_____
_____
_____

LA.6.2.2.3

Bones and Joints

What happens when you wiggle your fingers or touch your toes? Even though your bones are rigid, your body can bend in many ways. Your skeleton bends at its joints. A **joint** is a place in the body where two bones come together. For example, your elbow and your shoulder are two joints that move when you raise your hand.

Making Movement Happen

Muscles make bones move at their joints. Try standing on one leg and bending the other leg at the knee. Hold that position. You can feel that you are using the muscles at the back of your thigh. Now straighten your leg. You can feel the muscles in the back of your leg relax, but the muscles in the front of your leg are at work. Your nervous system controls when and how your muscles act on your bones. You will read more about the nervous system later in this lesson.

apply it!

1 Interpret Diagrams Circle three of the football player's joints.

2 Compare and Contrast Describe how your shoulder and elbow move in different ways.

_____
_____
_____

3 CHALLENGE From a standing position, bend down and grab your ankles. List six places or joints where your skeleton bends.

_____
_____

Lab zone Do the Lab Investigation
A Look Beneath the Skin.

Assess Your Understanding

got it? ....

○ **I get it!** Now I know that _____ and _____ work together to make the body move.

○ **I need extra help with** _____

Go to **my science COACH** online for help with this subject.

SC.6.L.14.5

Which Systems Move Materials in Your Body?

The trillions of cells that make up your body need materials to function. Cells also produce wastes that must be removed. If the processes of moving these materials were made into a movie, your nervous system would be the director. The movie set would include the muscular and skeletal systems. And the main characters would be some of your other systems. 🗝 **The circulatory, respiratory, digestive, and excretory systems play key roles in moving materials in your body.**

Transporting Materials Your circulatory system includes your heart, blood vessels, and blood. Blood vessels are found throughout your body. Blood that flows through these vessels carries materials such as water, oxygen, and food to every cell, as shown in **Figure 2.** Materials that your cells must get rid of, such as carbon dioxide and other cell wastes, are also moved through the body in the blood.

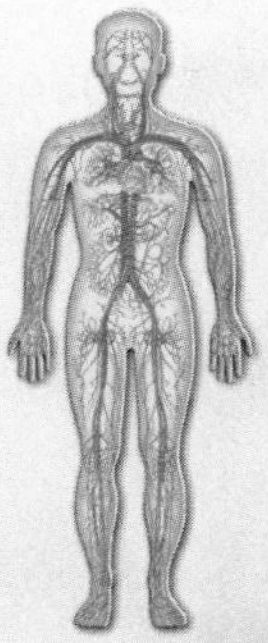

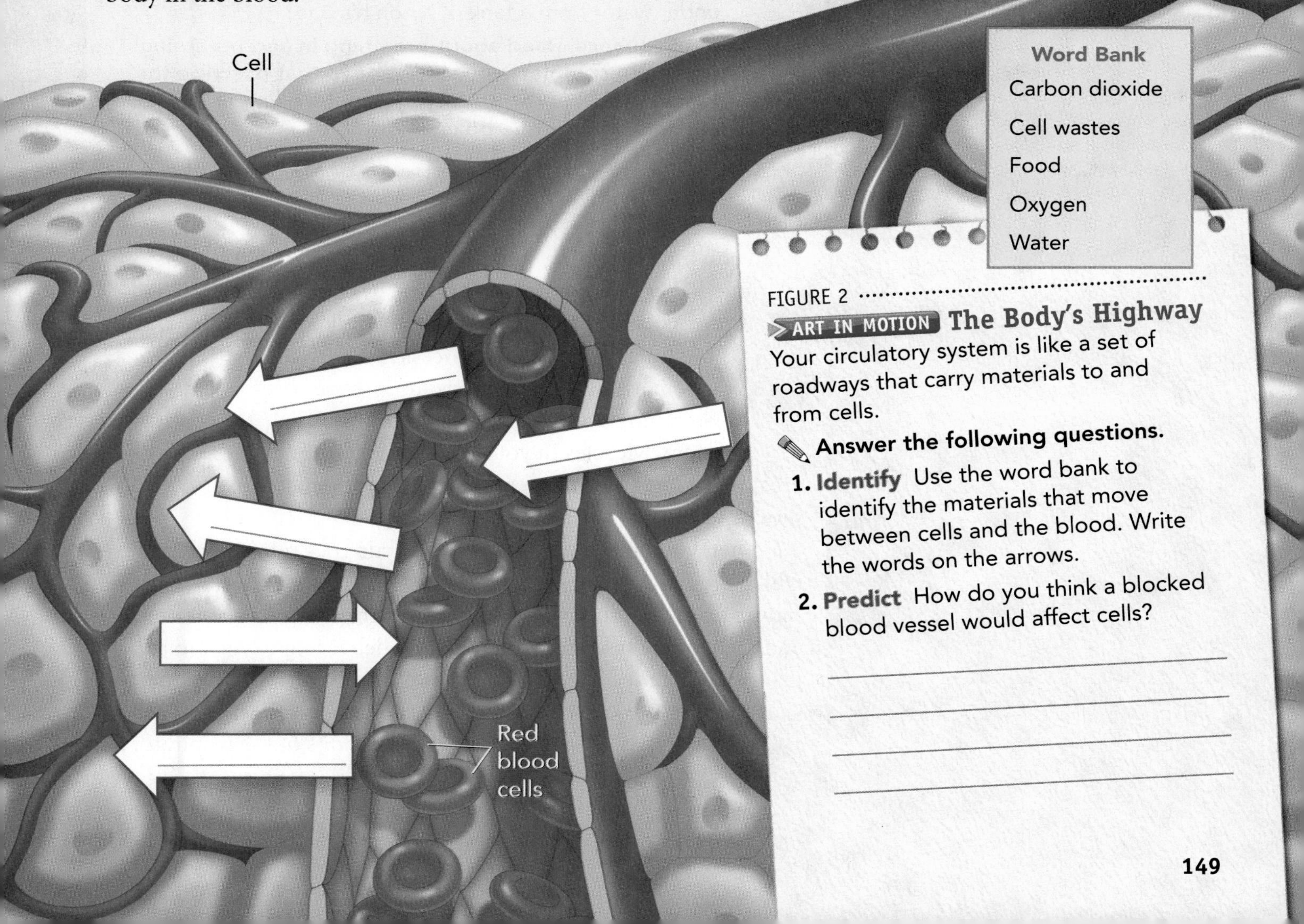

FLORIDA NGSSS

SC.6.L.14.5 Identify and investigate the general functions of the major systems of the human body (digestive, respiratory, circulatory, reproductive, excretory, immune, nervous, and musculoskeletal) and describe ways these systems interact with each other to maintain homeostasis.

LA.6.2.2.3 The student will organize information to show understanding.

Blood vessel

Cell

Word Bank

Carbon dioxide

Cell wastes

Food

Oxygen

Water

FIGURE 2 ....
ART IN MOTION The Body's Highway
Your circulatory system is like a set of roadways that carry materials to and from cells.

✏ **Answer the following questions.**

1. **Identify** Use the word bank to identify the materials that move between cells and the blood. Write the words on the arrows.

2. **Predict** How do you think a blocked blood vessel would affect cells?

Red blood cells

149

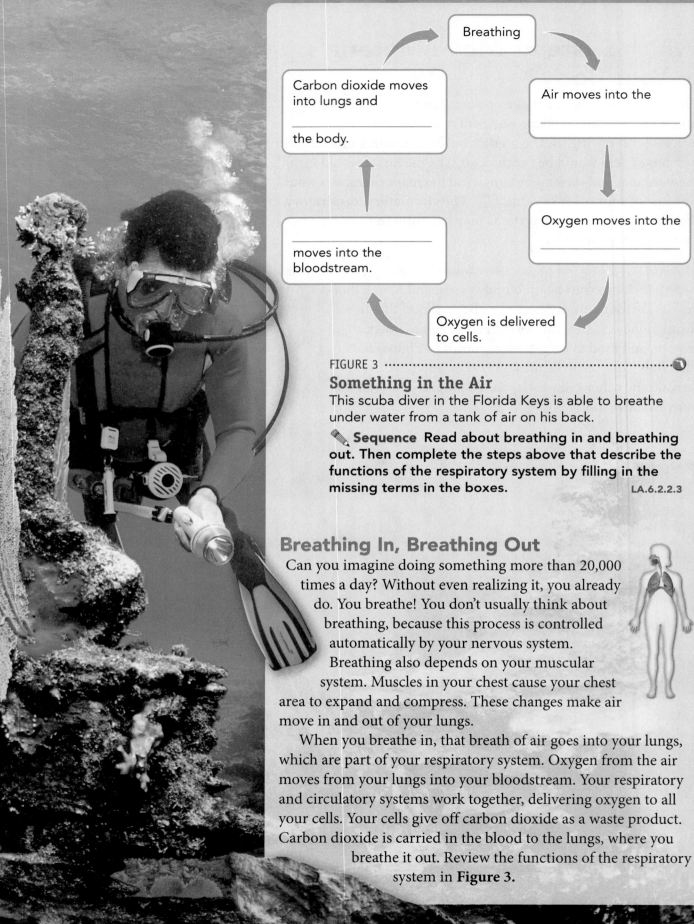

Breathing

Carbon dioxide moves into lungs and
_____
the body.

Air moves into the
_____

_____
moves into the bloodstream.

Oxygen moves into the
_____

Oxygen is delivered to cells.

FIGURE 3 ···

Something in the Air

This scuba diver in the Florida Keys is able to breathe under water from a tank of air on his back.

✎ **Sequence Read about breathing in and breathing out. Then complete the steps above that describe the functions of the respiratory system by filling in the missing terms in the boxes.** LA.6.2.2.3

Breathing In, Breathing Out

Can you imagine doing something more than 20,000 times a day? Without even realizing it, you already do. You breathe! You don't usually think about breathing, because this process is controlled automatically by your nervous system.

Breathing also depends on your muscular system. Muscles in your chest cause your chest area to expand and compress. These changes make air move in and out of your lungs.

When you breathe in, that breath of air goes into your lungs, which are part of your respiratory system. Oxygen from the air moves from your lungs into your bloodstream. Your respiratory and circulatory systems work together, delivering oxygen to all your cells. Your cells give off carbon dioxide as a waste product. Carbon dioxide is carried in the blood to the lungs, where you breathe it out. Review the functions of the respiratory system in **Figure 3.**

Getting Food

Your respiratory system takes in oxygen, and your circulatory system delivers it to your cells. Oxygen is used in cells to release energy from sugar molecules that come from the food you eat. But how do sugar molecules get to your cells? Your digestive system helps to break down foods into sugars and other nutrient molecules that your body can use. A **nutrient** is a substance that you get from food and that your body needs to carry out processes, such as contracting muscles. Through a process called **absorption,** nutrients move from the digestive system into the bloodstream. The circulatory system then delivers the nutrients to all the cells in your body. In this way, your digestive system and circulatory system work together to get food to your cells.

Moving Wastes

The excretory system eliminates wastes from your body. Your respiratory, circulatory, and digestive systems all have roles in the excretory system. You already read that carbon dioxide passes from the circulatory system into the respiratory system and leaves the body when you exhale. Other cellular wastes also pass into the blood. These wastes are filtered out of the blood by the kidneys. This process produces urine, which then carries the wastes out of your body. Materials that are not used by the digestive system leave the body as solid waste.

Vocabulary Suffixes The names of three body systems contain the suffix *-atory* or *-etory*, which both mean "of, or pertaining to." Circle the name of each of these systems once in the text on this page. Then underline sentences that describe what these systems do.

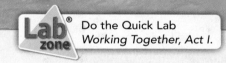

Lab zone® Do the Quick Lab *Working Together, Act I.*

🔑 Assess Your Understanding

1a. List Name four body systems that are involved in getting oxygen to your cells.

_____

_____

SC.6.L.14.5

b. Explain How is absorption an important function of the digestive system?

_____

_____

_____

SC.6.L.14.5

c. Draw Conclusions How does the circulatory system help other systems function?

_____

_____

_____

_____

_____

_____

_____

SC.6.L.14.5

got it? ·

○ **I get it!** Now I know that materials are moved within my body by the _____

_____

○ **I need extra help with** _____

Go to MY SCIENCE ⑤ COACH online for help with this subject.

SC.6.L.14.5

did you **know?**

Scientists at the McKnight Brain Institute at the University of Florida study how disease or injury affect the nervous system. They also study how radiation in outer space affects brain cells. This information could help make space travel safer.

SC.6.N.2.3

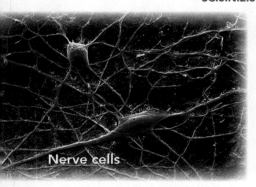
Nerve cells

Which Systems Control Body Functions?

To function properly, each part of your body must be able to communicate with other parts of your body. For example, if you hear a phone ring, that message must be sent to your brain. Your brain then directs your muscles to move your bones so you can answer the phone. These actions are controlled by the nervous system, which is made up of the brain, spinal cord, and nerves. In your nervous system, information travels through nerve cells.

Other messages are sent by chemical signals that are produced by the endocrine system. The endocrine system is made up of organs called **glands** that release chemical signals directly into the bloodstream. For example, when you exercise, your endocrine system sends signals that make you perspire, or sweat. As sweat evaporates, it helps you cool down. **The nervous system and the endocrine system work together to control body functions.**

Nervous System Your eyes, ears, skin, nose, and taste buds send information about your environment to your nervous system. Your senses let you react to bright light, hot objects, and freshly baked cookies. A signal in the environment that makes you react is called a **stimulus** (plural *stimuli*). A **response** is what your body does in reaction to a stimulus. Responses are directed by your nervous system but often involve other body systems. For example, your muscular and skeletal systems help you reach for a cookie. And your digestive system releases saliva before the cookie even reaches your mouth.

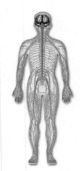

FIGURE 4 ··

Stimulus and Response

Have you ever been startled by something unexpected?

✎ **Use the pictures to complete these tasks.**

1. **Sequence** Use numbers 1, 2, and 3 to put the pictures in order.

2. **Explain** Use the terms *stimulus* and *response* to explain what happened.

_____

_____

_____

_____

_____

apply it!

Among the drugs that affect the nervous system, caffeine is one of the most commonly used worldwide. Caffeine is found in coffee, tea, soda, other beverages, and even in chocolate.

1 Explain How does caffeine reach the brain after someone drinks a cup of coffee or tea? In your answer, be sure to identify the systems involved.

_____

_____

_____

2 Infer Caffeine is addictive, which means that the body can become physically dependent on the drug. Which body system do you think would be most involved in an addiction? Explain your answer.

_____

_____

_____

Endocrine System

Endocrine System The chemical signals released by the endocrine system are called **hormones.** Hormones are transported through your body by the circulatory system. These chemicals affect many body processes. For example, one hormone interacts with the excretory system and the circulatory system to control the amount of water in the bloodstream. Another hormone interacts with the digestive system and the circulatory system to control the amount of sugar in the bloodstream. Hormones also affect the reproductive systems of both males and females.

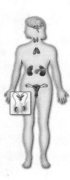

Lab zone ® Do the Quick Lab
Working Together, Act II.

🔑 Assess Your Understanding

2a. Compare and Contrast How are the nervous system and the endocrine system different?

_____

_____

_____

_____

SC.6.L.14.5

b. Apply Concepts Describe an example of a stimulus and response that involves your sense of hearing.

_____

_____

_____

_____

SC.6.L.14.5

got it? ....

O **I get it!** Now I know that the _____ system and _____ system work together to _____

O **I need extra help with** _____

Go to **my science** ⑤ **coach** online for help with this subject.

SC.6.L.14.5

Homeostasis

UNLOCK THE ESSENTIAL
?

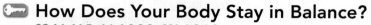 **How Does Your Body Stay in Balance?**
SC.6.L.14.5, LA.6.2.2.3, MA.6.S.6.2

my planet diary

SCIENCE STATS

Worried Sick—Not Just an Expression

Starting in the 1980s, scientists began to gather evidence that stress can affect the immune system. For example, the graph below shows the relationship between the length of time a person is stressed and the risk of catching a cold when exposed to a virus. Today, scientists know that high levels of stress and long periods of stress can increase a person's risk for many diseases. Therefore, managing stress is an important part of a healthy lifestyle. Many activities, including hanging out with friends, getting enough sleep, and exercising moderately, can help lower stress levels.

Read Graphs Use the graph to answer the questions.

1. Summarize the information given in the graph.

_____

_____

_____

2. What do you do to manage stress?

_____

_____

> PLANET DIARY Go to **Planet Diary** to learn more about homeostasis.

Stress and Catching a Cold

Increasing Risk of a Cold →

Less than 1 | 1–6 | 7–24 | More than 24

Months of Stress

 Lab zone® Do the Inquiry Warm-Up *Out of Balance.*

How Does Your Body Stay in Balance?

It may be summer or winter. You may be indoors or outdoors. You may be running or sitting still. Regardless, your internal body temperature is almost exactly 37°C. The conditions outside your body may change. But the conditions inside your body stay stable, or steady. Most of these conditions, including the chemical makeup of your cells, their water content, and your body temperature, stay about the same.

Homeostasis The condition in which an organism's internal environment is kept stable in spite of changes in the outside environment is called **homeostasis.** Keeping this balance is necessary for an organism to function properly and survive. **All of your body systems working together maintain homeostasis and keep the body in balance.**

FLORIDA NGSSS

SC.6.L.14.5 Identify and investigate the general functions of the major systems of the human body (digestive, respiratory, circulatory, reproductive, excretory, immune, nervous, and musculoskeletal) and describe ways these systems interact with each other to maintain homeostasis.

LA.6.2.2.3 The student will organize information to show understanding.

MA.6.S.6.2 Select and analyze the measures of central tendency.

FIGURE 1 ·······················

Keeping Warm in the Cold

Even in cold weather, this snowboarder keeps his temperature very close to 37°C. But over the course of a day, his temperature may vary a few degrees. Suppose his temperatures during the day were 37.1°C, 36.4°C, 36.9°C, and 37.2°C.

✏ **Analyze** Calculate the snowboarder's average temperature on this day.

_____

_____

_____

MA.6.S.6.2

Maintaining Homeostasis
You experience homeostasis in action when you shiver, sweat, or feel hungry, full, or thirsty. Your nervous and endocrine systems control these responses. Other systems, including the digestive, respiratory, circulatory, and muscular systems, also play roles in your body's responses.

Regulating Temperature When you are cold, your nervous system signals your muscles to make you shiver. Shivering produces heat that helps keep you warm. As explained in the diagram below, when you warm up, shivering stops. When you are too warm, your endocrine system releases hormones that make you perspire. As the sweat evaporates, your body cools. The circulatory system and skin also help regulate temperature. Changes in the amount of blood flow in the skin can help prevent heat loss or carry heat away. In this way, your body temperature stays steady.

Cold environment causes body temperature to drop.

Nervous system directs muscles to begin to shiver.

Heat from shivering muscles warms body.

Nervous system directs muscles to stop shivering.

Meeting Energy Needs If your body needs more energy, hormones from the endocrine system signal the nervous system to make you feel hungry. After you eat, other hormones tell your brain to make you feel full. Other body systems are also involved. For example, your muscular system helps move food through your digestive system. Your respiratory system takes in the oxygen that is used in cells to release energy from food.

FIGURE 2 ·······························
Hungry or Not?
Signals between your nervous system and your digestive system control your feelings of hunger.

✎ **Sequence** Fill in the missing steps in the cycle diagram. LA.6.2.2.3

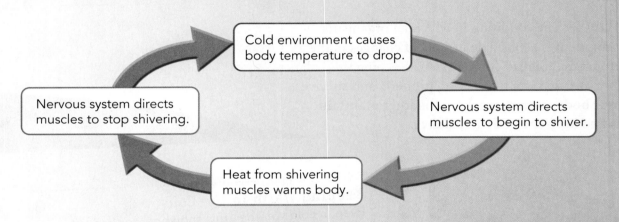

I feel hungry.

_____
_____

_____
_____

_____
_____

Maintaining Water Balance Life depends on water. All the chemical reactions that keep you alive happen within the watery environment of your cells. If your body needs more water, you feel thirsty. The water you drink passes from your digestive system into your circulatory system. Excess water leaves your body through your excretory system when you exhale, sweat, and urinate.

Keeping Your Balance You know that you hear with your ears. But did you know your ears also help you keep your balance? Structures in your inner ear sense the position of your head. They send this information to your brain, which interprets the signals. If your brain senses that you are losing your balance, it sends messages to your muscles to move in ways that help you stay steady, as in **Figure 3**.

Relate Cause and Effect
Complete the cause-and-effect table below to help you organize what you have learned about homeostasis. **LA.6.2.2.3**

Cause	Effect
_____ _____	Shivers
Body gets overheated.	_____
Body needs more energy.	_____
_____ _____ _____	Thirst

FIGURE 3 ···
Balancing Act
Signals from this diver's ears to her brain lead to movements that help her balance on the edge of the diving board.

✎ **Name** What systems of the diver's body play a role in keeping her balanced on her toes?

_____

_____

_____

_____

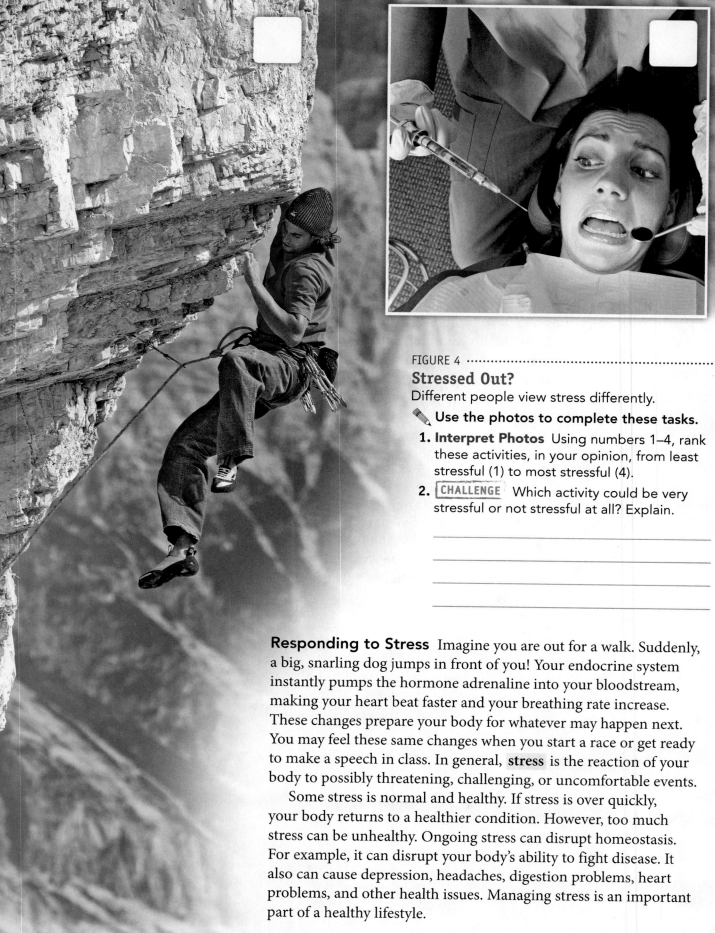

FIGURE 4 ··

Stressed Out?

Different people view stress differently.

✏ **Use the photos to complete these tasks.**

1. **Interpret Photos** Using numbers 1–4, rank these activities, in your opinion, from least stressful (1) to most stressful (4).

2. **CHALLENGE** Which activity could be very stressful or not stressful at all? Explain.

_____

_____

_____

_____

Responding to Stress Imagine you are out for a walk. Suddenly, a big, snarling dog jumps in front of you! Your endocrine system instantly pumps the hormone adrenaline into your bloodstream, making your heart beat faster and your breathing rate increase. These changes prepare your body for whatever may happen next. You may feel these same changes when you start a race or get ready to make a speech in class. In general, **stress** is the reaction of your body to possibly threatening, challenging, or uncomfortable events.

Some stress is normal and healthy. If stress is over quickly, your body returns to a healthier condition. However, too much stress can be unhealthy. Ongoing stress can disrupt homeostasis. For example, it can disrupt your body's ability to fight disease. It also can cause depression, headaches, digestion problems, heart problems, and other health issues. Managing stress is an important part of a healthy lifestyle.

apply it!

◢ **Communicate** A soccer game, a music recital, a class presentation, and many other events can cause stress. Think of an event from your life when you felt stress. Describe how your body responded during the event, and then after the event or when the stress went away.

_____

_____

_____

_____

_____

_____

_____

_____

_____

_____

_____

_____

_____

_____

_____

_____

Fighting Disease When your body systems are in balance, you are healthy. However, bacteria and viruses that cause disease can disrupt homeostasis and make you sick. Think about the last time you had a cold or influenza (the flu). You may have had a fever and less energy. You also may have slept more than usual. Over a few days, your immune system probably fought off the disease.

The immune system includes specialized cells that can attack and destroy viruses. When you are sick, these cells temporarily increase in number. Fighting infection sometimes causes your body temperature to go up. It also uses extra energy. As you get well, your fever goes away and your energy comes back. If you are sick for more than a few days, you may need medical attention to help your body fight the infection and become healthy again.

Systems in Action

How does your body work?

FIGURE 5 ···

> **REAL-WORLD INQUIRY** The body systems of this runner work together as she pushes herself to excel.

✎ **Apply Concepts** Read the descriptions of functions happening in the runner's body. Then identify the main systems involved.

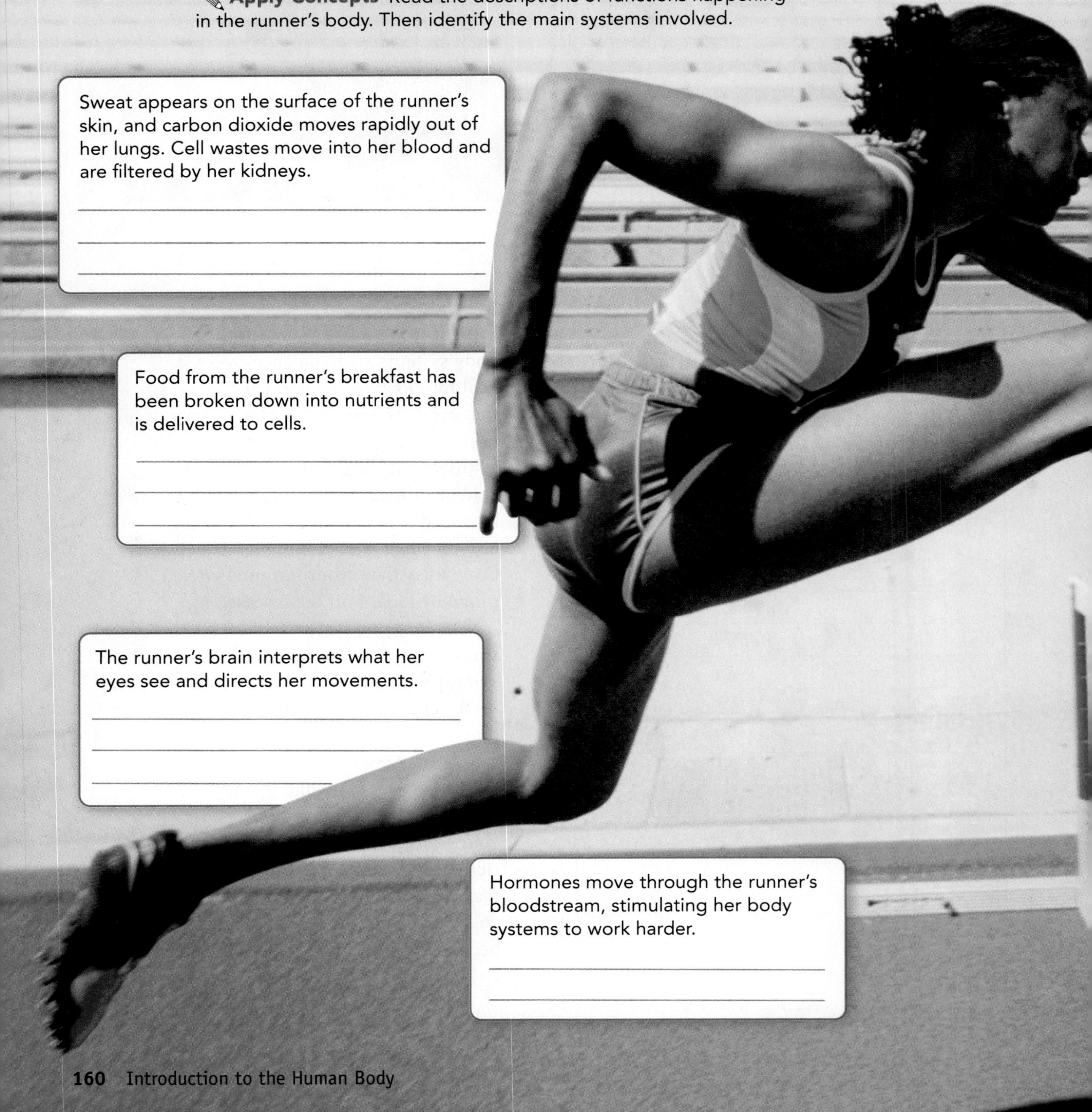

Sweat appears on the surface of the runner's skin, and carbon dioxide moves rapidly out of her lungs. Cell wastes move into her blood and are filtered by her kidneys.

_____

_____

_____

Food from the runner's breakfast has been broken down into nutrients and is delivered to cells.

_____

_____

_____

The runner's brain interprets what her eyes see and directs her movements.

_____

_____

_____

Hormones move through the runner's bloodstream, stimulating her body systems to work harder.

_____

_____

The runner's breathing rate and heart rate increase, supplying more oxygen to her muscle cells.

The runner's legs lift her off the ground and over the hurdle.

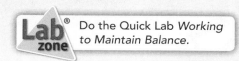 **Lab zone** Do the Quick Lab *Working to Maintain Balance.*

Assess Your Understanding

1a. Define What is homeostasis?

SC.6.L.14.5

b. Describe What is one way that your body systems interact with each other to help maintain homeostasis?

SC.6.L.14.5

c. Relate Cause and Effect Give an example of how stress can affect homeostasis.

SC.6.L.14.5

d. ANSWER THE ESSENTIAL ? How does your body work? Use what you have learned about how your body systems function to write your answer.

SC.6.L.14.5

got it? ....

○ **I get it!** Now I know that maintaining homeostasis depends on _____

_____

○ **I need extra help with** _____

Go to MY SCIENCE COACH *online for help with this subject.* SC.6.L.14.5

The Skeletal System

UNLOCK THE ESSENTIAL ?

🔑 **What Does the Skeleton Do?**
SC.6.L.14.5

🔑 **What Role Do Joints Play?**
SC.6.L.14.5

🔑 **What Are the Characteristics of Bones?**
SC.6.L.14.5, LA.6.4.2.2

my PLANET DiARY

Know Your Bones!

Here are some fascinating facts you may not know about your bones.

- You have the same number of bones in your neck as a giraffe. However, a single bone in the neck of a giraffe can be as long as 25 centimeters.

- You have 27 bones in each hand and 26 bones in each foot. They account for 106 of the 206 bones in your body.

- You do not have a funny bone. You have a sensitive spot on your elbow where a nerve passes close to the skin. If you hit this spot, the area feels funny.

- No one is truly "double-jointed." People who are able to twist in weird directions have very flexible joints.

FUN FACTS

Communicate Discuss the question with a partner. Then write your answer below.

Why do you think it is helpful for your hand to have 27 bones?

_____

_____

_____

_____

_____

_____

▸ **PLANET DIARY** Go to **Planet Diary** to learn more about bones.

Lab zone Do the Inquiry Warm-Up *Hard as a Rock?*

Vocabulary
- skeleton • vertebrae • joint • ligament
- compact bone • spongy bone • marrow
- cartilage • osteoporosis

Skills
- ↻ Reading: Summarize
- △ Inquiry: Classify

What Does the Skeleton Do?

If you have ever visited a construction site, you have seen workers assemble steel pieces into a rigid frame for a building. Once the building is finished, this framework is invisible.

Like a building, you have an inner framework. Your framework, or **skeleton,** is made up of all the bones in your body. Just as a building would fall without its frame, you would collapse without your skeleton. ⌫ **Your skeleton has five major functions. It provides shape and support, enables you to move, and protects your organs. It also produces blood cells and stores minerals and other materials until your body needs them.**

Shape and Support Your skeleton shapes and supports your body. It is made up of about 206 bones of different shapes and sizes. Your backbone, or vertebral column, is the center of your skeleton. A total of 26 small bones, or **vertebrae** (VUR tuh bray) (singular *vertebra*), make up your backbone. **Figure 1** shows how vertebrae connect to form the backbone or vertebral column.

> **FLORIDA** NGSSS
>
> **SC.6.L.14.5** Identify and investigate the general functions of the major systems of the human body (digestive, respiratory, circulatory, reproductive, excretory, immune, nervous, and musculoskeletal) and describe ways these systems interact with each other to maintain homeostasis.

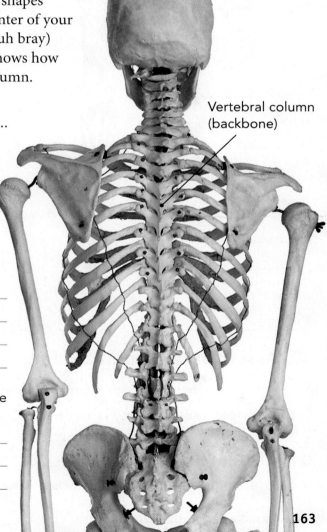

Vertebral column (backbone)

FIGURE 1 ·······

The Vertebral Column
Just like a flexible necklace of beads, your vertebrae move against each other, allowing you to bend and twist.

✎ **Use the photo to answer the questions about your vertebrae.**

1. **Interpret Photos** Which body parts does the vertebral column support?

_____

_____

_____

_____

2. CHALLENGE What is the advantage of having large vertebrae at the base of the vertebral column?

_____

_____

_____

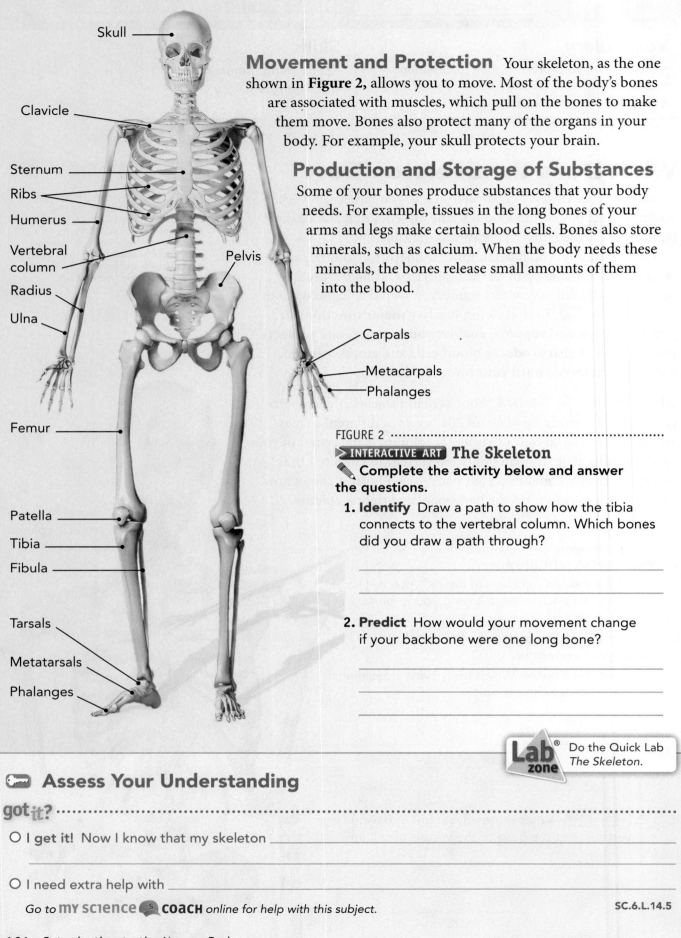

Skull

Clavicle

Sternum

Ribs

Humerus

Vertebral column

Radius

Ulna

Pelvis

Femur

Patella

Tibia

Fibula

Tarsals

Metatarsals

Phalanges

Carpals

Metacarpals

Phalanges

Movement and Protection
Your skeleton, as the one shown in **Figure 2**, allows you to move. Most of the body's bones are associated with muscles, which pull on the bones to make them move. Bones also protect many of the organs in your body. For example, your skull protects your brain.

Production and Storage of Substances
Some of your bones produce substances that your body needs. For example, tissues in the long bones of your arms and legs make certain blood cells. Bones also store minerals, such as calcium. When the body needs these minerals, the bones release small amounts of them into the blood.

FIGURE 2 ···

> **INTERACTIVE ART** **The Skeleton**
✎ **Complete the activity below and answer the questions.**

1. **Identify** Draw a path to show how the tibia connects to the vertebral column. Which bones did you draw a path through?

_____

_____

2. **Predict** How would your movement change if your backbone were one long bone?

_____

_____

_____

Lab ® Do the Quick Lab
zone *The Skeleton.*

🔑 Assess Your Understanding
got it? ··

○ **I get it!** Now I know that my skeleton _____

_____

○ **I need extra help with** _____

Go to **MY SCIENCE COACH** *online for help with this subject.*

SC.6.L.14.5

What Role Do Joints Play?

If your leg had only one long bone, how would you get out of bed? Luckily, your leg has many bones so you can move it easily. A **joint** is a place where two bones come together. 🔑 **Joints allow bones to move in different ways.** You have two kinds of joints: immovable and movable.

Immovable Joints Immovable joints connect bones but allow little or no movement. The bones of the skull are held together by immovable joints.

Movable Joints Most joints are movable. They allow the body to make many different movements such as those shown in **Figure 3**. The bones in movable joints are held together by **ligaments,** which are made of strong connective tissue.

FIGURE 3 ···

▶ **INTERACTIVE ART** **Movable Joints**
Movable joints allow you to move in different ways.

✏️ **Classify** **Write the name of another joint of each type on the line in each box.**

FLORIDA NGSSS

SC.6.L.14.5 Identify and investigate the general functions of the major systems of the human body (digestive, respiratory, circulatory, reproductive, excretory, immune, nervous, and musculoskeletal) and describe ways these systems interact with each other to maintain homeostasis.

✏️

Infer What would happen if your skull bones had movable joints?

_____

_____

_____

_____

Hinge Joint
This joint allows forward or backward motion. Your knee is a hinge joint that allows you to bend and straighten your leg.

_____

Ball-and-Socket Joint
This joint allows the greatest range of greatest range of motion. Your hip has a ball-and-socket joint that allows you to swing your leg in a circle.

_____

Pivot Joint
This joint allows one bone to rotate around another bone. You use this joint to turn your arm at your elbow side-to-side.

_____

Gliding Joint
This joint allows one bone to slide over another. Your wrist has a gliding joint that allows it to bend and flex.

_____

apply it!

Without movable joints, your body would be as stiff as a board.

❶ Observe Perform each activity below. Write the type of joint you use.

Move your arm from the shoulder in a circle. _____

Move your wrist to wave. _____

Turn your head from side to side. _____

❷ Classify In the chart, write the name of the type of joint each object has.

❸ Apply Concepts What type of joint do you have in your toes? Explain your answer.

Object	Type of Joint
Book	_____
Sliding Door	_____
Steering Wheel	_____

_____

_____

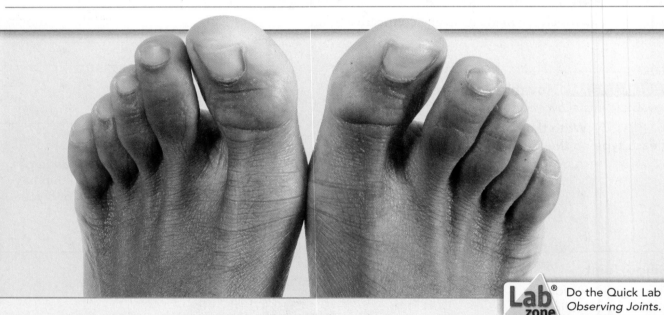

Do the Quick Lab
Observing Joints.

🔑 Assess Your Understanding

1a. Explain Why does your body need both immovable and movable joints?

_____

_____

_____

_____

SC.6.L.14.5

b. Relate Cause and Effect How would your legs move if your knees were ball-and-socket joints?

_____

_____

_____

SC.6.L.14.5

got it? ....

○ **I get it!** Now I know that joints _____

_____

○ **I need extra help with** _____

Go to **my science COACH** *online for help with this subject.*

SC.6.L.14.5

What Are the Characteristics of Bones?

The word *skeleton* comes from the Greek words meaning "a dried body." This suggests that a skeleton is dead, but bones are not dead at all.  **Bones are complex living structures that grow, develop, and repair themselves. Bones are also strong and lightweight.**

Bones are made up of bone tissue, blood vessels, and nerves. A thin, tough outer membrane covers all of a typical bone except the ends. Beneath the membrane is a thick layer of **compact bone,** which is hard and dense but not solid. Compact bone contains minerals that give bones strength. Small canals in the compact bone carry blood vessels and nerves from the bone's surface to its living cells.

Long bones, such as the femur in **Figure 4,** have a layer of spongy bone at the ends and under the compact bone. The small spaces within **spongy bone** make it lightweight but still strong. Bone also has two types of soft connective tissue called **marrow.** Red bone marrow fills the spaces in some of your spongy bone. It produces most of your blood cells. Yellow bone marrow is found in a space in the middle of the bone. It stores fat.

FIGURE 4 ·····························

Bone Structure

Many tissues make up the femur, the body's longest bone.

✎ **Relate Text and Visuals**
Write notes to describe each part of the bone and what it does.

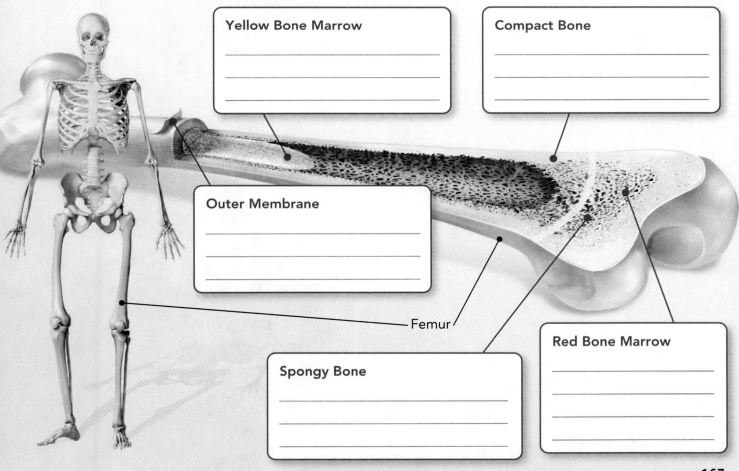

Yellow Bone Marrow
_____
_____
_____

Compact Bone
_____
_____
_____

Outer Membrane
_____
_____
_____

Femur

Spongy Bone
_____
_____
_____

Red Bone Marrow
_____
_____
_____

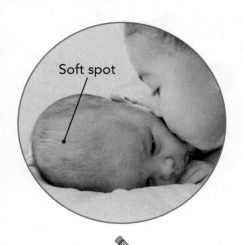

Soft spot

Bone Strength Bone is both strong and lightweight. Bones can absorb more force without breaking than concrete or granite rock can. Yet bones weigh much less than those materials. In fact, only about 20 percent of an average adult's body weight is bone. Bone feels as hard as a rock because it is made of tightly packed minerals—mainly phosphorus and calcium.

Bone Growth Because bones are alive, they form new bone tissue as you grow. Your bones are growing longer now, making you taller. Even after you are fully grown, bone tissue continues to form. For example, every time you play soccer or basketball, some of your bones absorb the force of your weight. They respond by making new bone tissue. New bone tissue also forms when a bone breaks.

Bone Development When you were born, most of your bones were cartilage. **Cartilage** is a strong connective tissue that is more flexible than bone. As you grew, most of that cartilage was replaced with bone. Some cartilage still protects the ends of your bones. You also have cartilage in your ears and at the tip of your nose.

Bone Strength	
Bone Growth	
Bone Development	

Healthy Bones A combination of a balanced diet and regular exercise are important for healthy bones. A balanced diet includes foods that contain enough calcium and phosphorus to keep your bones strong while they are growing. You should eat dairy products; meats; whole grains; and green, leafy vegetables.

Exercise helps build and maintain strong bones. During activities such as running and dancing, your bones support the weight of your entire body. These weight-bearing activities help your bones grow stronger. However, to prevent injury, always wear appropriate safety equipment when exercising.

As you age, your bones start to lose some minerals. This mineral loss can lead to **osteoporosis** (ahs tee oh puh ROH sis), a condition in which bones become weak and break easily. You can see how osteoporosis causes the spaces in a bone to become larger, reducing its density and strength in **Figure 5.**

FIGURE 5 ·······························

Osteoporosis
Regular exercise and a diet rich in calcium with vitamin D can help prevent osteoporosis later in life.

✎ **Compare and Contrast**
The photos show two bones. Label the healthy bone and the bone with osteoporosis. Then explain your choices.

_____

_____

_____

_____

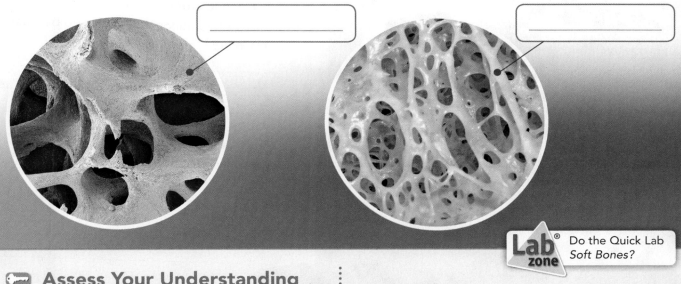

Lab zone® Do the Quick Lab *Soft Bones?*

🔑 **Assess Your Understanding**

2a. Explain How do eating a balanced diet and exercising regularly help your bones?

_____

_____

_____

SC.6.L.14.5

b. Apply Concepts How do you know that bone is living tissue?

_____

_____

_____

SC.6.L.14.5

got it?

○ **I get it!** Now I know that my bones are _____

_____

_____

_____

_____

○ **I need extra help with** _____

Go to **MY SCIENCE** 🅢 **COACH** *online for help with this subject.*

SC.6.L.14.5

The Muscular System

UNLOCK THE
ESSENTIAL
?

🔑 **What Muscles Are in Your Body?**
SC.6.N.3.3, SC.6.L.14.5, LA.6.4.2.2

🔑 **How Do Skeletal Muscles Work?**
SC.6.L.14.5

MY PLANET DIARY

BLOG

Posted by: Will

Location: Moore, Oklahoma

I hurt my shoulder while participating in tackling drills during football practice. The doctor said I had a deep muscle contusion, which is a bruise deep in a muscle. I was unable to lift my right arm for more than a week because of the injury. I had to take three tablets of ibuprofen every day for two weeks because it helped the swelling go down. I missed playing in only one game, and the pain eventually went away.

Answer the questions below.

1. What are two things Will had to do because of his injury?

_____

_____

_____

2. What can you do to avoid being injured when playing sports?

_____

_____

_____

_____

> PLANET DIARY Go to **Planet Diary** to learn more about muscles.

Lab **zone**® Do the Inquiry Warm-Up *How Do Muscles Work?*

Vocabulary
- involuntary muscle
- voluntary muscle
- skeletal muscle
- tendon
- smooth muscle
- cardiac muscle
- striated muscle

Skills
- ⏎ Reading: Compare and Contrast
- ⚠ Inquiry: Infer

What Muscles Are in Your Body?

Try to sit without moving any muscles. Can you do it? First, you probably need to breathe, so your chest expands to let air in. Then you swallow. Breathing and swallowing involve muscles, so it is impossible to sit still without any muscle movement.

Involuntary and Voluntary Muscles Some body movements, such as smiling, are easy to control. Other movements, such as breathing, are impossible to control completely. That is because some of your muscles are not under your conscious control. Those muscles are **involuntary muscles.** Involuntary muscles are responsible for other activities such as digesting food. The muscles under your conscious control are **voluntary muscles.** Smiling, writing, and getting out of your seat when the bell rings are all actions controlled by voluntary muscles.

 FLORIDA NGSSS

SC.6.N.3.3 Give several examples of scientific laws.

SC.6.L.14.5 Identify and investigate the general functions of the major systems of the human body and describe ways these systems interact with each other to maintain homeostasis.

LA.6.4.2.2 The student will organize information to show understanding.

FIGURE 1 ······························
Muscle Use
Some muscles are voluntary and others are involuntary.

✎ **Relate Text and Visuals**
Write how the person in each frame is using involuntary and voluntary muscles.

	Frame 1	Frame 2	Frame 3
Involuntary			
Voluntary			

Types of Muscle Tissue

Your body has skeletal, smooth, and cardiac muscle tissues. Some of these muscle tissues are involuntary, and some are voluntary.

Skeletal muscles provide the force that moves your bones. A strong connective tissue called a **tendon** attaches the muscle to a bone. Because you have conscious control of skeletal muscles, they are classified as voluntary muscles. In contrast, the inside of many internal body organs, such as the stomach and blood vessels, contain **smooth muscle** tissue. These are involuntary muscles. They work to control certain movements inside your body, such as moving food through your digestive system. The tissue called **cardiac muscle** is found only in your heart. Like smooth muscle, cardiac muscle is involuntary. Look at **Figure 2**.

FIGURE 2 ·······························

Muscle Tissue
You have three types of muscle tissue: skeletal, smooth, and cardiac.

✎ **Classify** In the table, identify the type of muscle tissue in each body structure.

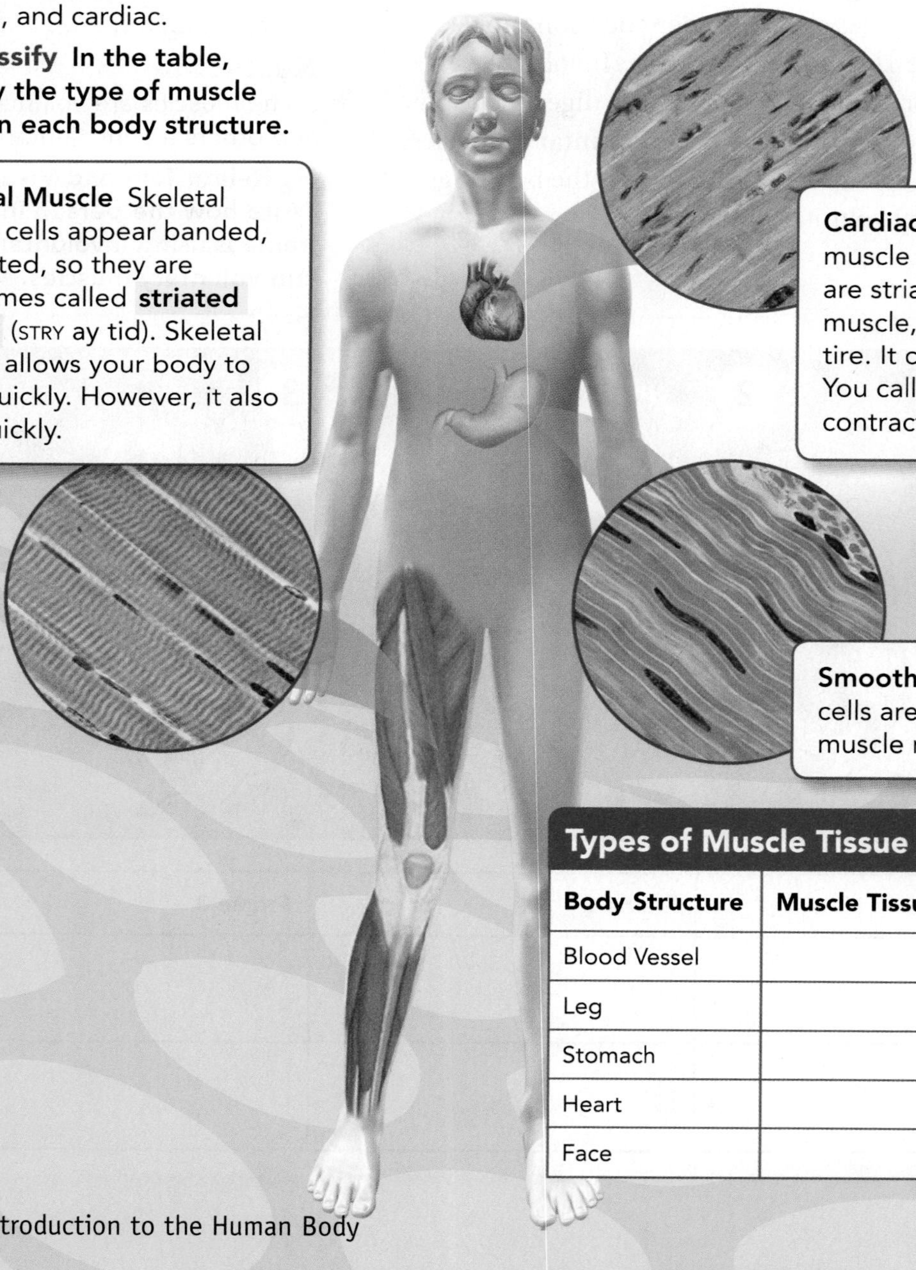

Skeletal Muscle Skeletal muscle cells appear banded, or striated, so they are sometimes called **striated muscle** (STRY ay tid). Skeletal muscle allows your body to react quickly. However, it also tires quickly.

Cardiac Muscle Like skeletal muscle cells, cardiac muscle cells are striated. But unlike skeletal muscle, cardiac muscle does not tire. It can contract repeatedly. You call those repeated contractions heartbeats.

Smooth Muscle Smooth muscle cells are not striated. This type of muscle reacts and tires slowly.

Types of Muscle Tissue

Body Structure	Muscle Tissue
Blood Vessel	
Leg	
Stomach	
Heart	
Face	

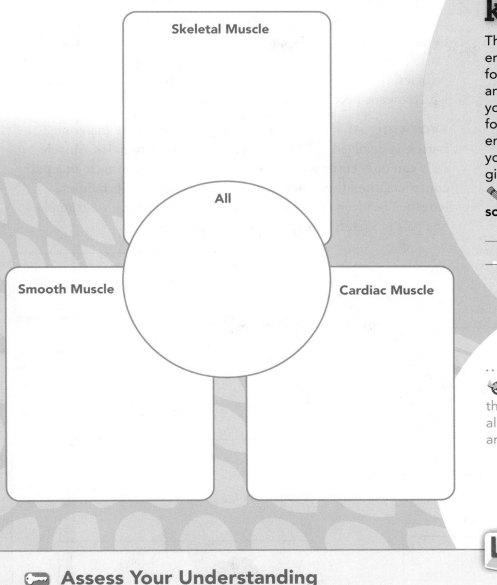

Skeletal Muscle

All

Smooth Muscle

Cardiac Muscle

did you know?

The law of conservation of energy states that when one form of energy is transformed to another, no energy is lost. When you eat, chemical energy in your food is changed into kinetic energy when you move using your muscles. Some energy is given off in the form of heat.

✏ **Identify** What is another scientific law?

_____

_____

SC.6.N.3.3

....

⟳ **Compare and Contrast** In the graphic organizer, write how all three muscle tissues are alike and how each type is different.

LA.6.4.2.2

 Lab zone® Do the Quick Lab *Observing Muscle Tissue.*

🔑 Assess Your Understanding

1a. Define What is the difference between voluntary and involuntary muscles?

_____

_____

_____

SC.6.L.14.5

b. ⚠**Infer** Why is it important that cardiac muscle tissue does not tire?

_____

_____

_____

SC.6.L.14.5

got it? ....

○ **I get it!** Now I know that the muscles in my body are _____

_____

○ **I need extra help with** _____

Go to **MY SCIENCE** Ⓢ **COACH** *online for help with this subject.*

SC.6.L.14.5

SC.6.L.14.5 Identify and investigate the general functions of the major systems of the human body (digestive, respiratory, circulatory, reproductive, excretory, immune, nervous, and musculoskeletal) and describe ways these systems interact with each other to maintain homeostasis.

How Do Skeletal Muscles Work?

Has anyone ever asked you to "make a muscle"? If so, you probably tightened your fist, bent your arm at the elbow, and made the muscles in your upper arm bulge, or contract. Like other skeletal muscles, the muscles in your arm do their work by contracting, which means becoming shorter and thicker.

Working in Pairs Each time you move, more than one muscle is involved. **Skeletal muscles work in pairs. Muscle cells can only contract, not lengthen. While one muscle in a pair contracts, the other muscle in the pair relaxes to its original length.** The biceps and triceps shown in **Figure 3** are an example of a pair of sketetal muscles in your upper arm.

FIGURE 3 ·····························

> **ART IN MOTION** Muscle Pairs

To bend your arm at the elbow, the biceps contracts while the triceps relaxes.

✏ **Interpret Diagrams** Tell what happens to each muscle as you straighten your arm.

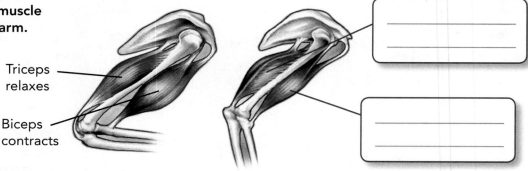

Triceps relaxes

Biceps contracts

apply it!

This girl's biceps and triceps work as a pair.

❶ Apply Concepts Below each photo, write which muscle is contracted.

1

2

_____

_____

❷ Infer What might happen if the biceps could not contract?

_____

Keeping Muscles Healthy

Regular exercise is important for maintaining the strength and flexibility of muscles. Exercise makes individual muscle cells grow bigger, so the whole muscle becomes thicker and stronger. Warming up before exercising increases the blood flow to your muscles. Stretching as you warm up helps your muscles become more flexible and prepares them for exercise. Exercise is important even in space, as shown in **Figure 4.**

Sometimes, muscles can become injured. A muscle strain can occur when muscles are overworked or overstretched. After a long period of exercise, a skeletal muscle can cramp, or contract and stay contracted. If you injure a muscle, be sure to follow medical instructions and rest the injured area so it can heal properly.

FIGURE 4 ·······························
Muscle Loss
Without gravity, astronauts in space can lose muscle mass. Therefore, they need to exercise daily.

✎ CHALLENGE **Explain why a lack of gravity might cause muscles to weaken.**

_____
_____
_____

 Lab ® Do the Quick Lab *Modeling How Skeletal Muscles Work.*

🔑 **Assess Your Understanding**

2a. Review How do muscles work in pairs?

_____
_____
_____

SC.6.L.14.5

b. Make Generalizations Why is it important to exercise both muscles in a pair?

_____
_____
_____

SC.6.L.14.5

got it? ························

○ **I get it!** Now I know that skeletal muscles work _____

_____

○ **I need extra help with** _____

Go to **my science** ⓢ **coach** *online for help with this subject.*

SC.6.L.14.5

The Skin

UNLOCK THE
ESSENTIAL
?

🗝 **What Are the Functions and Structures of the Skin?**
SC.6.L.14.5

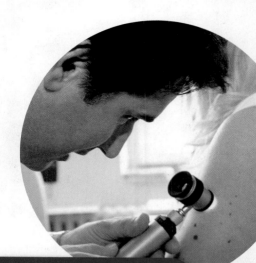

my PLANET DiaRY

CAREER

Would You Like to Be a Skin Doctor?

Did you know that there is a special type of doctor who studies and treats skin? This type of doctor, a dermatologist, specializes in caring for skin, hair, and nails. Dermatologists diagnose and treat a variety of skin problems ranging from acne to psoriasis to dangerous cancers.

To become a dermatologist, you need a lot of education. You may spend about ten years in schooling and training after you graduate high school. Then you must pass a certification test. Although becoming a dermatologist is not easy, it can be a rewarding career!

Communicate Discuss the question with a partner. Then write down your answer.

Why do you think dermatologists are important?

_____

_____

_____

_____

_____

_____

_____

▷ PLANET DIARY Go to **Planet Diary** to learn more about your skin.

Psoriasis

Lab zone Do the Inquiry Warm-Up *What Can You Observe About Skin?*

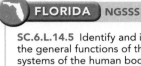

Vocabulary

- epidermis • melanin • dermis
- pore • follicle

Skills

- Reading: Relate Cause and Effect
- Inquiry: Observe

What Are the Functions and Structures of the Skin?

If an adult's skin were stretched out flat, it would cover an area about the size of a mattress on a twin bed. The skin is part of the integumentary system (in teg yoo MEN tur ee). In addition to the skin, this system includes hair, nails, sweat glands, and oil glands.

Functions of the Skin Your skin helps you in many ways. **The skin has two layers that protect the body. Skin helps regulate body temperature, eliminate wastes, gather information about the environment, and produce vitamin D.**

Protecting the Body The skin forms a barrier that keeps harmful substances outside the body. It also keeps important substances such as water and other fluids inside the body.

Maintaining Temperature The skin helps the body maintain a steady temperature. When you become too warm, like the runner in **Figure 1,** blood vessels in your skin enlarge. This widening of the vessels allows more blood to flow through them and body heat to escape into the environment. In addition, sweat glands produce perspiration in response to excess heat. As perspiration evaporates from your skin, your skin is cooled. When you get cold, blood vessels in your body contract. This reduces blood flow to the skin and helps your body conserve heat.

FLORIDA NGSSS

SC.6.L.14.5 Identify and investigate the general functions of the major systems of the human body (digestive, respiratory, circulatory, reproductive, excretory, immune, nervous, and musculoskeletal) and describe ways these systems interact with each other to maintain homeostasis.

FIGURE 1 ·····

Amazing Skin

As this runner exercises, his skin helps to cool him off.

✎ **Describe** On the notebook page, describe a time that your skin protected you, maintained your body temperature, or both.

177

Eliminating Wastes Perspiration contains dissolved waste materials that come from the breakdown of chemical processes. Your skin helps eliminate wastes whenever you perspire.

Gathering Information Nerves in your skin gather information from the environment. They provide information about things such as pressure, temperature, and pain. Pain messages warn you that something in your surroundings can injure you.

Producing Vitamin D Some skin cells produce vitamin D in the presence of sunlight. Vitamin D is important for healthy bones because it helps your body absorb the calcium in your food. Your skin cells need sunlight each day to produce enough vitamin D.

✎

⟳ **Relate Cause and Effect**
Describe the possible effect of not getting enough sunlight each day.

_____

_____

_____

FIGURE 2

Skin at Work
You may not notice that your skin is constantly working.

✎ **Complete the activity and answer the questions below.**

1. **Interpret Photos** Write below each photo the functions that the skin performs.

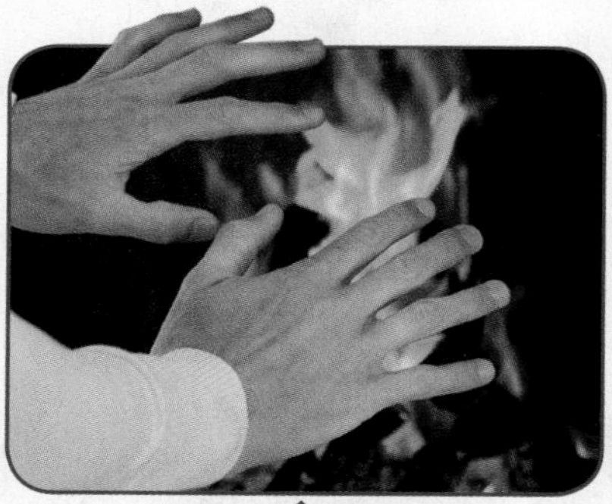

2. **Observe** Press down firmly on your arm with your fingertips. Then lightly pinch yourself. What information did you receive?

_____

_____

_____

_____

3. CHALLENGE What might happen if the nerves in your skin did not gather information?

_____

_____

_____

_____

Structures of the Skin The skin has two main layers, as shown in **Figure 3**. Together, these layers—an outer layer and an inner layer—perform all the skin's functions.

The **epidermis** is the outer layer of the skin. Deep in the epidermis, new cells form. As they mature, they move upward until they die. They then become part of the epidermal surface layer. This surface layer helps protect your skin. Cells stay in this layer for about two to three weeks until they are shed. Some cells deep in the epidermis produce **melanin,** a pigment that colors the skin.

The **dermis** is the inner layer of the skin. It is above a layer of fat. This fat layer pads the internal organs and helps keep heat in the body. The dermis includes nerves, blood vessels, sweat glands, hairs, and oil glands. **Pores** are openings that allow sweat to reach the surface. Strands of hair grow within the dermis in **follicles** (FAHL ih kulz). Oil produced in glands around the follicles keeps the surface of the skin moist and the hairs flexible.

FIGURE 3 ·······················

Structures of the Skin
✏ **Relate Text and Visuals On the lines, write the functions of the epidermis, the nerves, and the sweat gland.**

_____

_____

_____

_____

_____

_____

_____

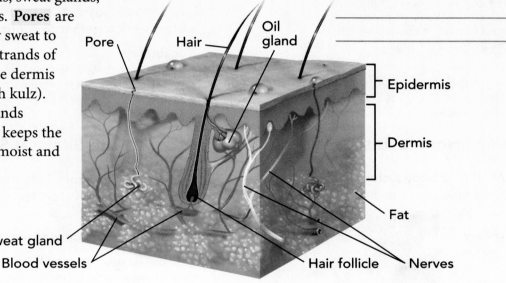

Pore   Hair   Oil gland

Epidermis

Dermis

Fat

Sweat gland
Blood vessels

Hair follicle   Nerves

Lab zone® Do the Quick Lab *Sweaty Skin.*

🔑 Assess Your Understanding

1a. Describe How does your skin gather information about the environment?

_____

_____

_____

SC.6.L.14.5

b. Summarize Explain how some structures in the skin protect your body.

_____

_____

_____

SC.6.L.14.5

got it? ···

○ **I get it!** Now I know that the skin has two layers that _____

_____

○ I need extra help with _____

Go to **MY SCIENCE S COACH** *online for help with this subject.*

SC.6.L.14.5

Cells, tissues, and organs make up organ _____ , which constantly interact
to help maintain _____ .

LESSON 1 Body Organization
SC.6.N.3.4, SC.6.L.14.5

The levels of organization in the human
body consist of cells, tissues, organs, and organ
systems.

Vocabulary
• cell • cell membrane • nucleus
• cytoplasm • tissue • muscle tissue
• nervous tissue • connective tissue
• epithelial tissue • organ • organ system

LESSON 2 System Interactions
SC.6.N.2.3, SC.6.L.14.5

Muscles, bones, and nerves work together
to make your body move.
The circulatory, respiratory, digestive, and
excretory systems play key roles in moving
materials in your body.
The nervous system and the endocrine
system work together to control body functions.

Vocabulary
• skeleton • skeletal muscle • joint • nutrient
• absorption • gland • stimulus • response
• hormone

LESSON 3 Homeostasis
SC.6.L.14.5

All of your body systems working together
maintain homeostasis and keep the body in
balance.

Vocabulary
• homeostasis
• stress

LESSON 4 The Skeletal System
SC.6.L.14.5

Your skeleton provides shape and support,
enables you to move, protects your organs,
produces blood cells, and stores minerals.

Joints allow bones to move in different ways.

Bones are complex living structures
that grow, develop, and repair themselves.

Vocabulary
• skeleton • vertebrae • joint • ligament
• compact bone • spongy bone • marrow
• cartilage • osteoporosis

LESSON 5 The Muscular System
SC.6.N.3.3, SC.6.L.14.5

Your body has skeletal, smooth, and cardiac
muscle tissues. Some of these muscle tissues are
involuntary, and some are voluntary.

Skeletal muscles work in pairs. Muscle cells
only contract, not lengthen. While one muscle in
a pair contracts, the other muscle relaxes.

Vocabulary
• involuntary muscle • voluntary muscle
• skeletal muscle • tendon • smooth muscle
• cardiac muscle • striated muscle

LESSON 6 The Skin
SC.6.L.14.5

The skin has two layers that protect the
body. Skin helps regulate body temperature,
eliminate wastes, and produce vitamin D.

Vocabulary
• epidermis
• melanin
• dermis
• pore
• follicle

Review and Assessment

LESSON 1 Body Organization

1. Bone tissue and fat tissue are examples of

   a. muscle tissue.   **b.** nervous tissue.

   c. epithelial tissue.   **d.** connective tissue.

                                                       SC.6.L.14.5

2. The _____ forms the outside border of a cell.

                                                       SC.6.L.14.5

3. Compare and Contrast How is a tissue different from an organ? How are they similar?

                                                       SC.6.L.14.5

LESSON 2 System Interactions

4. Signals from the _____ make skeletal muscles move.

   a. nervous system   **b.** digestive system

   c. respiratory system   **d.** muscular system

                                                       SC.6.L.14.5

5. _____ occurs when nutrients move from the digestive system into the bloodstream.

                                                       SC.6.L.14.5

6. Infer Your knee is called a hinge joint. It is called this because it bends like the hinge on a door. What are some other examples of joints in your body that work like a hinge?

                                                       SC.6.L.14.5

LESSON 3 Homeostasis

7. Under what circumstances would your endocrine system release adrenaline?

   a. sleep   **b.** sudden stress

   c. absorption   **d.** homeostasis

                                                       SC.6.L.14.5

8. Your body systems work together to maintain internal conditions, or

                                                       SC.6.L.14.5

9. Apply Concepts Imagine you are leading a workshop to help students deal with stress. Explain why it is important to reduce stress.

                                                       SC.6.L.14.5

LESSON 4 The Skeletal System

10. A soft connective tissue found inside bones is

   a. cytoplasm.   **b.** marrow.

   c. cartilage.   **d.** osteoporosis.

                                                       SC.6.L.14.5

11. The _____ make up your backbone.

                                                       SC.6.L.14.5

12. Draw Conclusions Does your body have more immovable or movable joints? Explain.

                                                       SC.6.L.14.5

LESSON 5 The Muscular System

13. Muscles that help the skeleton move are

   a. cardiac muscles.   **b.** smooth muscles.

   c. skeletal muscles.   **d.** involuntary muscles.

SC.6.L.14.5

14. Skeletal muscles must work in pairs because

muscle cells can only _____

SC.6.L.14.5

15. Compare and Contrast Write one similarity and one difference between skeletal muscle and cardiac muscle.

_____

_____

_____

SC.6.L.14.5

16. Predict What would happen if a tendon in your finger were cut?

_____

_____

SC.6.L.14.5

LESSON 6 The Skin

17. A pigment that colors the skin is

   a. the dermis.   **b.** the epidermis.

   c. a follicle.   **d.** melanin.

SC.6.L.14.5

18. Hair grows in _____

SC.6.L.14.5

19. Make Generalizations What skin layers are affected when a cut on your hand bleeds?

_____

_____

SC.6.L.14.5

20. Write About It You are out running with your friend on a hot day. Your body begins to warm up. Describe how your skin responds to the excess heat.

SC.6.L.14.5

 How does your body work?

21. Describe how the body systems of this boy function during and after the time he eats his lunch. Use at least four different body systems in your answer.

_____

_____

_____

_____

_____

_____

_____

_____

_____

_____

_____

_____

_____

_____

_____

_____

_____

SC.6.L.14.5

Florida Benchmarks Review

Circle the letter of the best answer.

1 Which term best fits the level of organization pictured in the diagram below?

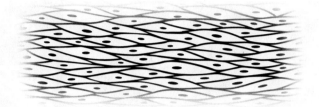

- **A** organ
- **B** tissue
- **C** single cell
- **D** organ system

SC.6.L.14.5

2 What is one way that stress can affect homeostasis?

- **A** disrupts ability to fight disease
- **B** increases water balance
- **C** maintains constant internal temperature
- **D** decreases the frequency of headaches

SC.6.L.14.5

3 Which two systems work together to respond to internal and external conditions and to control body functions?

- **A** skeletal and muscular systems
- **B** endocrine and nervous systems
- **C** muscular and digestive systems
- **D** respiratory and circulatory systems

SC.6.L.14.5

4 Which of the following is an important function of the integumentary system?

- **A** It produces blood cells.
- **B** It stores minerals until the body needs them.
- **C** It regulates body temperature.
- **D** It allows the body to move.

SC.6.L.14.5

5 Which of the following connects the bones in movable joints?

- **A** tendons
- **B** cartilage
- **C** marrow
- **D** ligaments

SC.6.L.14.5

Use the diagram below to answer Question 6.

6 What happens when the biceps contracts?

- **A** The triceps contracts.
- **B** The triceps relaxes.
- **C** The triceps shortens.
- **D** The triceps does not move.

SC.6.L.14.5

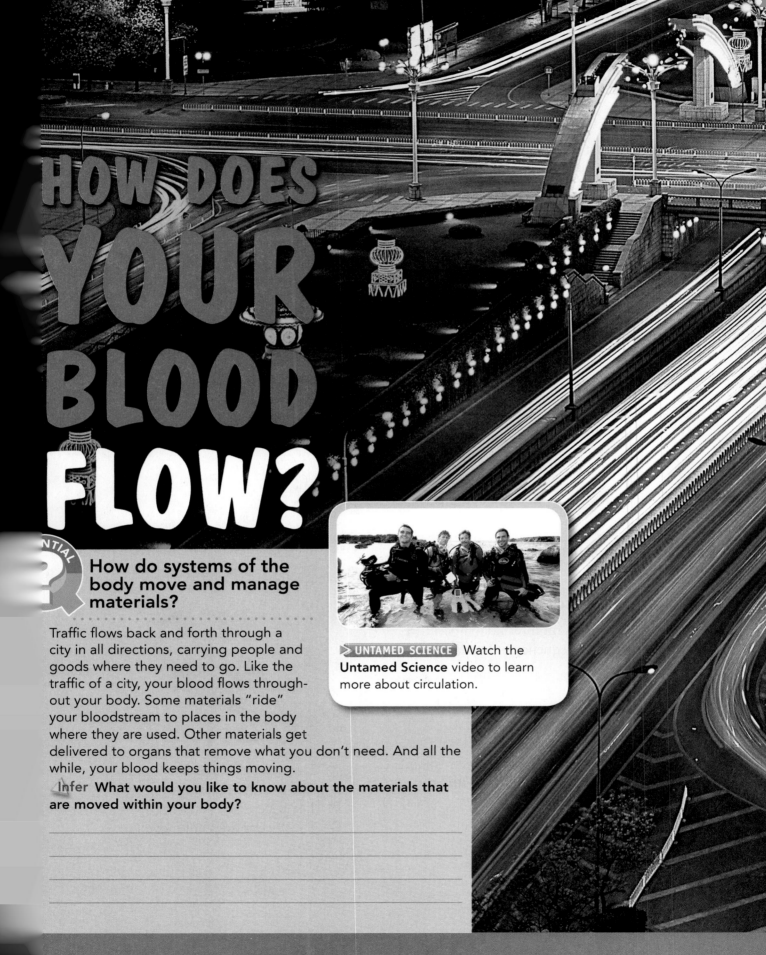

HOW DOES YOUR BLOOD FLOW?

How do systems of the body move and manage materials?

Traffic flows back and forth through a city in all directions, carrying people and goods where they need to go. Like the traffic of a city, your blood flows throughout your body. Some materials "ride" your bloodstream to places in the body where they are used. Other materials get delivered to organs that remove what you don't need. And all the while, your blood keeps things moving.

Infer What would you like to know about the materials that are moved within your body?

_____

_____

_____

_____

> **UNTAMED SCIENCE** Watch the **Untamed Science** video to learn more about circulation.

Managing Materials
in the Body

CHAPTER
5

FLORIDA

FLORIDA · Next Generation Sunshine State Standards

Big Idea 1: SC.6.N.1.5
Big Idea 14: SC.6.L.14.5

Language Arts: LA.6.2.2.3
Mathematics: MA.6.A.3.6

5 Getting Started

Check Your Understanding

1. **Background** Read the paragraph below and then answer the question.

> Each day, Ken **circulates** from the food pantry to senior centers around the city and then returns to the pantry. He **transports** meals and juice to the seniors and collects their empty bottles. Similarly, your blood circulates in your body. From the heart, your blood carries oxygen and **glucose** to your body cells. It picks up wastes before returning to the heart.

> To **circulate** is to move in a circle and return to the same point.

> To **transport** is to carry something from one place to another.

> **Glucose** is a sugar that is the major source of energy for the body's cells.

- What materials does your blood transport to your body cells?

_____

_____

▶ MY READING WEB If you had trouble completing the question above, visit **My Reading Web** and type in *Managing Materials in the Body.*

Vocabulary Skill

Identify Related Word Forms Learn related forms of words to increase your vocabulary. The table below lists forms of words related to key terms.

Verb	Noun	Adjective
respire, *v.* to obtain energy from the breakdown of food molecules	cellular respiration, *n.* the process by which cells obtain energy from the breakdown of food molecules	respiratory, *adj.* concerning respiration
excrete, *v.* to remove or eliminate waste	excretion, *n.* the process by which wastes are removed from the body	excretory, *adj.* concerning excretion

LA.6.1.6.1

2. **Quick Check** Fill in the blank with the correct form of *respire.*
- Obtaining energy from food is a _____ activity.

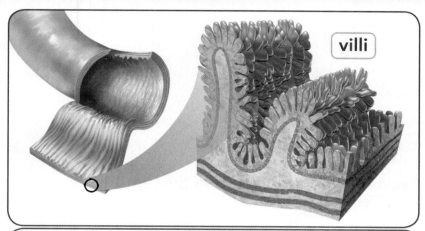

villi

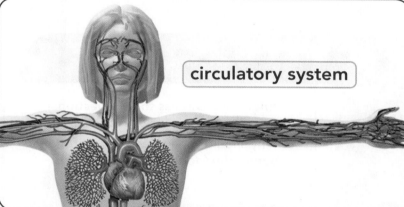

circulatory system

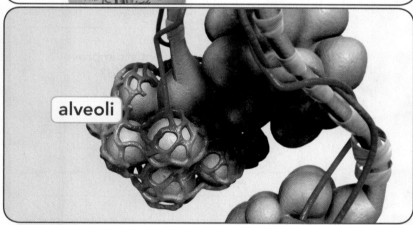

alveoli

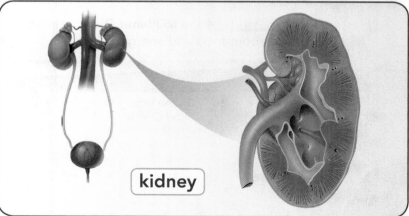

kidney

Chapter Preview

LESSON 1
- calorie • enzyme • esophagus
- peristalsis • villi

🔄 Reading: Chart
🔺 Inquiry: Develop Hypotheses

LESSON 2
- circulatory system • heart
- atrium • ventricle • valve
- artery • aorta • capillary • vein
- hemoglobin

🔄 Summarize
🔺 Observe

LESSON 3
- pharynx
- trachea
- cilia
- bronchi
- lungs
- alveoli
- diaphragm
- larynx
- vocal cords

🔄 Chart
🔺 Communicate

LESSON 4
- excretion
- urea
- urine
- kidney
- ureter
- urinary bladder
- urethra
- nephron

🔄 Identify the Main Idea
🔺 Infer

> **VOCAB FLASH CARDS** For extra help with vocabulary, visit **Vocab Flash Cards** and type in *Managing Materials in the Body.*

LESSON

1 Digestion

UNLOCK THE ESSENTIAL ?

🔑 **Why Do You Need Food?**
SC.6.L.14.5, MA.6.A.3.6

🔑 **What Happens in Your Digestive System?**
SC.6.L.14.5, LA.6.2.2.3

MY PLANET DIARY

The Science of Food

You know that you need to eat food every day. But did you know that for some people studying food is their job? People called food scientists research and improve the food products you buy at the grocery store. Sometimes, they even think up new foods!

Many food scientists spend a lot of time in a lab. They use what they know about biology and chemistry to test food for nutrition, taste, and shelf life, which is how long the food will last before it spoils. If you like science and food, being a food scientist might be the job for you!

CAREER

Communicate Discuss these questions with a partner. Then write your answers.

1. Why should food scientists test foods before the foods are sold?

_____

_____

_____

2. How might food scientists improve your favorite breakfast food?

_____

_____

_____

_____

▶ **PLANET DIARY** Go to **Planet Diary** to learn more about food and energy.

Lab zone® Do the Inquiry Warm-Up *Food Claims.*

188 Managing Materials in the Body

Vocabulary

- calorie • enzyme • esophagus
- peristalsis • villi

Skills

↪ Reading: Chart
△ Inquiry: Develop Hypotheses

Why Do You Need Food?

All living things need food to stay alive. ⚷ **Food provides your body with materials to grow and to repair tissues. It also provides energy for everything you do.** Exercising, reading, and sleeping require energy. Even maintaining homeostasis takes energy.

Calories When food is used for energy, the amount of energy released is measured in calories. One **calorie** is the amount of energy needed to raise the temperature of one gram of water by one degree Celsius. The unit *Calorie*, with a capital *C*, is used to measure the energy in foods. One Calorie equals 1,000 calories. Everyone needs a certain number of Calories to meet their daily energy needs. However, the more active you are, the more Calories you need.

FLORIDA NGSSS

SC.6.L.14.5 Identify and investigate the functions of the major systems of the human body.

MA.6.A.3.6 Construct and analyze tables, graphs, and equations to describe simple relations.

do the math!

The U.S. Department of Agriculture recommends that people do about 30 to 60 minutes of physical activity most days. The data table shows the Calories a 13-year-old weighing 45 kilograms burned in 30 minutes of each activity.

❶ **Graph** Use the data to draw a bar graph.

❷ **Name** Write a title for the bar graph.

❸ CHALLENGE Why does the type of physical activity change a person's dietary needs? Use the graph to explain your answer.

_____

_____

_____

_____

_____

_____

_____

Activity	Calories Burned in 30 minutes
Soccer	275
Dancing	115
Walking	75

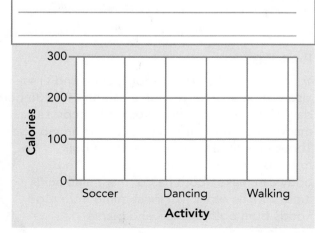

MA.6.A.3.6

What Nutrients Do You Need?
Your body breaks down the food you eat into nutrients. Nutrients are the substances in food that provide the raw materials and energy the body needs to carry out all its processes. People need six types of nutrients: carbohydrates, fats, proteins, vitamins, minerals, and water.

FIGURE 1 ·····································

> INTERACTIVE ART   **Feeding Your Body**
The nutrients your body needs comes from the foods you eat. **Make Judgments Why do you think it's important to eat a variety of foods everyday?**

_____

_____

_____

Carbohydrates
Carbohydrates (kahr boh HY drayts) are a major source of energy. They also provide raw materials to make cell parts. About 45 to 65 percent of your daily Calories should come from carbohydrates. Simple carbohydrates, called sugars, can give you a quick burst of energy. One sugar, glucose, is the major source of energy for your cells. Complex carbohydrates are made of many linked sugar molecules. Starch is a complex carbohydrate. Potatoes, rice, wheat, and corn contain starches. Your body breaks down starches into sugar molecules. In this way, starches provide a steady long-term energy source.

Fats
Like carbohydrates, fats are energy-containing nutrients. However, 1 gram of fat provides 9 Calories of energy, while 1 gram of carbohydrate provides only 4 Calories. Fats form part of the cell membrane. Fatty tissue also protects your organs and insulates your body. No more than 30 percent of your daily Calories should come from fats.

Proteins
Your body needs proteins for growth and tissue repair. Proteins also can be an energy source. About 10 to 35 percent of your daily Calorie intake should come from proteins. Proteins are made up of small, linked units called amino acids (uh MEE noh). Thousands of different proteins are built from about 20 different amino acids. Your body can make about half of the amino acids it needs. The other half must come from food. Foods from both animals and plants contain protein.

Vitamins and Minerals

Unlike some nutrients, vitamins do not provide the body with raw materials and energy. Instead, vitamins act as helper molecules in your body's chemical reactions. The body can make a few vitamins, such as vitamin D, but foods are the source of most vitamins.

Nutrients that are not made by living things are called minerals. Like vitamins, minerals do not provide your body with raw materials and energy. However, your body still needs small amounts of minerals to carry out chemical processes. For example, you need calcium to build bones and teeth, and iron to help red blood cells function. Plant roots absorb minerals from the soil. You obtain minerals by eating plants or animals that have eaten plants.

Water

Water is the most important nutrient because all the body's vital processes take place in water. In addition, water helps regulate body temperature and remove wastes. Water accounts for about 65 percent of the average healthy person's body weight because it makes up most of the body's fluids, including blood. Under normal conditions, you need to take in about 2 liters of water every day to stay healthy.

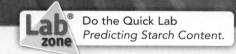

Lab zone® Do the Quick Lab
Predicting Starch Content.

🔑 Assess Your Understanding

1a. Define What does a Calorie measure?

_____

_____

SC.6.L.14.5

b. Draw Conclusions Why do active teenagers have high energy needs?

_____

_____

SC.6.L.14.5

c. Apply Concepts What do you think is meant by the phrase "a balanced diet?"

_____

_____

_____

_____

_____

_____

SC.6.L.14.5

got it? ·····································

○ **I get it!** Now I know that food provides the body with _____

_____

○ **I need extra help with** _____

Go to **MY SCIENCE COACH** *online for help with this subject.*

SC.6.L.14.5

What Happens in Your Digestive System?

Your digestive system is about 9 meters long from beginning to end. **Figure 2** shows the structures of the digestive system. 🔑 **The digestive system breaks down food, absorbs nutrients, and eliminates waste.** These functions occur one after the other in an efficient, continuous process.

Digestion The process by which your body breaks down food into small nutrient molecules is called digestion. Digestion can be mechanical or chemical. In mechanical digestion, bites of food are torn or ground into smaller pieces. This kind of digestion happens mostly in the mouth and stomach. In chemical digestion, chemicals break foods into their building blocks. Chemical digestion takes place in many parts of the digestive system. Substances made in the liver and pancreas help digestion occur.

Absorption and Elimination Absorption occurs after digestion. Absorption is the process by which nutrient molecules pass from your digestive system into your blood. Most absorption occurs in the small intestine. The large intestine eliminates materials that are not absorbed.

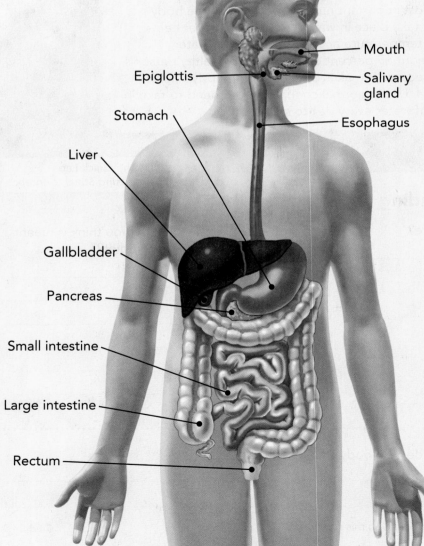

Epiglottis

Stomach

Liver

Gallbladder

Pancreas

Small intestine

Large intestine

Rectum

Mouth

Salivary gland

Esophagus

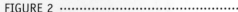

FIGURE 2 ·····

The Digestive System
Food passes directly through five organs of your digestive system.

✏️ **Identify** Circle the name(s) of the organ(s) where mechanical digestion mainly occurs. Check the name(s) of the organ(s) where most absorption occurs. Underline the name(s) of the organ(s) where elimination occurs.

The Mouth

Have you noticed that smelling food can be enough to start your mouth watering? This response happens because your mouth is where digestion begins. When you bite off a piece of food, both mechanical and chemical digestion begin inside your mouth. Your teeth and tongue carry out mechanical digestion. Your teeth cut, tear, crush, and grind food into small pieces. Your tongue pushes food toward your teeth.

As your teeth work, your saliva (suh LY vuh) moistens food into a slippery mass. Saliva is the fluid released by salivary glands when you eat. Saliva contains a chemical that can break down starches into sugars. This step begins the chemical digestion of your food.

The chemical in saliva that digests starch is an enzyme. An **enzyme** is a protein that speeds up chemical reactions in the body. Your body produces many different enzymes. Each enzyme has a specific chemical shape that enables it to speed up only one kind of reaction. Different enzymes are needed to complete the process of digestion. **Figure 3** shows how enzymes work.

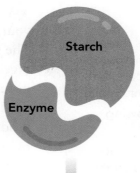

The starch molecule binds to an enzyme that has a matching shape.

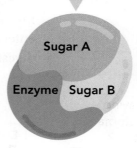

The starch molecule is broken down into two separate sugar molecules.

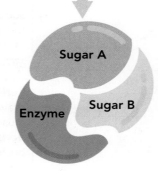

The enzyme and the sugar molecules all separate.

FIGURE 3 ···

How Enzymes Work
Enzymes help break down starches, proteins, and fats.

✎ **Observe** Which molecule does not change?

_____

_____

apply it!

You have four types of teeth. Each type has a specific function.

❶ **Name** Think about eating a carrot. Which type of teeth cuts the carrot into a bite-sized piece? _____

❷ **Identify** Which teeth at the back of your mouth crush and grind the carrot piece? _____ and _____

❸ **Interpret Diagrams** When people tear chicken off a bone, they use their pointed teeth called _____

❹ **Summarize** Write about all the teeth people use to eat an apple.

_____

_____

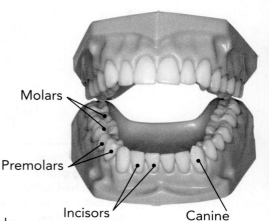

Molars
Premolars
Incisors
Canine

FIGURE 4 ·······························

The Stomach

The stomach wall has three muscle layers. The microscopic view shows you the cells that line the inside of the stomach.

✎ **Answer the following questions.**

1. **Classify** What type of digestion is aided by the action of stomach muscles?

_____

_____

_____

2. **Infer** How does having different layers of stomach muscles aid digestion?

_____

_____

_____

_____

_____

_____

To the Stomach Food moves from your mouth through your **esophagus** (ih SAHF uh gus) and then into your stomach. The stomach is a J-shaped muscular pouch where most mechanical digestion and some chemical digestion occur. Mechanical digestion occurs as layers of smooth muscle in the stomach wall contract, producing a churning motion. Chemical digestion occurs as the food mixes with digestive juice. Digestive juice is a fluid produced by cells that line the stomach. It contains the enzyme pepsin that chemically digests proteins into short chains of amino acids.

Food usually stays in your stomach for a few hours until mechanical digestion is complete. Now a thick liquid, the food enters the next part of the digestive system. That is where chemical digestion continues and absorption take place.

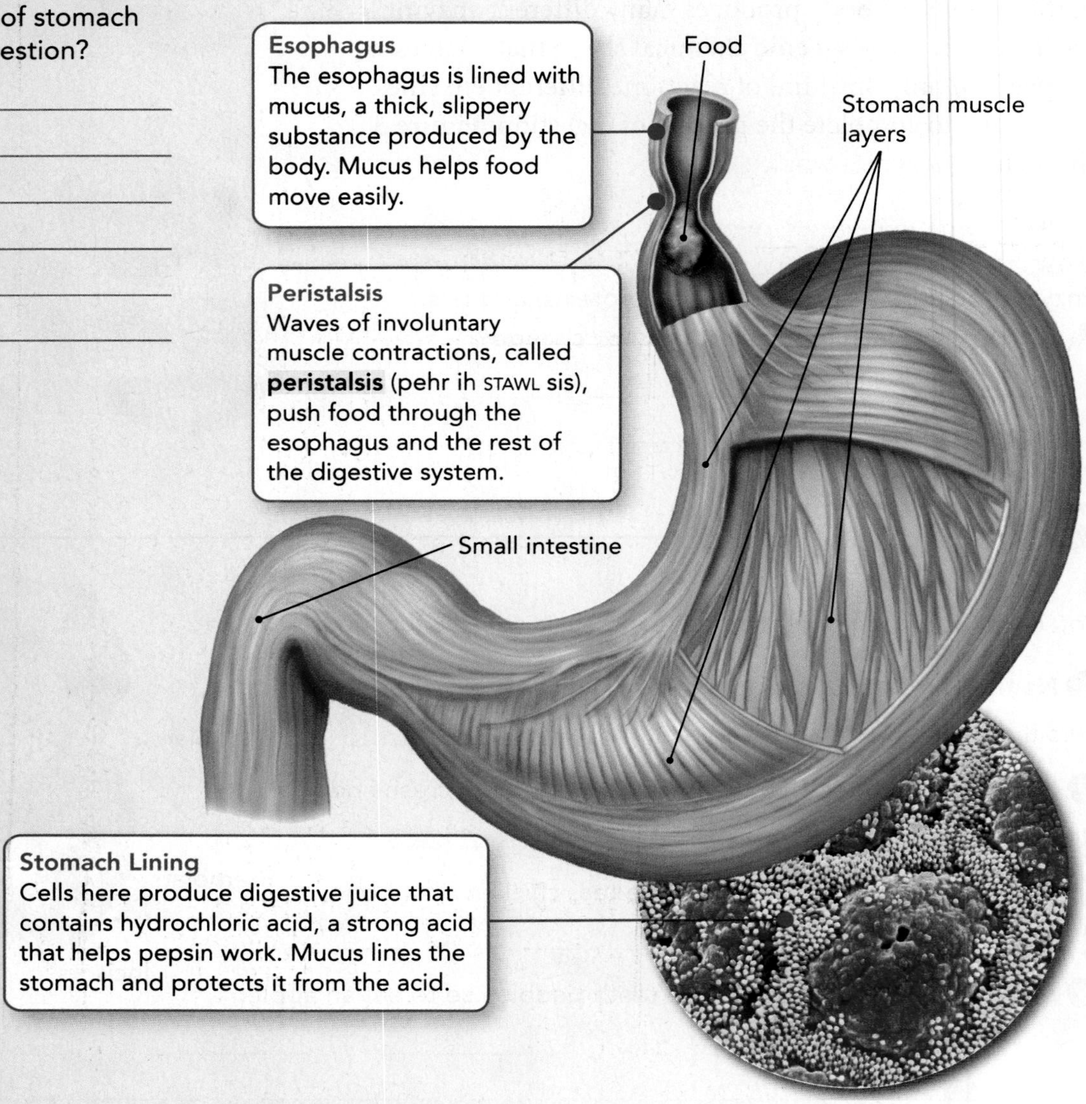

Esophagus
The esophagus is lined with mucus, a thick, slippery substance produced by the body. Mucus helps food move easily.

Food

Stomach muscle layers

Peristalsis
Waves of involuntary muscle contractions, called **peristalsis** (pehr ih STAWL sis), push food through the esophagus and the rest of the digestive system.

Small intestine

Stomach Lining
Cells here produce digestive juice that contains hydrochloric acid, a strong acid that helps pepsin work. Mucus lines the stomach and protects it from the acid.

The Small Intestine At about 6 meters—longer than some full-sized cars—the small intestine makes up two thirds of the length of the digestive system. The small intestine is the part of the digestive system where most chemical digestion and absorption take place. Its small diameter, from 2 to 3 centimeters wide, gives the small intestine its name.

A great deal happens in the small intestine. When food reaches it, starches and proteins have been partially broken down, but fats have not been digested. 🔑 **Substances produced by the liver, pancreas, and lining of the small intestine help to complete chemical digestion.** The liver and the pancreas send their substances into the small intestine through small tubes.

FIGURE 5 ·····························
> REAL-WORLD INQUIRY **Organs of Digestion**
The liver, pancreas, and gallbladder aid digestion in the small intestine.

✏ **Complete the tasks.**

1. **Identify** Fill in the missing labels.

2. ◭ **Develop Hypotheses** How may a blockage in the tube between the gall bladder and the small intestine affect digestion?

_____
_____
_____
_____
_____

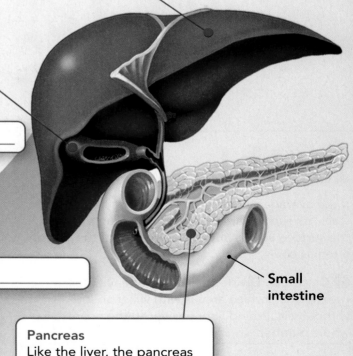

Gallbladder
The gallbladder stores bile and releases it into the small intestine.

Liver
The liver has many jobs. One job is making bile for the digestive system. Bile breaks fats into smaller droplets but is not involved in chemical digestion.

Small intestine

Pancreas
Like the liver, the pancreas has many jobs. One job is to produce enzymes that break down carbohydrates, proteins, and fats.

Absorption in the Small Intestine After chemical digestion takes place, the small nutrient molecules are ready for the body to absorb. The structure of the small intestine helps absorption occur. The inner surface of the small intestine is folded into millions of tiny finger-shaped structures called **villi** (VIL eye) (singular *villus*). Villi, shown in **Figure 6,** greatly increase the surface area of the small intestine. More surface area means that more nutrients can be absorbed. Nutrient molecules pass from cells on the surface of a villus into blood vessels and are then delivered to body cells.

FIGURE 6 ·································

Villi

Tiny villi line the folds of the small intestine.

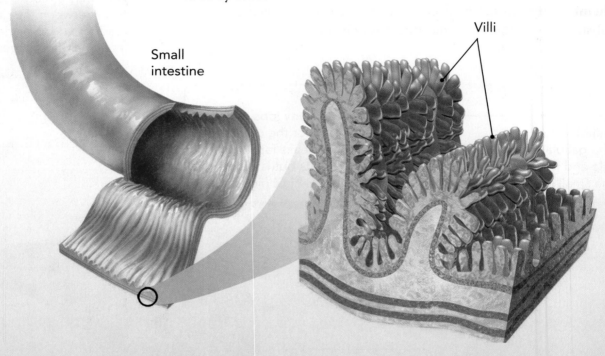

Small intestine

Villi

do the math!

If the average person's small intestine had smooth walls, its surface area would be 0.57 m². With villi, the surface area is about 250 m², about the size of a tennis court.

❶ **Calculate** Divide to find how many times greater the surface area is with villi than it is without villi. Round your answer to the nearest whole number.

❷ **Estimate** In Question 1, how did you know which number to divide by to get your answer?

_____

_____

_____

_____

_____

❸ CHALLENGE Some people have a wheat allergy that results in villi being destroyed. What problems might these individuals have?

_____

_____

_____

MA.6.A.5.3

The Large Intestine By the time material reaches the end of the small intestine, most nutrients have been absorbed. The water and undigested food that is left move from the small intestine into the large intestine. The large intestine is the last section of the digestive system. As the material moves through the large intestine, water is absorbed into the bloodstream. The remaining material is readied for elimination from the body.

The large intestine is about 1.5 meters long. It contains bacteria that feed on the material passing through. These bacteria normally do not cause disease. In fact, they are helpful because they make certain vitamins, including vitamin K.

The large intestine ends in a short tube called the rectum. In the rectum waste material is compressed into solid form. This waste material is eliminated from the body through the anus, a muscular opening at the end of the rectum.

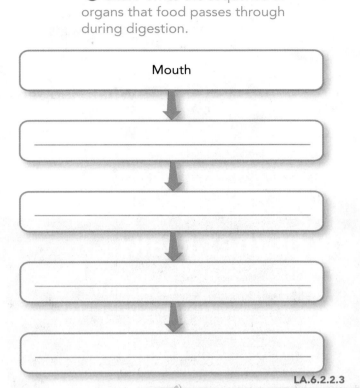

Chart Write the sequence of organs that food passes through during digestion.

Mouth

LA.6.2.2.3

Lab zone ® Do the Lab Investigation *As the Stomach Churns.*

🔑 Assess Your Understanding

2a. Define (Chemical/Mechanical) digestion occurs when enzymes break down foods into simpler substances.

SC.6.L.14.5

b. Apply Concepts How is the stomach similar to a washing machine?

_____

_____

_____

_____

SC.6.L.14.5

c. Explain How are the liver and pancreas involved in digestion?

_____

_____

_____

_____

SC.6.L.14.5

d. Relate Cause and Effect How do villi help the small intestine carry out its function?

_____

_____

SC.6.L14.5

got it? ....

○ **I get it!** Now I know that the digestive system works through the actions of organs that include

_____

_____

○ I need extra help with _____

Go to MY SCIENCE ⑤ COACH *online for help with this subject.*

SC.6.L14.5

Circulation

What Happens in Your Circulatory System?
SC.6.L.14.5

What Does Blood Contain?
SC.6.N.1.5, SC.6.L.14.5, LA.6.2.2.3

my pLaneT DiaRY

Your Heart, Your Health

Here are some fascinating facts that you may not know about your heart.

- In one year, your heart pumps enough blood to fill more than 30 competition-sized swimming pools!
- A drop of blood makes the entire trip through your body in less than a minute.
- Your heart beats about 100,000 times a day.
- Your heart pushes blood through about 100,000 kilometers of vessels. They would circle Earth more than twice!
- A child's heart is about the size of a fist. An adult's heart is about the size of two fists.

FUN FACTS

Read the following questions. Write your answers below.

1. Why is it important for a person's heart to be healthy?

_____

_____

_____

2. About how many times does your heart beat in a week? In a year?

_____

_____

_____

> **PLANET DIARY** Go to **Planet Diary** to learn more about the body's transport system.

Lab zone Do the Inquiry Warm-Up *Observing a Heart.*

FLORIDA NGSSS

SC.6.L.14.5 Identify and investigate the functions of the major systems of the human body and describe ways these systems interact with each other to maintain homeostasis.

What Happens in Your Circulatory System?

As shown in **Figure 1,** the circulatory system, or cardiovascular system, is made up of the heart, blood vessels, and blood. **The circulatory system delivers needed substances to cells, carries wastes away from cells, and helps regulate body temperature. In addition, blood contains cells that fight disease.**

Vocabulary

- circulatory system
- heart
- atrium
- ventricle
- valve
- artery
- aorta
- capillary
- vein
- hemoglobin

Skills

- Reading: Summarize
- Inquiry: Observe

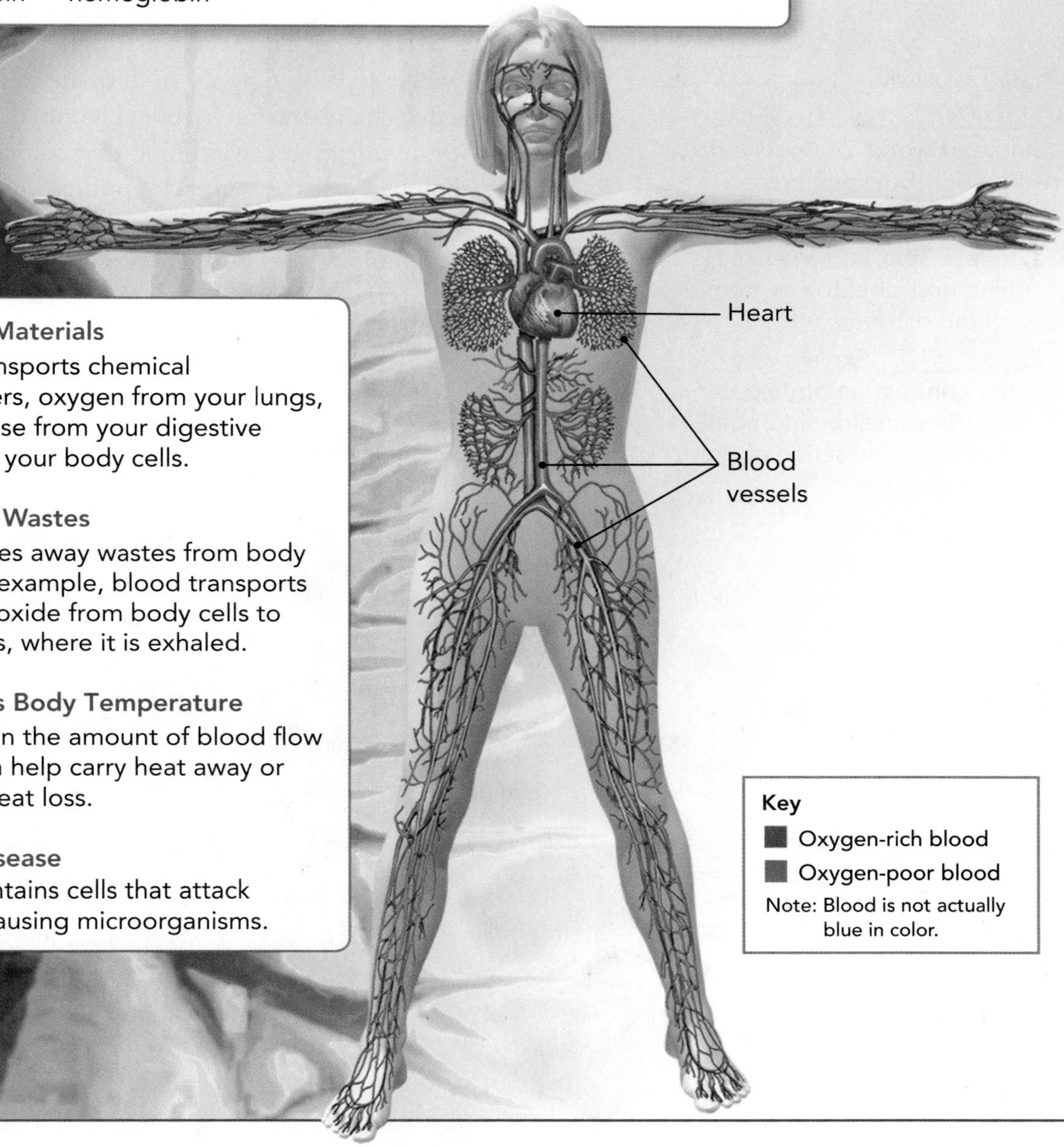

Delivers Materials
Blood transports chemical messengers, oxygen from your lungs, and glucose from your digestive system to your body cells.

Removes Wastes
Blood takes away wastes from body cells. For example, blood transports carbon dioxide from body cells to your lungs, where it is exhaled.

Regulates Body Temperature
Changes in the amount of blood flow in the skin help carry heat away or prevent heat loss.

Fights Disease
Blood contains cells that attack disease-causing microorganisms.

Heart

Blood vessels

Key
- Oxygen-rich blood
- Oxygen-poor blood

Note: Blood is not actually blue in color.

FIGURE 1 ·······································

The Circulatory System

Like roads that link all the parts of a town, your circulatory system links all the parts of your body.

✏ **Use the diagram to answer the questions.**

1. **Infer** What might happen if your circulatory system did not function properly?

_____

_____

2. **Pose Questions** After looking at the diagram, write a question that describes one thing you would like to learn about the circulatory system.

_____

_____

_____

_____

_____

The Heart
Without your heart, your blood would not go anywhere. As **Figure 2** shows, the **heart** is a hollow, muscular organ that pumps blood to the body through blood vessels.

The Heart's Structure The heart has a right side and left side that are completely separated by a wall of tissue called the septum. Each side has two chambers. Each upper chamber, called an **atrium** (AY tree um; plural *atria*), receives blood that comes into the heart. Each lower chamber, called a **ventricle,** pumps blood out of the heart. The pacemaker, a group of cells in the right atrium, sends out signals that regulate heart rate. These signals make the heart muscle contract.

FIGURE 2

▶ **INTERACTIVE ART** **The Heart**
Your heart works 24 hours a day, resting only between beats.

✎ **Complete the activities.**

1. **Relate Text and Visuals** Find and label the septum on the diagram.

2. CHALLENGE Explain why the contraction of the left ventricle must be stronger than the contraction of the right ventricle.

_____

_____

_____

_____

_____

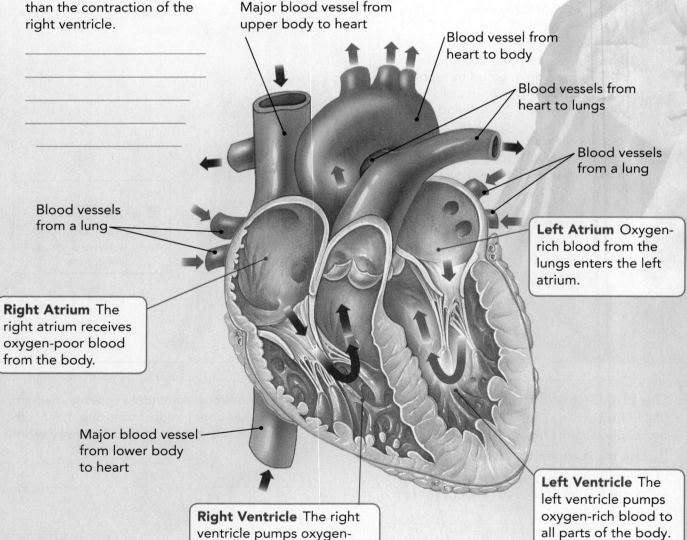

Major blood vessel from upper body to heart

Blood vessel from heart to body

Blood vessels from heart to lungs

Blood vessels from a lung

Left Atrium Oxygen-rich blood from the lungs enters the left atrium.

Blood vessels from a lung

Right Atrium The right atrium receives oxygen-poor blood from the body.

Major blood vessel from lower body to heart

Right Ventricle The right ventricle pumps oxygen-poor blood to the lungs.

Left Ventricle The left ventricle pumps oxygen-rich blood to all parts of the body.

How the Heart Works Valves separate the atria from the ventricles. A **valve** is a flap of tissue that prevents blood from flowing backward. Valves also separate the ventricles and the large blood vessels that carry blood away from the heart.

A heartbeat sounds something like *lub-dup*. First, the heart muscle relaxes and the atria fill with blood. Next, the atria contract, squeezing blood through valves, like those in **Figure 3,** and into the ventricles. Then the ventricles contract. This contraction closes the valves between the atria and ventricles, making the *lub* sound and squeezing blood into large blood vessels. Finally, the valves between the ventricles and blood vessels snap shut, making the *dup* sound. All this happens in less than one second.

The Path of Blood Flow
As you can see in **Figure 4,** the overall pattern of blood flow through the body is similar to a figure eight. The heart is at the center where the two loops cross. In the first loop, blood travels from the heart to the lungs and then back to the heart. In the second loop, blood travels from the heart throughout the body and then back to the heart.

Your body has three kinds of blood vessels: arteries, capillaries, and veins. **Arteries** carry blood away from the heart. For example, blood in the left ventricle is pumped into the **aorta** (ay AWR tuh), the largest artery in the body. From the arteries, blood flows into tiny vessels called **capillaries.** In the capillaries, substances are exchanged between the blood and body cells. From capillaries, blood flows into **veins,** which carry blood back to the heart.

FIGURE 4 ·····························
Blood Flow
Your heart can pump five liters of blood through the two loops each minute.

✎ **Interpret Diagrams** In each box, write where the blood from the heart travels. Then tell where blood travels after it leaves each part listed below.

Right atrium

_____

Veins from the body

_____

Arteries to the lungs

_____

FIGURE 3 ·····························
Heart Valves
Valves control the direction of blood flow through the heart.

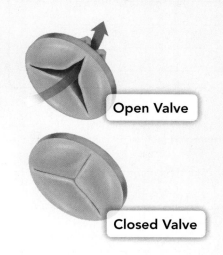

Open Valve

Closed Valve

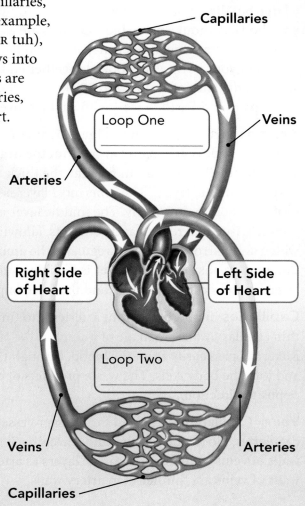

Capillaries

Veins

Loop One

Arteries

Right Side of Heart

Left Side of Heart

Loop Two

Veins

Arteries

Capillaries

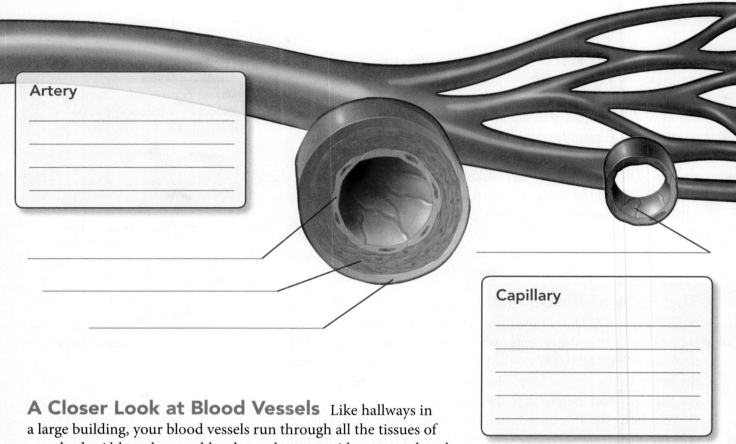

Artery

_____

_____

_____

_____

Capillary

_____

_____

_____

_____

_____

A Closer Look at Blood Vessels

Like hallways in a large building, your blood vessels run through all the tissues of your body. Although some blood vessels are as wide as your thumb, most of them are much finer than a human hair. If all the blood vessels in your body were hooked together end to end, they would stretch a distance of almost 100,000 kilometers. That's long enough to wrap around Earth twice—with a lot left over!

Arteries Arteries, shown in **Figure 5,** are thick-walled, muscular vessels. Arteries carry blood away from the heart. As they do, they split into smaller arteries. In general, the thick, elastic artery walls have three tissue layers. The innermost layer is epithelial tissue that enables blood to flow freely. The middle layer is mostly smooth muscle tissue that relaxes and contracts, allowing the artery to widen and narrow. This layer regulates the amount of blood sent to different organs. The outer layer is flexible connective tissue. These layers enable arteries to withstand the force of pumping blood.

Capillaries Blood flows from arteries into tiny capillaries. The thin capillary walls are made of a single layer of epithelial cells. Materials pass easily from the blood, through the capillary walls, and into the body cells. The waste products of cells pass in the opposite direction.

Veins Capillaries merge and form larger vessels called veins. From capillaries, blood enters veins and travels back to the heart. The walls of veins have the same tissue layers as arteries. However, the walls of veins are thinner than artery walls.

FIGURE 5 ·····································
Blood Vessels
✎ **Read the text before completing the tasks.**

1. **Identify** Underline in the text what happens to blood in each kind of vessel.

2. **Interpret Diagrams** In the diagram above, label the parts of each vessel. Then write in each box how the vessel's structure enables it to function.

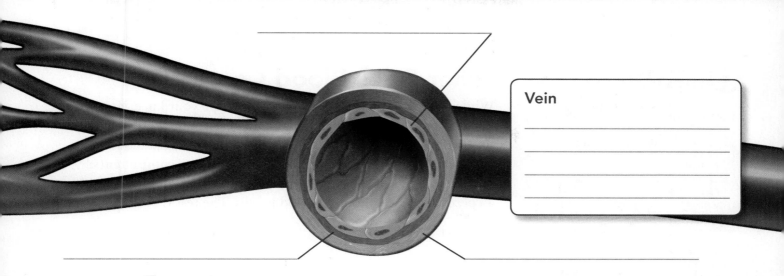

Vein

_____

_____

_____

_____

apply it!

Your pulse results from the alternating relaxation and contraction of arteries as blood is forced through them. Touch the inside of your wrist and find your pulse.

1 Observe How does your pulse feel through your fingertips?

_____

_____

_____

2 Observe How many heartbeats do you count in one minute?

_____

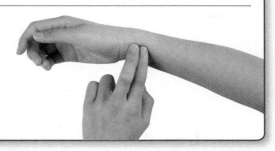

🔑 Assess Your Understanding

1a. Identify Blood returning from the lungs enters the heart at the (right atrium/left atrium/right ventricle/left ventricle).

SC.6.L.14.5

b. Identify In which direction do arteries carry blood?

_____

_____

_____

SC.6.L.14.5

c. Draw Conclusions Why is it important for your blood to complete both loops of circulation?

_____

_____

_____

_____

_____

_____

SC.6.L.14.5

got it? ....

○ **I get it!** Now I know that the circulatory system transports_____

_____

○ **I need extra help with** _____

_Go to_ **MY SCIENCE** 🅢 **COACH** _online for help with this subject._

SC.6.L.14.5

FIGURE 6 ·····························

> **VIRTUAL LAB** **Cells in Blood**

In addition to red blood cells and white blood cells, blood contains platelets and plasma.

✎ **Use the illustration about blood to complete the tasks.**

1. Identify What is the main function of hemoglobin in the blood?

_____

_____

_____

_____

2. Apply Concepts What do you think would happen to the number of white blood cells in the body when a person is fighting an infection? Explain your answer.

_____

_____

_____

_____

_____

_____

_____

What Does Blood Contain?

While riding your bike, you fall off and scrape your knee. Your knee stings, and blood oozes from the open wound. You go inside to clean the scrape. As you do, you wonder about what blood is.

Blood is a complex tissue. 🔑 **Blood has four components: plasma, red blood cells, white blood cells, and platelets.** About 45 percent of the volume of blood is cells. The rest is plasma.

Red Blood Cells

Red blood cells take up oxygen in the lungs and deliver it to cells throughout the body. Red blood cells, like most blood cells, are produced in bone marrow. Mature red blood cells have no nuclei. Without a nucleus, a red blood cell cannot reproduce or repair itself. Mature red blood cells live only about 120 days.

Hemoglobin

A red blood cell is made mostly of **hemoglobin** (HEE muh gloh bin), a protein that contains iron and binds chemically to oxygen molecules in the lungs. Hemoglobin releases oxygen as blood travels through the capillaries. Oxygen makes red blood cells bright red. Without it, the cells are dark red. Hemoglobin also picks up some carbon dioxide produced by cells and releases it into the lungs.

Plasma

Most materials transported in blood travel in the plasma. Plasma carries nutrients, such as glucose, fats, vitamins, and minerals. Plasma also carries chemical messengers that direct body activities, such as how your cells use glucose. In addition, plasma carries away most of the carbon dioxide and many other wastes that cell processes produce. Proteins in the plasma make it look pale yellow. Some of these proteins regulate water in the blood. Some help fight disease. Others help to form blood clots.

Summarize List and describe the materials that plasma carries.

LA.6.2.2.3

White Blood Cells

Like red blood cells, white blood cells are produced in bone marrow. White blood cells are the body's disease fighters. Some white blood cells recognize disease-causing organisms, such as bacteria, and alert the body to the invasion. Other white blood cells produce chemicals to fight the invaders. Still others surround and kill the organisms. White blood cells are larger than red blood cells and contain nuclei. They may live for days, months, or even years.

Platelets

Platelets (PLAYT lits) are cell fragments that help form blood clots. When a blood vessel is cut, platelets collect and stick to the vessel at the wound. The platelets release chemicals that produce a protein called fibrin (FY brin). Fibrin weaves a net of tiny fibers across the cut. Platelets and blood cells become trapped in the net, and a blood clot forms.

did you know? ....

Transfusions for patients in hospitals and other medical facilities create a constant need for blood. In Florida, blood centers across the state collect a total of more than 1,000,000 units of blood each year. (One unit is equal to 450 mL.)

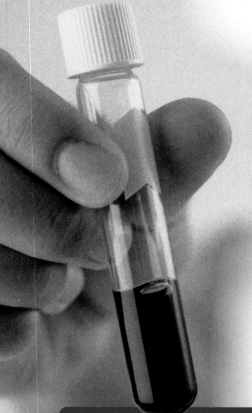

Marker Molecules and Transfusions A blood transfusion is the transfer of blood from one person to another. Most early attempts at blood transfusion failed, but no one knew why. In the early 1900s, a physician named Karl Landsteiner tried mixing blood samples from two people. Sometimes the two blood samples blended smoothly. At other times, the red blood cells clumped together. In a patient, this clumping would clog the capillaries, causing death.

Blood Types Landsteiner identified the four major types of blood: A, B, AB, and O. Blood types are determined by marker molecules on red blood cells. If your blood type is A, you have the A marker. If your blood type is B, you have the B marker. People with type AB blood have both A and B markers. People with type O blood do not have A or B markers.

Clumping proteins in your plasma recognize red blood cells with "foreign" markers that are not your type. The proteins make cells with foreign markers clump together. For example, blood type A contains anti-B clumping proteins that act against cells with B markers. Blood type O has clumping proteins for both A and B markers. In **Figure 7,** you can see all the blood type marker molecules and clumping proteins.

FIGURE 7 ··

Blood Types and Their Markers
Depending on your blood type, you may have certain marker molecules on your red blood cells and certain clumping proteins in your plasma.

✎ **Create Data Tables In the table, label the marker molecules and then identify the clumping proteins.**

Blood Types, Marker Molecules, and Clumping Proteins				
Blood Type Characteristic	**Blood Type A**	**Blood Type B**	**Blood Type AB**	**Blood Type O**
Marker Molecules on Red Blood Cells	A A A A A A			
Clumping Proteins	anti-B			

The marker molecules on your red blood cells determine the type of blood you can safely receive in transfusions. For example, a person with type A blood can receive transfusions of type A or type O blood. But type B blood would cause clumping and would not be safe. Through a process called cross-matching, a patient's blood type is checked so that safe donor types can be determined.

Blood Type	Safe Donor(s)	Unsafe Donor(s)
A	A, O	_____
B	_____	_____
AB	_____	_____
O	_____	_____

1 **Infer** Use what you know about blood types to complete the table.

2 **Predict** Which blood type may accept safe transfusions from any other blood type? Why?

_____

_____

_____

3 [CHALLENGE] Which blood type is a "universal donor," that is, a blood type that can be used in transfusions to anyone? Explain your reasoning.

_____

_____

_____

Rh Factor Landsteiner also discovered a protein on red blood cells that he called *Rh factor.* About 85 percent of the people he tested had this protein. The rest did not. As with blood type, a marker molecule on the red blood cells determines the presence of Rh factor. An Rh-positive blood type has the Rh marker. An Rh-negative blood type does not. Clumping proteins will develop in people with Rh-negative blood if they receive Rh-positive blood. This situation may be potentially dangerous.

Lab zone® Do the Quick Lab
Do You Know Your A-B-Os?

🔑 Assess Your Understanding

2a. Identify What is plasma?

_____

SC.6.L.14.5

b. Review What did Karl Landsteiner's observations lead him to discover?

_____

_____

SC.6.N.1.5, SC.6.L.14.5

c. Relate Cause and Effect How might a lack of iron in a person's diet affect his or her blood?

_____

_____

_____

SC.6.L.14.5

got it? ....

○ **I get it!** Now I know that blood contains _____

_____

○ **I need extra help with** _____

Go to MY SCIENCE ⓢ COACH *online for help with this subject.*
SC.6.L.14.5

3 The Respiratory System

UNLOCK THE ESSENTIAL ?

🔑 **What Is the Role of the Respiratory System?**
SC.6.L14.5

🔑 **What Happens When You Breathe?**
SC.6.L.14.5, LA.6.2.2.3

my planeT DiaRY

MISCONCEPTION

The Breath of Life

Misconception: The only gas you exhale is carbon dioxide.

Actually, about 16 percent of the air you exhale is oxygen. The air you inhale is made up of about 21 percent oxygen. Your body only uses a small portion of the oxygen in each breath, so the unused portion is exhaled.

Sometimes, this exhaled oxygen can mean the difference between life and death. If a person stops breathing, he or she needs to get more oxygen quickly. A rescuer can breathe into the person's mouth to give unused oxygen to the person. This process is called rescue breathing.

Read the following question. Then write your answer below.

Why would you want to learn to perform rescue breathing?

_____

_____

_____

_____

_____

_____

> PLANET DIARY Go to **Planet Diary** to learn more about the respiratory system.

Lab® zone Do the Inquiry Warm-Up *How Big Can You Blow Up a Balloon?*

FLORIDA NGSSS

SC.6.L.14.5 Identify and investigate the functions of the major systems of the human body and describe ways these systems interact with each other to maintain homeostasis.

What Is the Role of the Respiratory System?

In an average day, you may breathe 20,000 times. You breathe all the time because your body cells need oxygen, which comes from the air. 🔑 **Your respiratory system moves air containing oxygen into your lungs and removes carbon dioxide and water from your body. Your lungs and the structures that lead to them make up your respiratory system.**

Vocabulary

- pharynx • trachea • cilia • bronchi
- lungs • alveoli • diaphragm • larynx • vocal cords

Skills

↻ Reading: Chart

△ Inquiry: Communicate

Breathing and Homeostasis Your body needs oxygen for cellular respiration. During cellular respiration, cells break down glucose, releasing energy. You use energy for activities such as reading this book or playing ball. Your body also uses energy in carrying out processes that maintain homeostasis, such as removing wastes, growing, and regulating body temperature.

Breathing gets oxygen into your body. But cellular respiration depends on body systems working together. The digestive system supplies glucose from food. And the circulatory system carries this glucose and the oxygen from the respiratory system to all the cells in the body.

FIGURE 1 ·····
Systems Working Together
Body systems work together, getting the materials needed for cellular respiration to cells.

✎ **Describe System Interactions** Describe how each system provides cells with materials needed for cellular respiration. Then tell how cellular respiration helps the body maintain homeostasis.

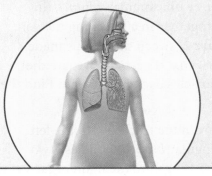

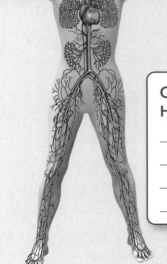

Circulatory System
_____
_____
_____
_____

Respiratory System
_____
_____
_____
_____

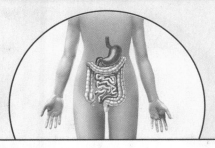

Digestive System
_____
_____
_____
_____

Cellular Respiration and Homeostasis
_____
_____
_____
_____

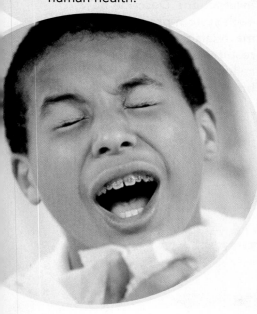

Breathing Structures When you breathe in, air and particles such as pollen and dust move through a series of structures and then into the lungs. You can see these structures—the nose, pharynx, trachea, and bronchi—on the right. These structures also warm and moisten the air you breathe.

Nose Air enters the body through the nose or the mouth. Hairs in the nose trap large particles. The air passes into spaces called nasal cavities. Some cells lining the nasal cavities produce mucus, a sticky material that moistens the air and traps more particles.

Pharynx and Trachea From the nose, air enters the **pharynx** (FAR ingks), or throat. Both the nose and the mouth connect to the pharynx. So air and food enter the pharynx. From the pharynx, air moves into the **trachea** (TRAY kee uh), or windpipe. When you swallow, a thin flap of tissue called the epiglottis covers the opening of the trachea to keep food out. Cells that line the trachea have **cilia** (SIL ee uh; singular *cilium*), tiny hairlike extensions that can move together in a sweeping motion. The cilia, like those shown in **Figure 2,** sweep the mucus made by cells in the trachea up to the pharynx. If particles irritate the trachea, you cough, sending the particles back into the air. Find the pharynx and trachea in **Figure 3.**

Bronchi and Lungs Air moves from the trachea into the left and right **bronchi** (BRAHNG ky; singular *bronchus*). These two passages take air into the lungs. The **lungs** are the main organs of the respiratory system. Inside the lungs, the bronchi branch into smaller and smaller tubes. At the end of the smallest tubes are **alveoli** (al VEE uh ly; singular *alveolus*), tiny, thin-walled sacs of lung tissue where gases can move between air and blood.

FIGURE 2 ·····································

Cilia

The photo shows a microscopic view of cilia.

✏ **Answer the questions below.**

1. **Relate Cause and Effect** How does coughing protect the respiratory system?

   _____

   _____

2. [CHALLENGE] What might happen if you did not have hairs in your nose and cilia in your trachea?

   _____

   _____

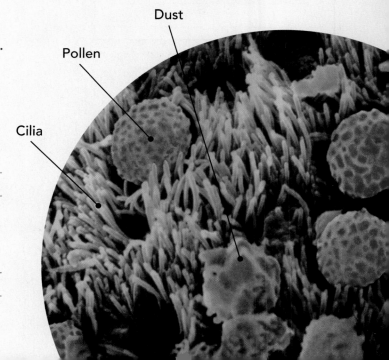

Dust

Pollen

Cilia

FIGURE 3 ······························

Structures of the Respiratory System

Particles in air are filtered out as the air moves through your respiratory system.

△ **Communicate** In your own words, write what each part of the respiratory system does.

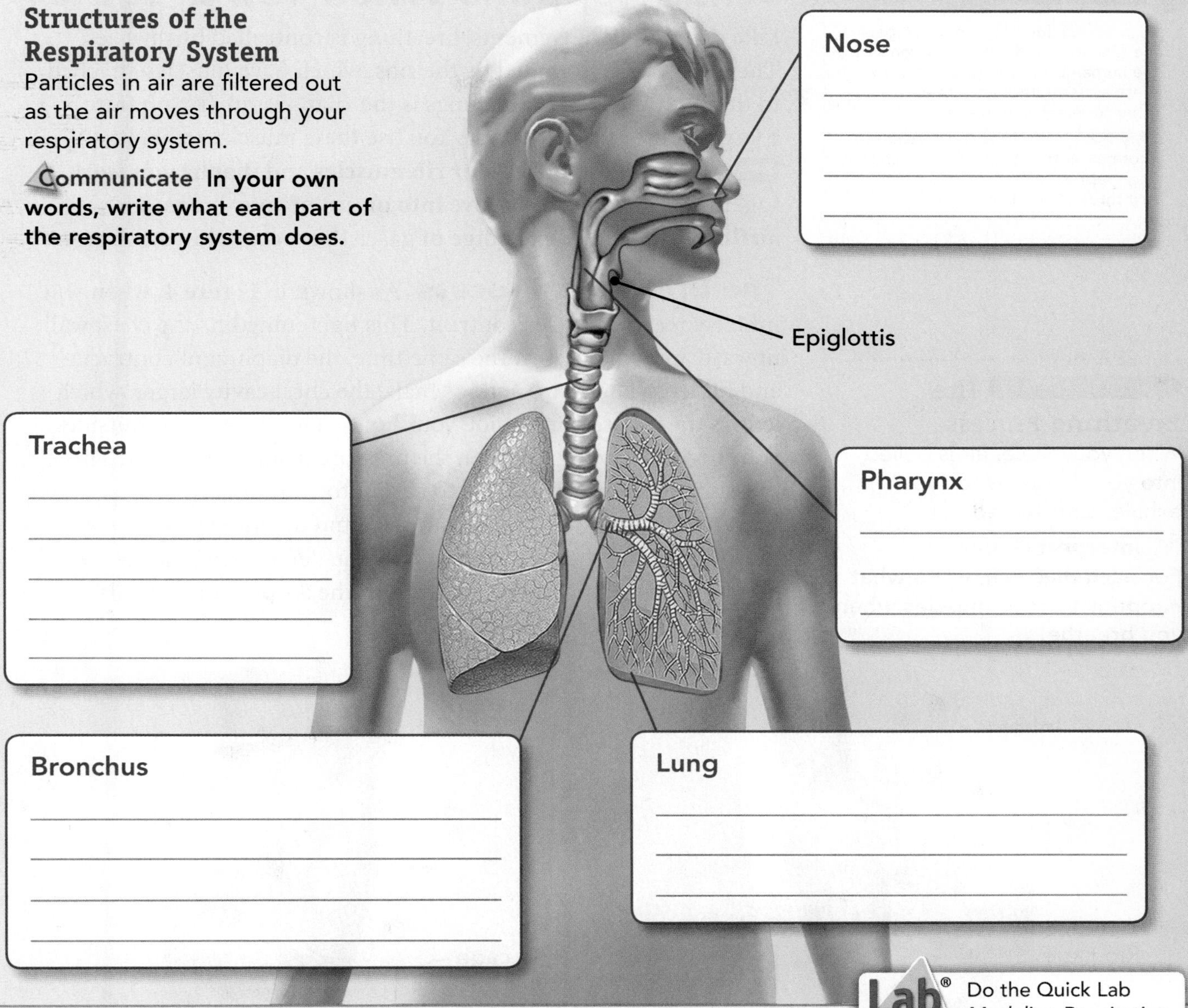

Nose
_____
_____
_____
_____

Epiglottis

Trachea
_____
_____
_____
_____

Pharynx
_____
_____
_____

Bronchus
_____
_____
_____
_____

Lung
_____
_____
_____
_____

Lab zone® Do the Quick Lab *Modeling Respiration.*

🔑 Assess Your Understanding

1a. Review What happens in the lungs?

_____
_____
_____

SC.6.L.14.5

b. Compare and Contrast How are breathing and cellular respiration different?

_____
_____
_____

SC.6.L.14.5

got it?

○ I get it! Now I know that the respiratory

system _____
_____
_____
_____
_____

○ I need extra help with _____

Go to **my science** 🔵 **coach** *online for help with this subject.*

SC.6.L.14.5

SC.6.L.14.5 Identify and investigate the functions of the major systems of the human body and describe ways these systems interact with each other to maintain homeostasis.

LA.6.2.2.3 The student will organize information to show understanding (e.g., representing main ideas within text through charting).

FIGURE 4 ·······················

> INTERACTIVE ART The **Breathing Process**
When you inhale, air is pulled into your lungs. When you exhale, air is forced out.

✏ **Interpret Diagrams**
For each diagram, write what happens to your muscles when you breathe.

What Happens When You Breathe?

Like other body movements, breathing is controlled by muscles. The lungs are surrounded by the ribs, which have muscles attached to them. At the base of the lungs is the **diaphragm** (DY uh fram), a large, dome-shaped muscle. You use these muscles to breathe. 🔑 **When you breathe, your rib muscles and diaphragm work together, causing air to move into or out of your lungs. This airflow leads to the exchange of gases that occurs in your lungs.**

The Breathing Process As shown in **Figure 4,** when you inhale your rib muscles contract. This tightening lifts the chest wall upward and outward. At the same time, the diaphragm contracts and flattens. These two actions make the chest cavity larger, which lowers the air pressure inside your lungs. The air pressure outside your body is now higher than the pressure inside your chest. This pressure difference causes air to rush into your lungs.

When you exhale, your rib muscles and diaphragm relax. As they relax, your chest cavity becomes smaller, making the air pressure inside your chest greater than the air pressure outside. As a result, air rushes out of your lungs.

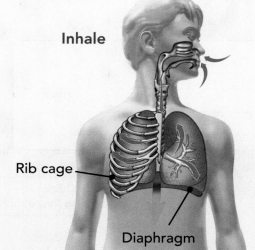

Inhale

Rib cage

Diaphragm

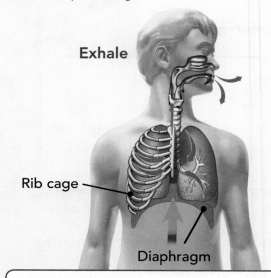

Exhale

Rib cage

Diaphragm

Rib Muscles

_____

_____

_____

Diaphragm

_____

_____

_____

Rib Muscles

_____

_____

_____

Diaphragm

_____

_____

_____

Breathing and Speaking Did you know that the air that moves out of your lungs when you breathe also helps you to speak? Your **larynx** (LAR ingks), or voice box, is located at the top of your trachea. Two **vocal cords,** which are folds of connective tissue, stretch across the opening of the larynx. When you speak, muscles make the vocal cords contract, narrowing the opening as air rushes through. Then the movement of the vocal cords makes air molecules vibrate, or move rapidly back and forth. This vibration causes a sound—your voice.

Chart In the text, underline and number the steps that help you speak. Then write these steps in the graphic organizer.

LA.6.2.2.3

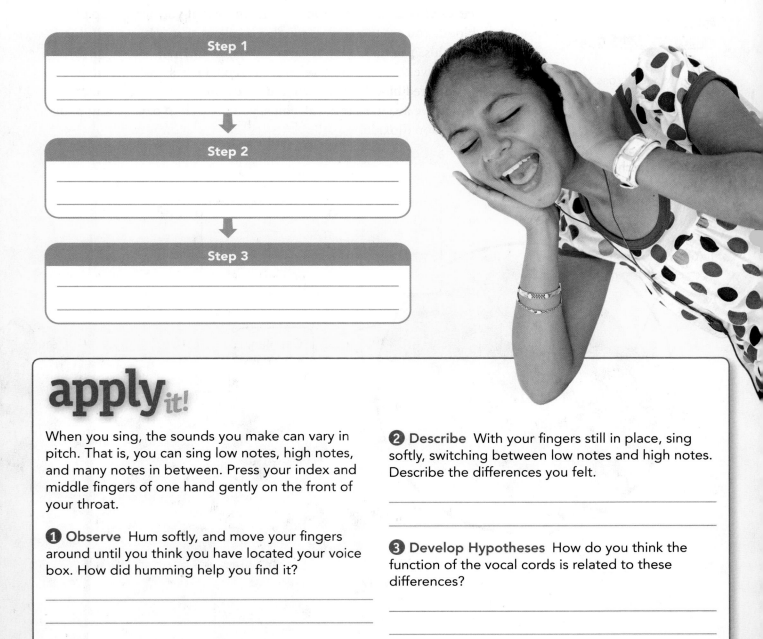

Step 1

Step 2

Step 3

apply it!

When you sing, the sounds you make can vary in pitch. That is, you can sing low notes, high notes, and many notes in between. Press your index and middle fingers of one hand gently on the front of your throat.

❶ **Observe** Hum softly, and move your fingers around until you think you have located your voice box. How did humming help you find it?

❷ **Describe** With your fingers still in place, sing softly, switching between low notes and high notes. Describe the differences you felt.

❸ **Develop Hypotheses** How do you think the function of the vocal cords is related to these differences?

213

Gas Exchange Air's final stop in its journey through the respiratory system is an alveolus in the lungs. An alveolus has thin walls and is surrounded by many thin-walled capillaries. **Figure 5** shows some alveoli.

Because the alveoli and the capillaries have very thin walls, certain materials can pass through them easily. After air enters an alveolus, oxygen passes through the wall of the alveolus and then through the capillary wall into the blood. Similarly, carbon dioxide and water pass from the blood into the air within the alveolus. This whole process is called gas exchange.

How Gas Exchange Occurs Imagine that you are a drop of blood. You are traveling through a capillary that wraps around an alveolus. You have a lot of carbon dioxide and a little oxygen. As you move through the capillary, oxygen attaches to the hemoglobin in your red blood cells. Carbon dioxide moves into the alveolus. As you move away from the alveolus, you are rich in oxygen and poor in carbon dioxide.

FIGURE 5 ·····························
▶ **ART IN MOTION** **Gas Exchange**
Gases move across the thin walls of both alveoli and capillaries.

✎ **Relate Text and Visuals** Label each arrow with the gas being exchanged and describe where it is coming from and moving to.

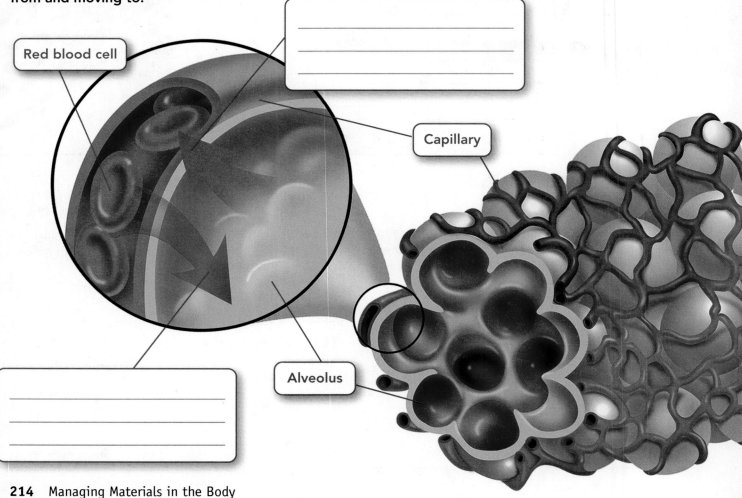

Red blood cell

Capillary

Alveolus

Surface Area for Gas Exchange Your lungs can absorb a large amount of oxygen because of the surface area of the alveoli. An adult's lungs have about 300 million alveoli. Together these alveoli have a surface area of about 100 meters squared (m^2)—the area of the floor in an average classroom! As a result, the alveoli provide a huge amount of surface area for exchanging gases. Therefore, healthy lungs can supply all the oxygen that a person needs—even when the person is very active.

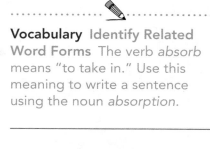

Vocabulary Identify Related Word Forms The verb *absorb* means "to take in." Use this meaning to write a sentence using the noun *absorption*.

_____

_____

_____

_____

Vessel with blood rich in oxygen from lungs

Branch of bronchus

Vessel with blood rich in carbon dioxide from body

Lab zone Do the Lab Investigation *A Breath of Fresh Air.*

Assess Your Understanding

2a. Identify Where is the larynx located?

_____

_____

SC.6.L.14.5

b. Explain When you inhale, why does air rush into your lungs?

_____

_____

_____

SC.6.L.14.5

c. Draw Conclusions How do the alveoli enable people to be very active?

_____

_____

_____

_____

SC.6.L.14.5

got it?

O **I get it!** Now I know that when I breathe, air _____

_____

O I need extra help with _____

Go to my science **COACH** *online for help with this subject.* SC.6.L.14.5

UNLOCK THE ESSENTIAL ?

🔑 **What Is the Role of the Excretory System?**
SC.6.L.14.5, MA.6.A.3.6

🔑 **How Does Excretion Help Your Body Maintain Homeostasis?**
SC.6.L.14.5, LA.6.2.2.3

my planet Diary

Useful Urine

You can recycle plastic, glass, and paper. Did you know that urine can be recycled, too? Some astronauts in space will see their urine turned into drinking water! NASA has developed a machine that will purify the astronauts' urine. The water that is recovered can be used for drinking, among other things.

Why do astronauts need this kind of machine? Large quantities of water are too heavy to carry into space. So the machine runs urine through a filtering system to remove waste. Then iodine is added to the filtered urine to kill any harmful bacteria. What remains is drinkable water.

FUN FACTS

Answer the questions below.

1. How else might the astronauts use the filtered urine?

_____

_____

_____

2. Do you think this system would be useful on Earth? Why or why not?

_____

_____

_____

_____

_____

> PLANET DIARY Go to **Planet Diary** to learn more about excretion.

Space shower

Lab zone Do the Inquiry Warm-Up *How Does Filtering a Liquid Change the Liquid?*

Vocabulary
- excretion • urea • urine • kidney • ureter
- urinary bladder • urethra • nephron

Skills
- Reading: Identify the Main Idea
- Inquiry: Infer

What Is the Role of the Excretory System?

The human body faces a challenge similar to keeping your room clean. Just as you must clean up papers that pile up in your room, your body must remove wastes from cellular respiration and other processes. The process of removing waste is called **excretion.**

If wastes were not removed from your body, they would pile up and make you sick. **The excretory system collects the wastes that cells produce and removes them from the body.** The system includes the kidneys, ureters, urinary bladder, urethra, lungs, skin, and liver. Two wastes that your body must eliminate every day are excess water and urea. **Urea** (yoo REE uh) is a chemical that comes from the breakdown of proteins. As you know, the lungs eliminate some water. Most remaining water is eliminated in a fluid called **urine,** which includes urea and other wastes.

FLORIDA NGSSS

SC.6.L.14.5 Identify and investigate the functions of the major systems of the human body.
MA.6.A.3.6 Construct and analyze tables, graphs, and equations to describe simple relations.

do the math! Analyzing Data

Urine is made up of water, organic solids, and inorganic solids. The organic solids include urea and acids. The inorganic solids include salts and minerals. The solids are dissolved in the water.

1 Calculate Calculate and label on the *Normal Urine Content* graph the percentage of urine that is solids. Calculate and label on the *Solids in Normal Urine* graph the percentage of solids that is urea.

2 CHALLENGE What might a sharp decrease in the percentage of water in a person's urine indicate about the health of that person?

_____

_____

_____

_____

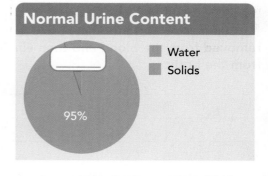

Normal Urine Content

- Water
- Solids

95%

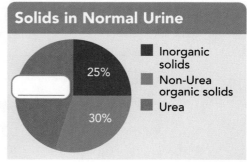

Solids in Normal Urine

- Inorganic solids
- Non-Urea organic solids
- Urea

25%

30%

MA.6.A.3.6

217

Structures That Remove Urine

Figure 1 shows the organs that remove urine from the body. Your two kidneys are the major organs of the excretory system. The **kidneys** act like filters. They remove urea and other wastes from the blood but keep materials that the body needs. These wastes are eliminated in the urine. Urine flows from the kidneys through two narrow tubes called **ureters** (yoo REE turz). The ureters carry urine to the **urinary bladder,** a muscular sac that stores urine. Urine leaves the body through a small tube called the **urethra** (yoo REE thruh).

Waste Filtration

Each kidney has about one million nephrons. A **nephron** is a tiny filtering factory that removes wastes from blood and produces urine. The nephrons filter wastes in two stages. First, both wastes and needed materials are filtered out of the blood. Next, much of the needed material is returned to the blood, and the wastes are eliminated from the body. Follow this process in **Figure 2.**

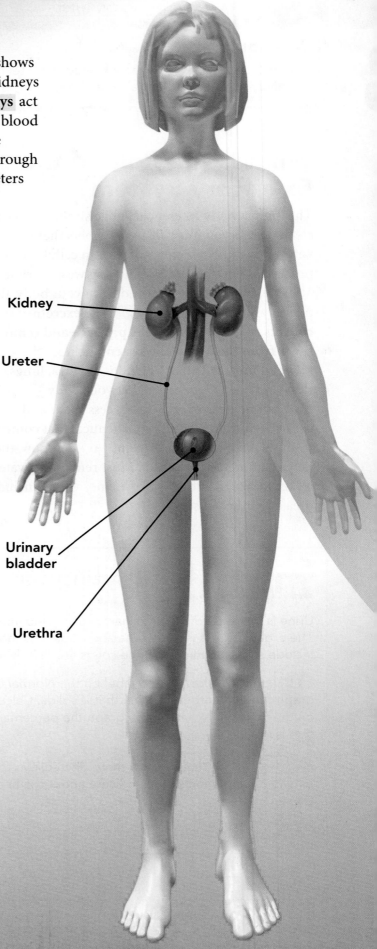

Kidney

Ureter

Urinary bladder

Urethra

FIGURE 1 ·······································
Removing Urine
Urine is produced in the kidneys and then removed from the body.

✎ **Summarize** Describe how urine is removed from the blood and then eliminated from the body.

_____

_____

_____

_____

_____

_____

_____

FIGURE 2 ···

How the Kidneys Work

Most of the work of the kidneys is done in the nephrons.

✏️ **Infer** In the key, write what each color represents in the diagram. Then explain below why it is important for capillaries to surround the nephron tube.

_____

_____

_____

_____

Key

◼ _____

_____

_____

◼ _____

_____

_____

◼ _____

Stage 1
- Blood flows into the cluster of capillaries in the thin-walled, hollow nephron capsule.
- Urea, glucose, and some water are filtered out of the blood and into the capsule.
- These materials then pass into the nephron tube.

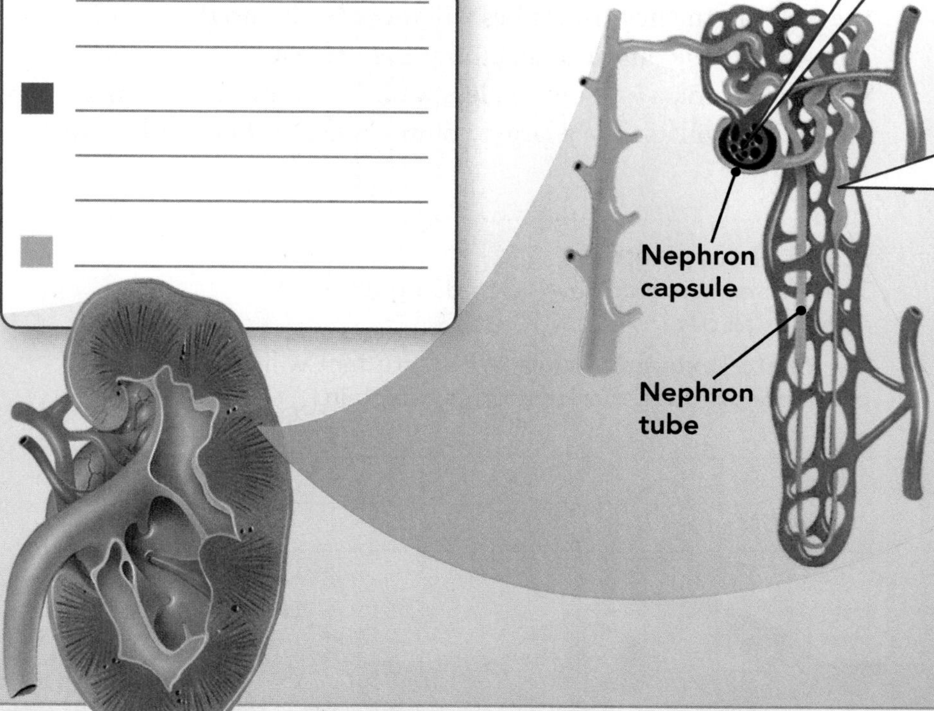

Stage 2
- As the material flows through the nephron tube, most of the needed glucose and water move back into the blood through the capillaries.
- Most of the urea and some of the water stay in the nephron tube and become urine.

Nephron capsule

Nephron tube

🗝️ **Assess Your Understanding**

1a. Name The chemical _____ comes from the breakdown of proteins.

SC.6.L.14.5

b. Draw Conclusions Why is it important for a kidney to have many nephrons?

_____

_____

_____

SC.6.L.14.5

Lab zone® Do the Quick Lab *Kidney Function.*

got it?

○ **I get it!** Now I know that the function of the excretory system is to _____

_____

○ **I need extra help with** _____

Go to **MY SCIENCE ⑤ COACH** online for help with this subject. SC.6.L.14.5

FLORIDA NGSSS

SC.6.L.14.5 Identify and investigate the functions of the major systems of the human body and describe ways these systems interact with each other to maintain homeostasis.

LA.6.2.2.3 The student will organize information to show understanding (e.g., representing main ideas within text through paraphrasing).

Vocabulary Identify Related Word Forms You know the noun *excretion* means "the process of removing wastes." Use this meaning to choose the correct meaning of the verb *excrete*.

○ relating to removing wastes

○ to remove wastes

○ the state of removing wastes

How Does Excretion Help Your Body Maintain Homeostasis?

A buildup of wastes such as urea, excess water, and carbon dioxide can upset your body's balance. 🔑 **Excretion helps to maintain homeostasis by keeping the body's internal environment stable and free of harmful levels of chemicals.** The organs of excretion include the kidneys, lungs, skin, and liver.

Kidneys As the kidneys filter blood, they regulate the amount of water in your body, helping to maintain homeostasis, or internal stability. Remember that as urine is being formed, needed water passes from the nephron tubes into the blood. The amount of water that returns to the blood depends on conditions both outside and inside the body. For example, on a hot day when you have been sweating a lot and have not had much to drink, almost all the water in the nephron tubes will move back into the blood. You will excrete only a small amount of urine. On a cool day when you have drunk a lot of water, less water will move back into the blood. You will excrete a larger volume of urine. Look at **Figure 3.**

FIGURE 3 ···

Fluid Absorption
These three students have been doing different activities all day.

✎ **Relate Text and Visuals** Which student will probably produce the least urine? Explain.

_____

_____

_____

Maria has been in classes all morning. She has had nothing to eat or drink.

Kari has been running sprints. She forgot to bring her water bottle.

Mike has been sitting on the bench and drinking water.

Lungs, Skin, and Liver Organs that function as part of other systems in your body also help keep you healthy by excreting wastes. For example, the lungs of the respiratory system remove carbon dioxide and some water when you exhale. The skin, part of your integumentary system, contains sweat glands that produce perspiration. Perspiration consists mostly of water, salt, and a small amount of urea.

The liver, which functions as part of the digestive system, also makes urea from the breakdown of proteins in the body. In addition, the liver breaks down other wastes into forms that can be excreted. For example, the liver breaks down old red blood cells. It even recycles some of their parts. In this way, you can think of the liver as a recycling factory.

Identify the Main Idea In your own words, write about each organ's role in excretion. LA.6.2.2.3

Lungs
_____
_____
_____

Skin
_____
_____
_____

Liver
_____
_____
_____
_____

Kidneys
_____
_____
_____
_____

221

EXPLORE THE ESSENTIAL ?

Moving Things Along

How do systems of the body move and manage materials?

FIGURE 4

The systems of the body work together, helping to maintain homeostasis by changing materials and moving them to where they can be used or excreted.

Complete the following tasks.

1. **Identify** For each system, identify its main function and tell what materials are managed or moved.
2. **Describe System Interactions** Which system is the link for moving materials among the other three systems?

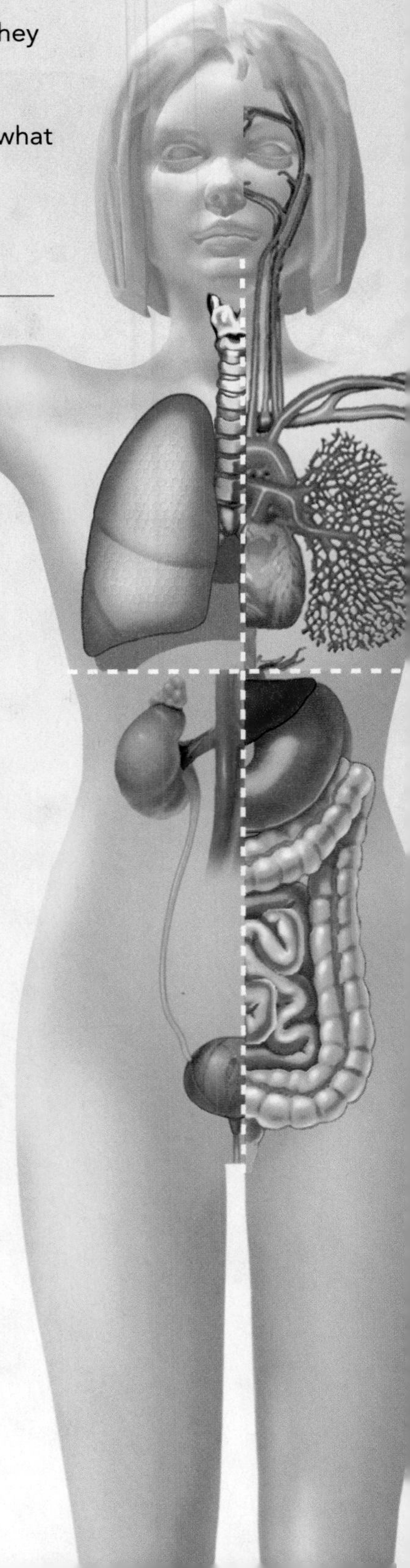

Respiratory System

Excretory System

Circulatory System

_____
_____
_____
_____
_____
_____
_____
_____
_____
_____
_____

Digestive System

_____
_____
_____
_____
_____
_____
_____
_____
_____
_____
_____

 Do the Quick Lab
Perspiration.

⚷ Assess Your Understanding

2a. Review How does removing wastes from the body help maintain homeostasis?

_____
_____

SC.6.L.14.5

b. Predict On a long bus trip, a traveler does not drink water for several hours. How will the volume of urine she produces that day compare to the volume on a day when she drinks several glasses of water? Explain.

_____
_____
_____
_____

SC.6.L.14.5

c. ANSWER THE ESSENTIAL **?** How do systems of the body move and manage materials?

_____
_____
_____
_____
_____
_____
_____
_____
_____
_____
_____

SC.6.L.14.5

got it? ....

O **I get it!** Now I know that excretion helps maintain homeostasis in my body by

_____
_____

O **I need extra help with** _____

_Go to_ **MY SCIENCE ⁵ COACH** _online for help with this subject._ SC.6.L.14.5

REVIEW THE ESSENTIAL ?

Materials in the body are managed and moved by the _____, _____, _____, and _____ systems.

LESSON 1 Digestion

SC.6.L.14.5

🔑 Food provides your body with materials for growth and repair. It also provides energy.

🔑 The digestive system breaks down food, absorbs nutrients, and eliminates waste.

🔑 Substances produced by the liver, pancreas, and lining of the small intestine help to complete chemical digestion.

Vocabulary
• calorie • enzyme • esophagus
• peristalsis • villi

LESSON 2 Circulation

SC.6.N.1.5, SC.6.L.14.5

🔑 The circulatory system delivers substances to cells, carries wastes away, and regulates body temperature. Blood cells fight disease.

🔑 Blood has four components: plasma, red blood cells, white blood cells, and platelets.

Vocabulary
• circulatory system • heart • atrium • ventricle
• valve • artery • aorta • capillary • vein
• hemoglobin

LESSON 3 The Respiratory System

SC.6.L.14.5

🔑 Your respiratory system moves air containing oxygen into your lungs and removes carbon dioxide and water from your body. Your lungs and the structures that lead to them make up your respiratory system.

🔑 When you breathe, your rib muscles and diaphragm work together, causing air to move into or out of your lungs. This airflow leads to the exchange of gases that occurs in your lungs.

Vocabulary
• pharynx • trachea • cilia • bronchi • lungs • alveoli
• diaphragm • larynx • vocal cords

LESSON 4 The Excretory System

SC.6.L.14.5

🔑 The excretory system collects the wastes that cells produce and removes them from the body.

🔑 Excretion helps maintain homeostasis by keeping the body's internal environment stable and free of harmful levels of chemicals.

Vocabulary
• excretion • urea • urine • kidney • ureter
• urinary bladder • urethra • nephron

Review and Assessment

LESSON 1   Digestion

1. Mechanical digestion begins in the

  a. liver.   **b.** esophagus.

  c. mouth.   **d.** small intestine.

                               SC.6.L.14.5

2. _____ is the involuntary contraction of muscles that pushes food forward.

                               SC.6.L.14.5

3. Interpret Diagrams How do you think acid reflux, the condition illustrated in the diagram below, affects the esophagus?

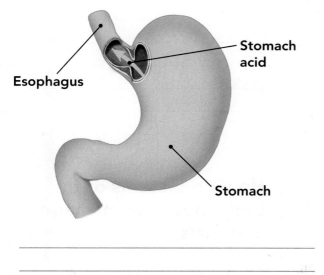

Esophagus   Stomach acid

                    Stomach

_____

_____

_____

                               SC.6.L.14.5

4. Apply Concepts How does the function of the digestive system contribute to homeostasis?

_____

_____

_____

_____

                               SC.6.L.14.5

5. **Write About It** Have you ever choked while eating? Explain what happens in a person's body when they choke. Describe some things people can do to avoid choking while eating.

                               SC.6.L.14.5

LESSON 2   Circulation

6. What structure regulates the direction of blood flow through the heart?

  a. ventricle   **b.** pacemaker

  c. valve   **d.** artery

                               SC.6.L.14.5

7. The _____ in your body carry blood back to your heart.

                               SC.6.L.14.5

8. Classify Which chambers of the heart below are the ventricles? Which chamber receives oxygen-poor blood from the body?

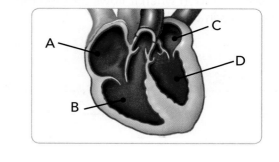

    A   C

                       D

        B

_____

_____

_____

                               SC.6.L.14.5

9. Predict Is it safe for a person with blood type O+ to receive a blood transfusion from a person who has blood type A+? Explain.

_____

_____

_____

_____

                      SC.6.N.1.5, SC.6.L.14.5

10. **Write About It** People who do not have enough iron in their diets sometimes develop anemia, a condition in which their blood cannot carry a normal amount of oxygen. Write a paragraph to explain why this is so.

                               SC.6.L.14.5

The Respiratory System

11. Your voice is produced by the

a. pharynx.   **b.** larynx.

c. trachea.   **d.** alveoli.

SC.6.L.14.5

12. Clusters of air sacs in the lungs are _____

SC.6.L.14.5

13. Classify What part of the respiratory system connects the mouth and nose?

_____

SC.6.L.14.5

14. Sequence What happens to the carbon dioxide in blood when it flows through the capillaries in the alveoli?

_____

_____

_____

_____

SC.6.L.14.5

15. Compare and Contrast How do mucus and cilia work together to remove dust that enters your nose? How do they differ?

_____

_____

_____

_____

_____

_____

_____

SC.6.L.14.5

16. **Write About It** Suppose you are a doctor with patients who are mountain climbers. Write a letter to these patients that explains how gas exchange is affected at the top of a mountain, where air pressure is lower and there is less oxygen than at lower elevations.

SC.6.L.14.5

The Excretory System

17. Urine leaves the body through the

a. ureters.   **b.** nephrons.

c. urinary bladder.   **d.** urethra.

SC.6.L.14.5

18. Urine is stored in the _____

SC.6.L.14.5

19. Relate Cause and Effect How do the kidneys help maintain homeostasis?

_____

_____

_____

_____

_____

_____

_____

_____

SC.6.L.14.5

APPLY THE ESSENTIAL **How do systems of the body move and manage materials?**

20. You eat an apple. Describe how the functions of your body systems working together can provide you with energy from the apple.

_____

_____

_____

_____

_____

_____

_____

_____

_____

SC.6.L.14.5

Florida Benchmarks Review

Circle the letter of the best answer.

1 What process is shown in the diagram below?

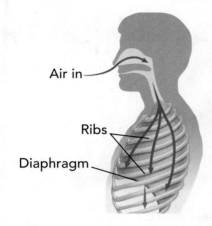

Air in

Ribs

Diaphragm

A   the process of inhaling
B   the process of exhaling
C   the process of cellular respiration
D   all of the above

SC.6.L.14.5

2 Which of the following parts of the digestive system is paired with its function?

A   esophagus—digests carbohydrates
B   stomach—digests fats
C   small intestine—begins mechanical digestion
D   large intestine—absorbs water

SC.6.L.14.5

3 Which of the following is true about blood in the aorta?

A   The blood is going to the lungs.
B   The blood is oxygen-poor.
C   The blood is rich in oxygen.
D   The blood is going to the heart.

SC.6.L.14.5

4 Which of the following organs functions as both a respiratory organ and an excretory organ?

A   the liver
B   the lungs
C   the skin
D   the kidneys

SC.6.L.14.5

5 The organs of the excretory system help maintain homeostasis by

A   removing harmful wastes from the body.
B   transporting needed materials to body cells.
C   circulating wastes.
D   carrying out cellular respiration.

SC.6.L.14.5

6 According to the table below, if a person eats a meal at noon, absorption cannot have begun by

Length of Time Food Usually Stays in Organs	
Organ	**Time**
Mouth	Less than 1 minute
Stomach	1 to 3 hours
Small Intestine	1 to 6 hours
Large Intestine	12 to 36 hours

A   1 P.M.
B   7 P.M.
C   9 P.M.
D   noon the next day.

SC.6.L.14.5

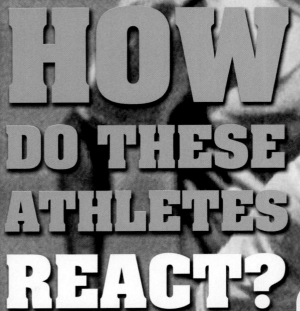

HOW DO THESE ATHLETES REACT?

What systems regulate and control body processes?

Soccer, known as football in most of the world, can be an exciting game. The Brazilian player in yellow is trying to advance the ball past the U.S. players in red and white. As they play the game, all these players rely on their body systems to sense what is happening, think about game strategy, react quickly, and sustain their energy.

Infer When you are about to collide with someone, how do you react?

_____

_____

_____

> **UNTAMED SCIENCE** Watch the **Untamed Science** video to learn more about the nervous system.

Controlling Body Processes

FLORIDA Next Generation Sunshine State Standards

Big Idea 2: SC.6.N.2.2
Big Idea 14: SC.6.L.14.5

Language Arts: LA.6.2.2.3, LA.6.4.2.2
Mathematics: MA.6.A.3.6

Check Your Understanding

1. **Background** Read the paragraph below and then answer the question.

Rajev wakes up gasping. Smoke enters his nose and stings his eyes. He feels the **involuntary** pounding of his heart. His **sense organs** send signals to his brain—alarms, shouts, smoke, heat, and sirens. Instantly, Rajev interprets the signals and takes **voluntary** action. He crawls to the window as the fire ladder rises below him.

> **Involuntary** action is not under a person's conscious control.
>
> **Sense organs,** such as eyes and ears, are body structures that gather information from your surroundings.
>
> **Voluntary** action is under a person's conscious control.

- Why is Rajev's crawling to the window a voluntary rather than an involuntary action?

_____

_____

> **MY READING WEB** If you had trouble completing the question above, visit **My Reading Web** and type in *Controlling Body Processes.*

Vocabulary Skill

Prefixes A prefix is a word part that is added to the beginning of a word to change its meaning. The table below lists prefixes that will help you learn terms in this chapter.

Prefix	Meaning	Term
inter-	between, among	interneuron, *n.* a neuron, or nerve cell, that is between other neurons
re-	back, over again	reflex, *n.* an automatic response that occurs rapidly without conscious control

LA.6.1.6.7

2. **Quick Check** The prefix *inter-* has more than one meaning. In the table above, circle the meaning of *inter-* that relates to the word *interneuron.*

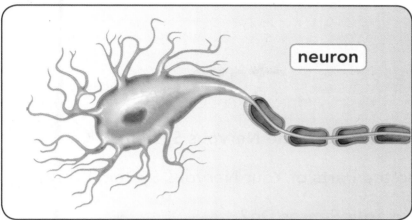

neuron

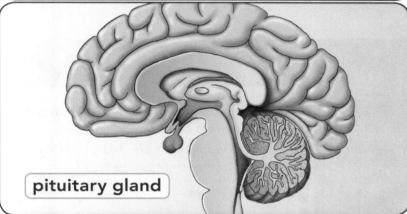

pituitary gland

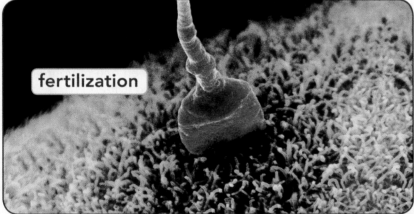

fertilization

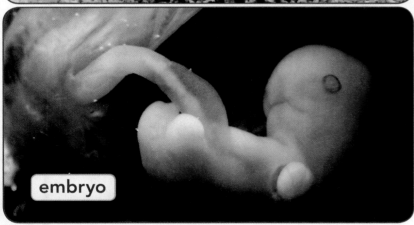

embryo

Chapter Preview

LESSON 1

- neuron • nerve impulse
- nerve • synapse
- central nervous system
- peripheral nervous system
- reflex

⟳ Identify Supporting Evidence
△ Infer

LESSON 2

- gland • duct • hormone
- target cell • hypothalamus
- pituitary gland
- negative feedback

⟳ Identify the Main Idea
△ Make Models

LESSON 3

- fertilization • egg • sperm
- zygote • testes • testosterone
- scrotum • semen • penis
- ovary • estrogen
- Fallopian tube • uterus • vagina
- menstrual cycle • menstruation
- ovulation

⟳ Sequence
△ Develop Hypotheses

LESSON 4

- embryo • fetus • amniotic sac
- placenta • umbilical cord

⟳ Compare and Contrast
△ Calculate

 VOCAB FLASH CARDS For extra help with vocabulary, visit **Vocab Flash Cards** and type in *Controlling Body Processes.*

231

The Nervous System

UNLOCK THE ESSENTIAL **?**

🔑 **What Is the Role of the Nervous System?**
SC.6.L.14.5

🔑 **How Do the Parts of Your Nervous System Work?**
SC.6.L.14.5, LA.6.2.2.3

🔑 **What Do Your Senses Do?**
SC.6.L.14.5

my planet diary

Wake Up!

Did you ever wake from a nap, only to find that your arm is "asleep"? What causes this "pins-and-needles" sensation? If you lie on your arm for a long period of time, too much pressure is placed on the nerves. The communication between your arm and brain no longer flows smoothly. A decrease in normal signals makes your arm feel odd. The pins-and-needles feeling actually happens when you remove the pressure from the nerves. They begin to send a normal flow of messages from your arm to your brain again. You slowly regain normal feeling in your arm. Remember to change your position often when you sit or lie down. If you don't, you'll end up having to wake up your arms and legs!

FUN FACTS

Read the following questions. Then write your answers below.

1. Why would your arm feel numb if you put too much pressure on it?

_____

_____

_____

_____

2. Describe a time when one of your limbs fell asleep. How did it feel?

_____

_____

_____

_____

_____

> PLANET DIARY Go to **Planet Diary** to learn more about the nervous system.

Lab zone® Do the Inquiry Warm-up
How Simple Is a Simple Task?

Vocabulary
- neuron • nerve impulse • nerve
- synapse • central nervous system
- peripheral nervous system • reflex

Skills
- ↪ Reading: Identify Supporting Evidence
- △ Inquiry: Infer

What Is the Role of the Nervous System?

You can use the Internet to chat with a friend hundreds of miles away. You can also use it to gather information from anywhere in the world. Like the Internet, your nervous system is a communications network. It includes the brain, the spinal cord, and the nerves that run throughout the body. It also includes the eyes, ears, and other sense organs. ☞ **Your nervous system receives information about what is happening both inside and outside your body. It directs how your body responds to this information. In addition, your nervous system helps maintain homeostasis.** Without your nervous system, you could not move, think, or sense the world around you.

Receiving Information Your nervous system makes you aware of what is happening around you. For example, if you were at a cookout like the one shown in **Figure 1,** you would know when the wind was blowing or a fly was buzzing around your head. Your nervous system also checks conditions inside your body, such as the level of glucose in your blood and your internal body temperature.

FLORIDA NGSSS

SC.6.L.14.5 Identify and investigate the general functions of the major systems of the human body (digestive, respiratory, circulatory, reproductive, excretory, immune, nervous, and musculoskeletal) and describe ways these systems interact with each other to maintain homeostasis.

FIGURE 1 ·····················
Gathering Information
The nervous system allows people to react to their environment.

✎ **Describe** List four things that your nervous system would help you notice if you were enjoying a meal with this family.

_____

_____

_____

_____

_____

Responding to Information

Any change or signal in the environment that an organism can recognize and react to is called a stimulus (STIM yoo lus; plural *stimuli*). For example, a buzzing fly is a stimulus. After your nervous system analyzes a stimulus, it directs a response. A response is a reaction to a stimulus. Some nervous system responses, such as swatting a fly, are voluntary, or under your control. But heart rate, breathing, sweating, and other necessary processes are involuntary responses to stimuli inside your body.

Maintaining Homeostasis

The nervous system helps maintain homeostasis by directing your body to respond properly to information it receives. For example, when your blood's glucose level drops, your nervous system signals that you are hungry. So, you eat. This action maintains homeostasis by supplying your body with needed nutrients and energy.

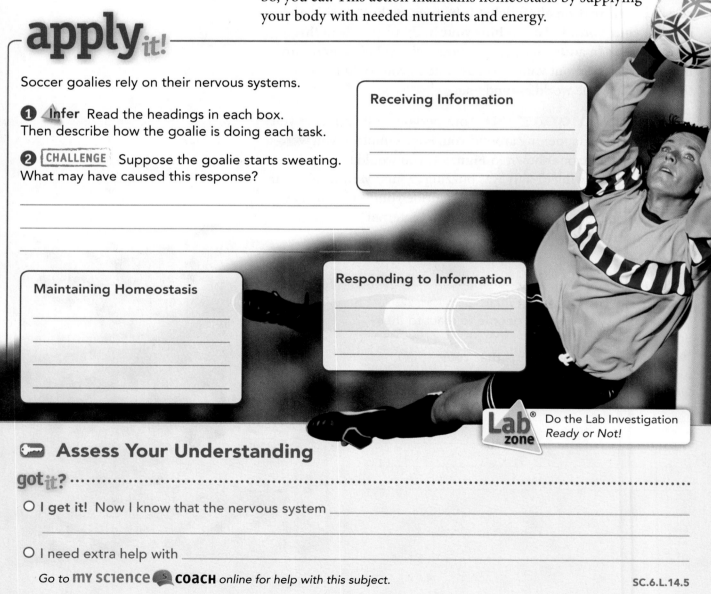

apply it!

Soccer goalies rely on their nervous systems.

❶ Infer Read the headings in each box. Then describe how the goalie is doing each task.

❷ CHALLENGE Suppose the goalie starts sweating. What may have caused this response?

_____

_____

_____

Receiving Information

_____

_____

_____

Maintaining Homeostasis

_____

_____

_____

Responding to Information

_____

_____

_____

Lab zone Do the Lab Investigation *Ready or Not!*

🔖 Assess Your Understanding

got it? ....

○ **I get it!** Now I know that the nervous system _____

_____

○ **I need extra help with** _____

Go to **MY SCIENCE COACH** online for help with this subject.

SC.6.L.14.5

How Do the Parts of Your Nervous System Work?

Your nervous system includes your brain, spinal cord, and the nerves that connect these organs to all parts of your body. Individual cells that carry information through your nervous system are called **neurons** (NOO rahnz), or nerve cells. The message that a neuron carries is called a **nerve impulse.** These impulses may occur as either electrical or chemical signals.

Neurons 🔑 **Neurons carry nerve impulses throughout the body.** A neuron has a large cell body that contains a nucleus, threadlike extensions called dendrites, and an axon, as shown in **Figure 2.** Nerve impulses begin in a dendrite and move through the neuron's cell body to the tips of the axon. Axons and their tissue covering make up nerve fibers. Nerve fibers are often arranged in parallel bundles covered with more connective tissue. They look like uncooked spaghetti wrapped in thin plastic. A bundle of nerve fibers is called a **nerve.**

Three Kinds of Neurons Your nervous system includes three kinds of neurons. A sensory neuron picks up a stimulus and converts it into a nerve impulse. The impulse travels along sensory neurons until it reaches an interneuron usually in the brain or spinal cord. An interneuron carries a nerve impulse to another interneuron or to a motor neuron. A motor neuron sends an impulse to a muscle or gland, enabling it to respond.

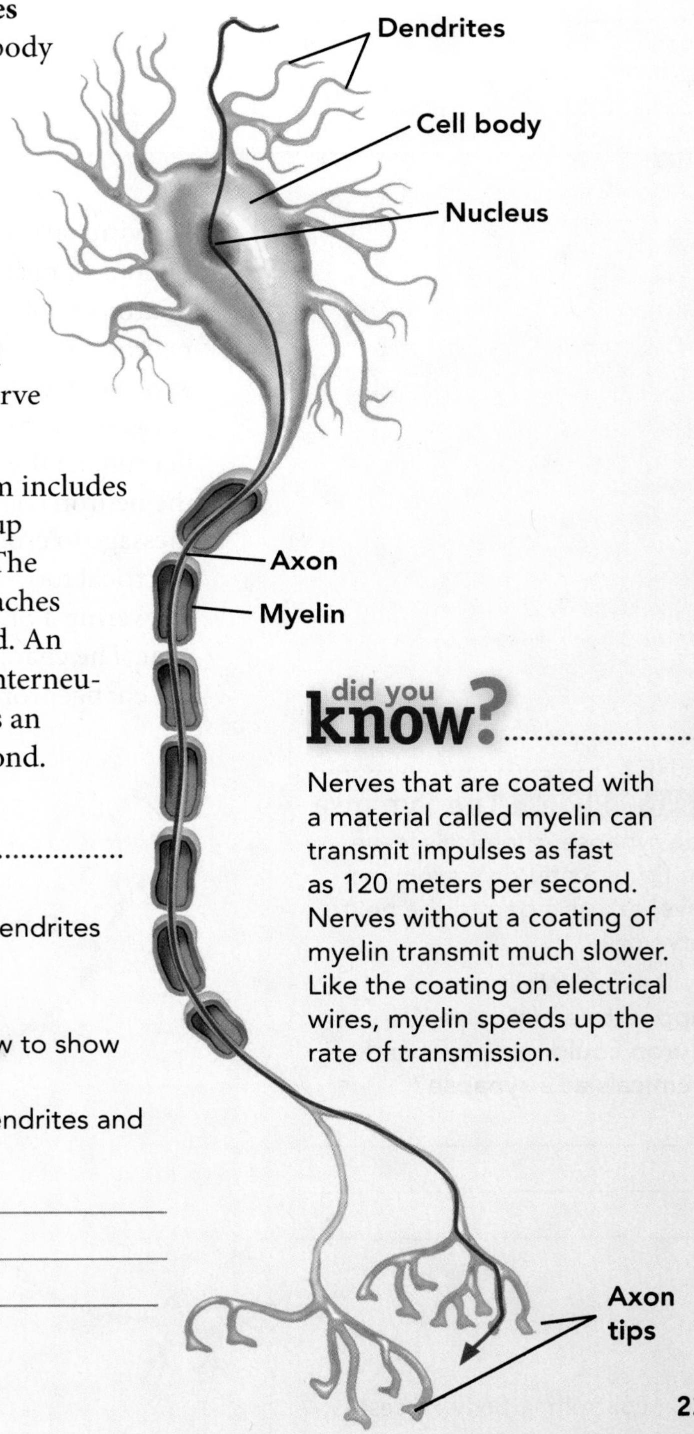

FLORIDA NGSSS

SC.6.L.14.5 Identify and investigate the general functions of the major systems of the human body (digestive, respiratory, circulatory, reproductive, excretory, immune, nervous, and musculoskeletal).

LA.6.2.2.3 The student will organize information to show understanding (e.g., representing main ideas within the text through summarizing).

FIGURE 2 ·······································

Structure of a Neuron

A neuron has only one axon but can have many dendrites that extend from the cell body.

✎ **Use the diagram to complete these tasks.**

1. **Interpret Diagrams** Draw a line with an arrow to show the path of a nerve impulse in the neuron.

2. **Draw Conclusions** How does having both dendrites and an axon help a neuron function?

_____

_____

_____

did you know? ·······················

Nerves that are coated with a material called myelin can transmit impulses as fast as 120 meters per second. Nerves without a coating of myelin transmit much slower. Like the coating on electrical wires, myelin speeds up the rate of transmission.

235

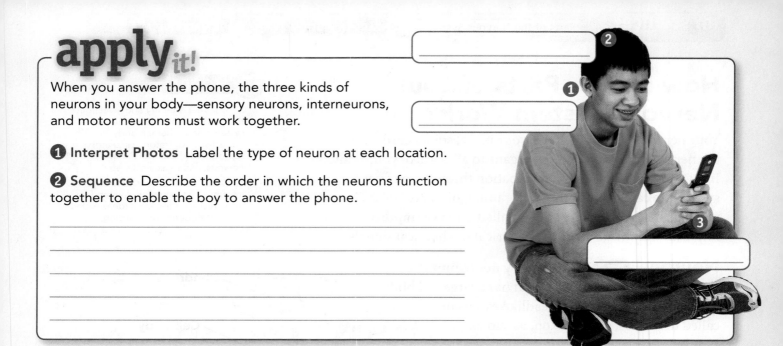

apply it!

When you answer the phone, the three kinds of neurons in your body—sensory neurons, interneurons, and motor neurons must work together.

1 Interpret Photos Label the type of neuron at each location.

2 Sequence Describe the order in which the neurons function together to enable the boy to answer the phone.

_____

_____

_____

_____

_____

Moving Impulses Between Neurons Every day, billions of nerve impulses travel through your nervous system from neurons to other neurons or body structures. The place where a neuron transfers an impulse to another structure is called a **synapse** (SIN aps). **Figure 3** shows the gap within the synapse between the axon tip of one neuron and the dendrite of another neuron. At the axon tips, electrical signals carried through the neuron change into a chemical form. This change allows the message to cross the gap. The message then continues in electrical form through the next neuron. These changes are like answering a phone and then writing down the information you hear. The change from hearing information to writing it is like the change from electrical to chemical form.

FIGURE 3 ·······························
> ART IN MOTION **The Synapse**
At a synapse, chemicals leave the tip of a neuron's axon and travel across a gap to the next nerve cell.

✎ **Predict** What would happen to an impulse if a neuron could not produce chemicals at a synapse?

_____

_____

_____

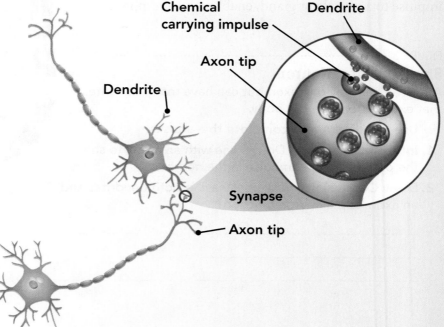

Chemical carrying impulse

Dendrite

Axon tip

Dendrite

Synapse

Axon tip

The Central Nervous System Like a traffic cop directing car drivers through a busy intersection, your nervous system directs your movements. It has two divisions that work together: the central nervous system and the peripheral nervous system. The **central nervous system** includes the brain and spinal cord and acts like the traffic cop. The **peripheral nervous system** includes all the nerves outside of the central nervous system, which are like the car drivers. **Figure 4** shows both systems.

The brain is the control center of the central nervous system. The spinal cord is a thick column of nervous tissue that links the brain to the peripheral nervous system. Most impulses from the peripheral nerves travel through the spinal cord to get to the brain. The brain then directs a response, which usually travels through the spinal cord and back to peripheral nerves.

FIGURE 4 ·······························

The Nervous System
All information about what is happening in the outside world and inside your body travels through your nervous system.

LA.6.2.2.3

✎ **Use the diagram and the boxes to complete these tasks.**

1. **Identify** Circle the name of each structure that is part of the central nervous system.

2. **Summarize** Explain in your own words the function of the structures in the diagram.

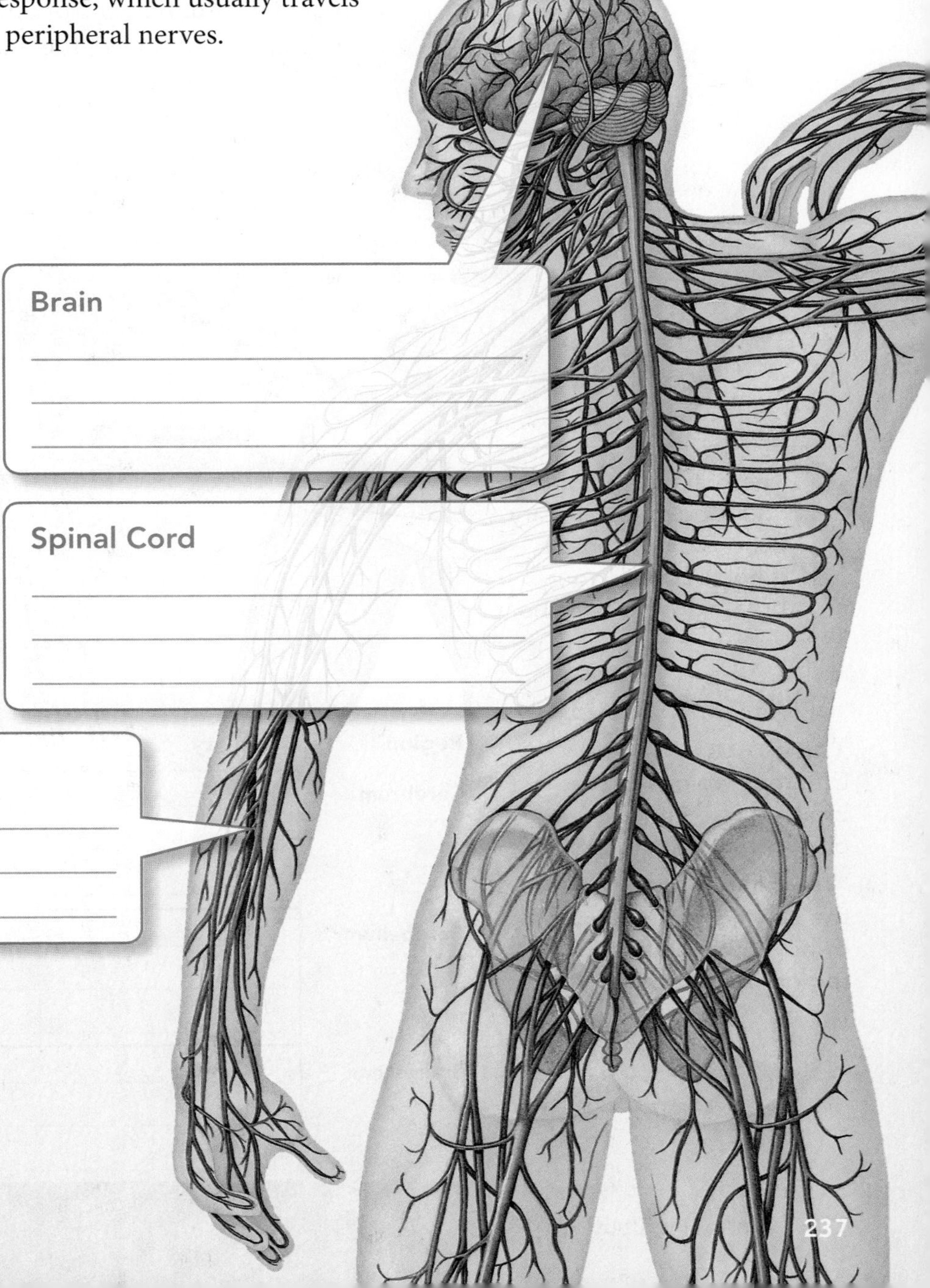

Brain
_____
_____
_____

Spinal Cord
_____
_____
_____

Peripheral Nerves
_____
_____
_____

✏️ **Identify Supporting Evidence** Which structures protect the brain from injury?

_____

_____

_____

The Brain Your brain has about 100 billion neurons, all of which are interneurons. Each of those neurons may receive up to 10,000 messages from other neurons and may send messages to about 1,000 more! Three layers of connective tissue under the skull cover the brain. Fluid fills the space between the middle layer and the innermost layer of connective tissue. The skull, the connective tissue, and the fluid all help protect the brain from injury. Three main regions of the brain are the brain stem, the cerebellum, and the cerebrum, as shown in **Figure 5**.

The Spinal Cord The brain stem connects to the spinal cord. Run your fingers down the center of your back to feel the bones of the vertebral column. The vertebral column surrounds and protects your spinal cord. Like the brain, layers of connective tissue cover the spinal cord. Also like the brain, fluid protects the spinal cord.

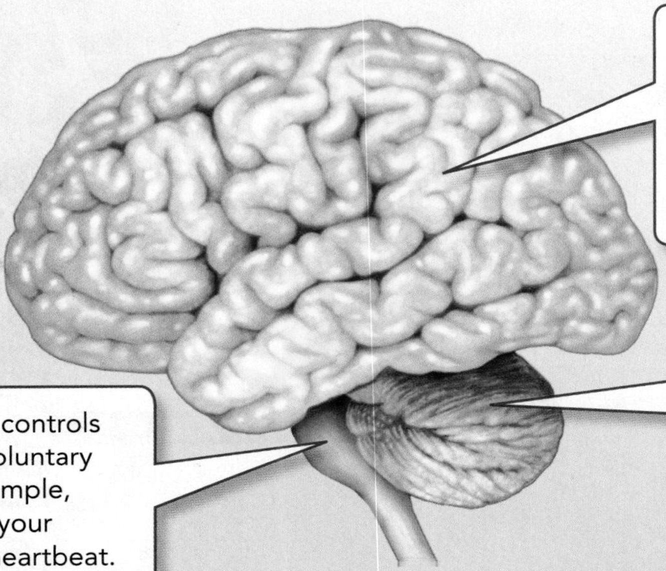

The *cerebrum* (suh REE brum) interprets input from your senses, controls movement, and carries out complex mental processes such as learning and remembering.

The *cerebellum* (sehr uh BEL um) coordinates your muscle actions and helps you keep your balance.

The *brain stem* controls your body's involuntary actions. For example, it helps control your breathing and heartbeat.

FIGURE 5

The Brain
Different regions of the brain receive and process different information.

✏️ **Apply Concepts** In the chart, write examples of how you use each region of your brain.

Region	Activity
Cerebrum	
Cerebellum	
Brain stem	

The Peripheral Nervous System The second
division of the nervous system is the peripheral nervous system.
The peripheral nervous system is a network of nerves that branches
out from the central nervous system and connects it to the rest of
the body. The peripheral nervous system is involved in both
involuntary and voluntary actions.

The peripheral nervous system has 43 pairs of nerves. Twelve
pairs begin in the brain. The other 31 pairs—the spinal nerves—
begin in the spinal cord. One nerve in each pair goes to the left
side of the body, and the other goes to the right. Look at the spinal
nerves shown in **Figure 6.** Each spinal nerve contains axons of
both sensory and motor neurons. The sensory neurons carry
impulses from the body to the central nervous system. In contrast,
the motor neurons carry impulses from the central nervous system
to the body.

Somatic and Autonomic Systems The peripheral
nervous system has two groups of nerves. They are the nerves
of the somatic (soh MAT ik) nervous system and those of the
autonomic (awt uh NAHM ik) nervous system. The somatic
nervous system controls voluntary actions, such as using a fork.
The autonomic nervous system controls involuntary actions, such
as digesting food.

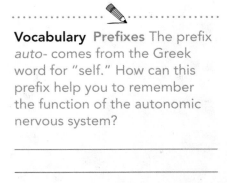

Vocabulary **Prefixes** The prefix
auto- comes from the Greek
word for "self." How can this
prefix help you to remember
the function of the autonomic
nervous system?

_____

_____

_____

FIGURE 6 ···

The Spinal Nerves
The spinal nerves leave the spinal cord
through spaces between the vertebrae.

**Infer On the diagram, circle the two
spinal nerves that are a pair. Then explain
how a spinal nerve is like a two-lane
highway.**

_____

_____

_____

_____

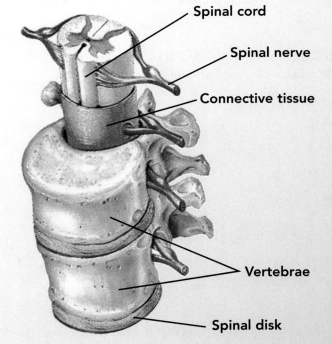

Spinal cord

Spinal nerve

Connective tissue

Vertebrae

Spinal disk

FIGURE 7 ···

▶ INTERACTIVE ART A Reflex Action

Reflexes help protect your body.

✎ **Relate Text and Visuals** On the diagram, number the steps in a reflex action.

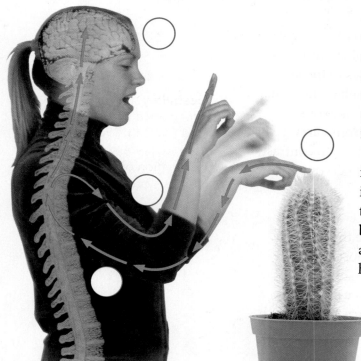

Reflexes The brain usually controls the contraction of skeletal muscles. Sometimes, however, skeletal muscles contract without involving the brain. A **reflex** is an automatic response that occurs rapidly without conscious control. For example, when your finger touches a sharp object, sensory neurons detect a pain stimulus. They send impulses to the spinal cord. Interneurons there pass those impulses directly to motor neurons. The motor neurons cause your arm muscles to contract, pulling your finger away from the sharp object like the cactus in **Figure 7.**

As the reflex action happens, other nerve impulses travel to your brain. As your brain interprets them, you feel a pain in your finger. It takes longer for the pain impulses to reach the brain and be interpreted than it does for the reflex action to occur. By the time you feel the pain, you have already jerked your hand away.

> **Lab** zone® Do the Quick Lab *How Does Your Knee React?*

🔑 Assess Your Understanding

1a. Name What is another name for a nerve cell?

_____

SC.6.L.14.5

b. Compare and Contrast How do the two groups of peripheral nerves differ?

_____

_____

_____

_____

SC.6.L.14.5

2a. Identify The part of the brain that helps you keep from falling is the _____.

SC.6.L.14.5

b. Draw Conclusions Why is it important for the brain to be so well protected?

_____

_____

_____

_____

SC.6.L.14.5

got it?···

○ I get it! Now I know that messages are carried through the nervous system among structures that

include _____

_____

○ I need extra help with _____

Go to MY SCIENCE ⑤ COACH online for help with this subject.

SC.6.L.14.5

What Do Your Senses Do?

Going to the movie theater can be a treat for your senses. Show times and titles flash on displays. Moviegoers chatter in line. As you walk into the theater, you can smell the popcorn. When you finally sit in your seat, you can feel the texture of the cushions on your body. You take a bite of your snack, and enjoy the show.

🔑 **Your eyes, ears, nose, mouth, and skin are specialized sense organs that enable you to get information from the outside world.** Each of these organs contains sensory neurons that send impulses to your brain. Your brain interprets them, enabling you to understand more about your environment.

How You See You would not be able to enjoy the visual experience of a movie without your sense of sight. Your eyes respond to the stimulus of light. They convert that stimulus into impulses that your brain interprets, enabling you to see.

The eye has many parts, as shown in **Figure 8.** Notice that light rays enter the eye through the pupil. Then they pass through the lens. Muscles attached to the lens adjust its shape and focus light rays on the retina. Because the lens bends light rays, it produces an upside-down image. The retina contains light-sensitive cells that produce nerve impulses. These impulses travel through the optic nerve to the brain. Your brain turns the image right-side up and combines the images from both eyes to produce a single image.

FLORIDA NGSSS

SC.6.L.14.5 Identify and investigate the general functions of the major systems of the human body (digestive, respiratory, circulatory, reproductive, excretory, immune, nervous, and musculoskeletal) and describe ways these systems interact with each other to maintain homeostasis.

FIGURE 8 ······················

The Eye

Light from an object produces an image on the retina.

✏️ **Develop Hypotheses** Hold your hand in front of your face. Look at it with one eye closed, then with the other. Explain why the image of your hand shifts.

_____

_____

_____

_____

_____

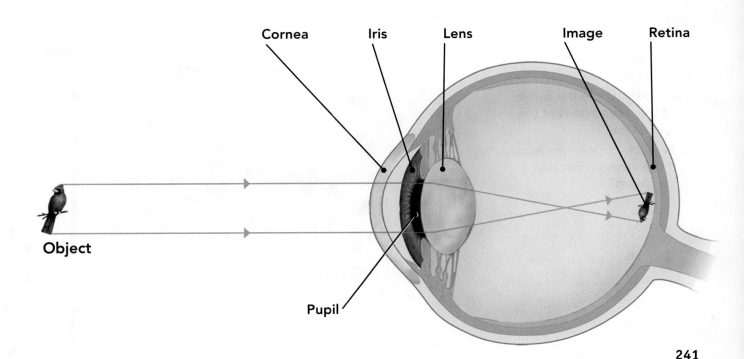

Cornea | Iris | Lens | Image | Retina

Object

Pupil

Taste and Smell The senses of taste and smell work together. Both depend on chemicals in the air or in food. The chemicals trigger responses in receptors in the nose and mouth. Nerve impulses then travel to the brain and are interpreted as smells or tastes.

The nose can distinguish at least 50 basic odors. In contrast, there are only five main taste sensations—sweet, sour, salty, bitter, and a meatlike taste called *umami*. When you eat, however, you experience a wider variety of flavors, since both smell and taste affect the flavor of food.

How You Hear When you hear your alarm clock ring, your brain tells you that it is time to get up. Most sounds are caused by the vibrations of air particles. The air particle vibrations move outward from the source of the sound, like waves moving out from a stone dropped in the water. In this way, sound is carried as waves. Ears are the sense organs that convert sound waves into nerve impulses that your brain interprets.

The three parts of the ear—outer, middle, and inner—are shown in **Figure 9.** Sound waves enter your outer ear through the ear canal. When the sound waves reach your eardrum, they cause it to vibrate. The vibrations pass to three tiny bones in your middle ear, which transmit the vibrations to your inner ear. There, sensory neurons in the cochlea convert these vibrations into nerve impulses. These impulses travel through the auditory nerve to the brain. Your brain interprets these impulses as sounds.

FIGURE 9

The Ear
Sound waves pass through the structures of the ear and are carried by nerve impulses to the brain.

✎ **Use the diagram to complete the tasks.**

1. **Identify** Circle the names of the three bones of the middle ear.

2. **Predict** What might happen if the eardrum became damaged?

_____

_____

_____

_____

_____

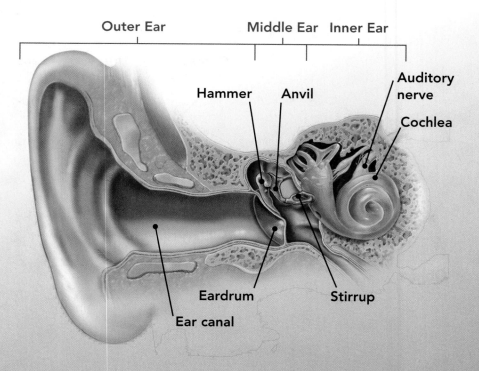

Outer Ear   Middle Ear   Inner Ear

Hammer   Anvil

Auditory nerve

Cochlea

Eardrum   Stirrup

Ear canal

Touch Unlike your other senses, the sense of touch is not found in one place. It is in all areas of your skin. Your skin has different kinds of touch receptors that respond to different stimuli. All of the touch receptors are located in the dermis, or the inner layer of skin.

The receptors that respond to light touch are in the upper part of the dermis. These receptors also let you feel textures, such as smooth glass and rough sandpaper. Receptors deeper in the dermis pick up the feeling of heavy pressure. For example, if you press down hard on your desk, you will feel pressure in your fingertips.

The dermis also contains receptors that respond to temperature and pain. Pain can be one of your most important sensations because it alerts you to danger.

FIGURE 10·······························
Touch
Your skin lets you feel the world around you.
✎ **Classify** In the box next to each photo, describe the kind of touch receptors each person is using.

Lab® zone Do the Quick Lab *Working Together.*

⚷ Assess Your Understanding

3a. Name Light-sensitive cells that produce nerve impulses are found in the _____
SC.6.L.14.5

b. Predict If a head cold interferes with your sense of smell, how do you think your sense of taste would be affected?

_____

_____

_____
SC.6.L.14.5

c. Describe Describe the eardrum's function.

_____

_____

_____
SC.6.L.14.5

d. Compare and Contrast How is the sense of touch different from the other senses?

_____

_____
SC.6.L.14.5

got it?···

○ **I get it!** Now I know that my sense organs enable me to _____

_____

○ **I need extra help with** _____

Go to **MY SCIENCE** ⓢ **COACH** *online for help with this subject.*
SC.6.L.14.5

 LESSON

2 The Endocrine System

 UNLOCK THE ESSENTIAL ?

🔑 **How Does the Endocrine System Function?**
SC.6.L.14.5, LA.6.2.2.3

🔑 **What Controls Hormone Levels?**
SC.6.L.14.5

my pLaneT DiaRY

The Cause of Acne

Misconception: Eating oily foods can cause acne.

Scientists have not found a link between eating certain foods and acne. So, what does cause acne? Much of the blame falls on certain hormones. Your body starts to produce these hormones when you enter adolescence. They stimulate your body to produce an oily substance called sebum. When your body produces too much sebum, some hair follicles in your skin may become blocked. This blockage causes bacteria to get trapped. Because the sebum and bacteria have nowhere to go, your skin becomes inflamed. The result is acne.

MISCONCEPTION

Communicate Discuss the following question with a partner. Write your answer below.

How would you explain to a friend what causes acne?

_____

_____

_____

_____

_____

_____

_____

_____

_____

_____

> PLANET DIARY Go to **Planet Diary** to learn more about the endocrine system.

 Lab zone Do the Inquiry Warm-Up *What's the Signal?*

Vocabulary

- gland • duct • hormone • target cell • hypothalamus
- pituitary gland • negative feedback

Skills

🔎 Reading: Identify the Main Idea

△ Inquiry: Make Models

How Does the Endocrine System Function?

Have you ever been so afraid that you heard your heart thump rapidly in your chest? When something frightens you, your body's endocrine system (EN duh krin) reacts.

Your body has two systems that regulate its activities: the nervous system and the endocrine system. The nervous system regulates most activities by sending nerve impulses throughout the body. 🔑 **The endocrine system regulates short-term and long-term activities by sending chemicals throughout the body. Long-term changes include growth and development.**

The endocrine system is made up of glands. A **gland** is an organ that produces or releases a chemical. Some glands, such as those producing saliva and sweat, release their chemicals into tiny tubes, or **ducts.** The ducts deliver the chemicals to specific places in the body or to the skin's surface. However, the glands of the endocrine system do not have delivery ducts. The endocrine glands produce and release chemicals directly into the blood. Then the blood carries those chemicals throughout the body.

FLORIDA   NGSSS

SC.6.L.14.5 Identify and investigate the general functions of the major systems of the human body.

LA.6.2.2.3 The student will organize information to show understanding (e.g. representing main ideas within the text through charting).

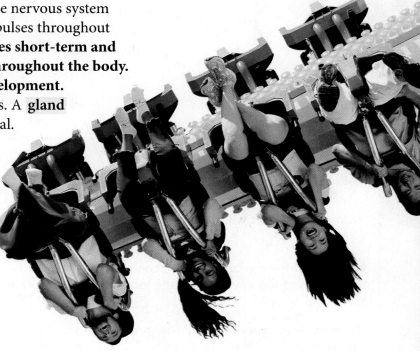

Main Idea

_____

_____

↓   ↓

Detail

_____

_____

_____

Detail

_____

_____

_____

🔎 **Identify the Main Idea**

In the graphic organizer, write the main idea of the third paragraph. Then write two details that support the main idea.

LA.6.2.2.3

Hormones

A chemical produced by an endocrine gland is called a **hormone.** Hormones are chemical messengers that travel in the blood. Hormones turn on, turn off, speed up, or slow down the activities of organs and tissues.

Nerve impulses from the brain act quickly. In contrast, hormones usually cause a slower, longer-lasting response. For example, if you see danger, your brain interprets the information and sends an impulse to an endocrine gland. The gland releases the hormone adrenaline into your blood. Adrenaline speeds up your heart rate and breathing rate. Even a quick hormonal response such as releasing adrenaline is much slower than a nerve response.

Each hormone affects specific target cells. **Target cells** are cells that are specialized in a way that enables them to recognize a hormone's chemical structure. Hormones travel in the blood until they find their target cells. Read about the endocrine glands and the hormones they produce in **Figure 1** on the next page.

apply it!

Hormones interact with target cells much like keys interact with locks.

❶ **Make Models** Look at Key A and Lock A. Then draw the shapes of the keyholes for the locks that Key B and Key C will unlock.

❷ **Draw Conclusions** How do a hormone and a target cell function like a key and a lock?

_____

_____

_____

_____

❸ CHALLENGE What body system does the endocrine system depend on to function? Explain.

_____

_____

_____

_____

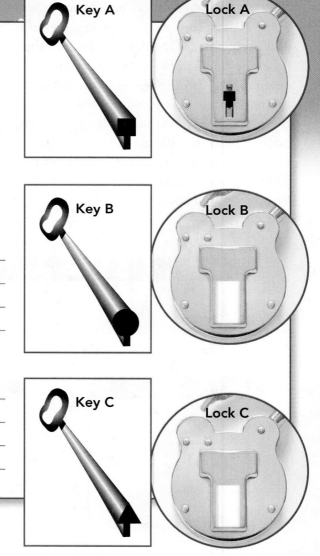

Key A   Lock A

Key B   Lock B

Key C   Lock C

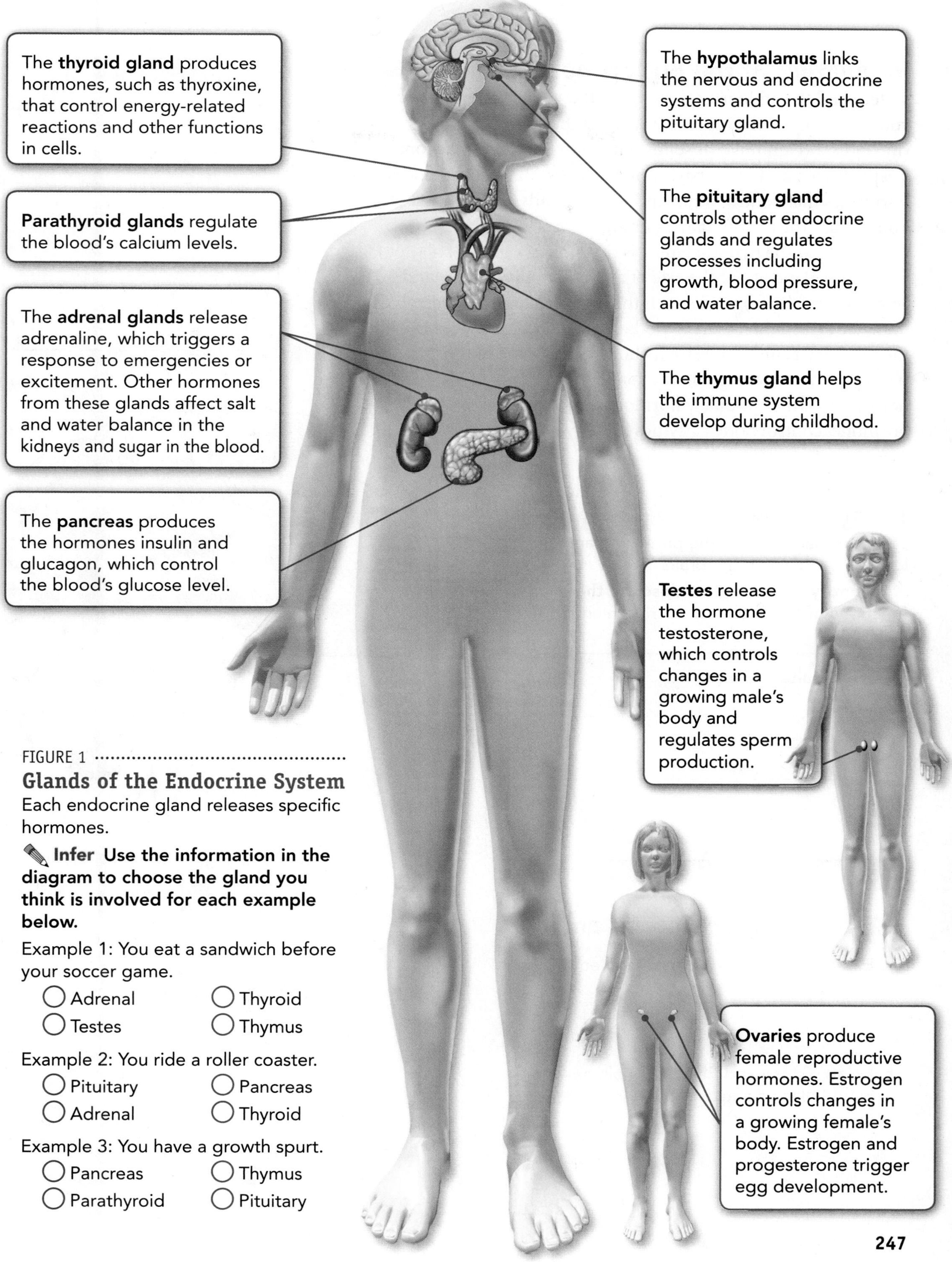

The **thyroid gland** produces hormones, such as thyroxine, that control energy-related reactions and other functions in cells.

Parathyroid glands regulate the blood's calcium levels.

The **adrenal glands** release adrenaline, which triggers a response to emergencies or excitement. Other hormones from these glands affect salt and water balance in the kidneys and sugar in the blood.

The **pancreas** produces the hormones insulin and glucagon, which control the blood's glucose level.

The **hypothalamus** links the nervous and endocrine systems and controls the pituitary gland.

The **pituitary gland** controls other endocrine glands and regulates processes including growth, blood pressure, and water balance.

The **thymus gland** helps the immune system develop during childhood.

Testes release the hormone testosterone, which controls changes in a growing male's body and regulates sperm production.

Ovaries produce female reproductive hormones. Estrogen controls changes in a growing female's body. Estrogen and progesterone trigger egg development.

FIGURE 1 ·····························
Glands of the Endocrine System
Each endocrine gland releases specific hormones.

✎ **Infer** Use the information in the diagram to choose the gland you think is involved for each example below.

Example 1: You eat a sandwich before your soccer game.
- ○ Adrenal
- ○ Testes
- ○ Thyroid
- ○ Thymus

Example 2: You ride a roller coaster.
- ○ Pituitary
- ○ Adrenal
- ○ Pancreas
- ○ Thyroid

Example 3: You have a growth spurt.
- ○ Pancreas
- ○ Parathyroid
- ○ Thymus
- ○ Pituitary

Regulators of the Endocrine System

The nervous system and the endocrine system work together. The part of your brain that links the two systems is the **hypothalamus** (hy poh THAL uh mus). It sends out nerve messages that control sleep, hunger, and other basic body processes. It also produces hormones that control other endocrine glands and organs. You can see the hypothalamus in **Figure 2**.

Just below the hypothalamus is the pituitary gland, an endocrine gland about the size of a pea. The **pituitary gland** (pih TOO ih tehr ee) works with the hypothalamus to control many body activities. The hypothalamus sends messages to the pituitary gland to release its hormones. Some of those pituitary hormones signal other endocrine glands to produce hormones. Other pituitary hormones, such as growth hormone, control body activities directly.

FIGURE 2 ·····························

The Hypothalamus and Pituitary Gland
The hypothalamus and the pituitary gland are located deep within the brain.

✎ **Identify** In the boxes, describe the functions of these two endocrine glands.

Hypothalamus

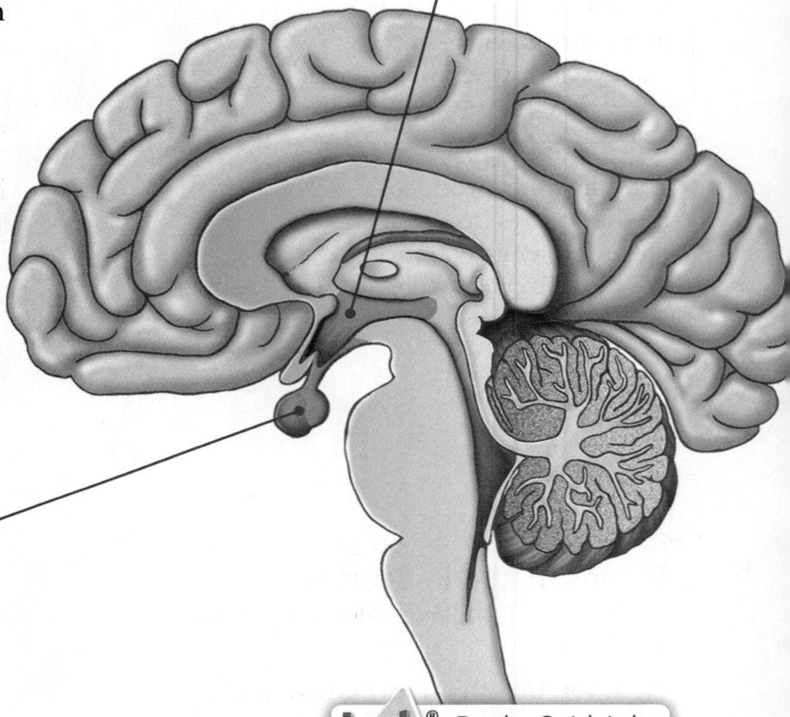

Pituitary Gland

Lab zone ® Do the Quick Lab *Making Models.*

🔑 Assess Your Understanding

1a. Explain How does adrenaline affect the heart?

_____

_____
SC.6.L.14.5

b. Relate Cause and Effect Explain how the hypothalamus affects growth.

_____

_____

_____
SC.6.L.14.5

got it?

○ **I get it!** Now I know that my endocrine system

_____

_____

_____

○ **I need extra help with** _____

Go to **MY SCIENCE** Ⓢ **COACH** *online for help with this subject.*
SC.6.L.14.5

What Controls Hormone Levels?

Suppose you set a thermostat at 20°C. If the room temperature falls below 20°C, the thermostat signals the furnace to turn on. When heat from the furnace warms the room to 20°C, the thermostat shuts off the furnace. In certain ways, the endocrine system works like a thermostat. It uses a process called **negative feedback** in which a system is turned off by the condition it produces.

🔑 **When the amount of a hormone in the blood reaches a certain level, the endocrine system sends signals that stop the release of that hormone.** In **Figure 3,** you can see how negative feedback regulates the level of the hormone thyroxine in the blood.

FLORIDA NGSSS

SC.6.L.14.5 Identify and investigate the general functions of the major systems of the human body (digestive, respiratory, circulatory, reproductive, excretory, immune, nervous, and musculoskeletal) and describe ways these systems interact with each other to maintain homeostasis.

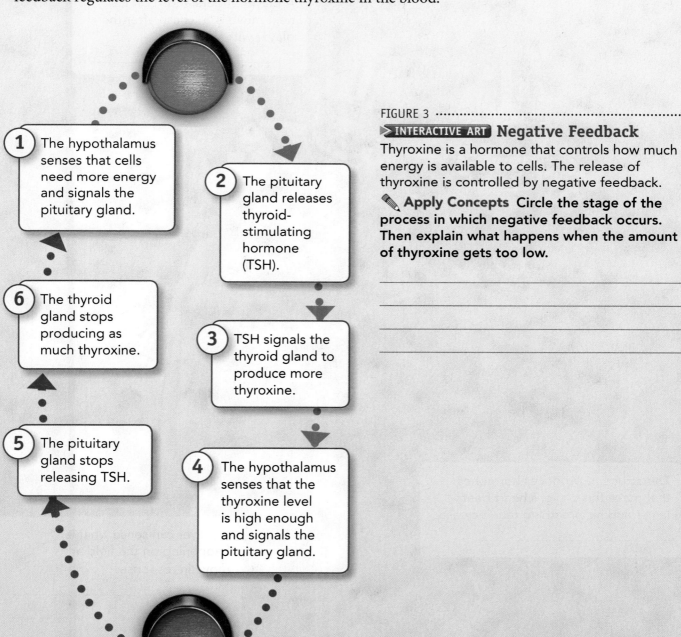

FIGURE 3 ....

▸ **INTERACTIVE ART** Negative Feedback
Thyroxine is a hormone that controls how much energy is available to cells. The release of thyroxine is controlled by negative feedback.

✏️ **Apply Concepts** Circle the stage of the process in which negative feedback occurs. Then explain what happens when the amount of thyroxine gets too low.

_____

_____

_____

_____

1. The hypothalamus senses that cells need more energy and signals the pituitary gland.

2. The pituitary gland releases thyroid-stimulating hormone (TSH).

3. TSH signals the thyroid gland to produce more thyroxine.

4. The hypothalamus senses that the thyroxine level is high enough and signals the pituitary gland.

5. The pituitary gland stops releasing TSH.

6. The thyroid gland stops producing as much thyroxine.

EXPLORE THE ESSENTIAL ?

Sense and Respond

What systems regulate and control body processes?

FIGURE 4 ⋯⋯⋯⋯⋯⋯⋯⋯⋯⋯⋯⋯⋯⋯⋯⋯⋯⋯⋯⋯

▶ **REAL-WORLD INQUIRY** The fans, players, and referee at this football game react to their surroundings because of their endocrine and nervous systems.

✎ Interpret Photos **Read the descriptions and identify what structures in the nervous system or endocrine system are involved.**

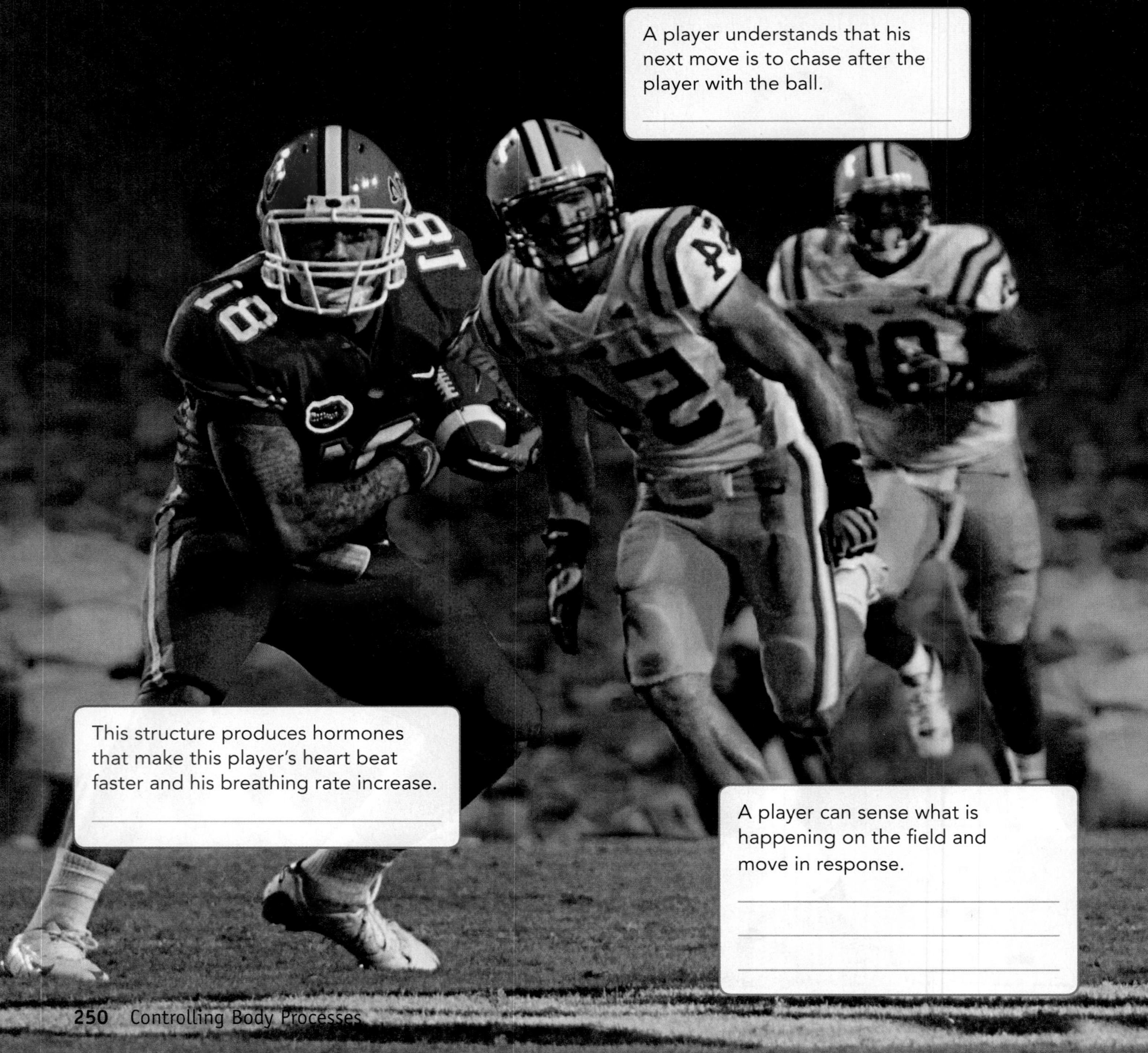

A player understands that his next move is to chase after the player with the ball.

_____

This structure produces hormones that make this player's heart beat faster and his breathing rate increase.

_____

A player can sense what is happening on the field and move in response.

_____

_____

_____

This structure produces hormones that help these fans get energy from the foods they eat.

_____

This structure produces hormones that control how this young fan grows.

_____

Lab zone® Do the Quick Lab *Modeling Negative Feedback.*

⚷ Assess Your Understanding

2a. Review Negative feedback works by turning a system (on/off) by the condition the system produces.

SC.6.L.14.5

b. Predict What do you think would happen to the level of a hormone in the blood if negative feedback didn't happen?

_____

_____

_____

SC.6.L.14.5

c. ANSWER THE ESSENTIAL ? What systems regulate and control body processes?

_____

_____

_____

SC.6.L.14.5

got it? ....

○ **I get it!** Now I know that negative feedback controls hormone levels by _____

_____

_____

_____

○ **I need extra help with** _____

Go to MY SCIENCE COACH *online for help with this subject.*
SC.6.L.14.5

The referee watches and listens to the action so he can make the correct calls.

_____

_____

LESSON 3

The Male and Female Reproductive Systems

UNLOCK THE ESSENTIAL ?

🔑 **What Are the Functions of the Reproductive Systems?**
SC.6.L.14.5, SC.6.N.2.2, LA.6.4.2.2

🔑 **What Happens During the Menstrual Cycle?**
SC.6.L.14.5, MA.6.A.3.6

MY PLANET DIARY

DISCOVERY

In Vitro Fertilization

By 1977, Dr. Patrick Steptoe and Dr. Robert Edwards had been working for years on an experimental procedure called in vitro fertilization. Their goal was to help women who could not get pregnant naturally. In vitro fertilization begins with retrieving an egg from a woman. The egg is placed in a lab dish along with a man's sperm. If the egg is successfully fertilized, it is placed back into the woman's body to grow into a baby.

Dr. Steptoe and Dr. Edwards were unsuccessful time and time again, until they met Lesley and John Brown. The doctors implanted a fertilized egg in Lesley. Nine months later, on July 25, 1978, the world's first in vitro baby was born. Her parents named her Louise Joy Brown.

Communicate Discuss the following questions with a partner. Write your answers below.

1. At what point during the in vitro fertilization process is the egg placed back into the woman's body?

_____

_____

_____

2. How did scientific knowledge about childbirth change as a result of Dr. Steptoe's and Dr. Edwards' work?

_____

_____

_____

▶ PLANET DIARY Go to **Planet Diary** to learn more about the male and female reproductive systems.

SC.6.N.2.2

Lab zone Do the Inquiry Warm-Up *What's the Big Difference?*

Louise Joy Brown
at birth

Louise Joy Brown
as an adult

Vocabulary

- fertilization • egg • sperm • zygote • testes
- testosterone • scrotum • semen • penis • ovary
- estrogen • Fallopian tube • uterus • vagina
- menstrual cycle • menstruation • ovulation

Skills

↻ Reading: Sequence

△ Inquiry: Develop Hypotheses

What Are the Functions of the Reproductive Systems?

Have you noticed how a child's body changes as the child grows? Two different endocrine glands—the ovaries and the testes—release hormones that control many of these changes. They also produce the sex cells that are part of sexual reproduction.

Sexual Reproduction You were once a single cell. That cell resulted from the joining of an egg cell and a sperm cell, which is a process called **fertilization.** An **egg** is the female sex cell. The male sex cell is a **sperm.** Both cells are shown in **Figure 1.** Fertilization is part of sexual reproduction, the process by which males and females produce new individuals. Sexual reproduction involves the production of eggs by the female and sperm by the male. When fertilization occurs, a fertilized egg, or **zygote,** is produced. The zygote contains all the information needed to produce a new human being.

FLORIDA NGSSS

SC.6.L.14.5 Identify and investigate the general functions of the reproductive system.

SC.6.N.2.2 Explain that scientific knowledge is durable because it is open to change as new evidence or interpretations are encountered.

LA.6.4.2.2 The student will record information (e.g., observations, notes, lists, charts, legends) related to a topic, including visual aids to organize and record information.

FIGURE 1 ··································

Egg and Sperm

An egg is one of the largest cells in the body. A sperm cell is much smaller than an egg and it can move. LA.6.4.2.2

✎ **Describe** In the table, describe each of the cells involved in fertilization.

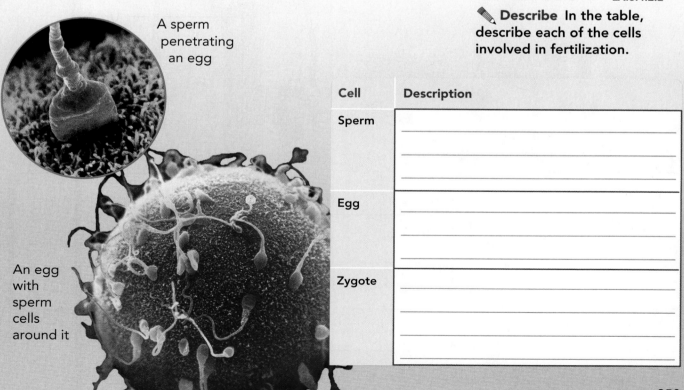

A sperm penetrating an egg

An egg with sperm cells around it

Cell	Description
Sperm	
Egg	
Zygote	

Sperm cells

Male Reproductive System

Look at the organs of the male reproductive system shown in **Figure 2.** The male reproductive system is specialized to produce sperm cells and the hormone testosterone. The structures of this system include the testes, scrotum, and penis.

The Testes The **testes** (TES teez; singular *testis*) are the organs in which sperm are produced. The testes consist of clusters of tiny, coiled tubes where sperm are formed. In addition to sperm, the testes produce testosterone. The hormone **testosterone** (tes TAHS tuh rohn) controls the development of adult male characteristics. These include facial hair, deepening of the voice, broadening of the shoulders, and the ability to produce sperm.

The testes are located in a pouch of skin called the **scrotum** (SKROH tum). The scrotum holds the testes away from the rest of the body. This distance keeps the testes about 2°C to 3°C below normal body temperature, which is 37°C. The cooler temperature is important because sperm cannot develop properly at 37°C.

FIGURE 2 ·······································

>INTERACTIVE ART **Structures of the Male Reproductive System**

✎ **Complete the tasks.**

1. **Identify** In the boxes, describe the structure and function of each organ.

2. **Calculate** Find the temperatures at which sperm develop properly.

_____

_____

_____

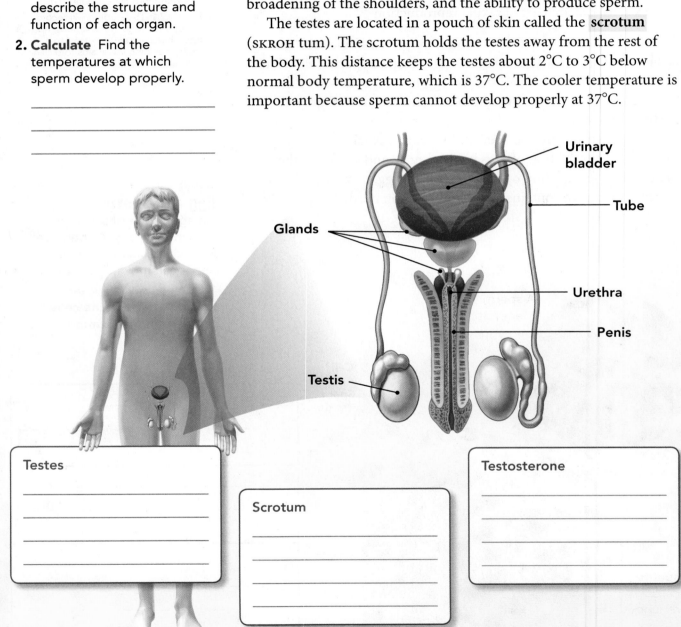

Glands

Urinary bladder

Tube

Urethra

Penis

Testis

Testes

_____
_____
_____
_____

Scrotum

_____
_____
_____
_____

Testosterone

_____
_____
_____
_____

Sperm The production of sperm cells begins during the teenage years. Each sperm cell has a head which contains chromosomes, and a long, whiplike tail. The chromosomes carry the information that controls inherited characteristics, such as blood type. The tail helps the sperm swim in fluid.

After forming in the testes, sperm travel through tubes in the male reproductive system. As they travel, sperm mix with fluids produced by nearby glands, as shown in **Figure 3.** This mixture of sperm cells and fluids is called **semen** (SEE mun). The fluids in semen provide an environment where sperm can swim. Semen also contains nutrients that the sperm use for energy.

Semen leaves the body through an organ called the **penis.** The semen travels through the tube in the penis called the urethra. Urine also leaves the body through the urethra. When semen passes through the urethra, however, muscles near the bladder contract. Those muscles prevent urine and semen from mixing.

Sequence Underline in the paragraphs the path that sperm take to leave the body. Then write the steps on the notepaper below.

FIGURE 3 ··········

Sperm Production and Passage From the Body

Sperm are produced in the testes and leave the body through the urethra.

✎ **Use the diagram to complete the tasks.**

1. **Relate Text and Visuals** On the diagram, draw arrows to trace the path that sperm travel through the male reproductive system.

2. **CHALLENGE** Why do sperm need to swim?

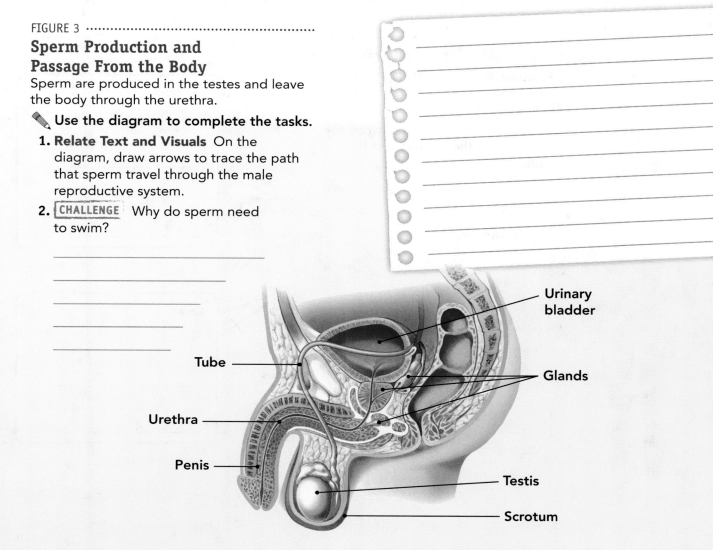

Urinary bladder

Tube

Glands

Urethra

Penis

Testis

Scrotum

When the female reproductive system becomes mature, the ovaries contain about 400,000 undeveloped eggs. However, only about 450 of those eggs will actually leave the ovaries and reach the uterus during a typical woman's life.

Female Reproductive System

The female reproductive system is specialized to produce eggs and nourish a developing baby until birth. It also produces estrogen and other hormones. The organs of this system include the ovaries, Fallopian tubes, uterus, and vagina.

The Ovaries The **ovaries** (OH vuh reez) are the female reproductive structures that produce eggs. They are located slightly below the waist, one on each side of the body, as shown in **Figure 4.** Like the testes in males, the ovaries are also endocrine glands that produce hormones. One hormone, **estrogen** (ES truh jun), triggers the development of some adult female characteristics. For example, estrogen causes the hips to widen and the breasts to develop. Estrogen is also involved in the development of egg cells. Each month, one of the ovaries releases a mature egg into the nearest oviduct, or Fallopian tube. A **Fallopian tube** is the passageway an egg travels from an ovary to the uterus. Fertilization usually occurs within a Fallopian tube.

FIGURE 4 ···

▶ **INTERACTIVE ART** **Structures of the Female Reproductive System**
The word *ovary* comes from the Latin word *ova*, meaning "eggs."

✏ **Identify** In the boxes, write the functions of the ovaries and the Fallopian tubes.

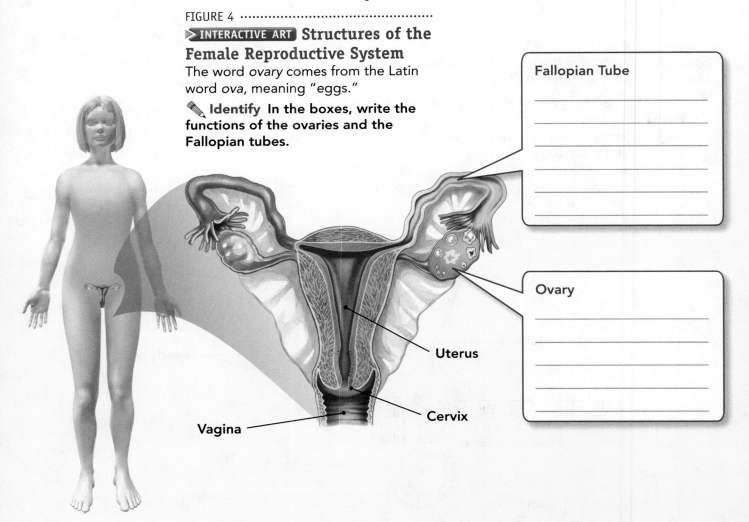

Fallopian Tube
_____
_____
_____
_____
_____

Ovary
_____
_____
_____
_____
_____

Uterus

Cervix

Vagina

Egg Cells From an ovary, an egg travels through the Fallopian tube to the uterus. The **uterus** (YOO tur us) is a hollow, muscular organ. If an egg has been fertilized in the Fallopian tube, it attaches to the wall of the uterus. An unfertilized egg breaks down in the uterus. It leaves through the cervix, an opening at the base of the uterus. The egg then passes through the vagina as it leaves the body. The **vagina** (vuh JY nuh) is a muscular passageway leading to the outside of the body. The vagina, or birth canal, is the passageway through which a baby leaves its mother's body during childbirth. **Figure 5** shows the female reproductive system.

Vocabulary Identify Related Word Forms When you know the meaning of a word, you can often identify and understand related word forms. How are the meanings of *fertilized* and *fertilization* related?

_____

_____

_____

FIGURE 5 ·················

Egg Production and Passage From the Body

Each month, an ovary produces an egg that leaves the body if it is not fertilized.

✎ **Describe** In the boxes, write the functions of the uterus and the vagina.

Fallopian tube

Ovary

Urinary bladder

Cervix

Urethra

Uterus

_____

_____

_____

Vagina

_____

_____

_____

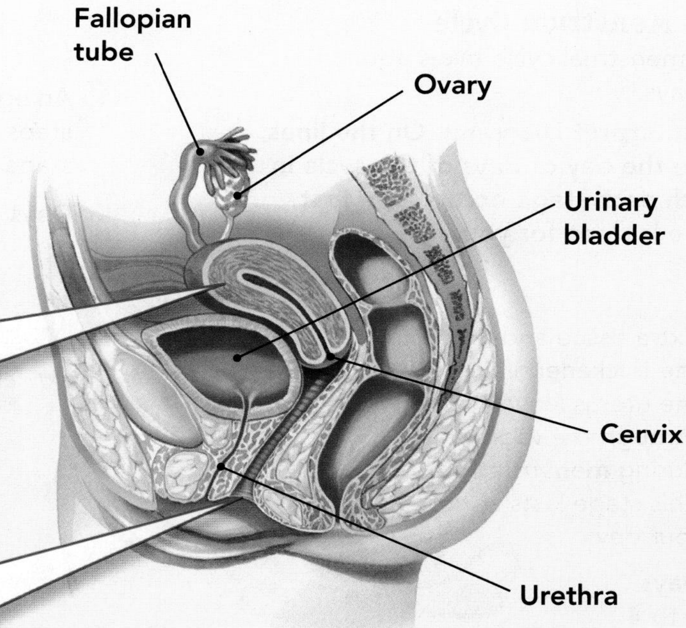

Lab zone Do the Quick Lab *Reproductive Systems.*

🔑 Assess Your Understanding

1a. Review What is fertilization?

_____

_____

SC.6.L.14.5

b. Relate Cause and Effect What changes does estrogen cause in a female's body?

_____

_____

_____

SC.6.L.14.5

got it?

○ I get it! Now I know that the male and female reproductive systems _____

_____

_____

○ I need extra help with _____

Go to **MY SCIENCE** ⓢ **COACH** online for help with this subject.

SC.6.L.14.5

FLORIDA NGSSS

SC.6.L.14.5 Identify and investigate the general functions of the reproductive system.

MA.6.A.3.6 Construct and analyze tables and graphs to describe simple relations using both common language and algebraic notation.

What Happens During the Menstrual Cycle?

Usually starting sometime during a girl's teenage years, an egg develops and is released about once a month. This event is part of the **menstrual cycle** (MEN stroo ul), or the monthly cycle of changes that occurs in females. 🔑 **During the menstrual cycle, an egg develops in an ovary. At the same time, the lining of the uterus thickens in a way that prepares the uterus for a fertilized egg.** Follow the stages of the menstrual cycle in **Figure 6.**

FIGURE 6 ···

The Menstrual Cycle
The menstrual cycle takes about 28 days.

✏️ **Interpret Diagrams** On the lines, write the day or days of the cycle in which each stage occurs. The first stage is done for you.

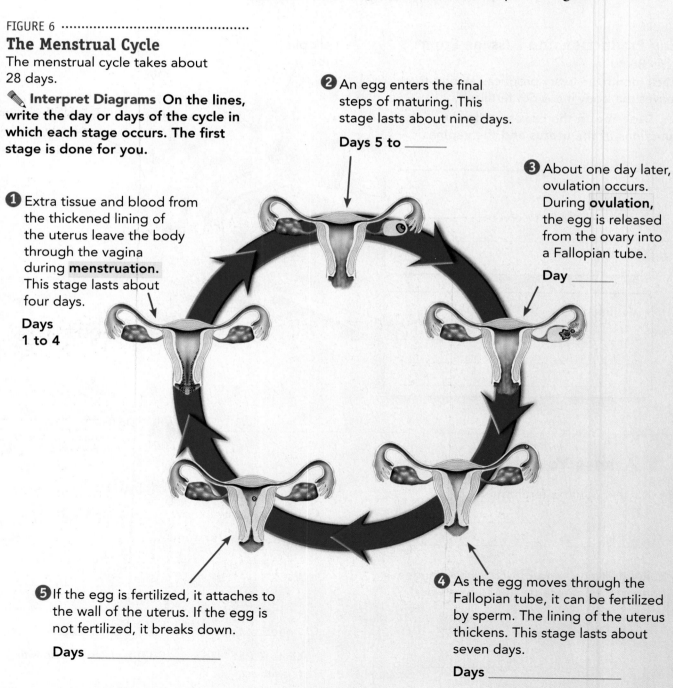

❶ Extra tissue and blood from the thickened lining of the uterus leave the body through the vagina during **menstruation.** This stage lasts about four days.

Days 1 to 4

❷ An egg enters the final steps of maturing. This stage lasts about nine days.

Days 5 to _____

❸ About one day later, ovulation occurs. During **ovulation,** the egg is released from the ovary into a Fallopian tube.

Day _____

❹ As the egg moves through the Fallopian tube, it can be fertilized by sperm. The lining of the uterus thickens. This stage lasts about seven days.

Days _____

❺ If the egg is fertilized, it attaches to the wall of the uterus. If the egg is not fertilized, it breaks down.

Days _____

do the math!

A woman's hormone levels change throughout her menstrual cycle. One such hormone is called LH.

1 Graph Use the data in the table to draw a line graph. Label the axes and write a title for the graph.

Day	1	5	9	13	17	22	25	28
Level of LH	12	13	13	70	12	12	8	10

2 Read Graphs On what day was the LH level the lowest? The highest?

_____

_____

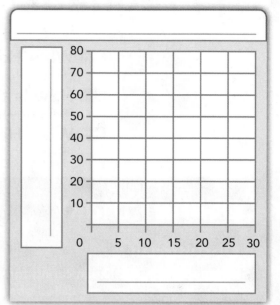

MA.6.A.3.6

3  **Develop Hypotheses** How might LH level and ovulation be related?

_____

_____

_____

Lab zone® Do the Quick Lab *Looking at Hormone Levels.*

🔑 Assess Your Understanding

2a. Identify In the menstrual cycle, what happens after ovulation occurs?

_____

_____

_____

SC.6.L.14.5

b. Infer What happens in the menstrual cycle if an egg is fertilized?

_____

_____

_____

SC.6.L.14.5

got it? ....

○ **I get it!** Now I know that during the menstrual cycle _____

_____

_____

○ **I need extra help with** _____

Go to MY SCIENCE ⓢ COACH *online for help with this subject.*

SC.6.L.14.5

Pregnancy and Birth

🔑 **What Happens Before Birth?**
SC.6.L.14.5

🔑 **How Is the Embryo Protected and Nourished?**
SC.6.L.14.5, LA.6.2.2.3, MA.6.A.3.6

🔑 **What Happens During Childbirth?**
SC.6.L.14.5

my planeT DiaRY

CAREER

Obstetrician

Some doctors specialize in caring for women during pregnancy. These doctors are called obstetricians. Obstetricians care for pregnant women, deliver babies, and make sure the mothers and new babies are healthy in the days that follow childbirth.

If you are interested in becoming an obstetrician, plan on spending at least ten years in school and training after you graduate high school. During this time you will learn how to care for mothers during pregnancy, childbirth, and after delivery. You will also learn about the serious conditions that babies may be born with. This career can be rewarding, even though it takes a lot of time and effort to get there.

Answer the questions below.

1. What are two responsibilities of an obstetrician?

_____

_____

_____

2. Why do you think a woman should see an obstetrician when she is pregnant?

_____

_____

_____

▶ PLANET DIARY   Go to **Planet Diary** to learn more about pregnancy and birth.

 Lab zone® Do the Inquiry Warm-Up *Prenatal Growth.*

 FLORIDA   NGSSS

SC.6.L.14.5 Identify and investigate the general functions of the major systems of the human body (digestive, respiratory, circulatory, reproductive, excretory, immune, nervous, and musculoskeletal) and describe ways these systems interact with each other to maintain homeostasis.

What Happens Before Birth?

When sperm are deposited into the vagina, they swim into and through the uterus and enter the Fallopian tubes. An egg can be fertilized in the Fallopian tubes during the first few days after ovulation. If a sperm fertilizes an egg, pregnancy can occur. The fertilized egg is called a zygote. 🔑 **Before birth, the zygote develops first into an embryo and then into a fetus.**

Vocabulary
- embryo • fetus • amniotic sac
- placenta • umbilical cord

Skills
- Reading: Compare and Contrast
- Inquiry: Calculate

Zygote and Embryo After fertilization, the zygote divides into two cells. These cells continue to divide as they travel toward the uterus. They form a hollow ball of more than one hundred cells by the time they reach the uterus. The ball attaches to the lining of the uterus. From the two-cell stage through the eighth week, a developing human is called an embryo (EM bree oh).

Fetus From the end of the eighth week until birth, a developing human is called a fetus (FEE tus). The internal organs that began to form in the embryo, such as the brain, continue to develop and start to function. The eyes, ears, and nose also develop, as you can see in **Figure 1**. The heart becomes large enough that a doctor can use a tool to hear it beat. The fetus begins to move and kick.

FIGURE 1 ·······························

> ART IN MOTION **Development of the Fetus**
An embryo develops into a fetus. Note: These photos do not show the actual sizes.

Interpret Photos In each box, describe the body parts of the embryo and fetus that you can see.

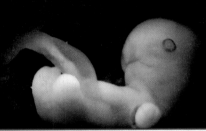

6-Week Embryo

_____

_____

_____

24-Week Fetus

_____

_____

_____

Lab zone® Do the Quick Lab Way to Grow!

Assess Your Understanding

got it? ···

O **I get it!** Now I know that before birth _____

_____

O **I need extra help with** _____

Go to MY SCIENCE COACH online for help with this subject.

SC.6.L.14.5

FLORIDA NGSSS

SC.6.L.14.5 Identify and investigate the general functions of the reproductive system.

LA.6.2.2.3 The student will organize information to show understanding (e.g., representing main ideas within the text through comparing/contrasting).

MA.6.A.3.6 Construct and analyze tables and graphs to describe simple relations using both common language and algebraic notation.

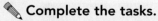

Compare and Contrast
In the paragraphs, underline how the amniotic sac and placenta are different. Then write how they are alike below. **LA.6.2.2.3**

_____

_____

_____

How Is the Embryo Protected and Nourished?

Soon after the embryo attaches to the uterus, new membranes and structures form. ☞ **The membranes and structures that form in the uterus during pregnancy protect and nourish the developing baby.**

Membranes **Figure 2** shows the two membranes that form during development. The **amniotic sac** (am NEE aht ik) surrounds the embryo and is filled with fluid. The fluid cushions and protects the embryo and later the fetus.

Another membrane helps form the **placenta** (pluh SEN tuh), which links the embryo and the mother. In the placenta, the embryo's blood vessels are next to the mother's blood vessels. Their blood does not mix, but substances are exchanged from one bloodstream to the other. The embryo's carbon dioxide and other wastes diffuse to the mother. Nutrients and oxygen diffuse from the mother to the embryo. In addition, drugs, alcohol, and chemicals in tobacco can diffuse from the mother to the embryo and cause it harm. However, most disease-causing organisms are prevented from reaching the embryo.

FIGURE 2

The Amniotic Sac and the Placenta
A fetus needs nourishment and protection to develop properly.

Complete the tasks.

1. **Identify** In the boxes, describe the functions of the amniotic sac and the placenta.

2. **CHALLENGE** How do you think it is possible for a baby to be born addicted to drugs?

_____

_____

_____

_____

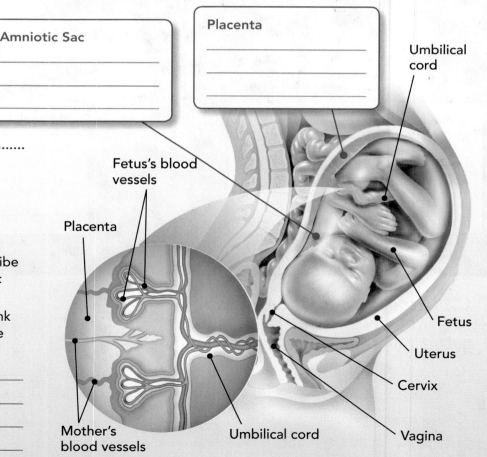

Amniotic Sac
_____
_____
_____

Placenta
_____
_____
_____

Umbilical cord

Fetus's blood vessels

Placenta

Mother's blood vessels

Umbilical cord

Fetus

Uterus

Cervix

Vagina

Structures

A ropelike structure, called the **umbilical cord,** begins to form between the embryo and the placenta. It contains blood vessels from the embryo that link the embryo to the placenta.

Umbilical cord

do the math!

A pregnancy is often divided into three stages called trimesters. Each trimester is three months.

① Interpret Tables How much mass does a developing fetus gain during each trimester?

First Trimester _____

Second Trimester _____

Third Trimester _____

② Calculate To find the percentage mass increase in a trimester, divide the mass gained in the trimester by the mass at the start of the trimester. Then multiply by 100. The percentage mass increase for the second trimester is as follows: $(614 \div 26) \times 100 =$ about 2,361 percent.

Find the percentage mass increase for the third trimester.

_____

_____

Change in Mass of a Developing Baby	
Month of Pregnancy	Mass (grams)
1	0.02
2	2
3	26
4	150
5	460
6	640
7	1,500
8	2,300
9	3,200

MA.6.A.3.6

 Do the Quick Lab *Egg-cellent Protection.*

🔑 Assess Your Understanding

1a. Explain What substances pass from the embryo or fetus to the mother?

_____

_____

_____

SC.6.L.14.5

b. Relate Cause and Effect Why is it dangerous for a pregnant woman to drink alcohol?

_____

_____

_____

SC.6.L.14.5

got it? ....

○ **I get it!** Now I know that an embryo or fetus is protected and nourished by _____

_____

○ **I need extra help with** _____

Go to MY SCIENCE COACH *online for help with this subject.*

SC.6.L.14.5

 **FLORIDA** NGSSS

SC.6.L.14.5 Identify and investigate the general functions of the major systems of the human body (digestive, respiratory, circulatory, reproductive, excretory, immune, nervous, and musculoskeletal) and describe ways these systems interact with each other to maintain homeostasis.

What Happens During Childbirth?

After about nine months of development inside a uterus, a baby is ready to be born. 🔑 **The birth of a baby takes place in three stages: labor, delivery, and afterbirth.**

Labor Labor is the first stage of birth. Strong muscle contractions of the uterus cause the cervix to open. Eventually, the opening is large enough for the baby to fit through. Labor may last from about two hours to more than 20 hours.

Delivery and Afterbirth The second stage of birth is called delivery. During a normal delivery the baby is pushed out of the uterus through the vagina. The head usually comes out first. Delivery can last several minutes to an hour or so. Shortly after delivery, the umbilical cord is cut about five centimeters from the baby's abdomen, as you can see in **Figure 3**. Seven to ten days later, the rest of the umbilical cord, which is now dried, falls off. It leaves a scar called the navel, or bellybutton.

Soon after delivery, muscles in the uterus contract, pushing the placenta and empty amniotic sac out through the vagina. This last stage, called afterbirth, usually takes less than an hour.

FIGURE 3 ·······························

Birth
Contractions in the uterus signal the start of labor.

✎ **Sequence In the boxes below, describe the events in each stage of birth.**

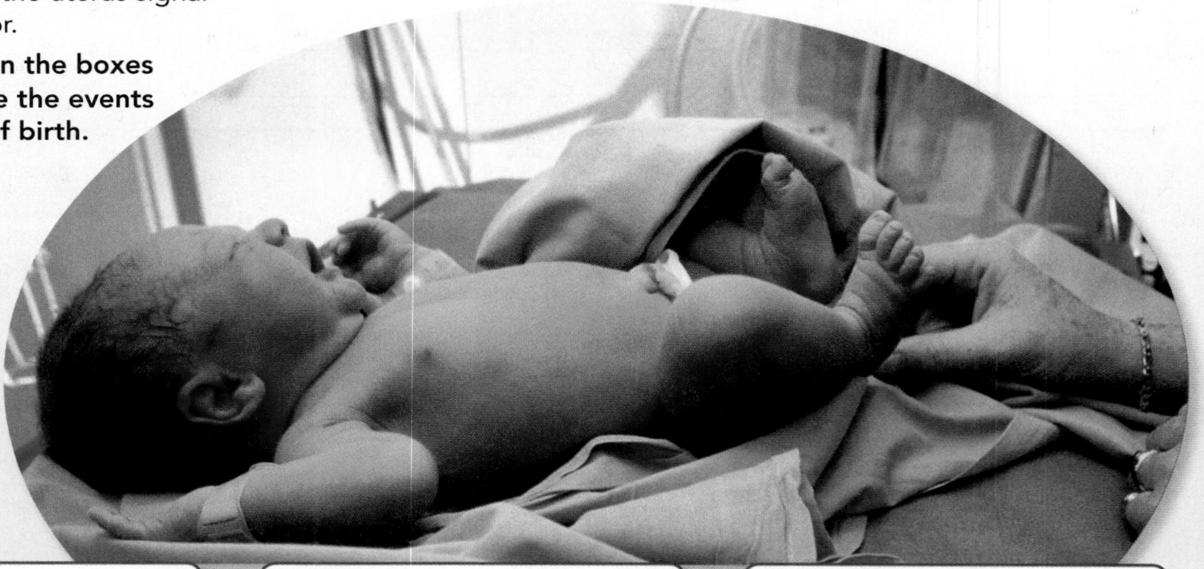

Labor		Delivery		Afterbirth
_____	➡	_____	➡	_____
_____		_____		_____
_____		_____		_____
_____		_____		_____

Birth and the Baby During birth, pressure caused by the muscle contractions briefly decreases the baby's oxygen supply. In response, the baby's endocrine system releases adrenaline, which increases the baby's heart rate. Seconds after delivery, the baby cries and begins breathing. The newborn's heart rate then slows down.

Multiple Births The delivery of more than one baby from a single pregnancy is called a multiple birth. Twin births are the most common multiple births. There are two types of twins: identical and fraternal. **Figure 4** shows how both types develop.

FIGURE 4 ······································
Multiple Births

Other multiple births, such as triplets, can also be fraternal or identical.

✎ **Interpret Diagrams** Explain on the notebook paper why fraternal twins can be different sexes and identical twins cannot.

Identical Twins

A sperm fertilizes a single egg.

The zygote splits and forms two embryos.

Fraternal Twins

Two sperm fertilize two eggs.

Each zygote forms an embryo.

Do the Quick Lab
Labor and Delivery.

🔑 Assess Your Understanding

2a. Name During labor, contractions cause the _____ to open.

SC.6.L.14.5

b. Apply Concepts Why must a baby start breathing right after birth?

_____

_____

SC.6.L.14.5

got it?

○ **I get it!** Now I know that childbirth involves

_____

○ **I need extra help with** _____

Go to my science ⓢ coach *online for help with this subject.*

SC.6.L.14.5

Study Guide

REVIEW THE ESSENTIAL

My _____ and _____ systems help regulate and control my body processes.

LESSON 1 The Nervous System

SC.6.L.14.5

🔑 Your nervous system receives information about what is happening both inside and outside your body. It directs how your body responds to this information and helps maintain homeostasis.

🔑 Neurons carry nerve impulses throughout the body. The brain is the control center of the central nervous system. The spinal cord links the brain to the peripheral nervous system.

🔑 Your eyes, ears, nose, mouth, and skin are specialized sense organs that enable you to get information from the outside world.

Vocabulary
- neuron • nerve impulse • nerve • synapse • central nervous system
- peripheral nervous system • reflex

LESSON 2 The Endocrine System

SC.6.L.14.5

🔑 The endocrine system regulates short-term and long-term activities by sending chemicals throughout the body. Long-term changes include growth and development.

🔑 When the amount of a hormone in the blood reaches a certain level, the endocrine system sends signals that stop the release of that hormone.

Vocabulary
- gland • duct • hormone • target cell • hypothalamus
- pituitary gland • negative feedback

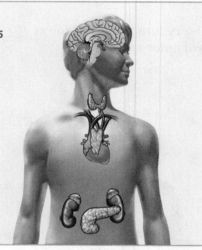

LESSON 3 The Male and Female Reproductive Systems

SC.6.L.14.5, SC.6.N.2.2

🔑 The male reproductive system produces sperm and testosterone. The female reproductive system produces eggs and estrogen. It also nourishes a developing baby until birth.

Vocabulary
- fertilization • egg • sperm • zygote
- testes • testosterone • scrotum • semen
- penis • ovary • estrogen • Fallopian tube
- uterus • vagina • menstrual cycle
- menstruation • ovulation

LESSON 4 Pregnancy and Birth

SC.6.L.14.5

🔑 Before birth, the zygote develops first into an embryo and then into a fetus.

🔑 The membranes and structures that form in the uterus during pregnancy protect and nourish the developing baby.

🔑 The birth of a baby takes place in three stages: labor, delivery, and afterbirth.

Vocabulary
- embryo • fetus • amniotic sac
- placenta • umbilical cord

Review and Assessment

LESSON 1 The Nervous System

1. Which structure links the brain and the peripheral nervous system?

a. the cerebrum   **b.** the cerebellum

c. the cochlea   **d.** the spinal cord

SC.6.L.14.5

2. The senses of _____ and _____ depend on chemicals in the air and food. The sense of _____ depends on the stimulus of light. The sense of _____ depends on the stimulus of sound. The sense of _____ is found in all areas of your skin.

SC.6.L.14.5

3. Make Generalizations How does the nervous system help maintain homeostasis?

_____

_____

_____

SC.6.L.14.5

4. Draw Conclusions What is the result if the spinal cord is cut?

_____

_____

_____

SC.6.L.14.5

5. Apply Concepts As a man walks barefoot along the beach, he steps on a sharp shell. His foot automatically jerks upward, even before he feels pain. What process is this an example of? How does it help protect the man?

_____

_____

_____

_____

SC.6.L.14.5

6. Write About It The cerebrum, the cerebellum, and the brain stem are regions of the brain that carry out specific functions. Write a brief job description for each of these regions of the brain.

SC.6.L.14.5

LESSON 2 The Endocrine System

7. The structure that links the nervous system and the endocrine system is the

a. thyroid gland.   **b.** umbilical cord.

c. target cell.   **d.** hypothalamus.

SC.6.L.14.5

8. _____ recognize a hormone's chemical structure.

SC.6.L.14.5

9. Make Generalizations What is the endocrine system's role?

_____

_____

_____

_____

SC.6.L.14.5

10. Infer Study the diagram below. Then suggest how the hormones glucagon and insulin might work together to maintain homeostasis in a healthy person.

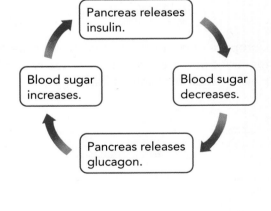

Pancreas releases insulin.

Blood sugar decreases.

Pancreas releases glucagon.

Blood sugar increases.

_____

_____

_____

_____

_____

SC.6.L.14.5

LESSON 3 **The Male and Female Reproductive Systems**

11. The release of an egg from an ovary is called

   a. ovulation.   **b.** menstruation.

   c. fertilization.   **d.** negative feedback.

                      SC.6.L.14.5

12. A mixture of sperm and fluids is called

   _____

                      SC.6.L.14.5

13. Draw Conclusions What is the role of the fluids in semen?

   _____

   _____

                      SC.6.L.14.5

14. Relate Cause and Effect What changes occur in the uterus during the menstrual cycle?

   _____

   _____

   _____

   _____

   _____

                      SC.6.L.14.5

15. Compare and Contrast In what ways are the functions of the ovaries and the testes similar? How do their functions differ?

   _____

   _____

   _____

   _____

                      SC.6.L.14.5

16. math! The average menstrual cycle is 28 days in length. But it can vary from 21 to 35 days. Ovulation usually occurs 14 days before the end of the cycle. On what day will ovulation occur after the start of a 21-day cycle? A 35-day cycle?

                      SC.6.L.14.5

LESSON 4 **Pregnancy and Birth**

17. The membrane that protects and cushions the embryo is called the

   a. umbilical cord.   **b.** scrotum

   c. amniotic sac.   **d.** ovary.

                      SC.6.L.14.5

18. The _____ contains blood vessels from the embryo that link the embryo and the placenta.

                      SC.6.L.14.5

19. Sequence What three stages of development does a fertilized egg go through before birth?

   _____

   _____

                      SC.6.L.14.5

20. Compare and Contrast Fraternal twins develop from (a single egg/two eggs). Identical twins develop from (a single egg/two eggs).

                      SC.6.L.14.5

APPLY THE ESSENTIAL ? What systems regulate and control body processes?

21. The body goes through many changes during adolescence. Suppose a tumor in the pituitary gland causes the gland to function incorrectly. How might a person's development during adolescence be affected? Explain.

   _____

   _____

   _____

   _____

   _____

   _____

   _____

   _____

                      SC.6.L.14.5

Florida Benchmarks Review

Circle the letter of the best answer.

1 What is the function of the part labeled A on the neuron shown below?

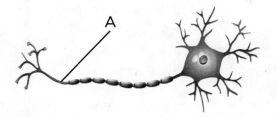

A It carries the nerve impulse toward the cell body.

B It protects the neuron from damage.

C It carries the nerve impulse away from the cell body.

D It picks up stimuli from the environment.

SC.6.L.14.5

2 A scientist studying the brain is studying part of the

A peripheral nervous system.

B somatic nervous system.

C autonomic nervous system.

D central nervous system.

SC.6.L.14.5

3 You can infer that a person who has lost his or her sense of smell is also likely to have a poor

A sense of balance.

B sense of taste.

C sense of touch.

D sense of hearing.

SC.6.L.14.5

4 You are riding your bike when a small child suddenly darts out in front of you. Which of your endocrine glands is most likely to release a hormone in response to this situation?

A pituitary gland

B adrenal gland

C thyroid gland

D parathyroid gland

SC.6.L.14.5

5 A woman gives birth to twins who developed from a single fertilized egg that split early in development. Which of the following is a reasonable prediction that you can make about the twins?

A They will be the same sex.

B They will have similar interests.

C They will not look alike.

D They will have different inherited traits.

SC.6.L.14.5

6 Look at the table below. At the twelfth week, a developing baby measures about 75 mm. By which week has the fetus grown to four times this length?

Length of Fetus			
Week of Pregnancy	Average Length (mm)	Week of Pregnancy	Average Length (mm)
4	4	24	300
8	30	28	350
12	75	32	410
16	180	36	450
20	250	38	500

A Week 4   B Week 12

C Week 24   D Week 32

SC.6.L.14.5

WHAT CAN YOU DO TO PREVENT DISEASE?

Why do you sometimes get sick?

This three-year-old girl from Somalia is getting a polio vaccine. Polio is spread through contaminated water or food, or by contact with a person infected with the virus. It used to be a common disease in Somalia. Polio has been almost eliminated in the United States because most babies receive the polio vaccine. Vaccines prevent some viral diseases. Other viral diseases, such as the common cold, have no vaccine.

Infer **What steps can you take to stop a virus such as a cold from spreading?**

_____

_____

_____

_____

> **UNTAMED SCIENCE** Watch the **Untamed Science** video to learn more about fighting disease.

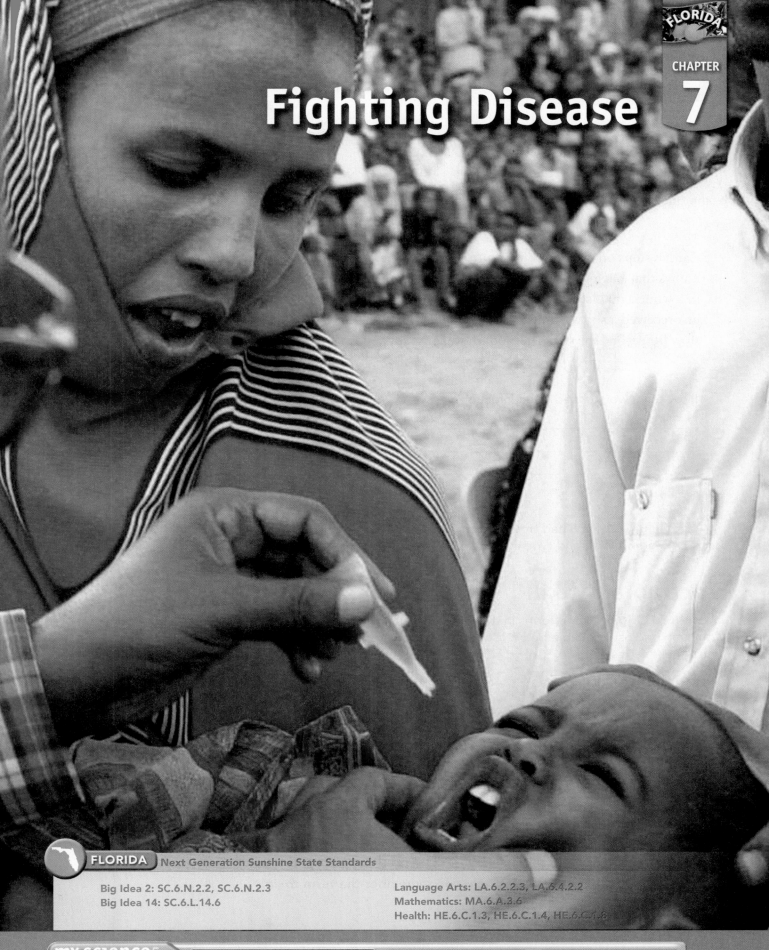

Fighting Disease

FLORIDA *Next Generation Sunshine State Standards*

Big Idea 2: SC.6.N.2.2, SC.6.N.2.3
Big Idea 14: SC.6.L.14.6

Language Arts: LA.6.2.2.3, LA.6.4.2.2
Mathematics: MA.6.A.3.6
Health: HE.6.C.1.3, HE.6.C.1.4, HE.6.C.1.8

7 Getting Started

Check Your Understanding

1. Background Read the paragraph below and then answer the question.

> Camila steps on a nail that punctures her foot. She knows that **bacteria** can cause a disease called tetanus in a wound that is **contaminated**. Fortunately, Camila just received a shot to prevent tetanus. However, to help stop **infection**, she soaks her foot in warm soapy water.

Bacteria are single-celled organisms that lack a nucleus.

An object that is **contaminated** has become unclean and could possibly infect the body.

Infection is the process in which disease-causing microorganisms invade the body and then multiply.

• How can a wound lead to an infection?

_____

_____

_____

> **MY READING WEB** If you had trouble completing the question above, visit **My Reading Web** and type in *Fighting Disease.*

Vocabulary Skill

Latin Word Origins Some terms in this chapter contain word parts with Latin origins. The table below lists some of the Latin words from which these terms come.

Latin Word	Meaning	Key Term
toxicum	poison	toxin, *n.* a poison produced by bacteria that damages cells
tumere	to swell	tumor, *n.* an abnormal mass of tissue that results from uncontrolled division of cells

LA.6.1.6.1

2. Quick Check In the table above, circle the meaning of the Latin word *toxicum.* The meaning may help you remember the term *toxin.*

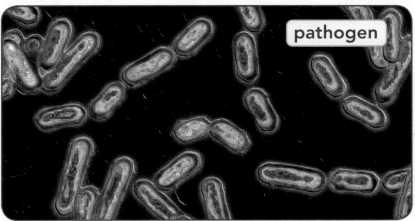

pathogen

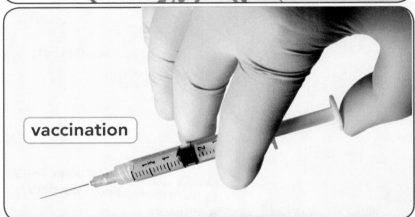

T cell

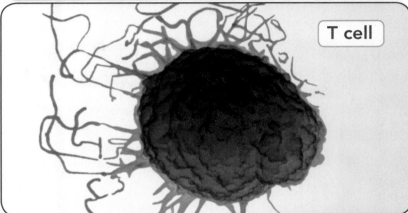

vaccination

allergen

Chapter Preview

LESSON 1
- microorganism   • pathogen
- infectious disease   • toxin
- parasite
- Identify the Main Idea
- Develop Hypotheses

LESSON 2
- inflammatory response
- phagocyte   • immune response
- lymphocyte   • T cell   • antigen
- B cell   • antibody
- Compare and Contrast
- Make Models

LESSON 3
- immunity   • active immunity
- vaccination   • vaccine
- passive immunity   • antibiotic
- Relate Cause and Effect
- Communicate

LESSON 4
- noninfectious disease   • allergy
- allergen   • histamine   • asthma
- insulin   • diabetes   • tumor
- carcinogen
- Summarize
- Draw Conclusions

LESSON 5
- AIDS   • HIV
- Sequence
- Graph

> VOCAB FLASH CARDS For extra help
with vocabulary, visit **Vocab Flash
Cards** and type in *Fighting Disease.*

1 Infectious Disease

UNLOCK THE ESSENTIAL ?

🔑 **How Do Pathogens Cause Disease?**
SC.6.N.2.2, SC.6.N.2.3, SC.6.L.14.6, LA.6.2.2.3

🔑 **What Pathogens Cause Infectious Disease and How Are They Spread?**
SC.6.L.14.6, LA.6.2.2.3

my planet diary

Fight the Flu

Misconception: You cannot catch the flu if you have gotten a flu shot.

The flu vaccine decreases your chances of catching the flu, but it does not protect you 100 percent. However, if you get the shot and still end up catching the flu, your symptoms probably will be milder than if you had not gotten vaccinated.

There are many strains of the flu virus. Each year, scientists choose the strains that they think will appear in the United States. Then a vaccine is made that contains those strains. The vaccine is given to people across the country. However, getting a flu shot will not protect you against any strain that is not in the vaccine.

MISCONCEPTION

Read the following questions. Write your answers below.

1. What is one challenge that scientists face when making the flu vaccine?

_____

_____

_____

2. Does a person need to get a flu shot every year? Why or why not?

_____

_____

_____

> PLANET DIARY Go to **Planet Diary** to learn more about infectious diseases.

 Lab zone Do the Inquiry Warm-Up *The Agents of Disease.*

Vocabulary
- microorganism • pathogen
- infectious disease • toxin • parasite

Skills
- Reading: Identify the Main Idea
- Inquiry: Develop Hypotheses

How Do Pathogens Cause Disease?

In ancient times, people had different ideas about what caused disease. They thought that things such as evil spirits or swamp air caused disease. In fact, they sometimes cut holes in the skulls of sick people to let the evil spirits out. The ancient Greeks thought that disease resulted from an imbalance of four body fluids: blood, phlegm (flem) or mucus, black bile, and yellow bile.

Louis Pasteur and Microorganisms
It was not until the 1860s that a French scientist named Louis Pasteur discovered the cause of some diseases. After investigating what causes foods to spoil, Pasteur concluded that **microorganisms,** living things too small to see without a microscope, were the cause. Pasteur thought that microorganisms might be causing disease in animals and people, too. So he investigated a disease attacking silkworms at the time. Pasteur found microorganisms inside silkworms with the disease. He was able to show that these organisms caused the disease. Pasteur's work led to an understanding of what causes most infectious diseases—microorganisms.

FLORIDA NGSSS

SC.6.N.2.2 Explain that scientific knowledge is durable because it is open to change as new evidence or interpretations are encountered.

SC.6.N.2.3 Recognize that scientists possess varied talents, interests, and goals.

SC.6.L.14.6 Compare and contrast types of infectious agents that may infect the human body, including viruses, bacteria, fungi, and parasites.

LA.6.2.2.3 The student will organize information to show understanding.

Identify the Main Idea
In the graphic organizer, write the main idea of the first paragraph. Then write three details that support the main idea.
LA.6.2.2.3

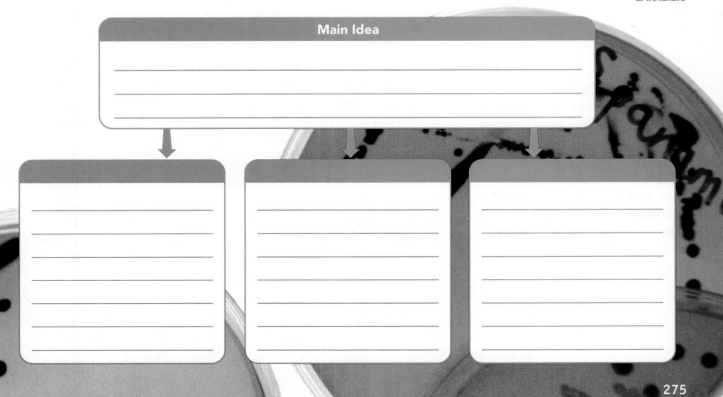

Main Idea

275

THEN

NOW

Then	Now

FIGURE 1 ·······················

Preventing Infection

A clean environment reduces the chance of infection after surgery.

✏ **Communicate** Observe the pictures above. In the table, describe the operating rooms then and now. Then in a small group, discuss how technology affects surgery today. Write your ideas below.

_____

_____

_____

_____

SC.6.N.2.2

Joseph Lister Pasteur's work influenced a British surgeon named Joseph Lister. Before the twentieth century, surgery was risky because most surgeons operated with dirty instruments and did not wash their hands. The sheets on hospital beds were rarely washed between patients. Even if people lived through an operation, many died later from an infection.

Lister hypothesized that microorganisms cause the infections that often followed surgery. He planned an experiment to test his hypothesis. Before performing operations, he washed his hands and surgical instruments with carbolic acid, a chemical that kills microorganisms. He also sprayed the patients with the acid, as shown in **Figure 1.** After the surgeries, he covered the patients' wounds with bandages dipped in carbolic acid.

Lister's results were dramatic. Before he used his new methods, about 45 percent of his surgical patients died from infection. With Lister's new techniques, only about 15 percent died.

Robert Koch In the 1870s and 1880s, the German physician Robert Koch showed that a specific microorganism causes each disease. For example, the microorganism that causes strep throat cannot cause chickenpox or other diseases. Look at **Figure 2** to see how Koch identified the microorganism for a disease called anthrax.

Organisms that cause disease are called **pathogens.** A disease caused by a pathogen is an **infectious disease.** 🔑 **When you have an infectious disease, pathogens are in your body causing harm.** Pathogens damage large numbers of individual cells, which makes you sick.

FIGURE 2 ······················

Koch's Experiment
Koch followed the scientific method in his research of pathogens.

✏️ **Draw Conclusions** How would Koch's conclusion have been different if Mouse B's blood had not contained the pathogen found in Mouse A's blood?

_____

_____

_____

_____

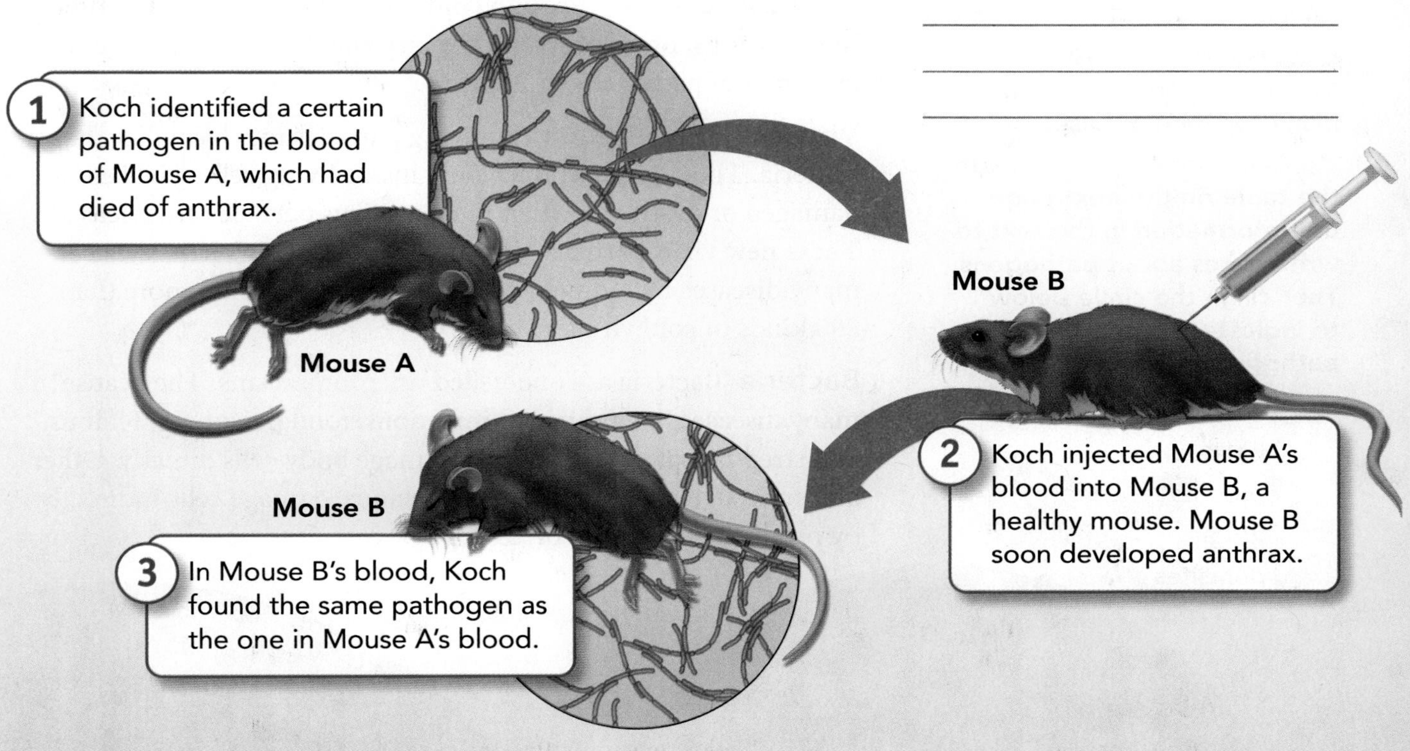

1 Koch identified a certain pathogen in the blood of Mouse A, which had died of anthrax.

Mouse A

Mouse B

Mouse B

3 In Mouse B's blood, Koch found the same pathogen as the one in Mouse A's blood.

2 Koch injected Mouse A's blood into Mouse B, a healthy mouse. Mouse B soon developed anthrax.

Lab zone ® Do the Quick Lab *How Do Pathogens Cause Disease?*

🔑 **Assess Your Understanding**

1a. Define What is an infectious disease?

_____

_____

SC.6.L.14.6

b. Summarize What was the goal of Lister's scientific work?

_____

_____

_____

SC.6.N.2.3, SC.6.L.14.6

got it?

◯ **I get it!** Now I know that pathogens cause disease by _____

_____

_____

◯ **I need extra help with** _____

Go to **MY SCIENCE** 💬 **COACH** *online for help with this subject.*
SC.6.L.14.6

FLORIDA NGSSS

SC.6.L.14.6 Compare and contrast types of infectious agents that may infect the human body, including viruses, bacteria, fungi, and parasites.

LA.6.2.2.3 The student will organize information to show understanding.

What Pathogens Cause Infectious Disease and How Are They Spread?

You share Earth with many kinds of organisms. Most of these organisms are harmless, but some can make you sick. Some diseases are caused by multicelled animals, such as worms. However, most pathogens can be seen only with a microscope.

Types of Pathogens

The five major types of human pathogens are viruses, bacteria, protists, fungi, and parasites. They can be spread through contact with a sick person, other living things, or an object in the environment. You can see some examples of pathogens in **Figure 3.**

Viruses Viruses are tiny nonliving particles much smaller than bacteria. They can reproduce only inside living cells. The cells are damaged or destroyed when the new virus particles are released. These new virus particles then infect other cells. Viruses cause many diseases including colds and the flu. There are more than 200 kinds of cold viruses alone.

Bacteria Bacteria are one-celled microorganisms. They cause many diseases, including ear infections, food poisoning, tetanus, and strep throat. Some bacteria damage body cells directly. Other bacteria, such as those that cause tetanus, damage cells indirectly by producing a poison, or **toxin.**

FIGURE 3 ·······

> VIRTUAL LAB **Pathogens**
Microscopic organisms cause many common diseases.

✎ **Compare and Contrast** In the table on the next page, use information in the text to write notes about pathogens. Then fill in the circle below to indicate which type of pathogen produces toxins.

LA.6.2.2.3

- ○ viruses
- ○ bacteria
- ○ protists
- ○ fungi
- ○ parasites

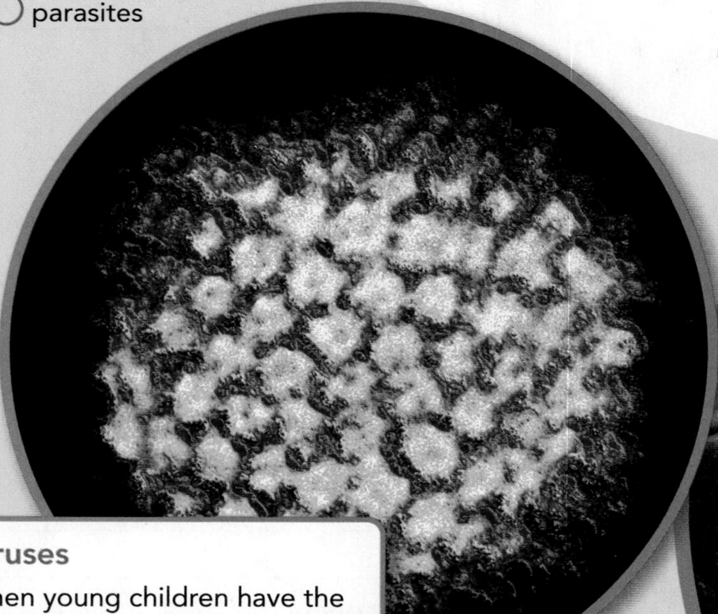

Viruses
When young children have the flu, this virus, called adenovirus, may be the cause of the runny nose and sore throat.

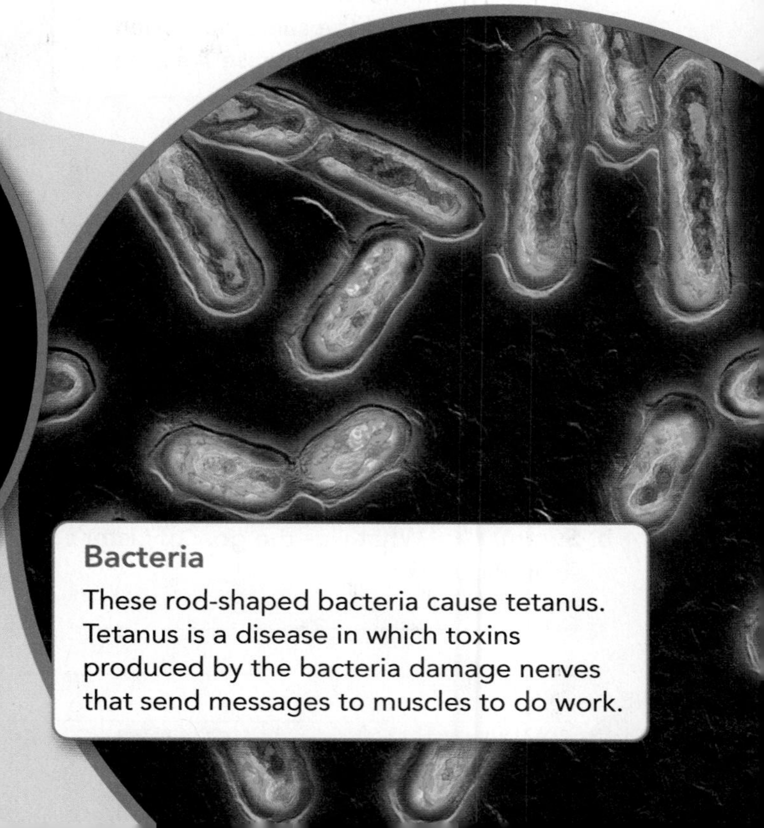

Bacteria
These rod-shaped bacteria cause tetanus. Tetanus is a disease in which toxins produced by the bacteria damage nerves that send messages to muscles to do work.

Protists Most protists are one-celled microorganisms and some can cause disease. They are larger than bacteria but still tiny. One type of protist causes the disease malaria, which is common in tropical areas. African sleeping sickness and hiker's disease are other diseases caused by protists.

Fungi Some fungi, such as molds and yeasts, also cause infectious diseases. Fungi that cause disease may be one-celled or multicelled organisms. Fungi grow best in warm, dark, moist areas of the body. Athlete's foot and ringworm are two fungal diseases.

Parasites The protist that causes malaria is an example of a **parasite** (PA ruh syt), or an organism that lives on or in a host and causes it harm. Multicellular organisms such as tapeworms, roundworms, fleas, ticks, mites, and mosquitoes are some parasitic animals that can cause disease. For instance, mites can cause scabies, a disease in which the skin becomes irritated and itchy.

Protists
This microorganism is called *Giardia* (jee AHR dee uh). People who drink from streams or lakes that contain this protist can get an intestinal disease called hiker's disease.

Fungi
This fungus causes a skin infection called athlete's foot.

Pathogen	Size	Characteristics	Types of Diseases
Viruses			
Bacteria			
Protists			
Fungi			
Parasites			

Pathogens are spread through contaminated water.

Apply Concepts If you have a cold, what can you do to prevent spreading it?

_____

_____

_____

_____

How Pathogens Are Spread

Pathogens can infect you in several ways. They can spread through contact with an infected person; through soil, food, or water; and through a contaminated object or an infected animal.

Infected People Pathogens often pass from one person to another through direct physical contact, such as kissing and shaking hands. For example, if you kiss someone with an open cold sore, the virus that causes cold sores can get into your body. Pathogens spread indirectly, too. For example, when a person with a cold sneezes, pathogens shoot into the air. People who inhale these pathogens may catch the cold.

Soil, Food, and Water Some pathogens occur naturally in the environment. For example, the bacteria that cause botulism, a severe form of food poisoning, live in soil. These bacteria can produce toxins in foods that have been improperly canned. Other pathogens contaminate food and water and sicken people who eat the food or drink the water. Cholera and dysentery, deadly diseases that cause severe diarrhea, are spread through contaminated food or water.

apply it!

Cholera is a deadly disease caused by bacteria in drinking water. This map shows the locations of cholera cases in the 1854 cholera epidemic in London, England, and the city's water pumps.

1 Develop Hypotheses Which pump was probably the source of the contaminated water? What evidence do you have?

_____

_____

_____

_____

2 Pose Questions Suppose a doctor at the time learned that two more people had died of cholera. What two questions would the doctor most likely have asked?

_____

_____

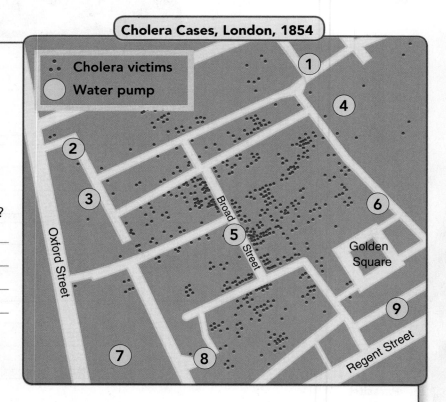

Cholera Cases, London, 1854

Cholera victims

Water pump

Contaminated Objects Some pathogens can survive for a time outside a person's body. People can contact pathogens by using objects, such as towels or keyboards, that an infected person has touched. Colds and flu can be spread in this way. Tetanus bacteria can enter the body if a contaminated nail or other object punctures the skin.

Infected Animals If an animal that is infected with certain pathogens bites a person, the pathogens can pass to the person. For example, people get rabies, a serious disease of the nervous system, from the bite of an infected animal, such as a dog or raccoon. In tropical regions, mosquito bites transfer the malaria protist to people. Deer ticks, as shown in **Figure 4,** live mostly in the northeastern and upper mideastern United States. The bites of some deer ticks spread Lyme disease. If left untreated, Lyme disease can damage joints and cause many other health problems.

FIGURE 4 ·····························

Deer Ticks and Lyme Disease

To prevent Lyme disease, wear a long-sleeved shirt and tuck your pants into your socks if you plan to walk where ticks may live.

✎ **Infer** Explain how a deer tick could infect you without your realizing it.

_____

_____

_____

_____

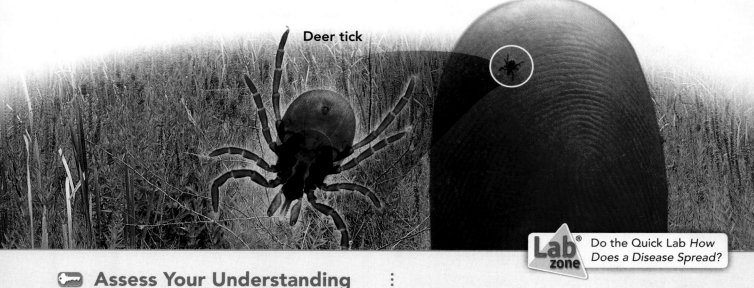

Deer tick

Lab zone Do the Quick Lab *How Does a Disease Spread?*

🔑 Assess Your Understanding

2a. Identify Name five types of pathogens that cause disease in humans.

_____

_____

SC.6.L.14.6

b. CHALLENGE How could people make bacteria-contaminated water safe to drink in order to prevent illness?

_____

_____

_____

_____

SC.6.L.14.6

got_it?

○ **I get it!** Now I know that disease-causing pathogens include _____

_____,

and they are spread by _____

_____

_____

○ **I need extra help with** _____

Go to **MY SCIENCE ⑤ COACH** online for help with this subject. SC.6.L.14.6

The Body's Defenses

🔑 **What Is the Body's First Line of Defense?**
SC.6.L.14.6, LA.6.4.2.2, LA.6.2.2.3

🔑 **What Are the Inflammatory and Immune Responses?**
SC.6.L.14.6, LA.6.2.2.3

MY PLANET DIARY

The Kissing Disease

Have you ever heard of mononucleosis? Also known as mono, or the kissing disease, mononucleosis is most common among older teenagers and people in their twenties. It got its nickname because the disease can be spread through kissing. But, be careful. Because mono is passed through saliva, it can also be spread by sharing cups, forks, straws, and other utensils.

Some common symptoms of mono are fever, sore throat, swollen glands, and fatigue. If you display these symptoms, you might want to pay your doctor a visit, even if you haven't kissed anyone!

FUN FACTS

Read the following questions. Write your answers below.

1. How can mononucleosis be spread?

_____
_____
_____
_____

2. What can you do to lower your chances of catching mono?

_____
_____
_____

▶ **PLANET DIARY** Go to **Planet Diary** to learn more about the body's defenses.

Lab® zone Do the Inquiry Warm-Up *Which Pieces Fit Together?*

Vocabulary
- inflammatory response • phagocyte
- immune response • lymphocyte • T cell
- antigen • B cell • antibody

Skills
Reading: Compare and Contrast
Inquiry: Make Models

What Is the Body's First Line of Defense?

You have probably battled invaders in video games. Video games have fantasy battles, but on and in your body, real battles against invading pathogens happen all the time. You are hardly ever aware of these battles because the body's disease-fighting system has lines of defense that effectively eliminate pathogens before they can harm your cells. **In the first line of defense, the surface of your skin, breathing passages, mouth, and stomach function as barriers to pathogens. These barriers trap and kill most pathogens with which you come into contact.**

Skin Your skin is an effective barrier to pathogens, as you can see in **Figure 1.** Pathogens on the skin are exposed to destructive chemicals in oil and sweat. Even if these chemicals do not kill them, the pathogens may fall off with dead skin cells. Most pathogens get through the skin only when it is cut. However, blood clots at a cut. Then a scab forms over the cut. So pathogens have little time to enter the body this way.

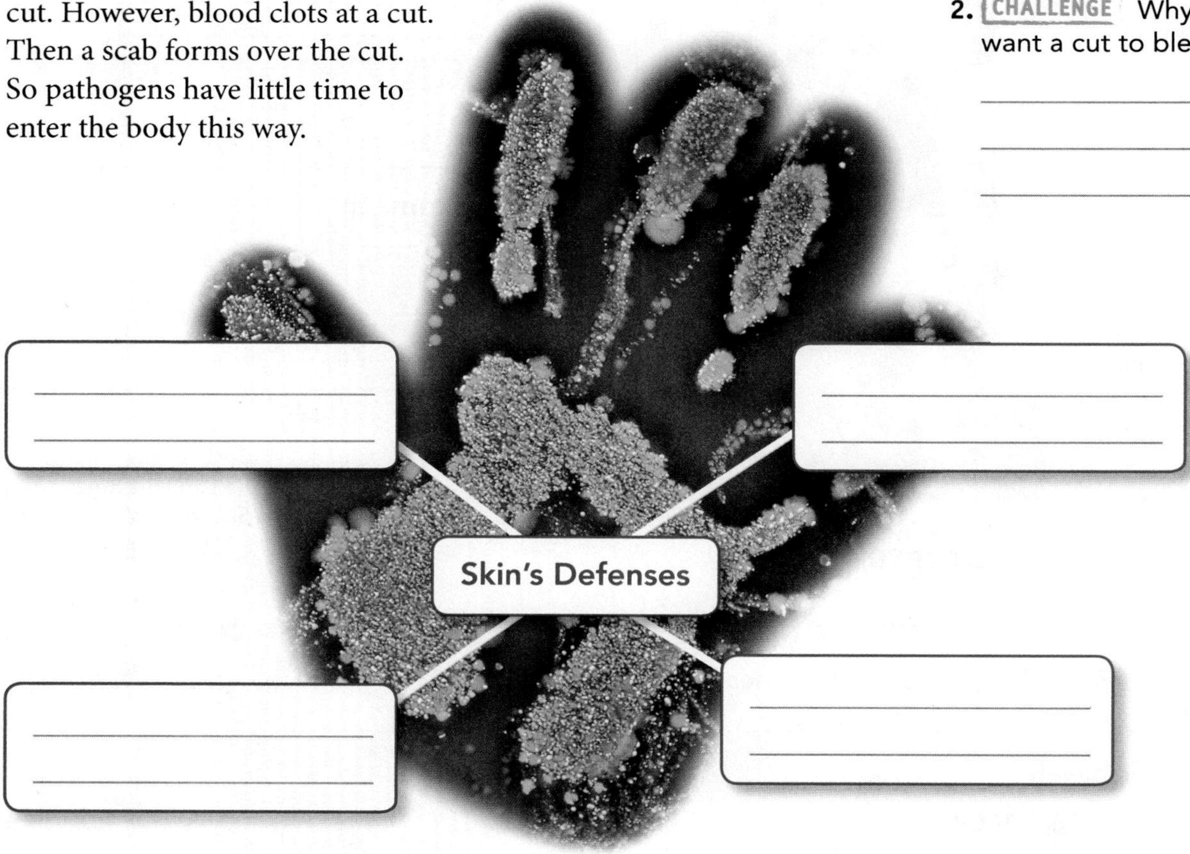

FLORIDA NGSSS

SC.6.L.14.6 Compare and contrast types of infectious agents that may infect the human body, including viruses, bacteria, fungi, and parasites.

LA.6.4.2.2 The student will record information related to a topic.

LA.6.2.2.3 The student will organize information to show understanding.

FIGURE 1 ······

Skin as a Barrier
The dots are groups of bacteria. The bacteria were on the skin of a person's hand.

✏ **Use the photo to complete the tasks.**

1. **Identify** In each box, write one of the skin's defenses against pathogens.

2. **CHALLENGE** Why would you want a cut to bleed some?

_____

_____

_____

Skin's Defenses

283

Breathing Passages Your breathing passages defend you from many pathogens you inhale. The nose, pharynx, trachea, and bronchi have hairs, mucus, and cilia, all of which trap pathogens from the air. In addition, you sneeze and cough when pathogens irritate your breathing passages. Sneezing and coughing force pathogens out of your body.

Mouth and Stomach Even if foods are handled safely, they still contain potential pathogens. Most of these pathogens are destroyed in your mouth or stomach. Saliva in your mouth contains destructive chemicals, and your stomach produces acid. **Figure 2** shows three of your body's barriers to pathogens.

FIGURE 2 ·····························
Barriers to Pathogens
Your breathing passages, mouth, and stomach are part of your first line of defense against pathogens.

✎ **Summarize** In each box, write how the barrier protects the body from pathogens.
LA.6.4.2.2

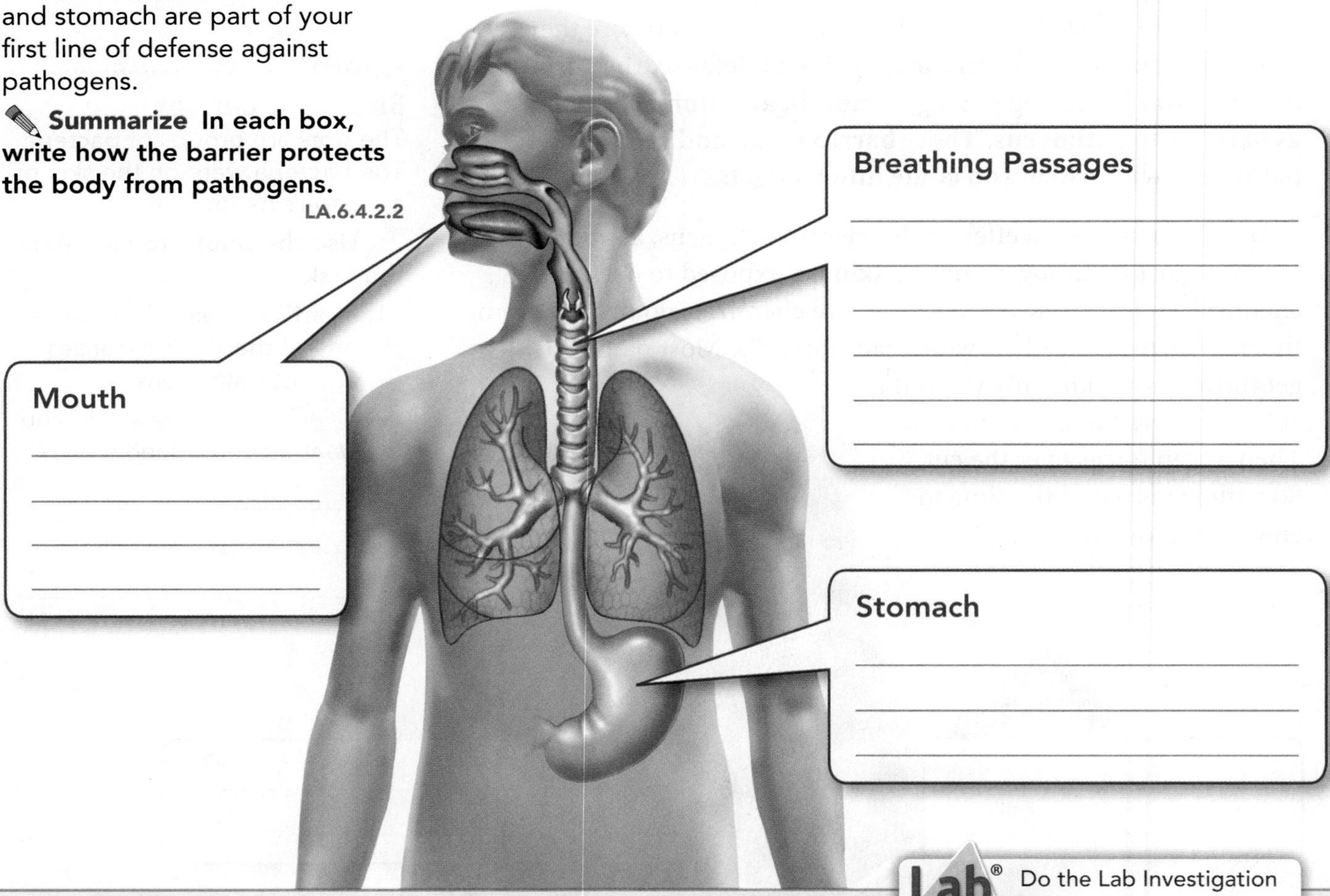

Mouth

Breathing Passages

Stomach

Lab zone® Do the Lab Investigation
The Skin as a Barrier.

🔑 Assess Your Understanding

got it? ···

○ **I get it!** Now I know that the body's first lines of defense are _____

_____

○ **I need extra help with** _____

Go to MY SCIENCE 🅢 COACH *online for help with this subject.*

SC.6.L.14.6

What Are the Inflammatory and Immune Responses?

Sometimes the first line of defense fails, and pathogens get into your body. Fortunately, your body has a second and third line of defense—the inflammatory response and the immune response. **In the inflammatory response, fluid and white blood cells leak from blood vessels and fight pathogens in nearby tissues. In the immune response, certain immune cells in the blood and tissues react to each kind of pathogen with a defense targeted specifically at the pathogen.**

Inflammatory Response

Have you ever scraped your knee? When body cells are damaged, they release chemicals that trigger the **inflammatory response,** which is your body's second line of defense. The inflammatory response is the same regardless of the pathogen, so it is a general defense. This response involves white blood cells, inflammation, and sometimes fever.

FLORIDA NGSSS

SC.6.L.14.6 Compare and contrast types of infectious agents that may infect the human body, including viruses, bacteria, fungi, and parasites.

LA.6.2.2.3 The student will organize information to show understanding.

Vocabulary Latin Word Origins The Latin word *inflammare* means "to set on fire." How does the Latin meaning relate to the word *inflammation*?

_____

_____

_____

Compare and Contrast Use the first paragraph of the text to list how the inflammatory and immune responses are alike and different in the Venn diagram.

LA.6.2.2.3

Inflammatory Response

Immune Response

Both

285

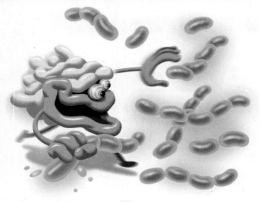

White Blood Cells

White Blood Cells Most white blood cells are disease fighters. However, each type of white blood cell has a particular function. The type of white blood cell involved in the inflammatory response is the phagocyte. A **phagocyte** (FAG uh syt) is a white blood cell that engulfs pathogens and destroys them by breaking them down.

Inflammation The inflammatory response is shown in **Figure 3**. During this response, capillaries widen in the area with pathogens. This enlargement increases blood flow to the area. Fluid and phagocytes leak out of the enlarged capillaries, and the affected area becomes red and swollen. In fact, if you touch the area, it will feel slightly warmer than usual. The phagocytes engulf the pathogens and destroy them.

Fever Chemicals produced during the inflammatory response sometimes cause a fever. Although a fever makes you feel bad, it helps your body fight the infection. Some pathogens do not grow or reproduce well at higher temperatures.

FIGURE 3

The Inflammatory Response
Inflammation is a sign your phagocytes are working.

✎ **Sequence** In the text above, underline the steps in the inflammatory response. In the boxes below, describe what is happening in each diagram.

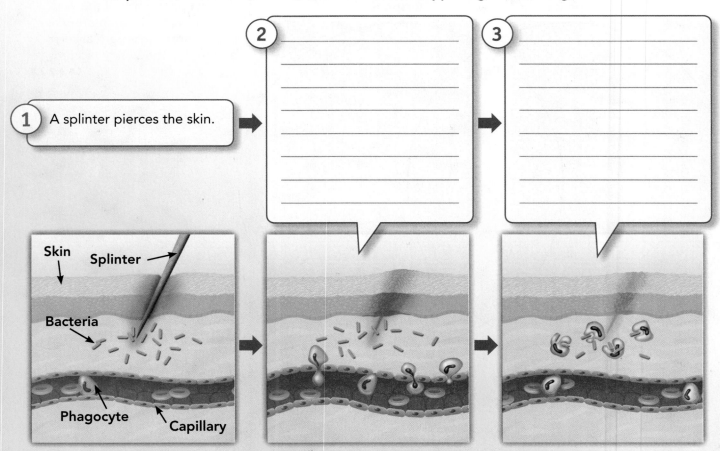

① A splinter pierces the skin.

②

③

Skin Splinter

Bacteria

Phagocyte Capillary

Immune Response If an infection from a pathogen is severe enough, it triggers the body's third line of defense—the **immune response.** The immune response is controlled by the immune system. The cells of the immune system can distinguish between different kinds of pathogens. They react to invaders with a defense targeted against that pathogen.

The white blood cells that distinguish between different kinds of pathogens are called **lymphocytes** (LIM fuh syts). Your body has two major kinds of lymphocytes: T cells and B cells.

T Cells A **T cell** is a lymphocyte that identifies pathogens and distinguishes one pathogen from another. Each kind of T cell recognizes a different kind of pathogen. What T cells actually recognize are a pathogen's marker molecules, which are called antigens. **Antigens** are molecules that the immune system recognizes either as part of your body or as coming from outside your body. Each different pathogen has its own antigen, with its own chemical structure. Look at **Figure 4** to see how T cells function.

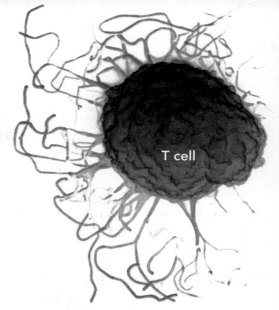

T cell

FIGURE 4 ·····················

T Cell Function
Healthy people have tens of millions of T cells in their blood.

✎ **Describe** **What two roles does a T cell play after it divides?**

_____

_____

_____

_____

_____

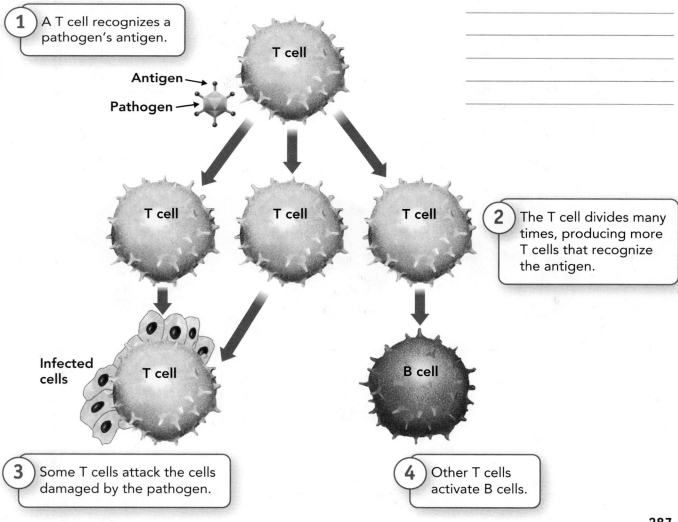

1 A T cell recognizes a pathogen's antigen.

T cell

Antigen →

Pathogen →

T cell   T cell   T cell

2 The T cell divides many times, producing more T cells that recognize the antigen.

Infected cells

T cell

B cell

3 Some T cells attack the cells damaged by the pathogen.

4 Other T cells activate B cells.

B Cells The lymphocytes called **B cells** produce proteins that help destroy pathogens. These proteins are called **antibodies.** Each kind of B cell produces only one kind of antibody, and each kind of antibody has a different structure. Antigen and antibody molecules fit together like pieces of a puzzle. When antibodies bind to the antigens on a pathogen, they mark the pathogen for destruction. Some antibodies make pathogens clump together like those shown in **Figure 5.** Others keep pathogens from attaching to the body cells they might harm. Still other antibodies make it easier for phagocytes to destroy the pathogens.

T cells activate B cells to make antibodies against a pathogen's antigens.

The antibodies then bind to antigens on any pathogens. The pathogens clump together and are destroyed by the phagocytes.

FIGURE 5 ···

▶ INTERACTIVE ART **B Cells**
B cells produce antibodies, which fit on specific antigens like pieces of a puzzle.

✎ **Make Models In the box below each B cell, draw an antigen that fits into the antibody on that B cell.**

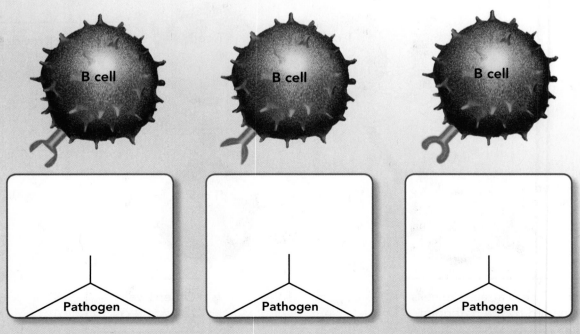

apply it!

Certain bacteria cause strep throat. Your T cells and B cells work together to combat the infection.

1 **Identify** Number each step in the immune response.

2 **Sequence** Describe each step of the immune response against the bacteria that causes strep throat.

_____

_____

_____

_____

_____

_____

_____

_____

_____

_____

_____

_____

T cell

Antigen →

Pathogen →

T cell   **T cell**   **T cell**

Infected throat cells →   **T cell**

B cell

Antibodies →

Antigen →

Lab® Do the Quick Lab *Stuck Together.*
zone

🔑 Assess Your Understanding

1a. Name Identify the key cells that are part of the immune response.

_____

_____

SC.6.L.14.6

b. Explain How does the inflammatory response defend against pathogens?

_____

_____

_____

SC.6.L.14.6

got it?

○ **I get it!** Now I know the inflammatory and immune responses are the body's _____

_____

_____

○ **I need extra help with** _____

Go to **MY SCIENCE** Ⓢ **COACH** *online for help with this subject.*

SC.6.L.14.6

Infectious Disease and Your Health

🔑 **How Can You Become Immune?**
SC.6.L.14.6, LA.6.4.2.2

🔑 **How Do Infectious Diseases Affect Body Systems?**
SC.6.L.14.6, HE.6.C.1.8

my planet diary
for Florida

BLOG

Posted by: Maddie
Location: Largo, Florida

A few years ago I stayed up all night at a friend's house. It was really fun until I started to feel sick. When I stayed up all night I really weakened my immune system and caught a cold. I believe I caught the cold from accidentally drinking out of a friend's water bottle and due to my lack of sleep the cold became more serious. I should have been more careful and paid more attention. If I had I wouldn't have gotten as sick and also by being careless I put all the kids who weren't sick at risk of the virus.

Write your answers to the questions below.

1. What was Maddie's explanation for why she got sick?

_____

_____

_____

_____

_____

2. What is one way Maddie could have prevented getting a cold?

_____

_____

_____

> PLANET DIARY Go to **Planet Diary** to learn more about how infectious diseases affect your health.

Lab zone® Do the Inquiry Warm-Up *Types of Immunity.*

Vocabulary
- immunity • active immunity • vaccination • vaccine
- passive immunity • antibiotic

Skills
- Reading: Relate Cause and Effect
- Inquiry: Communicate

How Can You Become Immune?

People get diseases. However, they get some diseases only once. This is because people develop immunity to some diseases once they recover from them. **Immunity** is the body's ability to destroy pathogens before they can cause disease. Immunity can be active or passive. **You acquire active immunity when your own immune system produces antibodies against a pathogen in your body. You acquire passive immunity when the antibodies come from a source outside your body.**

Active Immunity People who have had chickenpox were once invaded by the chickenpox virus. In response, their immune systems produced antibodies. The next time the chickenpox virus invades their bodies, their immune systems will produce antibodies quickly. So they will not become sick with chickenpox again. This reaction is called **active immunity** because the body has produced the antibodies that fight pathogens. Active immunity can result from either getting the disease or being vaccinated. It often lasts for many years. Sometimes it lasts for life.

FLORIDA NGSSS

SC.6.L.14.6 Compare and contrast types of infectious agents that may infect the human body, including viruses, bacteria, fungi, and parasites.

LA.6.4.2.2 The student will record information related to a topic.

LA.6.2.2.3 The student will organize information to show understanding.

Relate Cause and Effect
Complete the graphic organizer with the effects of contracting the chickenpox virus.

LA.6.4.2.2

Cause		Effect
Contract chickenpox virus the first time.	→	

Cause		Effect
Contract chickenpox virus the second time.	→	

291

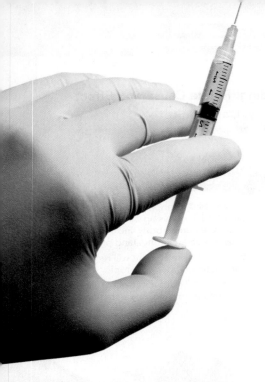

The Immune Response The immune system produces active immunity as part of the immune response. Recall that during the immune response, T cells and B cells help destroy pathogens. After the person recovers, some T cells and B cells keep the "memory" of the pathogen's antigen. If that kind of pathogen invades again, these memory cells recognize the antigen. They start the immune response so quickly that the person often does not get sick.

Vaccination Vaccination is another way of gaining immunity, as shown in **Figure 1. Vaccination** (vac suh NAY shun), or immunization, is the process by which harmless antigens are put into a person's body to produce active immunity. Vaccinations are given by injection, by mouth, or through a nasal spray.

The substance used in a vaccination is a vaccine. A **vaccine** (vak SEEN) usually consists of weakened or killed pathogens that trigger the immune response into action. The T cells and B cells still recognize and respond to the antigens of these weakened or killed pathogens and destroy them. So when you receive a vaccination, you usually do not get sick. However, after destroying these pathogens, your immune system responds by producing memory cells and active immunity to the disease.

FIGURE 1 ....
> ART IN MOTION **Vaccination**
A vaccine activates
the immune response.

✎ **Interpret Diagrams** In the
empty boxes, describe what is
happening in each diagram.

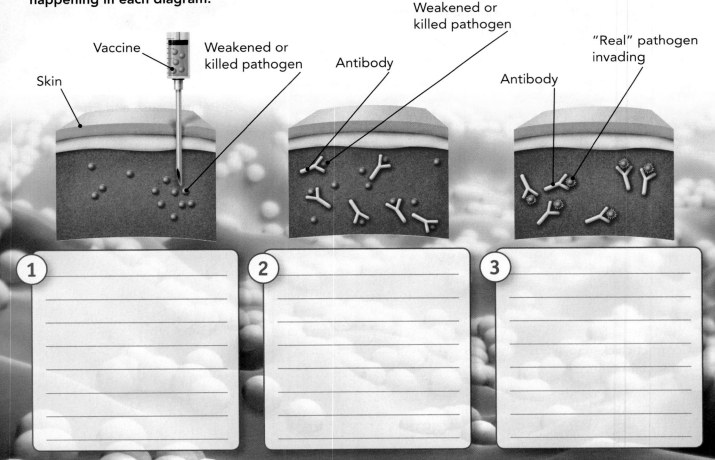

Passive Immunity Some diseases, such as rabies, are uncommon. So people rarely receive vaccinations against them. However, someone who is bitten by an animal with rabies is usually given injections containing antibodies to the rabies antigen. This type of protection is called passive immunity. **Passive immunity** results when antibodies are given to a person. Unlike active immunity, passive immunity usually lasts no more than a few months.

A baby acquires passive immunity to some diseases before birth. This immunity results from antibodies that are passed from the mother's blood into the baby's blood during pregnancy. After birth, these antibodies protect the baby for about six months.

FIGURE 2 ·····························
Immune Responses
Your body can destroy pathogens in two different ways.

✎ **Compare and Contrast**
Use the Venn diagram to compare and contrast active immunity and passive immunity.
LA.6.2.2.3

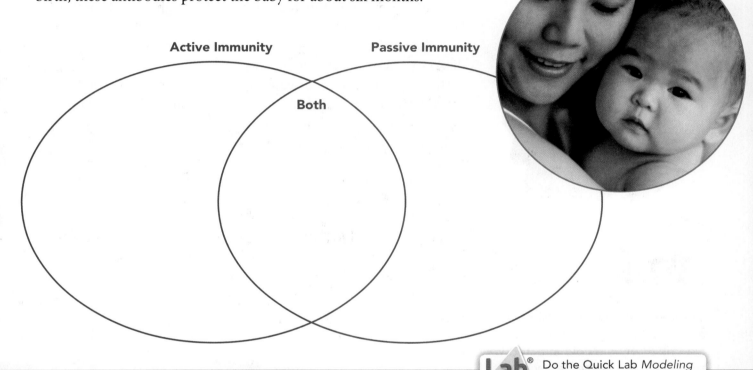

Active Immunity   **Passive Immunity**

Both

Lab zone ® Do the Quick Lab *Modeling Active and Passive Immunity.*

⚷ Assess Your Understanding

1a. Explain What are two ways that you could acquire active immunity?

_____

_____

_____
SC.6.L.14.6

b. Develop Hypotheses Why does passive immunity usually not last for long?

_____

_____

_____
SC.6.L.14.6

got it? ···

○ **I get it!** Now I know that I can become immune by _____

_____

○ **I need extra help with** _____

Go to **MY SCIENCE** ⓢ **COACH** *online for help with this subject.*
SC.6.L.14.6

FLORIDA NGSSS

SC.6.L.14.6 Compare and contrast types of infectious agents that may infect the human body, including viruses, bacteria, fungi, and parasites.

HE.6.C.1.8 Explain how body systems are impacted by hereditary factors and infectious agents.

How Do Infectious Diseases Affect Body Systems?

Bacteria and viruses are two types of pathogens that can cause infectious diseases that require treatment. 🔑 **Infectious diseases affect the normal function of body systems, such as the respiratory, circulatory, and digestive systems.**

Bacterial Diseases Some examples of bacterial diseases are tuberculosis and food poisoning. Tuberculosis is caused by the bacterium *Mycobacterium tuberculosis* and affects the respiratory system. Symptoms of tuberculosis include coughing and chest pain. Food poisoning is often caused by bacteria in the *Salmonella* genus. This illness affects the digestive system. It can cause vomiting, diarrhea, and stomach cramps.

If you get a bacterial disease, you may be given an antibiotic. An **antibiotic** (an tih by AHT ik) is a chemical that kills bacteria or slows their growth without harming body cells. Antibiotics are made naturally by some bacteria and fungi. They also are made in factories. Some antibiotics, such as amoxicillin, cause the cell walls of certain bacteria to burst.

Rod-shaped bacteria that cause tuberculosis

apply it!

Communicate Did you ever wake up with a cold? How did the cold make you feel? Describe how the cold affected your body systems in the space below.

_____

_____

_____

_____

_____

_____

_____

_____

_____

HE.6.C.1.8

Viral Diseases Viruses can also cause diseases that affect the body's systems. For instance, the virus that causes influenza, described in **Figure 3,** affects the respiratory and muscular systems. People with influenza have a cough, sore throat, and may feel muscle aches. Polio is another example of a disease caused by a virus. The polio virus attacks the nervous system. Some people infected by the polio virus only experience flulike symptoms. But the virus can also cause paralysis, meaning that a person can no longer move.

Medicines you take when you have a cold or the flu do not kill viruses because viruses are nonliving. But, medicines can reduce your symptoms so you feel better. Always follow the medicine's directions. To recover from a bacterial or viral disease, get plenty of rest and drink fluids..

FIGURE 3 ....
Cols and the Flu
✎ **Describe** Complete the common cold card. Use the flu card as a guide.

INFLUENZA (Flu)

Symptoms: High fever; sore throat; headache; cough

How It Spreads: Contact with contaminated people or objects; inhaling droplets

Treatment: Bed rest; fluids

Prevention: Vaccine (mainly for the high-risk ill, elderly, and young)

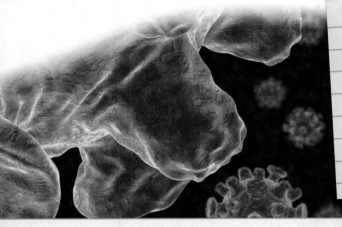

COMMON COLD

Symptoms:

How It Spreads:

Treatment:

Prevention:

Lab zone — Do the Quick Lab *What Substances Can Kill Pathogens?*

⚷ Assess Your Understanding

2a. Review What is the best treatment for viral diseases?

_____

_____

SC.6.L.14.6

b. Summarize What is one way that bacterial diseases affect body systems?

_____

_____

SC.6.L.14.6, HE.6.C.1.8,

○ **I get it!** Now I know that if I get sick, I can treat _____

and prevent _____

○ **I need extra help with** _____

Go to **my science** ⓢ **coach** online for help with this subject.

SC.6.L.14.6

Noninfectious Disease and Your Health

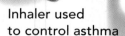

 **How Do People Get Noninfectious Diseases?**
SC.6.L.14.6, HE.6.C.1.3, HE.6.C.1.8

 **What Is Cancer and How Can It Be Treated?**
SC.6.L.14.6, HE.6.C.1.4

Inhaler used to control asthma

my planet Diary

Athletes With Asthma

Asthma is a disorder that causes shortness of breath and wheezing or coughing. You may think people who have asthma cannot excel in sports. But asthma does not have to stop anyone from succeeding. Here are some facts about asthma and athletics.

• One out of six athletes in the 1996 Summer Olympics had a history of asthma. Thirty percent of them won a medal.

• 22 percent of the athletes in the 1998 Winter Olympics suffered from asthma.

• Jerome Bettis (NFL football player), Jackie Joyner-Kersee (Olympic track and field medalist), Hakeem Olajuwon (NBA basketball player), and Amy VanDyken (Olympic swimmer) all live with asthma.

SCIENCE STATS

Answer the following questions.

1. Why might people think that someone with asthma cannot play sports?

_____
_____
_____
_____

2. What would you tell a friend who has asthma and wants to join the swim team?

_____
_____
_____

> PLANET DIARY Go to **Planet Diary** to learn more about noninfectious disease.

Lab zone® Do the Inquiry Warm-Up *Causes of Death, Then and Now*

Vocabulary

- noninfectious disease • allergy • allergen
- histamine • asthma • insulin • diabetes
- tumor • carcinogen

Skills

↻ Reading: Summarize

△ Inquiry: Draw Conclusions

How Do People Get Noninfectious Diseases?

Some diseases are infectious, meaning that they are caused by pathogens. A **noninfectious disease** is a disease that is not caused by pathogens. Unlike infectious diseases, noninfectious diseases cannot be spread from person to person. So how do people get noninfectious diseases? **Some noninfectious diseases are inherited. Other noninfectious diseases are a result of both inherited and environmental factors.**

Inherited Diseases Some noninfectious diseases, such as cystic fibrosis, are inherited diseases. This means that parents may pass the disease on to their children in their DNA.

Cystic fibrosis mostly affects the respiratory and digestive system. The disease causes the body to produce thick, sticky mucus. Normally, mucus is a watery, slimy substance. You may notice mucus in your nose when you have a cold. But a person with cystic fibrosis has thick mucus in their lungs, making it hard to breathe. This thick mucus may also clog up the pancreas, making it difficult for people with the disease to digest food.

FLORIDA NGSSS

SC.6.L.14.6 Compare and contrast types of infectious agents that may infect the human body, including viruses, bacteria, fungi, and parasites.

HE.6.C.1.3 Identify environmental factors that affect personal health.

HE.6.C.1.8 Explain how body systems are impacted by hereditary factors and infectious agents.

✐ **Summarize** Use your own words to summarize how cystic fibrosis affects body systems.

X-ray of lungs of a person with cystic fibrosis

This boy breathes in misty salt water to treat his cystic fibrosis.

HE.6.C.1.8

297

Other Noninfectious Diseases
Unlike cystic fibrosis, some noninfectious diseases result from more than just heredity. Whether or not the disease develops also depends on factors in the environment. Allergies, asthma, and diabetes are examples of this type of noninfectious disease.

Allergies People who sneeze a lot in the spring may not have a cold. Instead, they may be showing a symptom of an allergy. An **allergy** is a disorder in which the immune system is overly sensitive to a foreign substance—something not normally found in the body. Allergies may affect the respiratory and integumentary systems.

Any substance that causes an allergy is an **allergen.** Allergens include environmental factors such as pollen, dust, molds, some foods, pet dander (dead skin cells), and even some medicines.

Allergens may get into your body when you inhale them, eat them in food, or touch them. Allergens signal cells in the body to release a substance called histamine. **Histamine** (HIS tuh meen) is a chemical that is responsible for the symptoms of an allergy, such as a skin rash, sneezing, and watery eyes. Drugs that interfere with histamine, called antihistamines, may lessen this reaction. However, if you have an allergy, the best way to prevent allergy symptoms is to try to avoid the substance to which you are allergic.

Explain the Impact How is the respiratory system affected by allergies?

_____
_____
_____
_____
_____

apply it!

Suzy ate some strawberries. A short time later, she broke out in a rash.

❶ Identify What might have caused Suzy's rash?

_____

❷ Sequence Explain how eating strawberries can cause a rash.

_____
_____
_____

❸ Predict What might a doctor prescribe to relieve Suzy's rash?

_____
_____

Asthma Some allergic reactions can cause a condition called asthma. **Asthma** (AZ muh) is a disease which affects the respiratory system. During an asthma attack, the airways in the lungs narrow significantly. This narrowing causes wheezing, coughing, and shortness of breath. Asthma attacks may be triggered by stress and heavy exercise. Environmental factors, such as tobacco smoke, air pollution, strong odors, and respiratory infections can also trigger an attack.

Figure 1 shows a normal airway and an airway affected by asthma. During an asthma attack, the muscles around the airways tighten, narrowing the airways. At the same time, the inner walls of the airways become irritated, red, swollen, and warm. They produce mucus. The mucus clogs the airways and makes breathing even more difficult.

Someone who is having an asthma attack needs medicines, such as an inhaler, to open the airways and reduce swelling. A severe attack may require emergency care. An asthma attack can be fatal.

FIGURE 1 ....
Airways With and Without Asthma
Asthma is a common condition among young people.

✎ **Relate Text and Visuals** Look at the diagram of a normal airway. Then in each box of the second diagram, describe what happens in an airway affected by asthma.

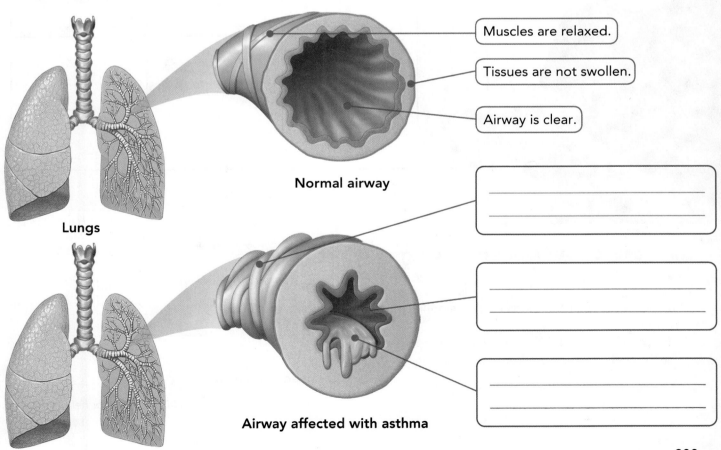

Muscles are relaxed.

Tissues are not swollen.

Airway is clear.

Normal airway

Lungs

Airway affected with asthma

FIGURE 2 ··

Glucose Testing

The student is using a device called a glucometer to measure the amount of glucose in his blood.

✏️ 🔁 **Summarize** Write notes in the table about Type I and Type II diabetes.

Diabetes One function of the pancreas, an organ of the digestive system, is to produce insulin. **Insulin** (IN suh lin) is a substance that enables body cells to take glucose from the blood and use it for energy. In the condition called **diabetes** (dy uh BEE teez), either the pancreas produces too little insulin or body cells do not use insulin properly. People with diabetes, or diabetics, have high levels of glucose in their blood but not enough of it in their body cells. If untreated, diabetics may lose weight and feel weak and hungry. They also may urinate often and feel thirsty.

Diabetes has two main forms. Type I diabetes often begins in childhood. The pancreas produces little or no insulin. People with this condition need insulin injections. Type II diabetes usually develops in adults. Either body cells stop responding normally to insulin or the pancreas stops making enough insulin. Some Type II diabetics can control their symptoms through diet, weight control, and exercise instead of insulin injections. An unhealthy diet and lack of exercise are environmental factors that may lead to Type II diabetes.

Type of Diabetes	Cause	Symptoms	Treatment
Type I			
Type II			

> **Lab** ® Do the Quick Lab *What Happens When Air Flow Is Restricted?*
> zone

🔑 Assess Your Understanding

1a. Name _____ is a disorder in which airways of the lungs narrow significantly.
SC.6.L.14.6

b. Relate Cause and Effect How is a person with asthma affected by environmental factors?

_____

_____

SC.6.L.14.6, HE.6.C.1.3

got it?

○ **I get it!** Now I know that noninfectious diseases can be _____

_____

_____

○ **I need extra help with** _____

Go to **my science** ⓢ **COACH** *online for help with this subject.*

SC.6.L.14.6

What Is Cancer and How Can It Be Treated?

Usually, the body produces new cells at about the same rate that other cells die. **However, cancer is a disease in which cells multiply uncontrollably, over and over, destroying healthy tissue. Treatments include surgery, radiation, and drugs.**

How Cancer Develops As cells divide over and over, they often form abnormal masses of cells called **tumors.** Not all tumors are cancerous. Cancerous tumors invade and destroy the healthy tissue around them. Eventually, cells from a tumor may break away from the tumor and enter the blood or lymph vessels. The blood or lymph carries the cancer cells to other parts of the body, where they may form new tumors. Unless stopped by treatment, cancer progresses through the body.

Causes of Cancer Different factors may work together to cause cancer. Inherited characteristics make some people more likely to develop certain cancers. For example, daughters of mothers who had breast cancer have an increased chance of developing breast cancer themselves. Factors in the environment, called **carcinogens** (kahr SIN uh junz), can also cause cancer. The tar in cigarette smoke is a carcinogen.

FLORIDA NGSSS

SC.6.L.14.6 Compare and contrast types of infectious agents that may infect the human body, including viruses, bacteria, fungi, and parasites.

HE.6.C.1.4 Recognize how heredity can affect personal health.

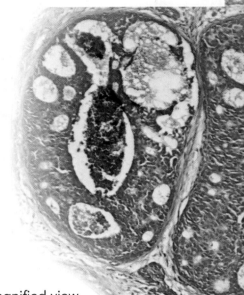

Magnified view of cancerous cells

do the math!

This data table shows the estimated number of new cases of different cancers in the United States in 1981 and 2007.

❶ **Interpret Tables** Which type of cancer has increased the most from 1981 to 2007 in men? In women?

Men _____

Women _____

❷ **Draw Conclusions** Explain why the number of new cancer cases might increase as tests to detect cancer improve.

_____

_____

_____

_____

_____

MA.6.A.3.6

Estimated New Cancer Cases

Type of Cancer	New Cases (1981)	New Cases (2007)
Men		
Prostate	70,000	218,890
Lung	88,000	114,760
Colon and Rectum	58,000	79,130
Oral Cavity and Pharynx	18,400	24,180
Women		
Breast	110,000	178,480
Lung	34,000	98,620
Colon and Rectum	62,000	74,630
Uterus	54,000	50,230

Cancer Treatment

Surgery, radiation, and drugs are used to treat cancer. If cancer is detected before it has spread, doctors may remove tumors with surgery. After surgery, radiation or drugs may be used to kill remaining cancer cells.

Radiation treatment uses high-energy waves to kill cancer cells. When these waves are aimed at tumors, the intense energy damages and kills cancer cells. Drug therapy is the use of chemicals to destroy cancer cells. It is often called chemotherapy. However, many of these chemicals can destroy some normal cells, too. Both radiation and chemotherapy can have side effects, such as nausea and hair loss.

Cancer and Personal Health

People, especially those people who inherit a risk of getting cancer, can change their health habits to reduce the risk of developing the disease. They should avoid carcinogens, such as those found in tobacco and sunlight. A low-fat diet can help prevent cancers of the digestive system.

The earlier cancer is detected, the more likely it can be treated successfully. In **Figure 3,** you can see a blackened spot on skin. This spot is a skin cancer called melanoma. Exposing unprotected skin to sunlight too often contributes to the development of skin cancer. It is especially important to avoid sunburns, which damage skin cells.

FIGURE 3 ·····························

Melanoma

Melanoma is the most serious skin cancer. It can affect many other organs in your body if not treated quickly.

✎ **On the notebook paper, write answers to the questions below.**

1. **Explain** What can you do to prevent skin cancer?
2. **CHALLENGE** What steps might a doctor take to treat melanoma?

Melanoma

INVISIBLE INVADERS

Why do you sometimes get sick?

FIGURE 4 ···
REAL-WORLD INQUIRY This boy's sneeze might be a symptom of a cold or an allergy.
✎ **Apply Concepts** Answer the questions in the boxes.

If this boy has a cold, what made him sick? Explain how you know.	How might he spread his sickness if it is a cold?	What might cause him to sneeze if he has an allergy?

Lab® zone Do the Quick Lab *What Does Sunlight Do to the Beads?*

🔑 Assess Your Understanding

2a. Review What is a tumor?

_____

_____

SC.6.L.14.6

b. Relate Cause and Effect What health habits reduce the risk of cancer?

_____

_____

SC.6.L.14.6, HE.6.C.1.4

c. ANSWER THE ESSENTIAL ? Why do you sometimes get sick?

_____

_____

_____

_____

_____

SC.6.L.14.6

got it? ···

○ **I get it!** Now I know that cancer is _____

_____

○ **I need extra help with** _____

Go to MY SCIENCE ⓢ COACH *online for help with this subject.*   SC.6.L.14.6

HIV and AIDS

 How Does HIV Affect the Body?
SC.6.L.14.6, MA.6.A.3.6

 How Is HIV Spread and Treated?
SC.6.L.14.6

my planet diary

The NAMES Project Foundation— AIDS Memorial Quilt

Headquarters: Atlanta, Georgia

How do you cope with loss? Some who have lost loved ones to AIDS express their feelings by making panels to add to the AIDS Memorial Quilt. Begun in 1987 in San Francisco, the NAMES Project Foundation takes care of the quilt. The quilt is made up of more than 47,000 individual panels from countries all around the world. The panels help people honor those whom they have lost to the tragic disease. The large number of panels sadly illustrates that AIDS has taken so many lives. Yet, the quilt is a symbol of unity that supports continuing research to find a cure for this devastating disease.

PROFILE

Communicate Discuss the following questions with a partner. Write your answers below.

1. The quilt is made up of panels from around the world. What does this tell you about AIDS?

   _____

   _____

2. Why do you think scientists are important in the fight against AIDS?

   _____

   _____

   _____

> **PLANET DIARY** Go to **Planet Diary** to learn more about HIV and AIDS.

Lab zone Do the Inquiry Warm-Up
How Does HIV Spread?

Vocabulary
- AIDS
- HIV

Skills
- Reading: Sequence
- Inquiry: Graph

How Does HIV Affect the Body?

Our immune system protects us well. So we usually do not even realize that our body has been attacked by a pathogen. But what happens when our immune system itself is sick?

Acquired immunodeficiency syndrome, or **AIDS,** is a disease caused by a virus that attacks the immune system. The virus that causes AIDS is called the human immunodeficiency virus, or **HIV.** **HIV is the only kind of virus known to attack the human immune system directly and destroy T cells.** Once inside the body, HIV enters T cells and reproduces. People can be infected with HIV—that is, have the virus living in their T cells—for many years before they become sick.

In 1981, the first case of AIDS was reported in the United States. Nearly one million Americans may now be infected with HIV. Many of these people—one in four—do not realize yet that they are infected. However, the disease is not found only in the United States. It is a worldwide epidemic.

FLORIDA NGSSS

SC.6.L.14.6 Compare and contrast types of infectious agents that may infect the human body, including viruses, bacteria, fungi, and parasites.

MA.6.A.3.6 Construct and analyze tables, graphs and equations to describe linear functions and other simple relations using both common language and algebraic notation.

do the math!

The table shows the number of men, women, and children under age 15 worldwide living with HIV in 2007.

1. **Graph** Use the data in the table to make a bar graph. Then write a title for the graph.

2. **Interpret Data** What do you notice about the number of men and women living with HIV in 2007?

_____

_____

_____

3. **Draw Conclusions** What conclusion can you make about the populations the virus affects?

_____

_____

_____

Populations Living With HIV in 2007	
Population	**Number of People**
Men	15.3 million
Women	15.5 million
Children under age 15	2 million

Number of People Living With HIV (millions)

20

15

10

5

0

Men   Women   Children under age 15

Population

MA.6.A.3.6

HIV and AIDS

When people first become infected with HIV, they often have no symptoms. A month or so later, they may seem to have the flu, but it goes away. Although they may not have symptoms at first, people can still spread the virus.

It may take ten years or more for severe symptoms to appear. However, in time, HIV begins to destroy the T cells it has infected. As the virus destroys T cells like the one shown in **Figure 1,** the body begins to lose its ability to fight disease. This is a symptom of the disease called AIDS.

Infections

People with AIDS start to get diseases that healthy people do not get normally. Development of these infections is one symptom of the disease AIDS. Most people infected with HIV eventually develop the symptoms of AIDS. Many survive attack after attack of infections. Yet, in time, their immune systems fail, and they die.

Sequence Complete the steps that happen after a person is infected with HIV and develops AIDS.

Step 1 A person is infected.

Step 2

_____

_____

_____

_____

Step 3

_____

_____

_____

_____

Step 4

_____

_____

_____

_____

Step 5

_____

_____

_____

FIGURE 1 ···

HIV

HIV reproduces inside T cells. It then bursts out to attack other T cells.

✎ [CHALLENGE] **Use what you see in the photo to explain why HIV destroys an immune system.**

_____

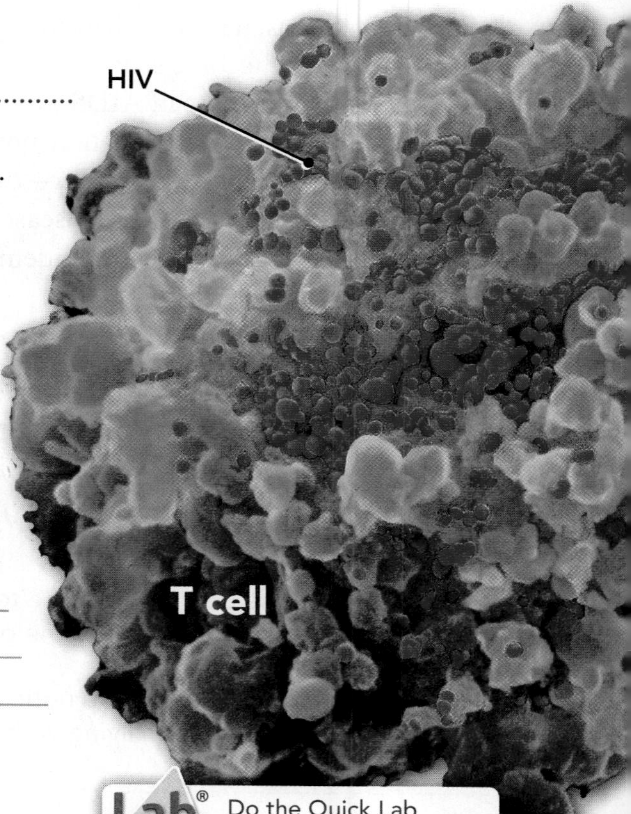

_____

_____

_____

_____

HIV

T cell

Lab® zone Do the Quick Lab
How Does HIV Attack?

🔑 Assess Your Understanding

got it? ··

○ **I get it!** Now I know that HIV affects the body by _____

_____

○ **I need extra help with** _____

Go to MY SCIENCE ⑤ COACH *online for help with this subject.*

SC.6.L.14.6

How Is HIV Spread and Treated?

FLORIDA NGSSS

SC.6.L.14.6 Compare and contrast types of infectious agents that may infect the human body, including viruses, bacteria, fungi, and parasites.

Like all other viruses, HIV can reproduce only inside cells. However, the virus can survive for a short time outside the human body in fluids. These fluids include blood and the fluids that the male and female reproductive systems produce.

🔑 **HIV can spread from one person to another if body fluids from an infected person come in contact with body fluids of an uninfected person.** Sexual contact is one way this transfer happens. HIV may also pass from an infected woman to her baby during pregnancy or childbirth, or through breast milk. Infected blood can also spread HIV. For example, drug users who share needles can pass HIV. Since 1985, all donated blood in the United States has been tested for HIV.

At this time, there is no cure for AIDS. However, combinations of drugs that fight the virus in different ways can delay the development of AIDS and extend life expectancy. See **Figure 2** for information about young people living with AIDS.

FIGURE 2 ···

Young People and AIDS

The graph shows how advances in HIV treatments enabled more people to live with AIDS.

✎ **Read Graphs** Using the graph, estimate how many 13- to 24-year-olds were living with AIDS in 2007.

_____

_____

_____

_____

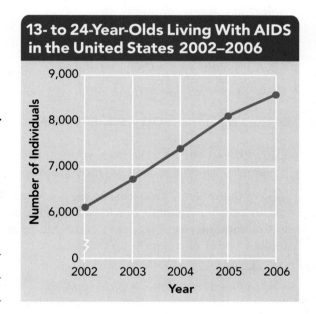

13- to 24-Year-Olds Living With AIDS in the United States 2002–2006

(graph: Number of Individuals vs. Year, 2002–2006)

🔑 **Assess Your Understanding**

1a. Review Where does HIV reproduce in people?

_____

_____

SC.6.L.14.6

b. Summarize How is AIDS treated?

_____

_____

SC.6.L.14.6

Lab zone Do the Quick Lab *What Will Spread HIV?*

got it? ···

○ **I get it!** Now I know that HIV can spread _____

○ **I need extra help with** _____

Go to **mY SCIEnce COACH** online for help with this subject.

SC.6.L.14.6

Study Guide

REVIEW THE ESSENTIAL

A _____ in my body may cause an _____ disease. My _____ system will try to fight the disease.

LESSON 1 Infectious Disease
SC.6.N.2.2, SC.6.N.2.3, SC.6.L.14.6

🔑 When you have an infectious disease, pathogens are in your body causing harm.

🔑 The five major types of human pathogens are viruses, bacteria, protists, fungi, and parasites. They can be spread through contact with a sick person, other living things, or an object in the environment.

Vocabulary
- microorganism • pathogen
- infectious disease • toxin • parasite

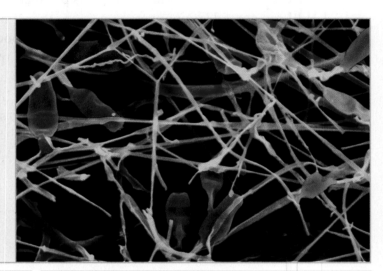

LESSON 2 The Body's Defenses
SC.6.L.14.6

🔑 The first line of defense is your outer coverings, which trap and kill most pathogens.

🔑 In the inflammatory response, fluid and white blood cells fight pathogens in nearby tissues. In the immune response, cells in the blood and tissues target each kind of pathogen.

Vocabulary
- inflammatory response • phagocyte
- immune response • lymphocyte • T cell
- antigen • B cell • antibody

LESSON 3 Infectious Disease and Your Health
SC.6.L.14.6

🔑 You acquire active immunity when your own immune system produces antibodies. You acquire passive immunity when the antibodies come from a source outside your body.

🔑 Infectious diseases affect the normal function of body systems.

Vocabulary
- immunity • active immunity • vaccination
- vaccine • passive immunity • antibiotic

LESSON 4 Noninfectious Disease and Your Health
SC.6.L.14.6

🔑 Some noninfectious diseases are inherited. Other noninfectious diseases are a result of both inherited and environmental factors.

🔑 Cancer is a disease in which cells multiply uncontrollably, destroying healthy tissue.

Vocabulary
- noninfectious disease • allergy
- allergen • histamine • asthma • insulin
- diabetes • tumor • carcinogen

LESSON 5 HIV and AIDS
SC.6.L.14.6

🔑 HIV is the only kind of virus known to attack the human immune system directly and destroy T cells.

🔑 HIV can spread from one person to another if body fluids from an infected person come in contact with body fluids of an uninfected person.

Vocabulary
- AIDS • HIV

Review and Assessment

LESSON 1 Infectious Disease

1. Organisms that cause disease are called

   a. histamines.   **b.** pathogens.

   c. phagocytes.   **d.** toxins.

                           SC.6.L.14.6

2. _____ are living things too small to see with a microscope that cause most infectious diseases.

                           SC.6.L.14.6

3. Classify What are the four ways in which a person can become infected with a pathogen?

_____

_____

_____

_____

_____

                           SC.6.L.14.6

4. Compare and Contrast Describe how bacteria and viruses are alike and different in terms of how they cause disease.

_____

_____

_____

_____

                           SC.6.L.14.6

5. Apply Concepts Can you catch a cold by sitting in a chilly draft? Explain.

_____

_____

_____

                           SC.6.L.14.6

6. Write About It Write a short speech that Joseph Lister might have delivered to other surgeons to convince them to use his surgical techniques. In the speech, Lister should explain why his techniques were so successful.

                     SC.6.N.2.3, SC.6.L.14.6

LESSON 2 The Body's Defenses

7. Proteins produced by B cells are called

   a. phagocytes.   **b.** T cells.

   c. antibodies.   **d.** pathogens.

                           SC.6.L.14.6

8. _____ engulf pathogens and destroy them.

                           SC.6.L.14.6

9. Communicate How does the body make it difficult for a pathogen to reach a part of the body where it can cause disease?

_____

_____

_____

_____

_____

                           SC.6.L.14.6

10. Interpret Diagrams In the diagram below, identify each labeled structure and its role in the immune response.

_____

_____

_____

_____

_____

_____

                           SC.6.L.14.6

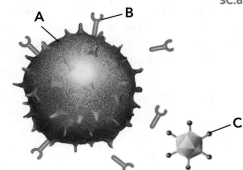

LESSON 3 Infectious Disease and Your Health

11. Which of the following produce active immunity without causing illness?

    a. vaccines   **b.** antibody injections

    c. antibiotics   **d.** phagocytes

                                SC.6.L.14.6

12. _____ are chemicals that can kill bacteria without harming body cells.

                                SC.6.L.14.6

13. Explain the Impact Describe one way that pathogens can affect body systems.

_____

_____

_____

_____

_____

_____

                SC.6.L.14.6, HE.6.C.1.8

LESSON 4 Noninfectious Disease and Your Health

14. Abnormal tissue masses are called

    a. allergies.   **b.** cancer.

    c. diabetes.   **d.** tumors.

                           SC.6.L.14.6

15. An _____ is any substance that causes an allergy.

                                SC.6.L.14.6

16. **Write About It** For some people, the dander of a cat causes an allergic reaction. On a separate piece of paper, describe how a person's body responds when exposed to this allergen. How can they lessen the reaction?

                                SC.6.L.14.6

LESSON 5 HIV and AIDS

14. HIV attacks the human immune system and destroys

    a. B cells.   **b.** antigens.

    c. antibodies.   **d.** T cells.

                              SC.6.L.14.6

15. HIV spreads from an infected person to an uninfected person through the contact of

_____

                              SC.6.L.14.6

16. Relate Cause and Effect How does the destruction of T cells interfere with the body's ability to fight disease?

_____

_____

_____

_____

                              SC.6.L.14.6

APPLY THE ESSENTIAL ? Why do you sometimes get sick?

20. You wake up one morning with a stuffy nose and a fever. Identify how you might have been infected by the virus that caused this cold. Then describe some steps your body will undertake to fight the virus.

_____

_____

_____

_____

_____

_____

_____

_____

_____

                              SC.6.L.14.6

Florida Benchmarks Review

Circle the letter of the best answer.

1 SARS is a respiratory disease caused by a virus. Use the data table to decide which statement below is true.

SARS Cases (Nov. 2002–July 2003)		
Country	No. of Cases	No. of Deaths
Canada	251	43
China, mainland	5,327	349
China, Taiwan	346	37
Singapore	238	33
United States	29	0

A Most of the people who got SARS died.
B Most SARS cases were in mainland China.
C Most SARS cases were in North America.
D Most SARS cases were in Singapore.

SC.6.L.14.6

2 All of the following are the body's defenses against pathogens *except*

A a physical barrier such as the skin.
B the inflammatory response.
C the immune response.
D attacks by red blood cells.

SC.6.L.14.6

3 A chemical that can kill disease-causing bacteria is called

A a vaccine.
B a phagocyte.
C an antibiotic.
D an active immunity.

SC.6.L.14.6

4 Which of these disorders occurs when the airways in the lungs narrow significantly during an allergic reaction?

A asthma
B diabetes
C AIDS
D melanoma

SC.6.L.14.6, HE.6.C.1.3

5 Which of the following is paired correctly?

A rabies: infectious disease
B diabetes: infectious disease
C AIDS: noninfectious disease
D allergy: infectious disease

SC.6.L.14.6

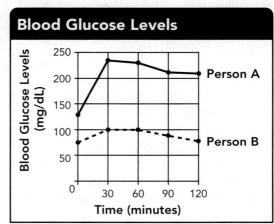

6 In a glucose tolerance test, a doctor gives a patient a sugar drink and measures the blood glucose level over time. The graph above shows test results from two people. Which person may have diabetes?

A Person A   **B** Person B
C Both people   **D** Neither person

SC.6.L.14.6

HOW ARE THIS MANATEE AND HYRAX ALIKE?

How are living things alike yet different?

Living in Florida waters, a manatee can grow to be longer than 3 meters and weigh over 360 kilograms. A rock hyrax is a small, tailless, rodentlike animal that lives in rocky areas of Africa. While these animals appear to be very different, they are actually related.

Develop Hypotheses What could these two animals have in common?

_____

_____

_____

_____

_____

_____

> UNTAMED SCIENCE Watch the **Untamed Science** video to learn more about living things.

Diversity of Life

FLORIDA   Next Generation Sunshine State Standards

Big Ideas 1, 3: SC.6.N.1.3, SC.6.N.3.1   Language Arts: LA.6.2.2.3, LA.6.4.2.2
Big Idea 15: SC.6.L.15.1   Mathematics: MA.6.A.3.6

my science online.com   Diversity of Life   > UNTAMED SCIENCE   > ESSENTIAL QUESTION   313

Getting Started

Check Your Understanding

1. **Background** Read the paragraph below and then answer the question.

> You eat **microscopic** organisms all the time without realizing it! Some microscopic organisms are necessary to prepare common foods. **Yeast,** for example, is a tiny organism that is used to make bread. **Bacteria** are used to make yogurt, sauerkraut, and many other foods.

> Something **microscopic** is so small that it cannot be seen without a magnifying lens or a microscope.
>
> **Yeast** is a single-celled organism that has a nucleus.
>
> **Bacteria** are single-celled organisms that do not have nuclei.

- What is one kind of food that bacteria are used to make?

_____

▶ **MY READING WEB** If you had trouble completing the question above, visit **My Reading Web** and type in *Diversity of Life.*

Vocabulary Skill

Greek Word Origins Many science words come from ancient Greek words. Learning the word parts that have Greek origins can help you understand some of the vocabulary in this chapter.

Greek Word Part	Meaning	Example
autos	self	autotroph, *n.* an organism that makes its own food
taxis	order, arrangement	taxonomy, *n.* the scientific study of how living things are classified
homos	similar, same	homeostasis, *n.* the maintenance of stable internal conditions

LA.6.1.6.7

2. **Quick Check** Circle the part of the word *taxonomy* that lets you know that the word's meaning has something to do with ordering or classifying things.

heterotroph

species

eukaryote

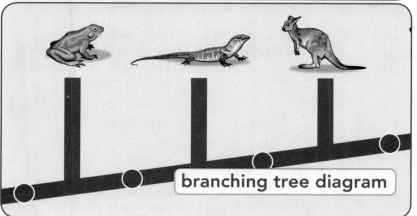

branching tree diagram

Chapter Preview

LESSON 1
- metabolism
- development
- asexual reproduction
- sexual reproduction
- spontaneous generation
- autotroph
- heterotroph

↻ **Compare and Contrast**
△ **Control Variables**

LESSON 2
- classification
- taxonomy
- binomial nomenclature
- genus
- species

↻ **Ask Questions**
△ **Observe**

LESSON 3
- prokaryote
- eukaryote

↻ **Identify the Main Idea**
△ **Classify**

LESSON 4
- evolution
- branching tree diagram
- shared derived characteristic
- convergent evolution

↻ **Summarize**
△ **Infer**

> **VOCAB FLASH CARDS** For extra help with vocabulary, visit **Vocab Flash Cards** and type in *Diversity of Life.*

What Is Life?

UNLOCK THE ESSENTIAL ?

🔑 **What Are the Characteristics of All Living Things?**
SC.6.L.15.1

🔑 **Where Do Living Things Come From?**
SC.6.L.15.1

🔑 **What Do Living Things Need to Survive?**
SC.6.L.15.1, LA.6.2.2.3

MY PLANET DiARY

TECHNOLOGY

It's Kismet!

If you hear a loud noise, do you turn toward the sound to see what caused it? When someone smiles at you, do you smile back? If somebody shook something in front of your face, would you back away? Most people react in these ways, and so does Kismet, a humanlike robot! Scientists developed Kismet to interact with, cooperate with, and learn from humans. Kismet can understand information that it sees and hears as if it were a young child. When responding to information, Kismet's face changes so that it seems interested, happy, or frightened. Kismet's expressions are so convincing that it is sometimes hard to remember that Kismet isn't really alive!

Answer the questions that follow.

1. What does Kismet do that makes it seem human?

_____

_____

_____

2. What are some things you think Kismet might not be able to do that humans can?

_____

_____

_____

_____

▶ PLANET DIARY Go to **Planet Diary** to learn more about living things.

 Lab zone® Do the Inquiry Warm-Up
Is It Living or Nonliving?

Vocabulary

- metabolism
- development
- asexual reproduction
- sexual reproduction
- spontaneous generation
- autotroph
- heterotroph

Skills

↻ **Reading:** Compare and Contrast

△ **Inquiry:** Control Variables

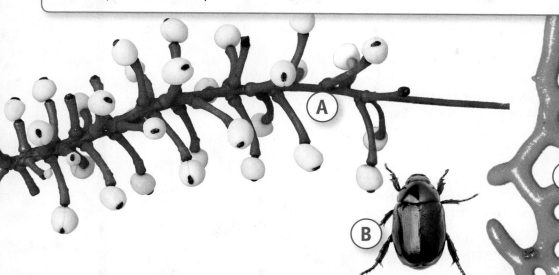

What Are the Characteristics of All Living Things?

If you were asked to name some living things, or organisms, you might name yourself, a pet, and some insects or plants. You would probably not mention a moss growing in a shady spot, the mildew on bathroom tiles, or the slime molds that ooze across lawns. But all of these things are organisms that share several important characteristics with all other living things. 🔑 **All living things have a cellular organization, contain similar chemicals, use energy, respond to their surroundings, grow and develop, and reproduce.**

FLORIDA   NGSSS

SC.6.L.15.1 Analyze and describe how and why organisms are classified according to shared characteristics with emphasis on the Linnaean system combined with the concept of Domains.

FIGURE 1 ·······························

It's Alive . . . or Is It?

✏ **Look at the photos. Then answer the questions.**

1. **Identify** List the letter of the photo(s) that you think show living thing(s). _____

2. **Describe** What characteristics helped you decide whether or not the things shown were living or nonliving?

_____

_____

_____

Cellular Organization

All organisms are made of small building blocks called cells. A cell, like the one shown here, is the basic unit of structure and function in an organism. Organisms may be composed of only one cell or of many cells.

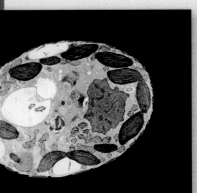

Single-celled organisms, like bacteria (bak TIHR ee uh), are unicellular organisms. The single cell is responsible for carrying out all of the functions necessary to stay alive. Organisms that are composed of many cells are multicellular. For example, you are made of trillions of cells. In many multicellular organisms, the cells are specialized to do certain tasks. Specialized cells in your body, such as muscle and nerve cells, work together to keep you alive. Nerve cells carry messages to your muscle cells, making your body move.

Characteristics of Living Things

The Chemicals of Life

The cells of living things are made of chemicals. The most abundant chemical in cells is water. Other chemicals, called carbohydrates (kahr boh HY drayts) are a cell's main energy source. Two other chemicals, proteins and lipids, are the building materials of cells, much as wood and bricks are the building materials of houses. Finally, DNA is the genetic material of cells—the chemical instructions that cells need to carry out the functions of life.

Energy Use

Organisms get energy from taking in and breaking down materials. The combination of chemical reactions through which an organism builds up or breaks down materials is called **metabolism.** The cells of organisms use energy to do what living things must do, such as grow and repair injured parts. An organism's cells are always hard at work. For example, as you read these words, not only are your eye and brain cells busy, but most of your other cells are working, too. Young sooty terns, like the one shown above, need lots of energy to fly. These birds can fly four to five years without ever setting foot on land!

FIGURE 2 ···

Living Things

All living things share the same characteristics.

✎ **Make Judgments** Which characteristic on these two pages do you think best identifies an object as a living thing? Explain your choice.

_____

_____

_____

_____

_____

_____

Response to Surroundings

If you've ever seen a plant in a sunny window, you may have observed that the plant's stems have bent so that the leaves face the sun. Like a plant bending toward the light, all organisms react to changes in their environment. A change in an organism's surroundings that causes the organism to react is called a stimulus (plural *stimuli*). Stimuli include changes in light, sound, and other factors.

An organism reacts to a stimulus with a response —an action or a change in behavior. For example, has someone ever knocked over a glass of water by accident during dinner, causing you to jump? The sudden spilling of water was the stimulus that caused your startled response.

Growth and Development

All living things grow and develop. Growth is the process of becoming larger. **Development** is the process of change that occurs during an organism's life, producing a more complex organism. As they develop and grow, organisms use energy and make new cells.

Reproduction

Another characteristic of organisms is the ability to reproduce, or produce offspring that are similar to the parents. Organisms reproduce in different ways. **Asexual reproduction** involves only one parent and produces offspring that are identical to the parent. **Sexual reproduction** involves two parents and combines their genetic material to produce a new organism that differs from both parents. Mammals, birds, and most plants sexually reproduce. Penguins lay eggs that develop into young penguins that closely resemble their parents.

Lab **zone** ® Do the Quick Lab *React!*

🔑 Assess Your Understanding

1a. Review A change in an organism's surroundings is a (stimulus/response).

SC.6.L.15.1

b. Infer A bird sitting in a tree flies away as you walk by. Which of the life characteristics explains the bird's behavior?

_____

SC.6.L.15.1

c. [CHALLENGE] Trees do not move like birds do, but they are living things. Why?

_____

_____

_____

_____

_____

SC.6.L.15.1

got it? ....

○ **I get it!** Now I know that all living things

_____

_____

_____

_____

○ I need extra help with _____

_____

Go to MY SCIENCE ⒮ COACH *online for help with this subject.* SC.6.L.15.1

 **FLORIDA** NGSSS

SC.6.L.15.1 Analyze and describe how and why organisms are classified according to shared characteristics with emphasis on the Linnaean system combined with the concept of Domains.

Where Do Living Things Come From?

Today, when people see weeds poking out of cracks in sidewalks or find mice in their cabinet, as shown in **Figure 3,** they know that these organisms are the result of reproduction. **Living things arise from other living things through reproduction.**

Four hundred years ago, however, people believed that life could appear from nonliving material. For example, when people saw flies swarming around decaying meat, they concluded that flies were produced by rotting meat. The mistaken idea that living things can arise from nonliving sources is called **spontaneous generation.** It took hundreds of years of experiments to convince people that spontaneous generation does not occur.

FIGURE 3 ···

Spontaneous Generation

Sometimes unexpected visitors, like this mouse, can be found in kitchen cabinets.

✎ **Answer the questions.**

1. **Develop Hypotheses** If you lived 400 years ago, where might you think the mouse in the cabinet came from?

   _____

   _____

   _____

2. CHALLENGE Describe a way in which you could test your hypothesis.

   _____

   _____

   _____

   _____

   _____

Redi's Experiment In the 1600s, an Italian doctor named Francesco Redi helped to disprove spontaneous generation. Redi designed a controlled experiment to show that maggots, which develop into new flies, do not arise from decaying meat. In a controlled experiment, a scientist carries out a series of tests that are identical in every respect except for one factor. The one factor that a scientist changes in an experiment is called the independent variable. The factor that changes as a result of changes to the independent variable is called the dependent variable. Redi's experiment is shown in **Figure 4.**

FIGURE 4 ....

Redi's Experiment

Francesco Redi designed one of the first controlled experiments. Redi showed that flies do not spontaneously arise from decaying meat. Here's how he did it:

STEP ① Redi placed meat in two identical jars. He left one jar uncovered. He covered the other jar with a cloth that let in air.

STEP ② After a few days, Redi saw maggots (young flies) on the decaying meat in the open jar. There were no maggots on the meat in the covered jar.

STEP ③ Redi reasoned that flies had laid eggs on the meat in the open jar. The eggs hatched into maggots. Because flies could not lay eggs on the meat in the covered jar, there were no maggots there. Redi concluded that decaying meat did not produce maggots.

Uncovered jar   Covered jar

apply it!

Use **Figure 4** to answer the following questions about Redi's experiment.

❶ Control Variables What is the independent variable in this experiment?

_____

_____

_____

❷ Control Variables What is the dependent variable?

_____

_____

_____

❸ Analyze Sources of Error Name two factors that would need to be kept constant in this experiment to avoid causing error. Why?

_____

_____

_____

_____

_____

_____

_____

Pasteur's Experiment Even after Redi's experiment, many people continued to believe in spontaneous generation. In the mid-1800s, Louis Pasteur, a French chemist, designed another experiment to test spontaneous generation. That experiment, shown in **Figure 5,** along with Redi's work, finally disproved spontaneous generation.

FIGURE 5 ···

> INTERACTIVE ART **Pasteur's Experiment**

Louis Pasteur's carefully controlled experiment demonstrated that bacteria arise only from existing bacteria. 🖋 **Design Experiments** Read each step of the experiment below. Why do you think flasks with curved necks were important?

_____

_____

_____

Step 1 Experiment Begins

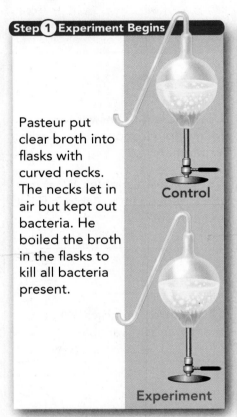

Pasteur put clear broth into flasks with curved necks. The necks let in air but kept out bacteria. He boiled the broth in the flasks to kill all bacteria present.

Control

Experiment

Step 2 A Year Passes

The boiled broth remained clear. Pasteur then left some of the flasks as is.

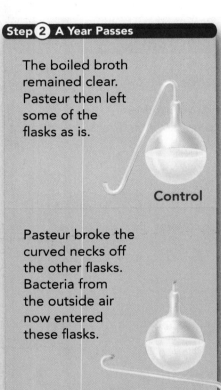

Control

Pasteur broke the curved necks off the other flasks. Bacteria from the outside air now entered these flasks.

Experiment

Step 3 A Few Days Later

The broth in the unbroken flasks remained clear. Pasteur concluded that bacteria could not arise from the broth.

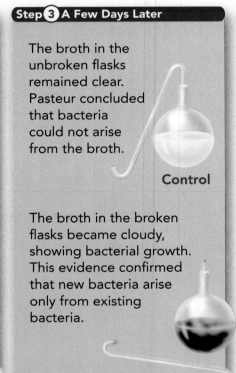

Control

The broth in the broken flasks became cloudy, showing bacterial growth. This evidence confirmed that new bacteria arise only from existing bacteria.

Experiment

Lab zone® Do the Quick Lab *Compare Broth Samples.*

🔑 Assess Your Understanding

2a. Identify A(n) _____ is the one factor that changes in a controlled experiment.

SC.6.L.15.1

b. Explain Why is the idea of spontaneous generation incorrect?

_____

_____

SC.6.L.15.1

got it?

○ **I get it!** Now I know that living things come from _____

_____

○ **I need extra help with** _____

Go to MY SCIENCE 🅢 COACH *online for help with this subject.*

SC.6.L.15.1

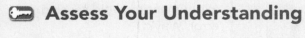

What Do Living Things Need to Survive?

Though it may seem surprising, flies, bacteria, and all other organisms have the same basic needs as you. 🔑 **All living things must satisfy their basic needs for food, water, living space, and stable internal conditions.**

Food Recall that organisms need a source of energy to live. They use food as their energy source. Organisms differ in the ways they obtain energy. Some organisms, such as plants, capture the sun's energy and use it to make food. Organisms that make their own food are called **autotrophs** (AW toh trohfs). *Auto-* means "self" and *-troph* means "feeder." Autotrophs use the food they make to carry out their own life functions.

Organisms that cannot make their own food are called **heterotrophs** (HET uh roh trohfs). Heterotrophs obtain energy by feeding on other organisms. Some heterotrophs eat autotrophs for food. Other heterotrophs consume heterotrophs that eat autotrophs. They use the energy in the autotrophs' bodies. Therefore, a heterotroph's energy source is also the sun—but in an indirect way. Animals, mushrooms, and slime molds are examples of heterotrophs.

FLORIDA NGSSS

SC.6.L.15.1 Analyze and describe how and why organisms are classified according to shared characteristics with emphasis on the Linnaean system combined with the concept of Domains.

LA.6.2.2.3 The student will organize information to show understanding (e.g., representing main ideas within text through comparing/contrasting).

🔄 **Compare and Contrast** As you read, circle how autotrophs and heterotrophs are similar and underline how they are different.
LA.6.2.2.3

Vocabulary Greek Word Origins The Greek word part *hetero-* means "other." How does this word help you to understand how heterotrophs get their food?

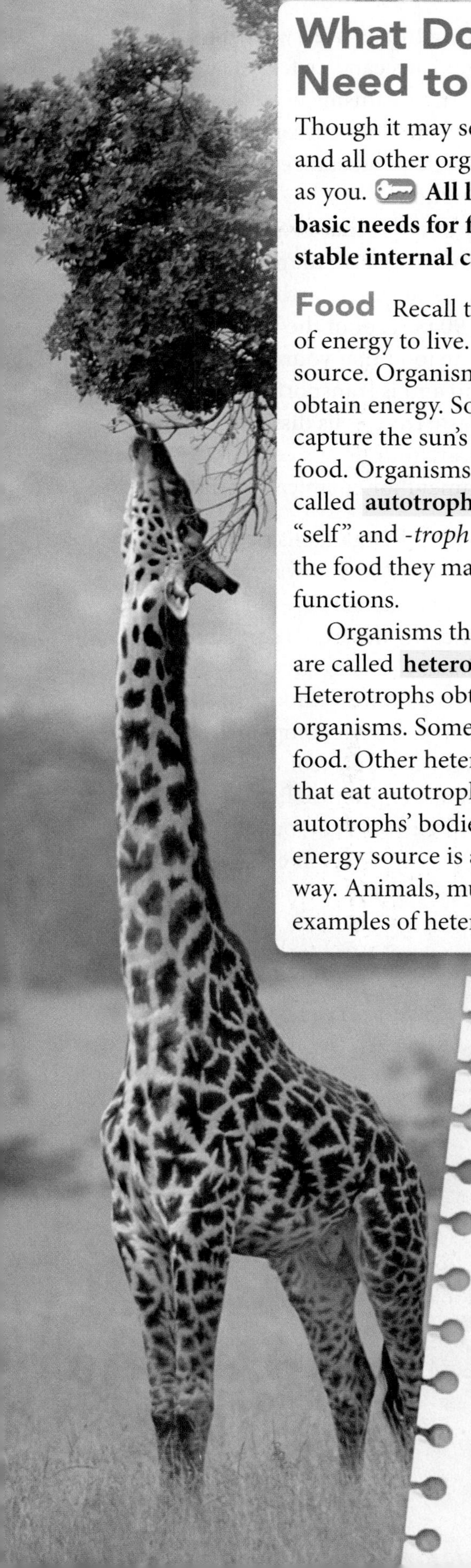

_____

_____

_____

_____

FIGURE 6 ....
Food
This giraffe, a heterotroph, obtains its energy by feeding on trees and shrubs.

✏️ **Identify** From your own habitat, name two examples of autotrophs and two examples of heterotrophs.

_____

_____

_____

_____

323

FIGURE 7 ·····················

Desert Oasis

You might be surprised to see so much green in the middle of a desert. In a desert oasis, there is water beneath the surface. The groundwater can bubble to the surface and create springs.

✏ **Draw Conclusions** How can a small area in the middle of a desert provide an organism what it needs to survive?

_____

_____

_____

_____

Water All living things need water to survive. In fact, most organisms can live for only a few days without water. Organisms need water to obtain chemicals from their surroundings, break down food, grow, move substances within their bodies, and reproduce.

One property of water that is vital to living things is its ability to dissolve more chemicals than any other substance on Earth. In fact, water makes up about 90 percent of the liquid part of your blood. The food that your cells need dissolves in blood and is transported to all parts of your body. Waste from cells dissolves in blood and is carried away. Your body's cells also provide a watery environment for chemicals to dissolve.

Living Space All organisms need a place to live—a place to get food and water and find shelter. Whether an organism lives in the freezing Arctic or the scorching desert, its surroundings must provide what it needs to survive.

Because there is a limited amount of space on Earth, some organisms must compete for space. Trees in a forest, for example, compete with other trees for sunlight above ground. Below ground, their roots compete for water and minerals.

FIGURE 8 ·································

Homeostasis

This southern coal skink is a lizard that lives mostly in the hillsides of pine woods in the Florida Panhandle. Basking in the sun helps the skink maintain a comfortable body temperature.

✎ **Make Generalizations** What are some challenges to maintaining homeostasis for animals and plants that live in Florida?

_____

_____

_____

_____

Do the Lab Investigation *Please Pass the Bread.*

Stable Internal Conditions

Organisms must be able to keep the conditions inside their bodies stable, even when conditions in their surroundings change significantly. For example, your body temperature stays steady despite changes in the air temperature. The maintenance of stable internal conditions is called homeostasis (hoh mee oh STAY sis).

Homeostasis keeps internal conditions just right for cells to function. Think about your need for water after a hard workout. When water levels in your body decrease, chemicals in your body send signals to your brain, which cause you to feel thirsty.

Other organisms have different mechanisms for maintaining homeostasis. Consider barnacles, which as adults are attached to rocks at the edge of the ocean. At high tide, they are covered by water. But at low tide, the watery surroundings disappear, and barnacles are exposed to hours of sun and wind. Without a way to keep water in their cells, they would die. Fortunately, a barnacle can close up its hard outer plates, trapping some water inside. In this way, a barnacle can keep its body moist until the next high tide. Refer to **Figure 8** to see another example of how an organism maintains homeostasis.

🔑 Assess Your Understanding

3a. Describe Which basic need is a fox meeting by feeding on berries?

_____

_____

SC.6.L.15.1

b. Apply Concepts The arctic fox has thick, dense fur in the winter and much shorter fur in the summer. How does this help the fox maintain homeostasis?

_____

_____

_____

_____

_____

SC.6.L.15.1

got it? ·····························

○ **I get it!** Now I know that to survive, living things need _____

_____

_____

○ **I need extra help with** _____

_____

_____

_____

Go to **MY SCIENCE** Ⓢ **COACH** *online for help with this subject.*   SC.6.L.15.1

LESSON 2 Classifying Life

🔑 **Why Do Biologists Classify Organisms?**
SC.6.N.1.3, SC.6.L.15.1, MA.6.A.3.6

🔑 **What Are the Levels of Classification?**
SC.6.L.15.1

🔑 **How Are Taxonomic Keys Useful?**
SC.6.L.15.1, LA.6.4.2.2

my planeT DiaRY

CAREER

Birds of a Feather

When people first began to travel in airplanes, birds often caused crashes. In 1960, 62 people were killed when birds flew into an airplane's engine. Something had to be done, but no one knew what kinds of birds were causing the crashes. Usually only a tiny, burnt piece of feather remained. Engineers didn't know how big or heavy the birds were, so they couldn't design planes to keep birds out of the engines. Then a scientist named Roxie Laybourne invented a way to classify birds using a tiny piece of feather. She identified the birds from many crashes. Her work helped engineers design engines to reduce bird collisions. She also helped develop bird management programs for major airports. Roxie's work has saved passengers' lives!

Answer the questions below.   SC.6.N.1.3

1. How was Roxie Laybourne's work different from an experiment?

_____

_____

_____

_____

2. What was the benefit of her invention?

_____

_____

_____

_____

_____

▶ PLANET DIARY Go to **Planet Diary** to learn more about classification.

Lab zone Do the Inquiry Warm-Up *Can You Organize a Junk Drawer?*

Vocabulary

- classification • taxonomy • binomial nomenclature
- genus • species

Skills

- Reading: Ask Questions
- Inquiry: Observe

Why Do Biologists Classify Organisms?

So far, scientists have identified more than one million kinds of organisms on Earth. That's a large number, and it keeps growing as scientists discover new organisms. Imagine how difficult it would be to find information about one particular organism if you had no idea even where to begin. It would be a lot easier if similar organisms were placed into groups.

Organizing living things into groups is exactly what biologists have done. Biologists group organisms based on similarities, just as grocers group milk with dairy products and tomatoes with other produce. **Classification** is the process of grouping things based on their similarities, as shown in **Figure 1**.

🔑 **Biologists use classification to organize living things into groups so that the organisms are easier to study.** The scientific study of how organisms are classified is called **taxonomy** (tak SAHN uh mee). Taxonomy is useful because once an organism is classified, a scientist knows a lot of information about that organism. For example, if you know that a crow is classified as a bird, then you know that a crow has wings, feathers, and a beak.

FLORIDA NGSSS

SC.6.N.1.3 Explain the difference between an experiment and other types of scientific investigations.

SC.6.L.15.1 Analyze and describe how and why organisms are classified according to shared characteristics.

MA.6.A.3.6 Construct and analyze tables, graphs, and equations to describe simple relations.

........................✏️........................

🔵 **Ask Questions** Before you read, preview the headings. Ask a *what*, *why*, or *how* question that you would like answered. As you read, write the answer to your question.

_____

_____

_____

_____

_____

FIGURE 1 ....

Classifying Insects

These bees and wasps belong to a large insect collection in a natural history museum. They have been classified according to the characteristics they share.

✏️ **Observe** What characteristics do you think may have been used to group these insects?

_____

_____

_____

_____

_____

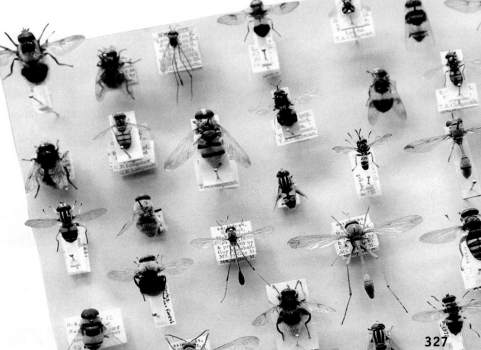

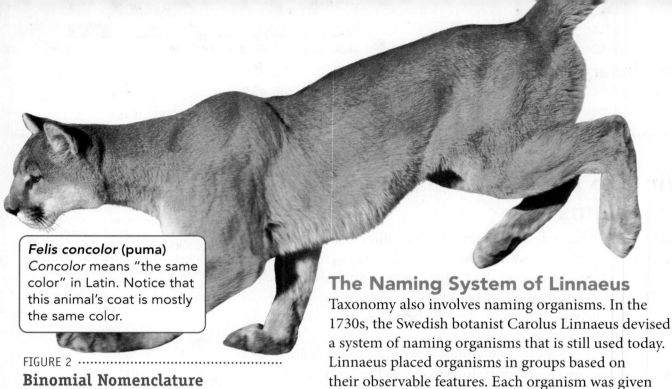

Felis concolor (puma)
Concolor means "the same color" in Latin. Notice that this animal's coat is mostly the same color.

FIGURE 2 ·······························

Binomial Nomenclature

These three different species of cats belong to the same genus. The cats' scientific names share the same first word, *Felis*. The second word of their names describes a feature of the animals.

✎ **Analyze and Describe** Suppose someone told you that a jaguarundi is classified in the same genus as house cats. What characteristics and behaviors do you think a jaguarundi might have?

_____

_____

_____

_____

The Naming System of Linnaeus

Taxonomy also involves naming organisms. In the 1730s, the Swedish botanist Carolus Linnaeus devised a system of naming organisms that is still used today. Linnaeus placed organisms in groups based on their observable features. Each organism was given a unique, two-part scientific name. This system is called **binomial nomenclature** (by NOH mee ul NOH men klay chur). *Binomial* means "two names."

Genus and Species The first word in an organism's scientific name is its genus. A **genus** (JEE nus; plural *genera*) is a classification grouping that contains similar, closely related organisms. As shown in **Figure 2**, pumas, house cats, and marbled cats are all classified in the genus *Felis*. Organisms that are classified in the genus *Felis* share characteristics such as sharp, retractable claws and behaviors such as hunting other animals.

The second word in a scientific name often describes a distinctive feature of an organism, such as where it lives or its appearance. Together, the two words form the scientific name of a unique kind of organism. A **species** (SPEE sheez) is a group of similar organisms that can mate with each other and produce offspring that can also mate and reproduce.

Felis domesticus (house cat)
Domesticus means "of the house" in Latin.

Felis marmorata (marbled cat)
Marmorata means "marble" in Latin. Notice the marbled pattern of this animal's coat.

Using Binomial Nomenclature A complete scientific name is written in italics. Only the first letter of the first word in a scientific name is capitalized. Notice that scientific names contain Latin words. Linnaeus used Latin words in his naming system because Latin was the language that scientists used during that time.

Binomial nomenclature makes it easy for scientists to communicate about an organism because everyone uses the same scientific name for the same organism. Using different names or common names for the same organism can get very confusing, as **Figure 3** describes.

FIGURE 3 ·····························

What Are You Talking About?

Is this animal a groundhog, a woodchuck, a marmot, or a whistlepig? Depending on where you live, all of these names are correct. Luckily, this animal has only one scientific name, *Marmota monax*.

✎ **Describe** How is a scientific name written?

_____

_____

_____

do the math!

Aristotle and Classification

Aristotle, an ancient Greek scholar, also developed a classification system for animals.

Animals With Blood

- 32%
- 46%
- 22%

■ Animals that swim (sharks, bass, dolphins)

■ Animals that fly (eagles, gulls, pigeons)

■ Animals that walk, run, or hop (tortoises, frogs, lions)

MA.6.A.3.6

❶ **Calculate** _____ percent of these animals either fly or swim.

❷ **Classify** What new categories would you use to make a graph that classifies animals that move in more than one way?

_____

_____

_____

_____

_____

Lab zone Do the Quick Lab *Classifying Seeds.*

🔑 Assess Your Understanding

1a. Define The scientific study of how living things are classified is called

_____

SC.6.L.15.1

b. Make Generalizations What is the advantage of using scientific names instead of using common names, like cat or dog?

_____

_____

_____

_____

_____

SC.6.L.15.1

got it? ·····························

○ **I get it!** Now I know that organisms are

classified _____

_____

○ **I need extra help with** _____

Go to **MY SCIENCE ⓢ COACH** online for help with this subject.

SC.6.L.15.1

FLORIDA NGSSS

SC.6.L.15.1 Analyze and describe how and why organisms are classified according to shared characteristics with emphasis on the Linnaean system combined with the concept of Domains.

What Are the Levels of Classification?

The classification system that scientists use today is based on the contributions of Linnaeus. But today's classification system uses a series of many levels to classify organisms.

To help you understand the levels of classification, imagine a room filled with everybody who lives in your state. First, all of the people who live in your town raise their hands. Then those who live in your neighborhood raise their hands. Then those who live on your street raise their hands. Finally, those who live in your house raise their hands. Each time, fewer people raise their hands. The more levels you share with others, the more you have in common with them.

The Major Levels of Classification Of course, organisms are not grouped by where they live, but by their shared characteristics. Most biologists today classify organisms into the levels shown in **Figure 4**. First, an organism is placed in a broad group, which in turn is divided into more specific groups.

🔑 **A domain is the broadest level of organization. Within a domain, there are kingdoms. Within kingdoms, there are phyla (FY luh; singular *phylum*). Within phyla are classes. Within classes are orders. Within orders are families. Each family contains one or more genera. Finally, each genus contains one or more species.** The more classification levels two organisms share, the more characteristics they have in common and the more closely related they are.

FIGURE 4 ·

▶ VIRTUAL LAB Levels of Classification

The figure on the facing page shows how the levels of organization apply to a great horned owl.

✎ **Answer the questions.**

1. **Analyze** List the characteristics that the organisms share at the kingdom level.

_____

_____

2. **Analyze** List the characteristics that the organisms share at the class level.

_____

_____

_____

3. **Analyze** List the characteristics that the organisms share at the genus level.

_____

_____

_____

4. **Draw Conclusions** How does the number of shared characteristics on your list change at each level? _____

_____

_____

5. **Interpret Diagrams** Robins have more in common with (lions/owls).

Levels of Classification

Domain Eukarya

Kingdom Animalia

Phylum Chordata

Class Aves

Order Strigiformes

As you move down these levels of classification, the number of organisms decreases. The organisms that remain share more characteristics with one another and are more related.

Family Strigidae

Genus *Bubo*

Species *Bubo virginianus*

Lab ® zone
Do the Quick Lab
Make a Classification Chart.

🔑 Assess Your Understanding

got it? ....

○ **I get it!** Now I know that the levels of classification are _____

_____

_____

_____

○ **I need extra help with** _____

_____

Go to **my science** ⓢ **coach** *online for help with this subject.*   SC.6.L.15.1

FLORIDA NGSSS

SC.6.L.15.1 Analyze and describe how and why organisms are classified according to shared characteristics with emphasis on the Linnaean system combined with the concept of Domains.

LA.6.4.2.2 The student will record information (e.g., observations) related to a topic.

How Are Taxonomic Keys Useful?

Why should you care about taxonomy? Suppose that you are watching television and feel something tickling your foot. Startled, you look down and see a tiny creature crawling across your toes. Although it's only the size of a small melon seed, you don't like the looks of its two claws waving at you. Then, in a flash, it's gone.

How could you find out what the creature was? You could use a field guide. Field guides are books with illustrations that highlight differences between similar-looking organisms. You could also use a taxonomic key. **Taxonomic keys are useful tools that help determine the identity of organisms.** A taxonomic key consists of a series of paired statements that describe the various physical characteristics of different organisms. The taxonomic key shown in **Figure 5** can help you identify the mysterious organism.

FIGURE 5 ···

> **INTERACTIVE ART** **Identifying Organisms**
The six paired statements in this taxonomic key describe physical characteristics of different organisms.

✎ **Analyze** _____ different organisms can be identified using this key. The mysterious organism is a _____

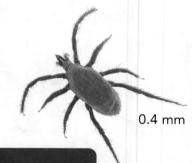

0.4 mm

Start Here ▶

First: For each set of statements, choose the one that best describes the organism; for example, 1a.

Second:
Follow the direction to the next step.

Third:
Continue process until organism is identified.

Taxonomic Key

Step		Characteristics	Organism
1	1a.	Has 8 legs	Go to Step 2.
	1b.	Has more than 8 legs	Go to Step 3.
2	2a.	Has one oval-shaped body region	Go to Step 4.
	2b.	Has two body regions	Go to Step 5.
3	3a.	Has one pair of legs on each body segment	Centipede
	3b.	Has two pairs of legs on each body segment	Millipede
4	4a.	Is less than 1 millimeter long	Mite
	4b.	Is more than 1 millimeter long	Tick
5	5a.	Has clawlike pincers	Go to Step 6.
	5b.	Has no clawlike pincers	Spider
6	6a.	Has a long tail with a stinger	Scorpion
	6b.	Has no tail or stinger	Pseudoscorpion

apply it!

Use the taxonomic key in **Figure 5** to answer the following questions.

1 Interpret Tables Identify each pictured organism.

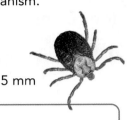

5 mm

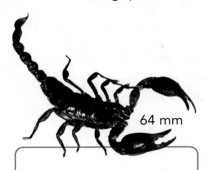

64 mm

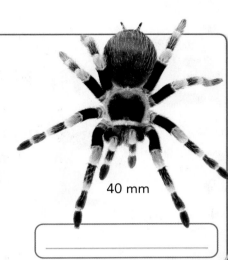

40 mm

50 mm

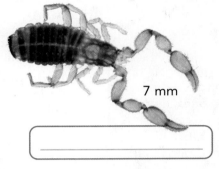

7 mm

25 mm

2 Draw Conclusions What other information could have been helpful in identifying these organisms?

_____

_____

_____

3 CHALLENGE Is this information necessary for the key in **Figure 5?** Explain your answer.

_____

_____

_____

LA.6.4.2.2

 Do the Quick Lab *Living Mysteries.*

🔑 Assess Your Understanding

got it? ···

○ **I get it!** Now I know that taxonomic keys are used to _____

_____

○ **I need extra help with** _____

Go to **MY SCIENCE** ⓢ **COACH** *online for help with this subject.*   SC.6.L.15.1

LESSON

3 Domains and Kingdoms

🔑 How Are Organisms Classified Into Domains and Kingdoms?

SC.6.L.15.1

my planet diary

Unbeelievable!

If you were classifying organisms, would you expect there to be more bees, more birds, or more mammals in the world? The table below shows the number of species of bees, mammals, and birds that scientists have found so far!

Number of Species		
Bees	**Mammals**	**Birds**
19,200	5,400	10,000

SCIENCE STATS

Answer the question below.

Why do you think that bee species outnumber mammal and bird species combined?

_____

_____

_____

_____

> PLANET DIARY Go to **Planet Diary** to learn more about domains and kingdoms.

 Do the Inquiry Warm-Up
What Organism Goes Where?

FLORIDA NGSSS

SC.6.L.15.1 Analyze and describe how and why organisms are classified according to shared characteristics with emphasis on the Linnaean system combined with the concept of Domains.

How Are Organisms Classified Into Domains and Kingdoms?

Suppose you helped Linnaeus classify organisms. You probably would have identified organisms as either plants or animals. That's because in Linnaeus' time there were no microscopes to see the tiny organisms that are known to exist today. Microscopes helped to discover new organisms and identify differences among cells.

Today, a three-domain system of classification is commonly used. As shown in the table on the top of the next page, the three domains are Bacteria, Archaea, and Eukarya. Within the domains are kingdoms. 🔑 **Organisms are placed into domains and kingdoms based on their cell type, their ability to make food, and the number of cells in their bodies.**

Vocabulary
- prokaryote
- eukaryote

Skills
🔁 Reading: Identify the Main Idea
△ Inquiry: Classify

Three Domains of Life					
Bacteria	Archaea	Eukarya			
		Protists	Fungi	Plants	Animals

Domain Bacteria
Although you may not know it, members of the domain Bacteria are all around you. You can find them on the surfaces you touch and inside your body. Some bacteria are autotrophs, while others are heterotrophs.

Members of the domain Bacteria are called prokaryotes (proh KA ree ohtz). **Prokaryotes** are unicellular organisms whose cells lack a nucleus. A nucleus (NOO klee us; plural *nuclei*) is a dense area in a cell that contains DNA—the chemical instructions that direct the cell's activities. In prokaryotes, nucleic acids are not contained within a nucleus.

Domain Archaea
Deep in the Pacific Ocean, hot gases and molten rock spew out from a vent in the ocean floor. It is hard to imagine that any living thing could exist in such harsh conditions. Surprisingly, a group of tiny organisms thrives in such a place. They are members of the domain Archaea (ahr KEE uh), whose name comes from the Greek word for "ancient."

Like bacteria, archaea are unicellular prokaryotes. And like bacteria, some archaea are autotrophs and others are heterotrophs. Archaea are classified in their own domain because their chemical makeup differs from that of bacteria. Bacteria and archaea also differ in the structure of their cells. The bacteria in **Figure 1** and the archaea in **Figure 2** have been stained and magnified to make them easier to see.

FIGURE 1 ·····························

Bacteria
Most bacteria, such as *Lactobacillus acidophilus,* are helpful. These bacteria help to produce yogurt and milk for people who are lactose intolerant.

FIGURE 2 ···

Archaea
Archaea can be found in extreme environments such as hot springs, very salty water, and the intestines of cows! Scientists think that the harsh conditions in which archaea live are similar to those of ancient Earth.

✎ **Compare and Contrast** How are archaea and bacteria similar? How are they different?

_____

_____

_____

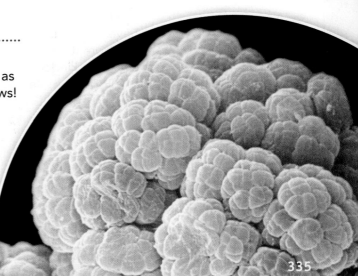

FIGURE 3 ·························

Eukarya

You can encounter organisms from all four kingdoms of Eukarya on a trip to a salt marsh.

Three Domains of Life

Bacteria	Archaea	Eukarya		
		Protists	Fungi	Plants	Animals

Domain Eukarya What do seaweeds, mushrooms, tomatoes, and dogs have in common? They are all members of the domain Eukarya. Organisms in this domain are **eukaryotes** (yoo KA ree ohtz)—organisms with cells that contain nuclei. Scientists classify organisms in the domain Eukarya into one of four kingdoms: protists, fungi, plants, or animals.

Marine dinoflagellates

Protists

A protist (PROH tist) is any eukaryotic organism that cannot be classified as a fungus, plant, or animal. Because its members are so different from one another, the protist kingdom is sometimes called the "odds and ends" kingdom. For example, some protists are autotrophs, while others are heterotrophs. Most protists are unicellular, but some, such as seaweeds, are multicellular.

Fungi

If you have eaten mushrooms, then you have eaten fungi (FUN jy). Mushrooms, molds, and mildew are all fungi. The majority of fungi are multicellular eukaryotes. A few, such as the yeast used in baking, are unicellular eukaryotes. Fungi are found almost everywhere on land, but only a few live in fresh water. All fungi are heterotrophs. Most fungi feed by absorbing nutrients from dead or decaying organisms.

Aspergillus fumigatus

apply it!

Classify While on a walk, you find an organism that you've never seen before. You are determined to figure out what kingdom it belongs to. Starting with the first observation below, circle the kingdom(s) the organism could fit into. Using the process of elimination, determine which kingdom the organism belongs to.

❶ There are nuclei present. (Protists/Fungi/Plants/Animals)

❷ You can count more than one cell. (Protists/Fungi/Plants/Animals)

❸ The organism cannot make its own food. (Protists/Fungi/Plants/Animals)

❹ The organism gets nutrients from dead organisms. (Protists/Fungi/Plants/Animals)

❺ Other members of this kingdom can be unicellular. (Protists/Fungi/Plants/Animals)

Plants

Dandelions on a lawn, peas in a garden, and the marsh grass shown here are familiar members of the plant kingdom. Plants are all multicellular eukaryotes, and most live on land. Also, plants are autotrophs that make their own food. Plants provide food for most of the heterotrophs on land.

The plant kingdom includes a great variety of organisms. Some plants produce flowers, while others do not. Some plants, such as giant redwood trees, can grow very tall. Others, like mosses, never grow taller than a few centimeters.

⬁ **Identify the Main Idea** In the text under Domain Eukarya, underline the main idea.

Snowy egret

Animals

A dog, a flea on the dog's ear, and a cat that the dog chases have much in common because all are animals. All animals are multicellular eukaryotes. In addition, all animals are heterotrophs. Animals have different adaptations that allow them to locate food, capture it, eat it, and digest it. Members of the animal kingdom live in diverse environments throughout Earth. Animals can be found from ocean depths to mountaintops, from hot, scalding deserts to cold, icy landscapes.

 Do the Quick Lab *Staining Leaves.*

🔑 Assess Your Understanding

1a. Define A cell that lacks a nucleus is called a (eukaryote/prokaryote).

SC.6.L.15.1

b. Describe Two ways that the members of the two domains of prokaryotes differ are in the

_____

_____

SC.6.L.15.1

c. CHALLENGE You learn that a dandelion is in the same kingdom as pine trees. Name three characteristics that these organisms share.

_____

_____

SC.6.L.15.1

got it?

○ **I get it!** Now I know that organisms are classified into domains and kingdoms based on their _____

_____

_____

○ **I need extra help with** _____

_____

Go to MY SCIENCE 🔊 COACH *online for help with this subject.*

SC.6.L.15.1

Evolution and Classification

🔑 **How Are Evolution and Classification Related?**

SC.6.N.3.1, SC.6.L.15.1, LA.6.2.2.3, LA.6.4.2.2

MY PLANET DIARY

DISCOVERY

If It Looks Like a Duck . . .

The first scientist to see the pelt of the platypus thought it was a joke. Could a four-legged, duck-billed, egg-laying mammal exist? How had it evolved? Native people from Australia believed that the first platypus was born when a water rat mated with a duck. But scientists put the platypus into a new group of egg-laying mammals. Then many years later, scientists began to argue. Had the platypus really evolved later with younger marsupials such as kangaroos? Would the platypus have to be reclassified? Scientists studied its DNA and discovered that the platypus was in the right place!

Answer the question below.
How did DNA help classify the platypus?

_____

_____

_____

_____

_____

_____

▶ PLANET DIARY Go to **Planet Diary** to learn more about evolution and classification.

 Lab® zone Do the Inquiry Warm-Up *Observing Similarities.*

 FLORIDA NGSSS

SC.6.N.3.1 Recognize and explain that a scientific theory is a well-supported and widely accepted explanation of nature.

SC.6.L.15.1 Analyze and describe how and why organisms are classified according to shared characteristics.

LA.6.2.2.3 The student will organize information to show understanding (e.g., summarizing).

LA.6.4.2.2 The student will record information related to a topic.

How Are Evolution and Classification Related?

When Linnaeus developed his classification system, people thought that species never changed. In 1859, a British naturalist named Charles Darwin published an explanation for how species could change over time. You may know that the process of change over time is called **evolution.** Darwin thought that evolution occurs by means of natural selection. Natural selection is the process by which individuals that are better adapted to their environment are more likely to survive and reproduce than other members of the same species.

Vocabulary

- evolution • branching tree diagram
- shared derived characteristic
- convergent evolution

Skills

- Reading: Summarize
- Inquiry: Infer

As understanding of evolution increased, biologists changed how they classify species. Scientists now understand that certain organisms may be similar because they share a common ancestor and an evolutionary history. The more similar the two groups are, the more recent the common ancestor probably is. Today's system of classification considers the history of a species. **Species with similar evolutionary histories are classified more closely together.**

Branching Tree Diagrams

Two groups of organisms with similar characteristics may be descended from a common ancestor. A **branching tree diagram,** like the one in **Figure 1,** shows probable evolutionary relationships among organisms and the order in which specific characteristics may have evolved. Branching tree diagrams begin at the base with the common ancestor of all the organisms in the diagram. Organisms are grouped according to their shared derived characteristics.

Summarize Name two things that similar organisms share.

_____

_____

_____

LA.6.2.2.3

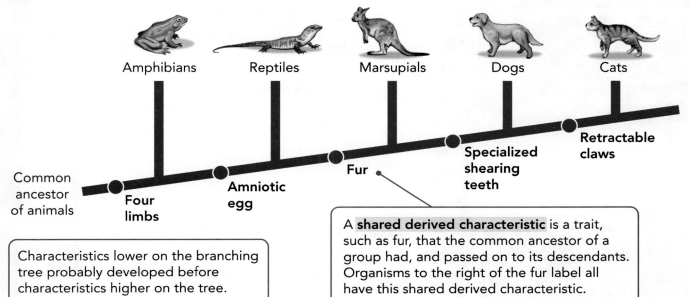

Characteristics lower on the branching tree probably developed before characteristics higher on the tree.

A **shared derived characteristic** is a trait, such as fur, that the common ancestor of a group had, and passed on to its descendants. Organisms to the right of the fur label all have this shared derived characteristic.

FIGURE 1 ···

> **ART IN MOTION** A Branching Tree

This branching tree diagram shows how cats have evolved.

✎ **Complete the tasks.**

1. **Interpret Diagrams** Put squares around the shared derived characteristics.

2. **Interpret Diagrams** Circle the animal(s) that belong to the smallest group.

3. **Apply Concepts** Cats are more closely related to (reptiles/marsupials).

339

Note the characteristics of Figures A, B, C, and D.

1 _Infer_ Which figure is the most similar to Figure B?

_____

2 [CHALLENGE] Suppose these shapes are fossils of extinct organisms. Which organism do you think might be the ancestor of all the others? Why?

_____

_____

_____

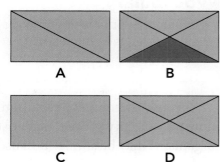

A   B

C   D

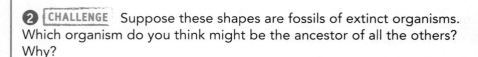

Finding a New Species

How are living things alike yet different?

FIGURE 2 ···

While on an expedition, you photograph what you think is a new species.

✏️ **Analyze and Describe** Use the camera image of the new species and the photos of organisms previously identified from the same area to record your observations in your field journal.

Laotian rock rat
Laonastes aenigmanus

Golden-crowned flying fox
Acerodon jubatus

FIELD JOURNAL

Location: Greater Mekong region of Asia

Date: _____

Organism's observable characteristics: _____

_____

_____

Observed habitat(s): _____

_____

Domain and kingdom: _____

_____

Additional information needed to determine if organism is a new

species: _____

_____

_____

Name (assuming it's a new species): _____

_____

Significance/meaning of name: _____

_____

LA.6.4.2.2

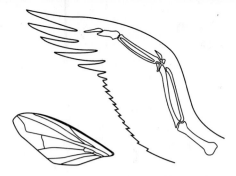

FIGURE 3

Convergent Evolution
Birds and insects both use wings to help them fly. However, these two organisms are not closely related.

Determining Evolutionary Relationships How do scientists determine the evolutionary history of a species? One way is to compare the structure of organisms. Scientists can also use information about the chemical makeup of the organisms' cells.

Sometimes unrelated organisms evolve similar characteristics because they evolved in similar environments, like organisms that move through the water or eat similar foods. Because the organisms perform similar functions, their body structures may look similar. Look at **Figure 3.** The process by which unrelated organisms evolve characteristics that are similar is called **convergent evolution.**

When studying the chemical makeup of organisms, sometimes new information is discovered that results in reclassification. For example, skunks and weasels were classified in the same family for 150 years. When scientists compared DNA from the cells of skunks and weasels, they found many differences. These differences suggest that the two groups are not that closely related. As a result, scientists reclassified skunks into a separate family.

 Do the Quick Lab *Common Ancestors.*

🔑 Assess Your Understanding

1a. Identify Look back at **Figure 1.** What characteristics do all reptiles share?

_____

_____

SC.6.L.15.1

b. ANSWER THE ESSENTIAL **?** How are living things alike yet different? _____

_____

_____

_____

SC.6.L.15.1

got it? ....

○ **I get it!** Now I know that evolution and classification are related because _____

_____

_____

_____

○ **I need extra help with** _____

_____

Go to **my science** Ⓢ **coach** *online for help with this subject.*   SC.6.N.3.1, SC.6.L.15.1

Study Guide

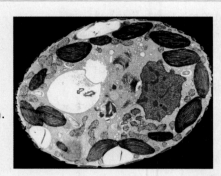

Living things can vary. For example, organisms may be prokaryotes or _____.
Yet all living things are made of _____, which grow, develop, and reproduce.

LESSON 1 What Is Life?

SC.6.L.15.1

🔑 All living things have a cellular organization, contain similar chemicals, use energy, respond to their surroundings, grow and develop, and reproduce.

🔑 Living things arise from other living things through reproduction.

🔑 All living things must satisfy their basic needs for food, water, living space, and stable internal conditions.

Vocabulary
• metabolism • development • asexual reproduction • sexual reproduction
• spontaneous generation • autotroph • heterotroph

LESSON 2 Classifying Life

SC.6.N.1.3, SC.6.L.15.1

🔑 Biologists use classification to organize living things into groups so that the organisms are easier to study.

🔑 The levels of classification are domain, kingdom, phylum, class, order, family, genus, and species.

🔑 Taxonomic keys are useful tools that help determine the identity of organisms.

Vocabulary
• classification • taxonomy • binomial nomenclature
• genus • species

LESSON 3 Domains and Kingdoms

SC.6.L.15.1

🔑 Organisms are placed into domains and kingdoms based on their cell type, ability to make food, and the number of cells in their bodies.

Vocabulary
• prokaryote
• eukaryote

LESSON 4 Evolution and Classification

SC.6.N.3.1, SC.6.L.15.1

🔑 Species with similar evolutionary histories are classified more closely together.

Vocabulary
• evolution
• branching tree diagram
• shared derived characteristic
• convergent evolution

Review and Assessment

LESSON 1 What Is Life?

1. An organism's reaction to a change in its surroundings is called

   a. a stimulus.   **b.** autotrophy.

   c. homeostasis.   **d.** a response.

                          SC.6.L.15.1

2. _____ involves only one parent and produces offspring that are identical to the parent.

                          SC.6.L.15.1

3. Apply Concepts Pick an organism in your home and describe how this organism meets the four basic conditions for survival.

                          SC.6.L.15.1

4. Control Variables A student is designing a controlled experiment to test whether the amount of water that a plant receives affects its growth. Which variables should the student hold constant and which variable should the student change?

                          SC.6.L.15.1

5. Write About It Suppose you are searching for new life forms as part of an expedition in a remote region of Alaska. At one site you find 24 greenish-brown objects, each measuring around 1 cm^3. The objects do not appear to have heads, tails, or legs, but you suspect they may be alive. Describe what you would do to determine if the objects are alive.

                          SC.6.L.15.1

LESSON 2 Classifying Life

6. Which of the following is the broadest level of classification?

   a. genus   **b.** species

   c. domain   **d.** kingdom

                          SC.6.L.15.1

7. The two-part naming system called

_____ was devised by Linnaeus in the 1700s.

                          SC.6.L.15.1

8. Analyze and Describe The scientific name for the red maple tree is *Acer rubrum*. Another organism is called *Acer negundo*. Based on its name, what can you predict about this organism? Explain.

                          SC.6.L.15.1

9. Make Models Develop a taxonomic key that a person could use to identify each of the plants shown below.

White ash   Red oak   White oak   Pasture rose

                          SC.6.L.15.1

LESSON 3 Domains and Kingdoms

10. Which four kingdoms belong to the domain Eukarya?

   a. prokarya, archaea, eukarya, bacteria

   b. protists, fungi, plants, animals

   c. mite, tick, scorpion, spider

   d. class, order, family, genus

   SC.6.L.15.1

11. All eukaryotes belong to domain Eukarya, while _____ belong to domain Bacteria or domain Archaea.

   SC.6.L.15.1

12. **Compare and Contrast** Both plants and fungi belong to the domain Eukarya. What is one main difference between these organisms?

   _____

   _____

   _____

   _____

   SC.6.L.15.1

LESSON 4 Evolution and Classification

13. Which of the following factors is most important when classifying an organism?

   a. size   b. shape

   c. habitat   d. evolutionary history

   SC.6.L.15.1

14. A diagram that shows probable evolutionary relationships among organisms is called a

   _____

   SC.6.L.15.1

15. **Recognize and Explain** If you discovered two unrelated organisms that looked very similar, how could you explain it?

   _____

   _____

   _____

   _____

   SC.6.N.3.1, SC.6.L.15.1

 APPLY THE ESSENTIAL ## How are living things alike yet different?

16. With the advances in commercial space travel, some day you may have the opportunity to visit another planet and see things you've never seen before! How would you go about identifying things on the other planet as being living or nonliving? If an object turns out to be living, what characteristics would you look for in order to classify it?

_____

_____

_____

_____

_____

_____

_____

_____

_____

_____

_____

_____

_____

_____

_____

SC.6.N.3.1, SC.6.L.15.1

Florida Benchmarks Review

Circle the letter of the best answer.

1 What information in the chart below tells you that the smooth-leaved elm is the tree most different from the other three trees?

Some Types of Trees

Common Name of Tree	Kingdom	Family	Species
Bird cherry	Plants	Rosaceae	*Prunus avium*
Flowering cherry	Plants	Rosaceae	*Prunus serrula*
Smooth-leaved elm	Plants	Ulmaceae	*Ultimus minor*
Whitebeam	Plants	Rosaceae	*Sorbus aria*

  A It belongs to a different family.
  B It belongs to a different species.
  C It is not a cherry tree.
  D This chart does not give enough information.

SC.6.L.15.1

2 According to the system of binomial nomenclature, which of the following is a properly written scientific name?

  A Acer rubrum
  B Acer Rubrum
  C *Acer rubrum*
  D *acer rubrum*

SC.6.L.15.1

3 Which of the following is an example of an autotroph?

  A a lion
  B a tree
  C an eagle
  D a mushroom

SC.6.L.15.1

4 Which domain does NOT contain prokaryotes?

  A Archaea
  B Bacteria
  C Eukarya
  D None of the above. All three domains contain prokaryotes.

SC.6.L.15.1

5 A branching tree diagram shows evolutionary relationships by

  A grouping organisms according to their differences.
  B determining the identity of organisms.
  C grouping organisms according to their shared derived characteristics.
  D giving an organism a unique, two-part scientific name.

SC.6.N.3.1, SC.6.L.15.1

6 How many kingdoms are represented by the organisms shown below?

  A 1
  B 2
  C 3
  D 4

SC.6.L.15.1

Bones in Space

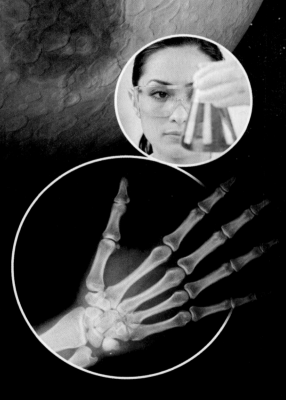

You're a crew member on the first manned mission to Mars. You'll travel at great speeds in microgravity. What will happen to your body during the year-long trip? That's one of the many important questions scientists at the Space Life Sciences Lab (SLSL) at the Kennedy Space Center in Florida are working on. The SLSL has 25 laboratories with state-of-the-art equipment. This equipment helps scientists study plants, animals and microorganisms under special conditions, such as extremely cold temperatures, lack of light, and microgravity.

Microgravity is the condition of experiencing weightlessness in space. It can affect living organisms in many ways. One major problem for astronauts is that microgravity decreases bone density. You may have heard of a disease called osteoporosis. As people get older, they lose calcium from their bones. Their bones become less dense, weaker, and can break more easily. The same thing happens to astronauts in space—but their bones deteriorate at a much faster rate. Astronauts can lose up to one percent of their bone mass per month! Scientists don't fully understand why this happens in microgravity. SLSL investigators plan to explore this issue by studying bone tissue in an artificial microgravity environment created at the lab. Their research will not only enable future missions to Mars, but will also help astronauts and people who suffer from osteoporosis today.

Research It Use resources to research the causes and treatments of osteoporosis. Then, use your findings to make a pamphlet that teaches astronauts about what they should do to prevent osteoporosis while in the microgravity conditions of space.

 FLORIDA NGSSS

SC.6.N.1.5 Recognize that science involves creativity, in designing experiments, and creating explanations.

SC.6.L.14.5 Investigate the functions of the major systems of the human body and how they maintain homeostasis.

Colwell's Gift

Cholera is an infection of the intestines that is spread by drinking water or eating food contaminated with cholera bacteria. It causes diarrhea, vomiting, and cramps. When cholera strikes, approximately one victim in 20 can become seriously ill and may die within hours. Because most places in the United States have safe drinking water, we don't see a lot of cholera here. But in many developing countries, cholera is still common.

For a long time, scientists could not predict cholera epidemics. Outbreaks happened suddenly, with no warning. And after the epidemic, scientists could not detect the cholera bacteria in the water. So, where did the bacteria go, and how did they reappear so suddenly?

Rita Colwell suspected that the cholera bacteria were present in the water in an inactive state between outbreaks. She thought that the bacteria became active when the water temperature rose.

After many years, Colwell proved her hypothesis. Using new methods, scientists were able to detect the inactive cholera bacteria in water where they had not previously been able to detect cholera. Satellite data also confirmed that cholera outbreaks occur when ocean temperatures rise. Warmer water causes cholera bacteria to multiply. Now, scientists use this information to help prevent future cholera outbreaks.

Write About It Satellite observation and technology helped prove Rita Colwell's hypothesis. Research some satellites and what kind of observations they are able to make from far distances. Prepare an information card that outlines the benefits and limitations of these observations on human life.

FLORIDA NGSSS

SC.6.N.1.3 Explain the difference between an experiment and other types of scientific investigation, and explain the relative benefits and limitations of each.

SC.6.L.14.6 Compare and contrast types of infectious agents that may infect the human body.

HE.6.C.1.3 Identify environmental factors that affect personal health.

Limpkins, a type of bird, live year-round throughout Florida. Their long, curved bills probe freshwater marshes and swamps for animals to eat, such as snails, insects, and worms.

Summarizing

Life Science

In this Life Science unit, you learned about the characteristics shared by all living things. You learned about cell structure and function and the levels of organization in living things. You also learned about the processes needed for life and how organisms maintain homeostasis.

How is this bird's body organized?

_____

_____

_____

_____

_____

_____

_____

_____

_____

How does the bird get energy?

_____

_____

_____

_____

_____

_____

_____

_____

_____

_____

As you study this unit, look for answers to these questions.

How is **DNA** important to these young armadillos?

In what ways do these animals **INTERACT** with their environment?

These nine-banded armadillo pups have a tough, scaly skin that acts like armor and helps to protect them from predators.

Introducing

Life Science

 Florida Big Idea 15

Diversity and Evolution of Living Organisms

A. The scientific theory of evolution is the organizing principle of life science.

B. The scientific theory of evolution is supported by multiple forms of evidence.

C. Natural Selection is a primary mechanism leading to change over time in organisms.

 How do life forms change over time?

 Florida Big Idea 16

Heredity and Reproduction

A. Reproduction is characteristic of living things and is essential for the survival of species.

B. Genetic information is passed from generation to generation by DNA; DNA controls the traits of an organism.

C. Changes in the DNA of an organism can cause changes in traits, and manipulation of DNA in organisms has led to genetically modified organisms.

 Why don't offspring always look like their parents?

 How can genetic information be used?

 Florida Big Idea 17

Interdependence

A. Plants and animals, including humans, interact with and depend upon each other and their environment to satisfy their basic needs.

B. Both human activities and natural events can have major impacts on the environment.

C. Energy flows from the sun through producers to consumers.

 How do living things affect one another?

DOES THIS FISH HAVE LEGS?

ESSENTIAL

How do life forms change over time?

This is not your average fish. Besides having bright red lips, the rosy-lipped batfish is a poor swimmer. Instead of using its pectoral fins for swimming, the batfish uses them to crawl along the seafloor.

Develop Hypotheses How do you think the batfish's leglike fins help it survive?

_____

_____

_____

_____

_____

_____

▶ **UNTAMED SCIENCE** Watch the **Untamed Science** video to learn more about adaptations.

Change Over Time

FLORIDA Next Generation Sunshine State Standards

Big Ideas 1, 3: SC.7.N.1.7, SC.7.N.3.1
Big Idea 15: SC.7.L.15.1, SC.7.L.15.2, SC.7.L.15.3

Language Arts: LA.7.4.2.2, LA.7.2.2.3
Mathematics: MA.6.S.6.2

Check Your Understanding

1. Background Read the paragraph below and then answer the question.

Last fall, Jerome collected more than 100 seeds from a species of plant called a sunflower. In the spring, he planted all the seeds. The new sunflowers varied in many ways. Jerome knows that, because of sexual reproduction, each plant's DNA is different.

- How are the plants' different traits related to sexual reproduction?

_____

_____

A **species** is a group of similar organisms that can mate with each other and produce fertile offspring.

Sexual reproduction results in offspring that are genetically different from each parent.

DNA is genetic material that carries information about an organism and is passed from parent to offspring.

> **MY READING WEB** If you had trouble completing the question above, visit **My Reading Web** and type in *Change Over Time.*

Vocabulary Skill

Identify Multiple Meanings Familiar words may mean something else in science. Look at the different meanings of the words below.

Word	Everyday Meaning	Scientific Meaning
theory	*n.* a guess **Example:** Sue has a theory that soccer is harder to play than basketball.	*n.* a well-tested concept that explains a wide range of observations **Example:** The cell theory says that all organisms are made of cells.
adaptation	*n.* a change in an individual's behavior **Example:** Talia's adaptation to her new school was hard, but she did it.	*n.* a trait that helps an individual survive and reproduce **Example:** Fur is an adaptation to cold.

LA.7.1.6.9

2. Quick Check Circle the sentence that uses the scientific meaning of the word *theory.*

- Evolutionary *theory* describes change over time.
- Do you have a *theory* about why Sarah is a vegetarian?

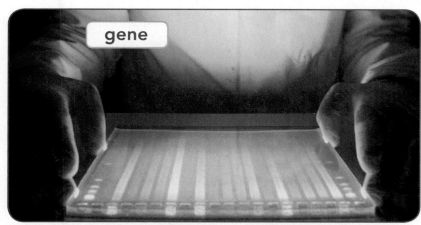

gene

trait

biodiversity

endangered species

Chapter Preview

LESSON 1
- evolution
- gene
- homologous structures
- Identify the Main Idea
- Communicate

LESSON 2
- adaptation
- scientific theory
- trait
- natural selection
- variation
- Relate Cause and Effect
- Develop Hypotheses

LESSON 3
- biodiversity
- extinction
- endangered species
- threatened species
- Summarize
- Predict

> **VOCAB FLASH CARDS** For extra help with vocabulary, visit **Vocab Flash Cards** and type in *Change Over Time.*

Evidence of Evolution

UNLOCK THE ESSENTIAL ?

🔑 **What Is Evolution?**
SC.7.L.15.1, LA.7.4.2.2

🔑 **What Evidence Supports Evolution?**
SC.7.N.1.7, SC.7.L.15.1

my planeT DiaRY

Moving On Up

In 2004, researchers on Ellesmere Island, Nunavut, in the Canadian Arctic, found a fossil that provides information about when fish first came onto land. The fossil, called *Tiktaalik*, is 375 million years old. *Tiktaalik* has characteristics of both fish and four-legged animals. Like other fish, it has fins. However, the fins have interior bones that helped push the animal up in the shallow waters close to shore to find food. The discovery of *Tiktaalik* has provided new fossil evidence to help scientists understand the relationship between marine vertebrates and land vertebrates.

Researcher from
Ellesmere Island

Communicate Discuss these questions with a partner. Write your answers below.

1. What characteristics does *Tiktaalik* have that are like a fish and a four-legged animal?

_____

_____

_____

_____

2. Do you think *Tiktaalik* spent most of its time on land or in water? Why?

_____

_____

_____

▶ PLANET DIARY Go to **Planet Diary** to learn more about fossil evidence.

This model of *Tiktaalik* shows what it may have looked like 375 million years ago.

 Lab zone® Do the Inquiry Warm-Up *How Can You Classify a Species?*

Vocabulary
- evolution • gene
- homologous structures

Skills
- Reading: Identify the Main Idea
- Inquiry: Communicate

What Is Evolution?

On a trip to the local science museum, you and your classmates wander into the natural history exhibit. Inside, you see bones and models of organisms that lived thousands, even millions of years ago. Some of the things you see remind you of organisms still living today. For example, woolly mammoths remind you of elephants. But there are some things that look very different from anything you've seen before. You've never seen flying reptiles, armored fish, or such large birds! Why do some of these organisms look familiar, but others look so different?

The diversity of life today and in the past can be explained by evolution. **Evolution** is change over time. 🔑 **The scientific theory of evolution explains how living things descended from earlier organisms.** Over millions and millions of years, evolution has resulted in organisms no longer living, as well as the ones alive today. By understanding evolution, we can begin to understand the history of life on Earth.

FLORIDA NGSSS

SC.7.L.15.1 Recognize that fossil evidence is consistent with the scientific theory of evolution that living things evolved from earlier species.

LA.7.4.2.2 The student will record information related to a topic.

FIGURE 1 ....

Wooly Mammoth
Wooly mammoths are no longer living, but they share a common ancestor with Asian elephants.

✏️ **Observe** List one similarity that you can see between these two organisms. Then list one difference.

_____

_____

_____

_____

_____

LA.7.4.2.2

Asian elephants live in countries such as India.

Wooly mammoths went extinct about 11,000 years ago.

Lab zone Do the Quick Lab *Understanding Evolution.*

🔑 **Assess Your Understanding**

got it? ....

○ **I get it!** Now I know that the scientific theory of evolution_____

_____

○ **I need extra help with** _____

Go to **my science** 🔵 **coach** online for help with this subject.

SC.7.L.15.1

FLORIDA NGSSS

SC.7.N.1.7 Explain that scientific knowledge is the result of a great deal of debate and confirmation within the scientific community.

SC.7.L.15.1 Recognize that fossil evidence is consistent with the scientific theory of evolution that living things evolved from earlier species.

What Evidence Supports Evolution?

How do we know that organisms change over time? Scientists have found a great deal of evidence that supports the theory of evolution. 🔑 **Fossils, similarities in DNA and protein structures, similar body structures, and patterns of early development all provide evidence that organisms have changed over time.**

Fossils Have you ever seen a movie with dinosaurs in it? How do we know how dinosaurs moved or acted? Scientists can answer these questions using fossils. Recall that fossils are preserved remains or traces of an organism that lived in the past. Scientists can infer the structures of ancient organisms by looking at fossils. Fossil evidence also supports the theory that living things evolved from earlier organisms. For instance, scientists in Florida have found fossils of *Metatomarctus canavus*, an ancient doglike creature. This animal looked similar to modern dogs, wolves, and foxes.

The millions of fossils that scientists have collected are called the fossil record. The fossil record provides clues about how and when a new species evolved and how organisms are related. Recall that a species is a group of similar organisms that can mate with each other and produce offspring that can also mate and reproduce.

FIGURE 2 ··•🔵

A Florida Fossil
The jawbone of *Metatomarctus canavus* is shown here with a modern dog's jawbone.
✏️ **Look at the two jawbones and answer the questions below.** SC.7.N.1.7

1. **Observe** How do these jawbones look similar?

_____

_____

_____

_____

2. **Recognize** How do these bones help to confirm the theory of evolution?

_____

_____

_____

_____

_____

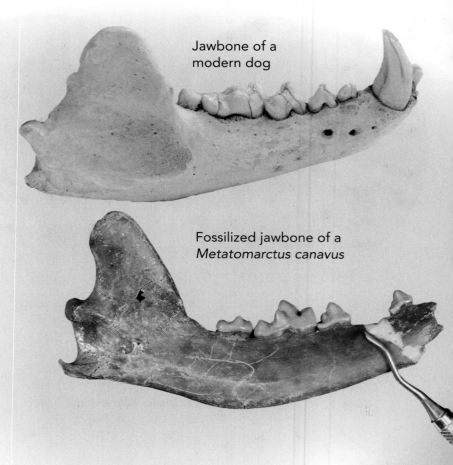

Jawbone of a modern dog

Fossilized jawbone of a *Metatomarctus canavus*

Similarities in DNA and Protein Structure

Why do some species have similar body structures or similar patterns of development? Scientists infer that the species inherited many of the same genes from a common ancestor.

Genes are segments of DNA that determine characteristics in an organism. Recall that DNA is the genetic material inside a cell that carries information about an organism. Scientists compare the sequence of nitrogen bases in the DNA of different species to infer how closely related two species are. The more similar the DNA sequences, the more closely related the species are. The DNA bases in a gene specify what type of protein will be produced. Therefore, scientists can also compare the order of amino acids in a protein to see how closely two species are related.

In most cases, evidence from DNA and protein structure has confirmed conclusions based on fossils, embryos, and body structure. For example, DNA comparisons show that dogs are more similar to wolves than to coyotes. Scientists had already reached this conclusion based on similarities in the structure and development of these three species.

apply it!

The table shows the sequence of amino acids in one region of a protein, cytochrome *c*, for five different animals. Each letter corresponds to a different amino acid in the protein.

1 Interpret Tables Which species is most distantly related to the horse?

_____

2 Communicate Explain how amino acid sequences provide information about evolutionary relationships among organisms.

_____
_____
_____
_____
_____
_____
_____

SC.7.N.1.7

Section of Cytochrome *c* Protein in Animals

Animal	Amino Acid Position in the Sequence											
	39	40	41	42	43	44	45	46	47	48	49	50
Horse	N	L	H	G	L	F	G	R	K	T	G	Q
Donkey	N	L	H	G	L	F	G	R	K	T	G	Q
Rabbit	N	L	H	G	L	F	G	R	K	T	G	Q
Snake	N	L	H	G	L	F	G	R	K	T	G	Q
Turtle	N	L	N	G	L	I	G	R	K	T	G	Q

Similarities in Body Structure

An organism's body structure is its basic body plan, which in vertebrates includes how its bones are arranged. Fishes, amphibians, reptiles, birds, and mammals all have an internal skeleton with a backbone. This similarity provides evidence that these animal groups all evolved from a common ancestor.

Similar structures that related species have inherited from a common ancestor are known as **homologous structures** (hoh MAHL uh gus). In **Figure 3,** you can see some examples of homologous structures. These include a bird's wing, a dolphin's flipper, and a dog's leg.

Sometimes fossils show structures that are homologous with structures in living species. For example, scientists have recently found fossils of ancient whalelike creatures. The fossils show that the ancestors of today's whales had legs and walked on land. This evidence supports other evidence that whales and other vertebrates share a common ancestor that had a skeleton with a backbone.

Identify the Main Idea
Describe the main idea on this page.

_____

_____

_____

_____

_____

FIGURE 3 ·······

> INTERACTIVE ART **Homologous Structures**
The bones in a bird's wing, a dolphin's flipper, and a dog's leg have similar structures.

✎ **Interpret Diagrams** Use the drawing of the dog's leg as a guide. Color in the matching bones in the bird's wing and the dolphin's flipper with the appropriate colors.

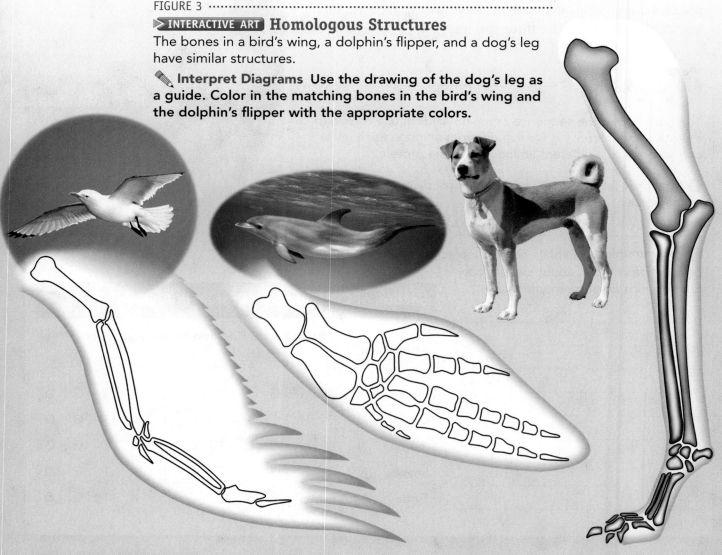

Similarities in Early Development Scientists also infer evolutionary relationships by comparing the early development of different organisms. For example, the organisms in **Figure 4** look similar during the early stages of development. All four organisms have a tail. They also have a row of tiny slits along their throats. The similarities suggest that these vertebrate species are related and share a common ancestor.

FIGURE 4 ······································
Similarities in Development
These four organisms all look similar during their early development.

✎ **Complete each task.**

1. **Observe** Circle at least two similarities shared by all four organisms.

2. **Describe** What are some differences between the organisms?

_____

_____

_____

_____

_____

_____

_____

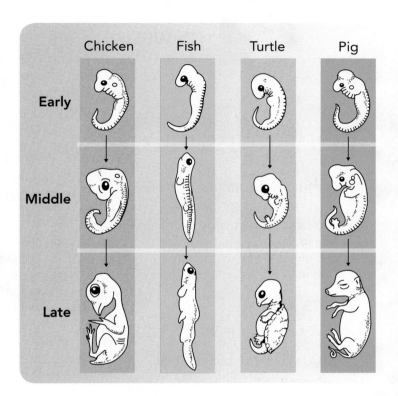

Chicken   Fish   Turtle   Pig

Early

Middle

Late

🔑 **Assess Your Understanding**

1a. Define _____ structures are structurally similar body parts in related species.
SC.7.L.15.1

b. [CHALLENGE] Bats and birds both have wings. What kinds of evidence might show whether or not bats and birds are closely related? Explain.

_____

_____

_____

_____

SC.7.L.15.1

Lab zone® Do the Quick Lab *Finding Proof.*

got it?

○ **I get it!** Now I know that the theory of evolution is supported by evidence that includes _____

_____

_____

_____

○ **I need extra help with** _____

Go to **MY SCIENCE** ⬤ˢ **COACH** *online for help with this subject.*
SC.7.L.15.1

Darwin's Theory

🔑 **What Was Darwin's Hypothesis?**
SC.7.N.3.1, SC.7.L.15.2, LA.7.4.2.2

🔑 **What Is Natural Selection?**
SC.7.N.3.1, SC.7.L.15.2, LA.7.2.2.3, MA.6.S.6.2

my planet diary

Charles Darwin

In 1839, Charles Darwin published his book *The Voyage of the Beagle.* Read the following excerpt about an animal Darwin encountered while in the Galápagos Islands.

The inhabitants believe that these animals are absolutely deaf; certainly they do not overhear a person walking close behind them. I was always amused when overtaking one of these great monsters, as it was quietly pacing along, to see how suddenly, the instant I passed, it would draw in its head and legs, and uttering a deep hiss fall to the ground with a heavy sound, as if struck dead. I frequently got on their backs, and then giving a few raps on the hinder part of their shells, they would rise up and walk away; — but I found it very difficult to keep my balance.

VOICES FROM HISTORY

Communicate **Discuss these questions with a classmate. Write your answers below.**

1. What kind of animal do you think Darwin was describing?

_____

_____

2. Describe your reaction to an unusual animal that you may have seen at a zoo, at an aquarium, or in a pet store. What was your first impression of the animal?

_____

_____

_____

▶ PLANET DIARY Go to **Planet Diary** for more information about Charles Darwin.

Lab zone® **Do the Inquiry Warm-Up**
How Do Living Things Vary?

Vocabulary
- adaptation • scientific theory
- trait • natural selection
- variation

Skills
- ↻ Reading: Relate Cause and Effect
- △ Inquiry: Develop Hypotheses

What Was Darwin's Hypothesis?

In 1831, the British ship HMS *Beagle* set sail from England on a five-year trip around the world. Charles Darwin was on board. Darwin was a naturalist—a person who observes and studies the natural world.

Diversity Darwin was amazed by the diversity of living things that he saw during the voyage. He wondered why they were so different from those in England. Darwin saw insects that looked like flowers. He also observed sloths, slow-moving animals that spent much of their time hanging in trees. Today, scientists know that organisms are even more diverse than Darwin thought. In fact, scientists have identified more than 1.6 million species of organisms on Earth. The exact number of species is unknown because many areas of Earth have not yet been studied.

Fossils Darwin saw fossils of animals that had died long ago. Recall that a fossil is the preserved remains or traces of an organism that lived in the past. Darwin was puzzled by some of the fossils he observed. For example, he saw fossils that resembled the bones of living sloths but were much larger in size. He wondered what had happened to the ancient, giant ground sloths. See **Figure 1**.

FLORIDA NGSSS

SC.7.N.3.1 Recognize and explain the difference between theories and laws and give several examples of scientific theories and the evidence that supports them.

SC.7.L.15.2 Explore the scientific theory of evolution by recognizing and explaining ways in which genetic variation and environmental factors contribute to evolution by natural selection and diversity of organisms.

LA.7.4.2.2 The student will record information related to a topic.

FIGURE 1 ·······························
Sloth Similarities
Darwin thought that the fossil bones of the giant ground sloths (left) resembled the bones of modern-day sloths (above).

✎ **Observe** List two similarities that you notice between the two sloths.
LA.7.4.2.2

Similarities
_____
_____
_____
_____

The Galápagos penguin is the northernmost penguin in the world! It lives on the equator and is kept cool by ocean currents. The Galápagos penguin is the rarest penguin species and is endangered.

Galápagos Organisms
The *Beagle* made many stops along the Atlantic and Pacific coasts of South America. From the Pacific coast, the ship traveled west to the Galápagos Islands. Darwin observed many unusual life forms there. He compared organisms from the Galápagos Islands to organisms that lived elsewhere. He also compared organisms living on the different islands.

Comparisons to South American Organisms
Darwin discovered many similarities between Galápagos organisms and those found in South America. Many of the birds and plants on the islands resembled those on the mainland. However, he also noted important differences between the organisms. For instance, you can see differences between island and mainland iguanas in **Figure 2**.

Darwin became convinced that species do not always stay the same. Instead, he thought species could change and even produce new species over time. Darwin began to think that maybe the island species were somehow related to South American species. Perhaps, he thought, the island species had become different from their mainland relatives over time.

FIGURE 2 ···
Comparing Iguanas

The iguanas on the Galápagos Islands have large claws that allow them to grip slippery rocks so they can feed on seaweed.

The iguanas on the mainland have smaller claws that allow them to climb trees so they can eat leaves.

✎ **Infer** The color of each iguana is an adaptation to its

○ food.   ○ habitat.

○ predators.   ○ climate.

Explain your answer.

_____

_____

_____

FIGURE 3 ·

INTERACTIVE ART Galápagos Finches

The structure of each bird's beak is an adaptation to the type of food the bird eats. Birds with long, pointed, sharp beaks pick at cacti. Those with short, thick beaks crush seeds.

Birds with narrow, pointed beaks grasp insects. Those with short, hooked beaks tear open fruit.

✎ **Interpret Diagrams** Look at the different beak structures. Draw a line from each finch to the type of food you think it eats.

Comparisons Among the Islands Darwin also discovered many differences among organisms on the different Galápagos Islands. For example, the tortoises on one island had dome-shaped shells. Those on another island had saddle-shaped shells. A government official in the islands told Darwin that he could tell which island a tortoise came from just by looking at its shell.

Adaptations Birds were also different from one island to the next. Look at **Figure 3.** When Darwin returned to England, he learned that the different birds were all finches. Darwin concluded that the finch species were all related to a single ancestor species that came from the mainland. Over time, different finches developed different beak shapes and sizes that were well suited to the food that they ate. Beak shape is an example of an **adaptation,** a trait that increases an organism's ability to survive and reproduce.

· · · · · · · · · · · · · · ✎ · · · · · · · · · · · · · ·

Vocabulary Identify Multiple Meanings Write a sentence using the everyday meaning of the word *adapt*.

_____

_____

_____

_____

_____

Darwin's Hypothesis Darwin thought about what he had seen during his voyage on the *Beagle*. By this time, Darwin was convinced that organisms change over time. Darwin, however, wanted to know *how* organisms change. Over the next 20 years, he consulted with other scientists and gathered more information. Based on his observations, Darwin reasoned that plants or animals that arrived on the Galápagos Islands faced conditions that were different from those on the nearby mainland. **Darwin hypothesized that species change over many generations and become better adapted to new conditions.**

Darwin's ideas are often referred to as a theory of evolution. A **scientific theory** is a well-supported and widely accepted explanation of nature. From the evidence he collected, Darwin concluded that organisms on the Galápagos Islands had changed over time.

apply it!

The first labradoodle dog was bred in 1989. A labradoodle is a cross between a standard poodle and a Labrador retriever. The poodle is very smart and has fur that sheds very little. The poodle may be less irritating for people allergic to dogs. Labradors are gentle, easily trained, and shed seasonally.

Standard poodle   Labrador retriever   Labradoodle

1 Make Generalizations Why do you think people breed these two dogs together?

_____

_____

2 Develop Hypotheses Would you expect the first labradoodle puppies to be the same as puppies produced several generations later? Explain.

_____

Artificial Selection Darwin studied the offspring of domesticated animals that were produced by artificial selection to understand how evolution might occur. In artificial selection, only organisms with a desired trait are bred. A **trait** is a specific characteristic that an organism can pass to its offspring. Darwin had bred pigeons with large, fan-shaped tails. By allowing only those pigeons with many tail feathers to mate, Darwin produced pigeons with two or three times the usual number of tail feathers. Darwin thought that a process similar to artificial selection might happen in nature. But he wondered what natural process selected certain traits.

FIGURE 4 ·······························
Artificial Selection
The pigeons that Darwin bred were all descended from the rock dove (left). Pigeons can be bred for characteristics such as color, beak shape, wingspan, and feather patterns.

✎ **Describe** If you were to breed an animal, what would it be and what traits would you want it to have?

_____

_____

_____

Lab zone® Do the Quick Lab
Bird Beak Adaptations.

🔑 Assess Your Understanding

1a. List Make a list of three observations that Darwin made during the *Beagle's* voyage.

_____

_____

_____
SC.7.L.15.2

b. Describe An adaptation is a trait that

increases an organism's ability to _____

and _____
SC.7.L.15.2

c. ◢ **Develop Hypotheses** How does artificial selection support Darwin's hypothesis?

_____

_____

_____

_____

_____
SC.7.N.3.1, SC.7.L.15.2

got it? ···

○ **I get it!** Now I know that Darwin's hypothesis was _____

_____

○ **I need extra help with** _____

Go to **MY SCIENCE** ⓢ **COACH** *online for help with this subject.*
SC.7.L.15.1

367

SC.7.N.3.1 Recognize and explain the difference between theories and laws and give several examples of scientific theories and the evidence that supports them.

SC.7.L.15.2 Explore the scientific theory of evolution by recognizing and explaining ways in which genetic variation and environmental factors contribute to evolution by natural selection and diversity of organisms.

LA.7.2.2.3 The student will organize information to show understanding.

MA.6.S.6.2 Select and analyze measures of central tendency.

What Is Natural Selection?

In 1858, Darwin and Alfred Russel Wallace, another British biologist, both proposed the same explanation for how evolution occurs. The next year, Darwin described his explanation in his book *The Origin of Species.* In this book, Darwin proposed that evolution occurs by means of natural selection. **Natural selection** is the process by which individuals that are better adapted to their environment are more likely to survive and reproduce than other members of the same species. Darwin identified factors that affect the process of natural selection: overproduction, variation, and competition. **Figure 5** shows how natural selection might happen in a group of sea turtles.

Overproduction Darwin knew that most species produce far more offspring than can possibly survive. In many species, so many offspring are produced that there are not enough resources—food, water, and living space—for all of them.

Factors That Affect Natural Selection
How do life forms change over time?

FIGURE 5 ···

> **REAL-WORLD INQUIRY** Overproduction, variation, and competition are factors that affect the process of natural selection.

✎ **Summarize** Examine the sequence below that shows how natural selection could affect a group of sea turtles over time. Label each factor in the illustration and write a brief caption explaining what is occurring.　　LA.7.2.2.3

Variation Members of a species differ from one another in many of their traits. Any difference between individuals of the same species is called a **variation.** For example, sea turtles may differ in color, size, the ability to swim quickly, and shell hardness.

Competition Since food, space, and other resources are limited, the members of a species must compete with one another to survive. Competition does not always involve physical fights between members of a species. Instead, competition is usually indirect. For example, some turtles may not find enough to eat. A slower turtle may be caught by a predator, while a faster turtle may escape. Only a few turtles will survive to reproduce.

Selection Darwin observed that some variations make individuals better adapted to their environment. Those individuals are more likely to survive and reproduce. Their offspring may inherit the helpful characteristic. The offspring, in turn, will be more likely to survive and reproduce, and pass the characteristic to their offspring. After many generations, more members of the species will have the helpful characteristic.

In effect, the environment selects organisms with helpful traits to become parents of the next generation. 🗝 **Darwin proposed that, over a long time, natural selection can lead to change. Helpful variations may accumulate in a species, while unfavorable ones may disappear.**

➲ **Relate Cause and Effect**
Fill in the graphic organizer to identify the factors that cause natural selection. **LA.7.2.2.3**

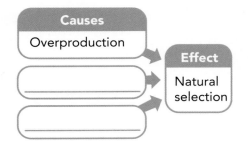

Causes
Overproduction
⟶

Effect
Natural selection

369

Environmental Change A change in the environment can affect an organism's ability to survive and therefore lead to natural selection. For example, monkey flowers are plants that do not normally grow in soil that has a high concentration of copper. However, because of genetic variation, some varieties of monkey flower now grow near copper mines. In **Figure 6** you can see how natural selection might have resulted in monkey flowers that can grow in copper-contaminated soil.

Genes and Natural Selection Without variations, all the members of a species would have the same traits and the same chance of surviving and reproducing. But where do variations come from? How are they passed on from parents to offspring?

Darwin could not explain what caused variations or how they were passed on. As scientists later learned, variations can result from changes in genes and the shuffling of different forms of genes when egg and sperm join. Genes, such as those for hair color and height, are passed from parents to their offspring. Only traits that are inherited, or controlled by genes that are passed on to offspring, can be acted upon by natural selection.

do the math!

The typical clutch size, or number of eggs, a loggerhead sea turtle can lay at once is around 113. Even with producing so many offspring, the loggerhead sea turtle is endangered in many areas. Suppose that scientists counted the number of eggs laid at seven different nesting sites along the southeast coast of the United States. The following year, scientists check the nesting sites to see how many offspring survived and returned.

Loggerhead Sea Turtle Data							
Site	A	B	C	D	E	F	G
Clutch Size	114	103	121	118	107	103	104
Returning Turtles	45	35	55	53	40	66	38

❶ **Select and Analyze** Which measure of central tendency would you use to find the average clutch size? Calculate that measure. _____
_____
_____

❷ **Interpret Data** Do you think clutch size influences the survival rates of the offspring? Use the data to support your answer.
_____
_____
_____
_____

❸ CHALLENGE Hypothesize why Site F had the largest number of returning turtles.
_____
_____
_____

MA.6.S.6.2, MA.7.A.3.1

Monkey flowers grow successfully in healthy, unpolluted soil.

Copper seeps into the soil around the copper mine. Most monkey flowers cannot grow in this polluted soil, and they begin to die.

Some monkey flowers have genetic variations that allow them to survive and reproduce in copper-contaminated soil.

_____
_____
_____
_____

FIGURE 6 ···

Environmental Change

When copper contaminated the soil surrounding the monkey flowers, the environment changed. Due to a genetic variation, some varieties of monkey flower are now able to survive in that soil.

✎ **Draw Conclusions** In the last circle, draw what you think the area will look like in ten years' time. Write a caption describing what has taken place.

Lab zone®   Do the Lab Investigation *Nature at Work.*

🔑 Assess Your Understanding

2a. Define A variation is any (similarity/ difference) between individuals of the same species.

SC.7.L.15.2

b. ANSWER THE ESSENTIAL ? How do life forms change over time?

_____

_____

SC.7.L.15.2

c. Explain How does genetic variation contribute to the diversity of organisms?

_____

_____

_____

_____

SC.7.L.15.2

got it? ··

○ **I get it!** Now I know that natural selection occurs _____

_____

_____

○ **I need extra help with** _____

Go to MY SCIENCE ⁵ COACH *online for help with this subject.*

3 Biodiversity and Extinction

 UNLOCK THE ESSENTIAL ?

🔑 **How Do New Species Form?**
SC.7.L.15.2

🔑 **What Factors Affect Biodiversity?**
SC.7.L.15.2, LA.7.2.2.3

🔑 **Why Do Species Go Extinct?**
SC.7.L.15.3

MY PLANET DIARY

Crickets, Maggots, and Flies, Oh My!

A male cricket chirps to attract a mate. Unfortunately, chirping also attracts a parasitic fly. Parasitic flies listen for chirping crickets. When a cricket is located, a female fly deposits larvae onto the cricket's back. The larvae, or maggots, burrow into the cricket. The maggots come out seven days later, killing the cricket in the process. Parasitic flies reduced the cricket population on the Hawaiian island of Kauai between 1991 and 2001. By 2003, the cricket population on Kauai had increased. The male crickets were silent! In about 20 cricket generations, the crickets had evolved into an almost silent population.

Lab zone Do the Inquiry Warm-Up *How Much Variety Is There?*

FUN FACT

Communicate Discuss these questions with a classmate. Write your answers below.

1. Why do you think the crickets on Kauai evolved so quickly?

_____

_____

2. If most of the male crickets can no longer chirp, how do you think it might affect the size of the cricket population?

_____

_____

_____

_____

> **PLANET DIARY** Go to **Planet Diary** to learn more about evolution.

 **FLORIDA** NGSSS

SC.7.L.15.2 Explore the scientific theory of evolution by recognizing and explaining ways in which genetic variation and environmental factors contribute to evolution by natural selection and diversity of organisms.

How Do New Species Form?

Natural selection explains how variations can lead to changes in a species. But how could an entirely new species form? 🔑 **A new species can form when a group of individuals remains isolated from the rest of its species long enough to evolve different traits that prevent reproduction.** Isolation, or complete separation, occurs when some members of a species become cut off from the rest of the species. One way this can happen is when a natural barrier, such as a river, separates group members.

Vocabulary
- biodiversity
- extinction
- endangered species
- threatened species

Skills
- Reading: Summarize
- Inquiry: Predict

FIGURE 1 ·····················

Kaibab and Abert's Squirrels

The Kaibab squirrel (left) and the Abert's squirrel (right) have been isolated from each other for a long time. Eventually, this isolation may result in two different species.

✎ **Identify** What conditions might differ from one side of the Grand Canyon to the other that would cause the squirrels to be different colors?

_____

_____

Key

| | Range of Kaibab squirrel | | Range of Abert's squirrel |

As you can see in **Figure 1,** the populations of Kaibab and Abert's squirrels are separated by the Grand Canyon. The two kinds of squirrels are the same species, but they have slightly different characteristics. For example, the Kaibab squirrel has a black belly, while Abert's squirrel has a white belly. It is possible that one day these squirrels will become so different that they will no longer be able to mate with each other and will become separate species.

 Do the Quick Lab
Large-Scale Isolation.

🔑 Assess Your Understanding

got it? ··

○ **I get it!** Now I know that new species form when _____

_____

○ **I need extra help with** _____

Go to **MY SCIENCE** 💬 **COACH** *online for help with this subject.*

 NGSSS

SC.7.L.15.2 Explore the scientific theory of evolution by recognizing and explaining ways in which genetic variation and environmental factors contribute to evolution by natural selection and diversity of organisms.

LA.7.2.2.3 The student will organize information to show understanding.

What Factors Affect Biodiversity?

No one knows exactly how many species live on Earth. More than 1.5 million species have been identified so far. The number of different species in an area is called its **biodiversity.** It is difficult to estimate the total biodiversity on Earth because many areas of the planet have not been thoroughly studied. Some scientists think that the deep oceans alone could contain 10 million new species! Protecting biodiversity is a major environmental issue today. Biodiversity varies from place to place on Earth. **Factors that affect biodiversity in an ecosystem include area, climate, genetic diversity, and diversity of niches.**

Summarize In the space provided, write a summary of how each factor influences biodiversity.   LA.7.2.2.3

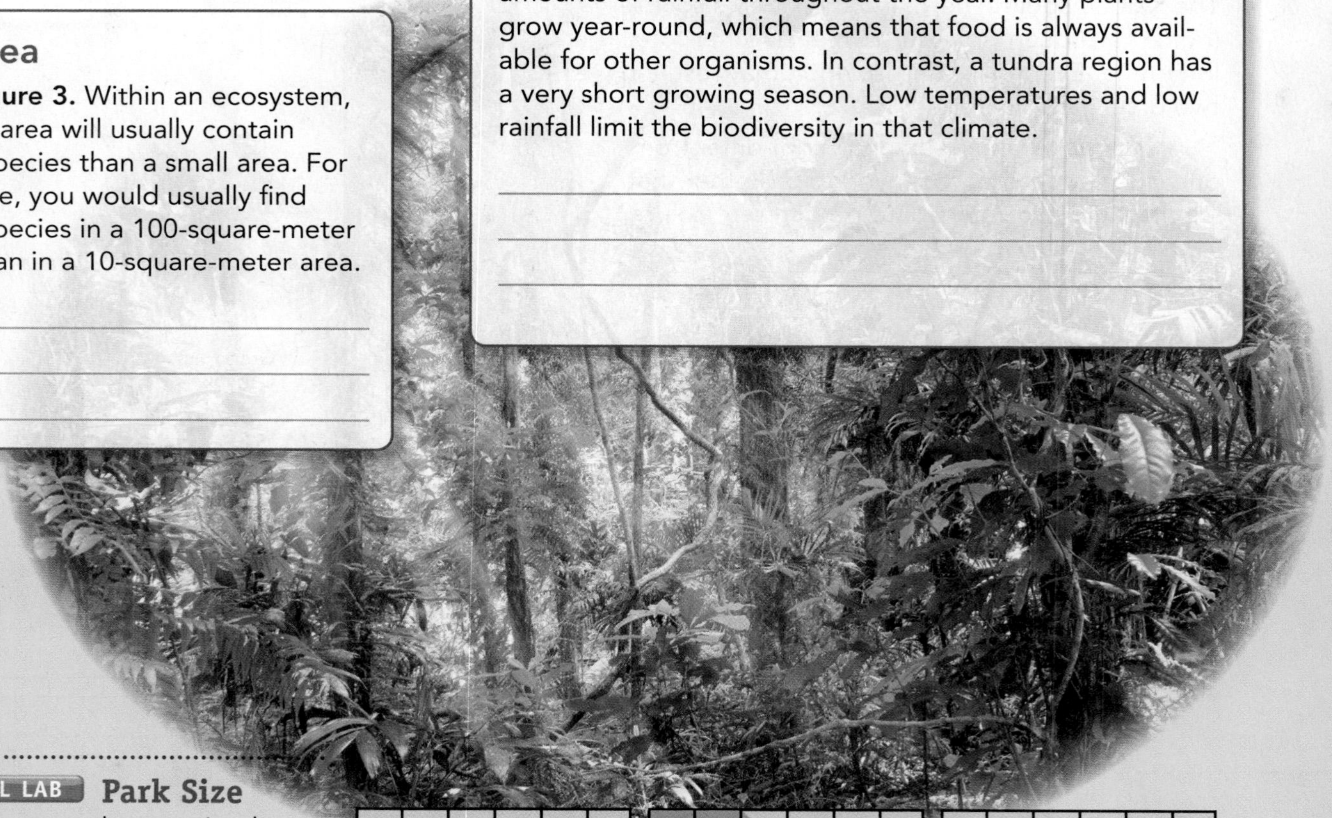

❶ Area

See **Figure 3.** Within an ecosystem, a large area will usually contain more species than a small area. For example, you would usually find more species in a 100-square-meter area than in a 10-square-meter area.

_____

_____

_____

❷ Climate

Climate affects the biodiversity in a certain area. For example, tropical rain forests are the most diverse ecosystems in the world. They are warm and have large amounts of rainfall throughout the year. Many plants grow year-round, which means that food is always available for other organisms. In contrast, a tundra region has a very short growing season. Low temperatures and low rainfall limit the biodiversity in that climate.

_____

_____

_____

FIGURE 3

▷ VIRTUAL LAB Park Size

A park manager has received three park plans. The dark green area represents the park.

✎ **Identify Circle the plan the manager should choose to support the most biodiversity.**

□] 10 m

10 m

❸ Genetic Diversity

Diversity is very important within a species. Organisms in a healthy population have diverse traits such as color and size. These traits are determined by genes, which organisms inherit from their parents. Organisms in a species share many genes. But each organism also has some genes that differ from those of other individuals. Both the shared genes and the genes that differ among individuals make up the total gene pool of that species. Species with a diverse gene pool are better able to adapt to and survive changes in the environment.

_____

_____

❹ Niche Diversity

Coral reefs are the second most diverse ecosystems in the world. Found only in shallow, warm waters, coral reefs are often called the rain forests of the sea. A coral reef supports many different niches. Recall that a niche is the role of an organism in its habitat, or how it makes its living. A coral reef enables a greater number of species to live in it than a more uniform habitat, such as a flat sandbar, does.

_____

_____

 Do the Quick Lab
Grocery Gene Pool.

🔑 Assess Your Understanding

1a. Review A (smaller/larger) area will contain more species than a (smaller/larger) area.
SC.7.L.15.2

b. Explain How is biodiversity related to niches?

_____

_____

_____

SC.7.L.15.2

c. Apply Concepts You have been elected as the environmental manager of your country. What could you do to protect biodiversity?

_____

_____

_____

_____

SC.7.L.15.2

got it? ···

○ **I get it!** Now I know that the factors that affect biodiversity include _____

_____

○ **I need extra help with** _____

Go to **MY SCIENCE** ⁵ **COACH** *online for help with this subject.*
SC.7.L.15.2

Why Do Species Go Extinct?

The biodiversity of an ecosystem can also be affected by extinction. When all the members of a species disappear from Earth, it is called **extinction**. 🔑 **Extinction usually occurs when a species is unable to adapt within a changing environment.**

Process of Extinction

How does extinction occur? Imagine a species of insect that depends on a certain plant for food. Now suppose that the plant has died out. If this insect is not able to adapt to these new circumstances by eating another food source, individuals of the species will begin to die. Once the size of a population drops below a certain level, the species may not be able to recover and will become extinct. Species in danger of becoming extinct in the near future are called **endangered species.** Species that could become endangered in the near future are called **threatened species.**

Schaus butterfly

FIGURE 4 ·· ⓘ

Endangered Species

The green sea turtle is a well-known endangered species in Florida. But did you know that Florida also has endangered insect species? The Schaus butterfly is endangered because its forest habitat is shrinking. ✏️ **Infer Why do you think some endangered species get more attention than others?**

_____

_____

_____

_____

Green sea turtle

Extinction and Human Activities

Extinction is a natural process that usually happens gradually. However, most scientists think that extinction rates have increased in recent years due to human activities. One example of a species affected by human activity is the Florida panther. The number of panthers in the wild has decreased in the last 100 years. Scientists estimate that fewer than 100 Florida panthers survive today. What happened to the panther population?

As people moved to Florida, they used land for farming and building homes. This reduced the amount of habitat in which the panthers could find food. People also hunted and killed the panthers. Unable to adapt to the quickly changing environment, the panthers began to die out. To prevent this species from becoming extinct, Florida has declared panthers an endangered species. It is now illegal to hunt or harm them.

FIGURE 4 ·······················
Slow Down for Panthers!
Road signs such as this one warn drivers in Florida to watch out for panthers in the road.

do the math!

Wildlife biologists in Florida keep a close eye on the panther population. When a panther dies, biologists try to find the cause of death and record it. This pie chart shows the causes of death for Florida panthers between 1997 and 2007.

1 Interpret Data What is the leading cause of death for Florida panthers?

_____

_____

2 Predict To reduce the amount of panthers hit by cars, scientists have installed tunnels under major roadways. The tunnels allows panthers to cross roads unharmed. What is another way that you could reduce the number of panther deaths each year?

_____

_____

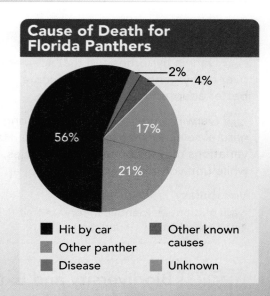

Cause of Death for Florida Panthers

2%
4%
56%
17%
21%

■ Hit by car   ■ Other known causes
■ Other panther
■ Disease   ■ Unknown

Lab zone Do the Quick Lab
Disappearing Act.

🔑 Assess Your Understanding

got it? ···

○ I get it! Now I know that a species may go extinct because _____

_____

○ I need extra help with _____

Go to **my science** ⓢ **coach** *online for help with this subject.*

SC.7.L.15.3

REVIEW THE ESSENTIAL ?

Living things change over time, or _____, through a process called _____

LESSON 1 Evidence of Evolution
SC.7.N.1.7, SC.7.L.15.1

🔑 The scientific theory of evolution explains how living things descended from earlier organisms.

🔑 Fossils, similarities in DNA and protein structures, similar body structures, and patterns of early development all provide evidence that organisms have changed over time.

Vocabulary
• evolution • gene • homologous structures

LESSON 2 Darwin's Theory
SC.7.N.3.1, SC.7.L.15.2

🔑 Darwin hypothesized that species change over many generations and become better adapted to new conditions.

🔑 Darwin proposed that, over a long time, natural selection can lead to change. Helpful variations may accumulate in a species, while unfavorable ones may disappear.

Vocabulary
• adaptation • scientific theory • trait
• natural selection • variation

LESSON 3 Biodiversity and Extinction
SC.7.L.15.2, SC.7.L.15.3

🔑 A new species can form when a group of individuals remains isolated from the rest of its species long enough to evolve different traits that prevent reproduction.

🔑 Factors that affect biodiversity in an ecosystem include area, climate, genetic diversity, and diversity of niches.

🔑 Extinction usually occurs when a species is unable to adapt within a changing environment.

Vocabulary
• biodiversity • extinction
• endangered species • threatened species

Review and Assessment

LESSON 1   Evidence of Evolution

1. Similar structures that related species have inherited from a common ancestor are called

   a. adaptations.

   b. fossils.

   c. ancestral structures.

   d. homologous structures.

                                SC.7.L15.1

2. The scientific theory of _____ explains how living things are descended from earlier organisms.

                                SC.7.L15.1

3. Draw Conclusions Look at the drawing, at the right, of the bones in a crocodile's leg. Do you think that crocodiles share a common ancestor with birds, dolphins, and dogs? Support your answer with evidence.

Crocodile

                                SC.7.L15.1

4. Make Judgments What type of evidence is the best indicator of how closely two species are related? Explain your answer.

                          SC.7.N.1.7, SC.7.L15.1

LESSON 2   Darwin's Theory

5. A trait that helps an organism to survive and reproduce is called a(n)

   a. variation.   **b.** adaptation.

   c. species.   **d.** selection.

                                SC.7.L15.2

6. Two organisms that can mate and produce fertile offspring are members of the same

                                SC.7.L15.2

7. Recognize and Explain What evidence did Darwin use to support his theory of evolution?

                        SC.7.N.3.1, SC.7.L15.2

8. Apply Concepts What is one factor that affects natural selection? Give an example.

                                SC.7.L15.2

9. Compare and Contrast What is a difference between the processes of natural selection and artificial selection?

                                SC.7.L15.2

10. **Write About It** You are a reporter in the 1800s interviewing Charles Darwin about his theory of evolution. Write three questions you would ask him. Then write answers that Darwin might have given.

                                SC.7.L15.2

LESSON 3 **Biodiversity and Extinction**

11. When all the members of a species disappear from Earth, it is called

   a. adaptation.

   b. evolution.

   c. natural selection.

   d. extinction.

SC.7.L.15.3

12. _____ is the number of different species in an area.

SC.7.L.15.3

13. Apply Concepts A population of deer lives in a forest. Draw a picture that illustrates how a geographic feature could isolate this deer population into two separate groups. Label the geographic feature.

SC.7.L.15.3

14. Draw Conclusions Florida panthers have had to adapt to a changing environment. How did this almost cause the extinction of the species?

_____

_____

_____

_____

_____

_____

SC.7.L.15.3

 How do life forms change over time?

15. Suppose that over several years, the climate in an area becomes much drier than it was before. How would plants, like the ones shown below, be affected? Using the terms *variation* and *natural selection,* predict what changes you might observe in the plants as a result of this environmental change.

_____

_____

_____

_____

_____

_____

_____

_____

_____

_____

_____

_____

_____

_____

SC.7.L.15.1, SC.7.L.15.2, SC.7.L.15.3

Florida Benchmarks Review

Circle the letter of the best answer.

① The illustration below has no title. Which of the following titles would best describe the concept shown in this illustration?

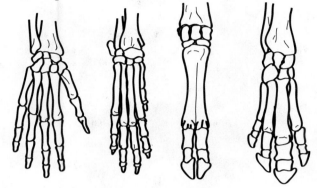

- **A** Wrist Bone Adaptations
- **B** Similarities in Wrist Bone Development
- **C** Evolutionary Change Through Variation
- **D** Homologous Structures in Four Animals

SC.7.L.15.1

② The process by which individuals that are better adapted to their environment are more likely to survive and reproduce than other members of the same species is called

- **A** natural selection.
- **B** evolution.
- **C** competition.
- **D** overproduction.

SC.7.N.15.2

③ Which of the following is the best example of an adaptation that helps organisms survive in their environment?

- **A** green coloring in lizards living on gray rocks
- **B** a thick coat of fur on animals that live in the desert
- **C** an extensive root system in desert plants
- **D** thin, delicate leaves on plants in a cold climate

SC.7.L.15.2

④ Which of the following sets of factors did Darwin identify as affecting natural selection?

- **A** adaptation, predation, and evolution
- **B** overproduction, variation, and competition
- **C** adaptations, traits, and variations
- **D** predation, competition, and mutualism

SC.7.L.15.2

⑤ Which of the following is an example of something that would decrease biodiversity?

- **A** A law is passed to protect coral reefs.
- **B** Logging is outlawed in rain forests.
- **C** A species' gene pool becomes less diverse.
- **D** In a forest, 100,000 acres are set aside as a national park.

SC.7.L.15.2

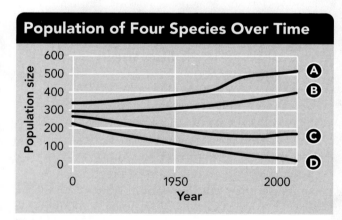

⑥ Which one of these animal species is most likely to be endangered by the year 2050?

- **A** Species A
- **B** Species B
- **C** Species C
- **D** Species D

SC.7.L.15.3

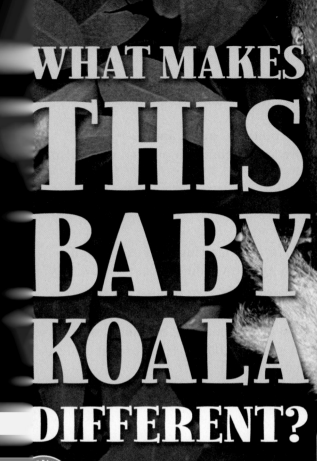

WHAT MAKES THIS BABY KOALA DIFFERENT?

Why don't offspring always look like their parents?

Even though this young koala, or joey, has two fuzzy ears, a long nose, and a body shaped like its mom's, you can see that the two are different. You might expect a young animal to look exactly like its parents, but think about how varied a litter of kittens or puppies can look. This joey is an albino—an animal that lacks the usual coloring in its eyes, fur, and skin.

△ Observe **Describe how this joey looks different from its mom.**

_____

_____

_____

_____

> UNTAMED SCIENCE Watch the **Untamed Science** video to learn more about heredity.

Genetics and DNA: The Science of Heredity

FLORIDA | Next Generation Sunshine State Standards

Big Idea 1: SC.7.N.1.5, SC.7.N.1.6
Big Idea 2: SC.7.N.2.1
Big Idea 16: SC.7.L.16.1, SC.7.L.16.2, SC.7.L.16.3

Language Arts: LA.7.2.2.3
Mathematics: MA.6.A.3.6

10 Getting Started

Check Your Understanding

1. **Background** Read the paragraph below and then answer the question.

> Kent's cat just had six kittens. All six kittens look different from one another—and from their two parents! Kent knows each kitten is unique because cats reproduce through **sexual reproduction,** not **asexual reproduction.** Before long, the kittens will grow bigger and bigger as their cells divide through **mitosis.**

- In what way are the two daughter cells that form by mitosis and cell division identical?

_____

> **MY READING WEB** If you had trouble completing the question above, visit **My Reading Web** and type in *Genetics and DNA: The Science of Heredity.*

Sexual reproduction involves two parents and combines their genetic material to produce a new organism that differs from both parents.

Asexual reproduction involves only one parent and produces offspring that are identical to the parent.

During **mitosis,** a cell's nucleus divides into two new nuclei, and one copy of DNA is distributed into each daughter cell.

Vocabulary Skill

Suffixes A suffix is a word part that is added to the end of a word to change its meaning. For example, the suffix *-tion* means "process of." If you add the suffix *-tion* to the verb *fertilize,* you get the noun *fertilization. Fertilization* means "the process of fertilizing." The table below lists some other common suffixes and their meanings.

Suffix	Meaning	Example
-ive	performing a particular action	recessive allele, *n.* an allele that is masked when a dominant allele is present
-ance or *-ant*	state, condition of	codominance, *n.* occurs when both alleles are expressed equally

LA.7.1.6.7

2. **Quick Check** Fill in the blank with the correct suffix.

- A domin_____ allele can mask a recessive allele.

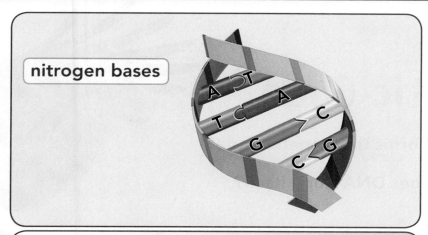

nitrogen bases

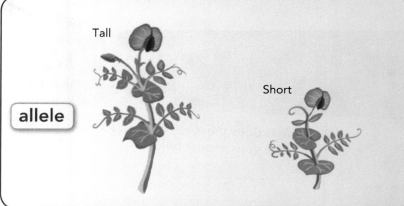

Tall

Short

allele

phenotype

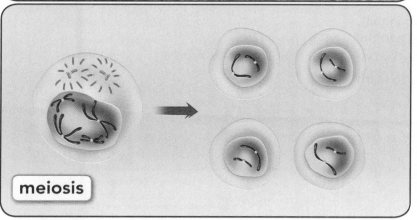

meiosis

Chapter Preview

LESSON 1
- nitrogen bases
- DNA replication
- ↻ Identify the Main Idea
- △ Infer

LESSON 2
- heredity
- genetics
- fertilization
- purebred
- allele
- dominant allele
- recessive allele
- hybrid
- ↻ Identify Supporting Evidence
- △ Predict

LESSON 3
- probability
- Punnett square
- pedigree
- phenotype
- genotype
- homozygous
- heterozygous
- ↻ Summarize
- △ Draw Conclusions

LESSON 4
- meiosis
- ↻ Relate Cause and Effect
- △ Design Experiments

> **VOCAB FLASH CARDS** For extra help with vocabulary, visit **Vocab Flash Cards** and type in *Genetics and DNA: The Science of Heredity.*

The Genetic Code

🔑 **What Forms the Genetic Code?**
SC.7.L.16.1, LA.7.2.2.3

🔑 **How Does DNA Copy Itself?**
SC.7.L.16.1

MY PLANET DIARY

BIOGRAPHY

DNA Debut

In 1951, English scientist Rosalind Franklin discovered that DNA could exist in a dry form and a wet form. Franklin made an image of the wet form of DNA by exposing it to X-rays. The X-rays bounced off the atoms in the DNA to make the image. The image (see the background on the next journal page) was so clear that it helped scientists understand the structure of DNA for the first time. Her discovery was important for figuring out how genetic information is passed from parent to offspring. Franklin's contribution to science was not only in her research, but also in that she succeeded at a time when many people thought women shouldn't be scientists.

> PLANET DIARY Go to **Planet Diary** to learn more about the genetic code.

What does the X-ray of DNA look like to you? Write your answer below.

_____

_____

_____

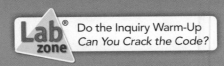
Lab zone® Do the Inquiry Warm-Up
Can You Crack the Code?

Vocabulary
- nitrogen bases
- DNA replication

Skills
- Reading: Identify the Main Idea
- Inquiry: Infer

(1) Everglades snail kite

What Forms the Genetic Code?

It took almost 100 years after the discovery of DNA for scientists to figure out that it looks like a twisted ladder. When James Watson and Francis Crick published the structure of DNA in 1953, they added another clue to how traits are passed from parent to offspring. DNA contains the genetic information for cells to make proteins. Proteins determine a variety of traits, from hair color to an organism's ability to digest food.

The Structure of DNA Parents pass traits to their offspring through chromosomes. Chromosomes are composed mostly of proteins and DNA and are located in a cell's nucleus. Look at **Figure 1.** The twisted ladder structure of DNA is also known as a "double helix." The sides of the double helix are made up of sugar molecules called deoxyribose, alternating with phosphate molecules. The name DNA, or deoxyribonucleic acid (DEE ahk see ry boh noo klee ik), comes from this structure.

The rungs of DNA are made of nitrogen bases. **Nitrogen bases** are molecules that contain nitrogen and other elements. DNA has four kinds of nitrogen bases: adenine (AD uh neen), thymine (THY meen), guanine (GWAH neen), and cytosine (SY tuh seen). The capital letters *A, T, G,* and *C* are used to represent the bases.

FLORIDA NGSSS

SC.7.L.16.1 Understand and explain that every organism requires a set of instructions that specifies its traits, that this hereditary information (DNA) contains genes located in the chromosomes of each cell.

LA.7.2.2.3 The student will organize information to show understanding or relationships among facts, ideas, and events (e.g., representing main ideas within the text).

FIGURE 1

> ART IN MOTION **Genetic Structures**
Everglades snail kites, like all organisms, contain all of the genetic structures below.

✎ **Sequence** Put the structures in order from largest to smallest by writing the numbers two through five in the blank circles.

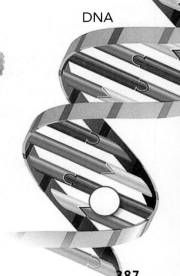

DNA

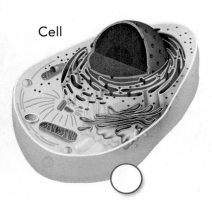

Cell

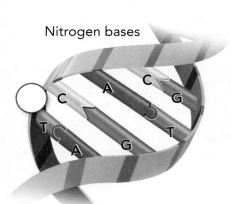

Nitrogen bases

Chromosome

387

Chromosomes, Genes, and DNA

In **Figure 2,** you can see the relationship among chromosomes, genes, and DNA. A gene is a section of a DNA molecule that contains the information to code for one specific protein. A gene is made up of a series of bases in a row. The bases in a gene are arranged in a specific order—for example, ATGACGTAC. A single gene on a chromosome may contain anywhere from several hundred to a million or more of these bases. Each gene is located at a specific place on a chromosome.

Because there are so many possible combinations of bases and genes, each individual organism has a unique set of DNA. DNA can be found in all of the cells of your body except for red blood cells. DNA can be found in blood samples, however, because white blood cells do contain DNA.

FIGURE 2 ·······························

Chromosomes and Genes
Humans have between 20,000 and 25,000 genes on their chromosomes. The corals that make up ocean reefs are thought to have as many as 25,000 genes too!

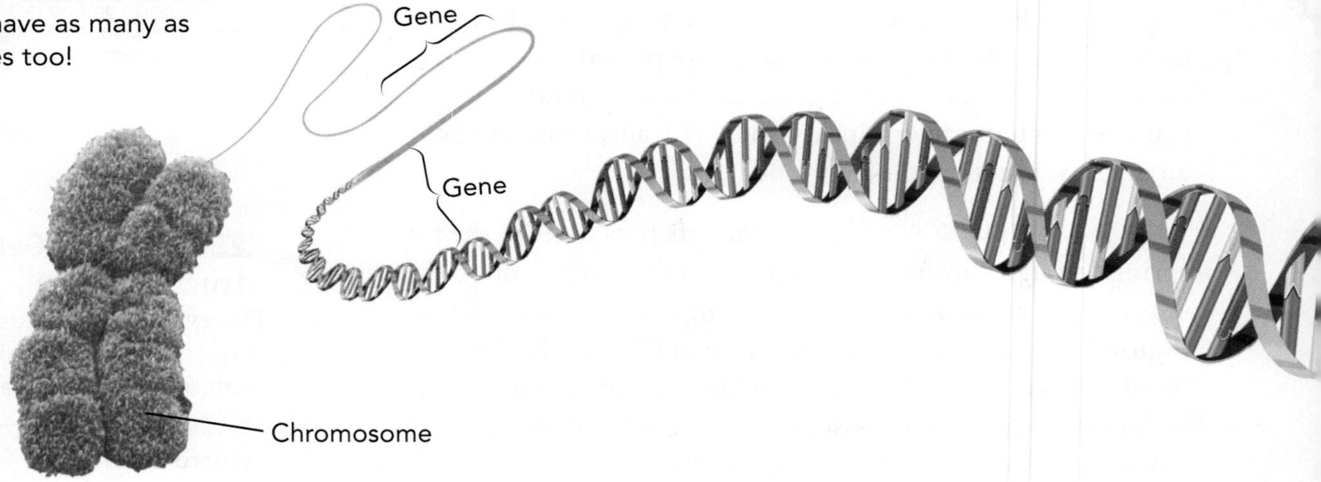

Gene

Gene

Chromosome

apply it!

Can you help solve the crime?

Someone robbed a jewelry store. The robber's DNA was extracted from skin cells found on the broken glass of a jewelry case. The police collected DNA samples from three suspects. The letters below represent the sequences of nitrogen bases in the DNA. Based on the DNA found at the crime scene, circle the DNA of the guilty suspect.

Robber: GACCAGTTAGCTAAGTCT

Suspect 1: TAGCTGA

Suspect 2: GACGAGT

Suspect 3: CTAAGTC

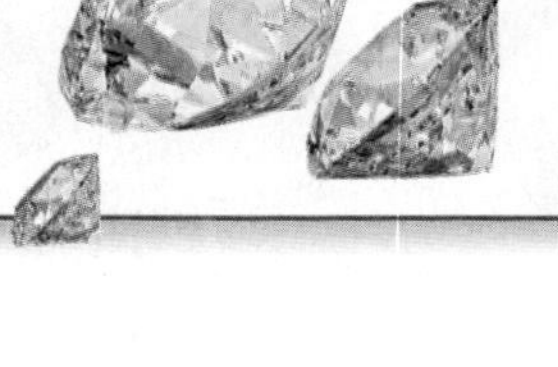

❶ **Explain** Why can you solve crimes using DNA?

_____

_____

_____

❷ **Infer** Could the police have used blood on the broken glass to test for DNA? Why or why not?

_____

_____

_____

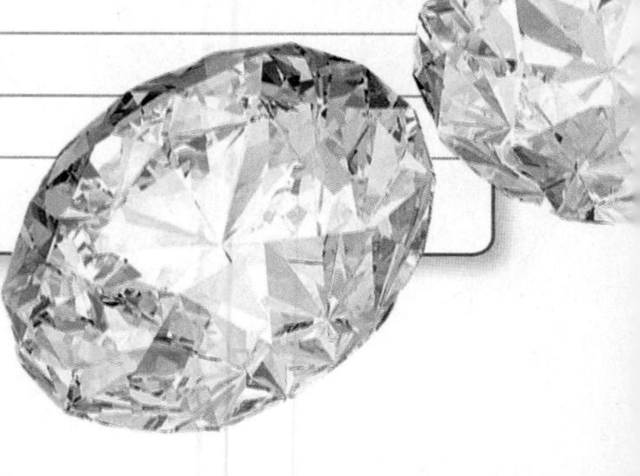

Order of the Bases A gene contains the code that determines the structure of a protein. 🔑 **The order of the nitrogen bases along a gene forms a genetic code that specifies what type of protein will be produced.** Remember that proteins are long-chain molecules made of individual amino acids. In the genetic code, a group of three DNA bases codes for one specific amino acid. For example, the three-base sequence CGT (cytosine-guanine-thymine) always codes for the amino acid alanine. The order of the three-base code units determines the order in which amino acids are put together to form a protein.

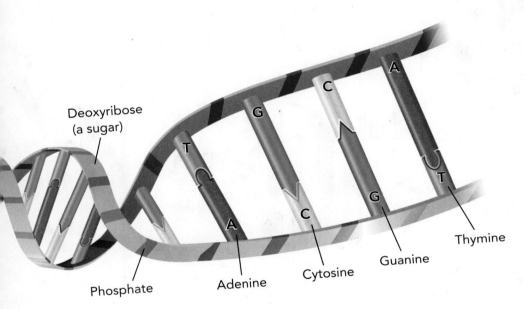

Deoxyribose (a sugar)

Phosphate

Adenine

Cytosine

Guanine

Thymine

FIGURE 3 ·······························

DNA Bases
Notice the sequence in the DNA bases.

✏️ **Interpret Diagrams**
Which base always pairs with cytosine?

_____

_____

Lab zone ® Do the Lab Investigation
Guilty or Innocent?

🔑 **Assess Your Understanding**

1a. Identify These letters represent the nitrogen bases on one strand of DNA: GGCTATCCA. What letters would form the other strand of the helix?

_____
                                    SC.7.L.16.1

b. Explain How do parents pass traits such as eye color to their offspring?

_____

_____

_____
                                    SC.7.L.16.1

got it?

○ **I get it!** Now I know that the genetic code of nitrogen bases specifies_____

_____

_____

○ **I need extra help with** _____

_____

Go to **my science** 🄢 **coach** *online for help with this subject.*
                                    SC.7.L.16.1

FIGURE 4 ·····························

>INTERACTIVE ART DNA Replication

Without DNA replication, daughter cells could not carry out their life functions.

✎ **Interpret Diagrams Fill in the missing bases on the new strand of DNA. Then complete the sentences below.**

Steps in DNA Replication

❶ _____ unzips.

❷ Nitrogen bases in the cell _____ pair up with the bases on the DNA halves.

❸ Two new identical DNA molecules are formed.

FLORIDA NGSSS

SC.7.L.16.1 Understand and explain that every organism requires a set of instructions that specifies its traits, that this hereditary information (DNA) contains genes located in the chromosomes of each cell, and that heredity is the passage of these instructions from one generation to another.

How Does DNA Copy Itself?

Two new cells, or daughter cells, result when a cell divides. To ensure that each daughter cell has the genetic information it needs to carry out its activities, DNA copies itself. **DNA replication** is the process in which an identical copy of a DNA strand is formed for a new cell. Replication is very important, since daughter cells need a complete set of DNA to survive.

DNA replication begins when the two sides of a DNA molecule unwind and separate, like a zipper unzipping, between the nitrogen bases. Next, nitrogen bases in the nucleus pair up with the bases on each half of the DNA. 🔑 **Because of the way the nitrogen bases pair up, the order of the bases in each new DNA strand matches the order in the original DNA strand.** This pattern is key to understanding how DNA replication occurs. Adenine always pairs with thymine, while guanine always pairs with cytosine. At the end of replication, two identical DNA molecules are formed.

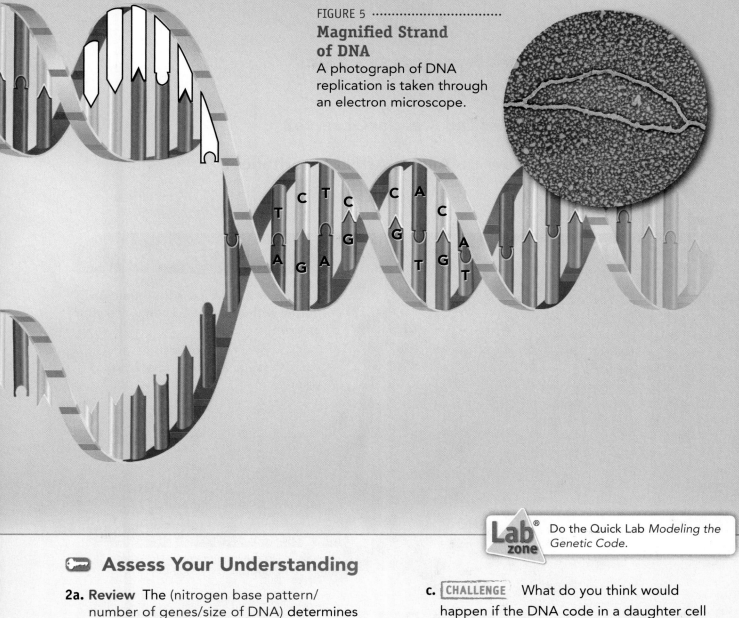

FIGURE 5 ·······························
Magnified Strand of DNA
A photograph of DNA replication is taken through an electron microscope.

Do the Quick Lab *Modeling the Genetic Code.*

🔑 **Assess Your Understanding**

2a. Review The (nitrogen base pattern/ number of genes/size of DNA) determines how DNA is replicated.   SC.7.L.16.1

b. Describe Where in the cell does DNA replication take place?

_____

_____

_____
                                      SC.7.L.16.1

c. CHALLENGE   What do you think would happen if the DNA code in a daughter cell did not match the code in the parent cell?

_____

_____

_____

_____
                                      SC.7.L.16.1

got it? ···

○ **I get it!** Now I know that DNA replication is the process in which_____

○ **I need extra help with** _____

   Go to my science ⑤ coach *online for help with this subject.*   SC.7.L.16.1

🔑 **What Did Mendel Observe?**
SC.7.L.16.1, SC.7.N.2.1, LA.7.2.2.3

🔑 **How Do Alleles Affect Inheritance?**
SC.7.L.16.1, SC.7.N.2.1

MY PLANET DiARY

Almost Forgotten

When scientists make great discoveries, sometimes their work is praised, criticized, or even forgotten. Gregor Mendel was almost forgotten. He spent eight years studying pea plants, and he discovered patterns in the way characteristics pass from one generation to the next. For almost 40 years, people overlooked Mendel's work. When it was finally rediscovered, it unlocked the key to understanding heredity.

BIOGRAPHY

Communicate **Discuss the question below with a partner. Then write your answer.**

Did you ever rediscover something of yours that you had forgotten? How did you react?

_____

_____

_____

▶ **PLANET DIARY** Go to **Planet Diary** to learn more about heredity.

Lab zone Do the Inquiry Warm-Up *What Does the Father Look Like?*

FLORIDA NGSSS

SC.7.L.16.1 Understand and explain that every organism requires a set of instructions and that heredity is the passage of these instructions from one generation to another.

SC.7.N.2.1 Identify an instance from the history of science in which scientific knowledge has changed when new evidence was encountered.

LA.7.2.2.3 The student will organize information to show understanding or relationships among facts, ideas, and events (e.g., representing main ideas within the text through comparing and contrasting).

What Did Mendel Observe?

In the mid-nineteenth century, a priest named Gregor Mendel tended a garden in a central European monastery. Mendel's experiments in that peaceful garden would one day transform the study of heredity. **Heredity** is the passing of physical characteristics, or traits, from parents to offspring.

Mendel wondered why different pea plants had different traits. Some pea plants grew tall, while others were short. Some plants produced green seeds, while others had yellow seeds. Mendel observed that the forms of the pea plants' traits were often similar to those of their parents. Sometimes, however, the forms differed.

Vocabulary

- heredity • genetics • fertilization • purebred
- allele • dominant allele • recessive allele • hybrid

Skills

⟳ Reading: Identify Supporting Evidence

△ Inquiry: Predict

Mendel's Experiments Mendel experimented with thousands of pea plants. Today, Mendel's discoveries form the foundation of **genetics,** the scientific study of heredity. **Figure 1** shows the parts of a pea plant's flower. The pistil produces female sex cells, or eggs. The stamens produce pollen, which contains the male sex cells, or sperm. A new organism begins to form when egg and sperm cells join in the process called **fertilization.** Before fertilization can happen in pea plants, pollen must reach the pistil of a pea flower. This process is called pollination.

Pea plants are usually self-pollinating. In self-pollination, pollen from a flower lands on the pistil of the same flower. Mendel developed a method by which he cross-pollinated, or "crossed," pea plants. **Figure 1** shows his method.

Mendel decided to cross plants that had contrasting forms of a trait—for example, tall plants and short plants. He started with purebred plants. A **purebred** organism is the offspring of many generations that show the same form of a trait. For example, two purebred tall pea plants always produce tall offspring.

FIGURE 1 ⋯⋯⋯⋯⋯⋯⋯⋯⋯⋯

Crossing Pea Plants

Mendel devised a way to cross-pollinate pea plants.

✏ **Use the diagram to answer the questions about Mendel's procedure.**

1. Observe How does flower B differ from flower A?

_____

_____

2. Infer Describe how Mendel cross-pollinated pea plants.

_____

_____

_____

_____

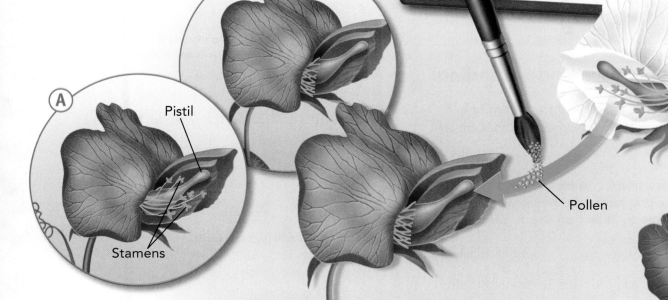

B

A

Pistil

Stamens

Pollen

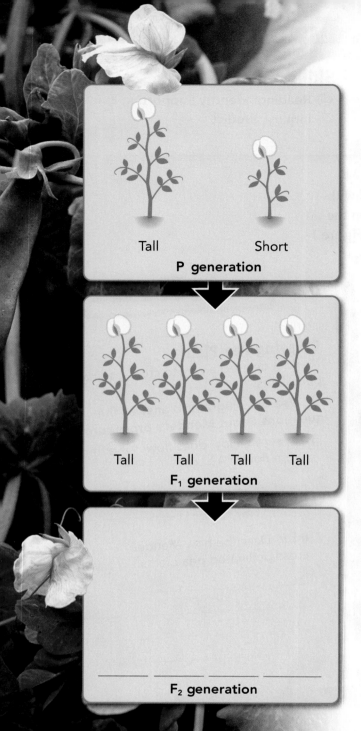

Tall   Short

P generation

Tall   Tall   Tall   Tall

F₁ generation

_____

F₂ generation

The F₁ and F₂ Offspring

Mendel crossed purebred tall plants with purebred short plants. Scientists call these plants the parental, or P, generation. The resulting offspring are the first filial (FIL ee ul), or F₁, generation. The word *filial* comes from *filia* and *filius*, the Latin words for "daughter" and "son."

Look at **Figure 2** to see the surprise Mendel found in the F₁ generation. All the offspring were tall. The shortness trait seemed to have disappeared!

When these plants were full-grown, Mendel allowed them to self-pollinate. The F₂ (second filial) generation that followed surprised Mendel even more. He counted the plants of the F₂ generation. About three fourths were tall, while one fourth were short.

Experiments With Other Traits

Mendel repeated his experiments, studying other pea-plant traits, such as flower color and seed shape. **In all of his crosses, Mendel found that only one form of the trait appeared in the F₁ generation. However, in the F₂ generation, the "lost" form of the trait always reappeared in about one fourth of the plants.**

FIGURE 2 ....
Results of a Cross
In Mendel's crosses, some forms of a trait were hidden in one generation but reappeared in the next.

✎ **Interpret Diagrams** Draw and label the offspring in the F₂ generation.

Lab zone®   Do the Quick Lab *Observing Pistils and Stamens.*

🔑 Assess Your Understanding

1a. Explain The passage of traits from one generation to the next generation is called

_____

SC.7.L.16.1

b. Compare and Contrast In Mendel's cross for stem height, how did the plants in the F₂ generation differ from the F₁ plants?

_____

SC.7.L.16.1, LA.7.2.2.3

got it?

○ **I get it!** Now I know that Mendel found that one form of a trait _____

_____

_____

○ **I need extra help with** _____

Go to **MY SCIENCE** ⓢ **COACH** online for help with this subject.   SC.7.L.16.1

How Do Alleles Affect Inheritance?

Mendel reached several conclusions from his experimental results. He reasoned that individual factors, or sets of genetic "information," must control the inheritance of traits in peas. The factors that control each trait exist in pairs. The female parent contributes one factor, while the male parent contributes the other factor. Finally, one factor in a pair can mask, or hide, the other factor. The tallness factor, for example, masked the shortness factor.

Genes and Alleles Today, scientists know that genes control the inheritance of traits. **Alleles** (uh LEELZ) are the different forms of a gene. The gene that controls stem height in peas has one allele for tall stems and one allele for short stems. Each pea plant inherits two alleles—one from the egg and the other from the sperm. A plant may inherit two alleles for tall stems, two alleles for short stems, or one of each.

🔑 **An organism's traits are controlled by the alleles it inherits from its parents. Some alleles are dominant, while other alleles are recessive.** A **dominant allele** is one whose trait always shows up in the organism when the allele is present. A **recessive allele,** on the other hand, is hidden whenever the dominant allele is present. **Figure 3** shows dominant and recessive alleles of the traits in Mendel's crosses.

FLORIDA NGSSS

SC.7.L.16.1 Understand and explain that every organism requires a set of instructions and that heredity is the passage of these instructions from one generation to another.

SC.7.N.2.1 Identify an instance from the history of science in which scientific knowledge has changed when new evidence was encountered.

FIGURE 3 ·····················

Alleles in Pea Plants

Mendel studied the inheritance of seven different traits in pea plants.

✎ **Use the table to answer the questions.**

1. **Draw Conclusions** Circle the picture of the dominant allele in the P generation for each trait.

2. **Predict** Under what conditions would the recessive form of one of these traits reappear?

_____

_____

Inheritance of Pea Plants Studied by Mendel

	Seed Shape	Seed Color	Pod Shape	Pod Color	Flower Color	Flower Position	Stem Height
P	Wrinkled	Yellow	Pinched	Green	Purple	Tip of stem	Tall
	X	X	X	X	X	X	X
	Round	Green	Smooth	Yellow	White	Side of stem	Short
F₁	Round	Yellow	Smooth	Green	Purple	Side of stem	Tall

FIGURE 4 ·······························

> VIRTUAL LAB Dominant and Recessive Alleles

Symbols serve as a shorthand way to identify alleles.

✎ **Complete each row of the diagram.**

1. **Identify** Fill in the missing allele symbols and descriptions.

2. **Summarize** Use the word bank to complete the statements. (Terms will be used more than once.)

3. **Relate Cause and Effect** Draw the two possible ways the F₂ offspring could look.

Alleles in Mendel's Crosses In Mendel's cross for stem height, the purebred tall plants in the P generation had two alleles for tall stems. The purebred short plants had two alleles for short stems. But each F₁ plant inherited one allele for tall stems and one allele for short stems. The F₁ plants are called hybrids. A **hybrid** (HY brid) organism has two different alleles for a trait. All the F₁ plants are tall because the dominant allele for tall stems masks the recessive allele for short stems.

Symbols for Alleles Geneticists, scientists who study genetics, often use letters to represent alleles. A dominant allele is symbolized by a capital letter. A recessive allele is symbolized by the lowercase version of the same letter. For example, *T* stands for the allele for tall stems, and *t* stands for the allele for short stems. When a plant has two dominant alleles for tall stems, its alleles are written as *TT*. When a plant has two recessive alleles for short stems, its alleles are written as *tt*. These plants are the P generation shown in **Figure 4.** Think about the symbols that would be used for F₁ plants that all inherit one allele for tall stems and one for short stems.

P

Tall
T
___
Purebred

Short
t
___
Purebred

Word Bank
dominant
recessive

F₁

___
T
___

All plants inherit one _____ allele and one _____ allele. These plants are all tall.

F₂

Plants may inherit two _____ alleles. These plants are tall.

Plants may inherit one _____ allele and one _____ allele. These plants are tall.

Plants may inherit two _____ alleles. These plants are short.

apply it!

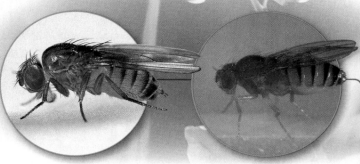

In fruit flies, long wings are dominant over short wings. A scientist crossed a purebred long-winged fruit fly with a purebred short-winged fruit fly.

1 If *W* stands for long wings, write the symbols for the alleles of each parent fly.

_____

2 ⚠ **Predict** What will be the wing length of the F_1 offspring?

_____

3 ⚠ **Predict** If the scientist crosses a hybrid male F_1 fruit fly with a hybrid F_1 female, what will their offspring probably be like?

_____

_____

_____

Significance of Mendel's Contribution

Mendel's discovery of genes and alleles eventually changed scientists' ideas about heredity. Before Mendel, most people thought that the traits of an individual organism were simply a blend of the parents' characteristics. Mendel showed that offspring traits are determined by individual, separate alleles inherited from each parent. Unfortunately, the value of Mendel's discovery was not known during his lifetime. But when scientists in the early 1900s rediscovered Mendel's work, they quickly realized its importance. Because of his work, Mendel is often called the Father of Genetics.

🔾 **Identify Supporting Evidence** What evidence showed Mendel that traits are determined by separate alleles?

_____

_____

_____

_____

 Lab zone ® Do the Quick Lab *Inferring the Parent Generation.*

🗝 Assess Your Understanding

2a. Identify How did Mendel's work change scientific knowledge about genetics?

_____

_____

_____

SC.7.L.16.1, SC.7.N.2.1

b. Relate Cause and Effect Why is a pea plant tall when it is a hybrid for stem height?

_____

_____

_____

SC.7.L.16.1

got it?

○ **I get it!** Now I know that an organism's traits are controlled by _____

_____

_____

_____

○ **I need extra help with** _____

Go to **my science** Ⓢ **coach** *online for help with this subject.*

SC.7.L.16.1

3 Probability and Heredity

UNLOCK THE ESSENTIAL ?

🔑 **How Is Probability Related to Inheritance?**
SC.7.L.16.2, MA.6.A.3.6

🔑 **What Are Phenotype and Genotype?**
SC.7.L.16.2

MY PLANET DIARY
for Florida

Storm on the Way?

Have you ever watched a hurricane form? Weather forecasters at the National Hurricane Center (NHC) in Miami, Florida, have. From May 15 to November 30, the NHC Operations Area is staffed around the clock with forecasters. They study data from aircraft, ocean buoys, and satellites to develop computer models. These models predict the probable paths of a storm. If the probability of a certain path is high, the NHC issues a warning that helps save lives and reduce damage.

FIELD TRIP

Communicate Answer the question below. Then discuss your answer with a partner.

Local weather forecasters often talk about the percent chance for rainfall. What do you think they mean?

_____

_____

_____

_____

_____

> **PLANET DIARY** Go to **Planet Diary** to learn more about probability and weather.

Lab zone ® Do the Inquiry Warm-Up *What's the Chance?*

FLORIDA NGSSS

SC.7.L.16.2 Determine the probabilities for genotype and phenotype combinations using Punnett Squares and pedigrees.

MA.6.A.3.6 Construct and analyze tables, graphs, and equations to describe linear functions and other simple relations using both common language and algebraic notation.

How Is Probability Related to Inheritance?

Before the start of a football game, the team captains stand with the referee for a coin toss. The team that wins the toss chooses whether to kick or receive the ball. As the referee tosses the coin, the visiting team captain calls "heads." What is the chance that the visitors will win the toss? To answer this question, you need to understand the principles of probability.

Vocabulary
- probability
- pedigree
- genotype
- heterozygous
- Punnett square
- phenotype
- homozygous

Skills
- Reading: Summarize
- Inquiry: Draw Conclusions

What Is Probability? Each time you toss a coin, there are two possible ways it can land—heads up or tails up. **Probability** is a number that describes how likely it is that an event will occur. In mathematical terms, you can say the probability that a tossed coin will land heads up is 1 in 2. There's also a 1 in 2 probability that the coin will land tails up. A 1 in 2 probability is expressed as the fraction $\frac{1}{2}$ or as 50 percent.

The laws of probability predict what is *likely* to occur, not what *will* occur. If you toss a coin 20 times, you may expect it to land heads up 10 times and tails up 10 times. But you may get 11 heads and 9 tails, or 8 heads and 12 tails. The more tosses you make, the closer your actual results will be to those predicted by probability.

Do you think the result of one toss affects the result of the next toss? Not at all. Each event occurs independently. Suppose you toss a coin five times and it lands heads up each time. What is the probability that it will land heads up on the next toss? If you said the probability is still 1 in 2, or 50 percent, you're right. The results of the first five tosses do not affect the result of the sixth toss.

do the math!

Percentage

One way to express probability is as a percentage. A percentage is a number compared to 100. For example, 50 percent, or 50%, means 50 out of 100. Suppose you want to calculate percentage from the results of a series of basketball free throws in which 3 out of 5 free throws go through the hoop.

STEP 1 Write the comparison as a fraction.

$$3 \text{ out of } 5 = \frac{3}{5}$$

STEP 2 Calculate the number value of the fraction.

$$3 \div 5 = 0.6$$

STEP 3 Multiply this number by 100%.

$$0.6 \times 100\% = 60\%$$

.... Practice! ....

1 Calculate Suppose 5 out of 25 free throws go through the hoop. Write this result as a fraction.

_____

2 Calculate Express your answer in Question 1 as a percentage.

_____

_____

_____

MA.7.P.7.1, MA.7.P.7.2

Probability and Genetics How is probability related to genetics? Think back to Mendel's experiments. He carefully counted the offspring from every cross. When he crossed two plants that were hybrid for stem height (*Tt*), about three fourths of the F₁ plants had tall stems. About one fourth had short stems.

Each time Mendel repeated the cross, he observed similar results. He realized that the principles of probability applied to his work. He found that the probability of a hybrid cross producing a tall plant was 3 in 4. The probability of producing a short plant was 1 in 4. Mendel was the first scientist to recognize that the principles of probability can predict the results of genetic crosses.

Punnett Squares

A tool that can help you grasp how the laws of probability apply to genetics is called a Punnett square. A **Punnett square** is a chart that shows all the possible ways alleles can combine in a genetic cross. Geneticists use Punnett squares to see these combinations and to determine the probability of a particular outcome, or result. 🔑 **In a genetic cross, the combination of alleles that parents can pass to an offspring is based on probability.**

Figure 1 shows how to make a Punnett square. In this case, the cross is between two hybrid pea plants with round seeds (*Rr*). The allele for round seeds (*R*) is dominant over the allele for wrinkled seeds (*r*). Each parent can pass either one allele or the other to an offspring. The boxes in the Punnett square show the possible combinations of alleles that the offspring can inherit.

FIGURE 1 ·······························

▶ **INTERACTIVE ART** **How to Make a Punnett Square**

You can use a Punnett square to find the probabilities of a genetic cross.

✎ **Follow the steps in the figure to fill in the Punnett square.**

1. **Predict** Determine the probability that an offspring will have wrinkled seeds.

_____

2. **Interpret Tables** Determine the probability that an offspring will have round seeds? Explain your answer.

_____

_____

_____

2 The male parent's alleles are written along the top of the square. Fill in the female parent's alleles along the left side.

R   r

1 Start by drawing a box and dividing it into four squares.

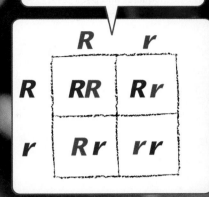

5 The completed square shows all the possible allele combinations the offspring can have.

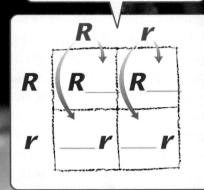

4 Copy the male parent's alleles into the boxes beneath them.

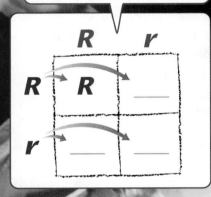

3 Copy the female parent's alleles into the boxes to their right. The first one is done for you.

Pedigrees

A Punnett square shows why Mendel got the results he saw in the F$_2$ generations. But a Punnett square is not the only tool scientists can use to trace a particular trait. A **pedigree** is a chart or "family tree" that shows the presence or absence of a trait according to the relationships within a family across several generations. Doctors use pedigrees to trace and diagnose genetic disorders. You will learn more about pedigrees in Chapter 13.

✏️ **Summarize** In your own words, describe what a Punnett square shows about combinations of alleles.

_____

_____

_____

_____

_____

 Do the Quick Lab *Coin Crosses.*

🔑 Assess Your Understanding

1a. Review What is probability?

_____

_____

SC.7.L.16.2

b. Apply Concepts What is the probability that a cross between a hybrid pea plant with round seeds and one with wrinkled seeds will produce offspring with wrinkled seeds? (Draw a Punnett square on other paper to find the answer.)

_____

SC.7.L.16.2, MA.6.A.3.6

got it?

○ **I get it!** Now I know that the combination of alleles parents can pass to offspring _____

_____

○ **I need extra help with** _____

Go to my science COACH *online for help with this subject.*

SC.7.L.16.2

FLORIDA NGSSS

SC.7.L.16.2 Determine the probabilities for genotype and phenotype combinations using Punnett Squares and pedigrees.

What Are Phenotype and Genotype?

Two terms that geneticists use are **phenotype** (FEE noh typ) and **genotype** (JEN uh typ). 🔑 **An organism's phenotype is its physical appearance, or visible traits. An organism's genotype is its genetic makeup, or alleles.** In other words, genotype is an organism's alleles. Phenotype is how a trait looks or is expressed.

To compare phenotype and genotype, look at **Figure 2.** The allele for smooth pea pods (*S*) is dominant over the allele for pinched pea pods (*s*). All the plants with at least one *S* allele have the same phenotype. That is, they all produce smooth pods. However, these plants can have two different genotypes—*SS* or *Ss*. If you were to look at the plants with smooth pods, you would not be able to tell the difference between those that have the genotype *SS* and those with the genotype *Ss*. The plants with pinched pods, on the other hand, would all have the same phenotype—pinched pods—as well as the same genotype—*ss*.

Geneticists use two additional terms to describe an organism's genotype. An organism that has two identical alleles for a trait is said to be **homozygous** (hoh moh ZY gus) for that trait. A smooth-pod plant that has the alleles *SS* and a pinched-pod plant with the alleles *ss* are both homozygous. An organism that has two different alleles for a trait is **heterozygous** (het ur oh ZY gus) for that trait. A smooth-pod plant with the alleles *Ss* is heterozygous. Recall that Mendel used the term *hybrid* to describe heterozygous pea plants.

Vocabulary Suffixes The suffix *-ous* means "having." Circle this suffix in the highlighted terms *homozygous* and *heterozygous* in the paragraph at the right. These terms describe the organism as having

_____

_____

_____

FIGURE 2 ·····························

Describing Inheritance

An organism's phenotype is its physical appearance. Its genotype is its genetic makeup.

✎ **Based on what you have read, answer these questions.**

1. **Classify** Fill in the missing information in the table.

2. **Interpret Tables** How many genotypes are there for the smooth-pod phenotype?

_____

Phenotypes and Genotypes

Phenotype	Genotype	Homozygous or Heterozygous
Smooth pods	_____	_____
Smooth pods	_____	_____
Pinched pods	_____	_____

apply it!

Mendel's principles of heredity apply to many other organisms. For example, in guinea pigs, black fur color (*B*) is dominant over white fur color (*b*). Suppose a pair of black guinea pigs produces several litters of pups during their lifetimes. The graph shows the phenotypes of the pups. Write a title for the graph.

1 **Read Graphs** How many black pups were produced? How many white pups were produced?

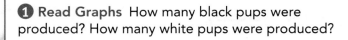

2 **Infer** What are the possible genotypes of the offspring?

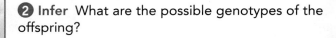

3 **Draw Conclusions** What can you conclude about the genotypes of the parent guinea pigs? Explain your answer.

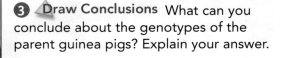

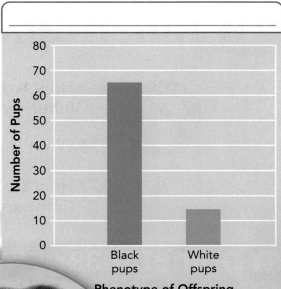

Number of Pups (y-axis: 0, 10, 20, 30, 40, 50, 60, 70, 80)

Black pups | White pups

Phenotype of Offspring

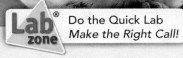
Lab zone® Do the Quick Lab
Make the Right Call!

🔑 Assess Your Understanding

2a. **Relate Cause and Effect** Explain how two organisms can have the same phenotype but different genotypes.

_____

_____

_____

SC.7.L.16.2

b. **CHALLENGE** In their lifetimes, two guinea pigs produce 40 black pups and 40 white pups. On a separate paper, make a Punnett square and find the likely genotypes of these parents.

_____

SC.7.L.16.2

got it?

○ **I get it!** Now I know that phenotype and genotype are terms that describe _____

_____

_____

_____

_____

○ **I need extra help with** _____

Go to **my science** ⓢ **coach** *online for help with this subject.*

SC.7.L.16.2

Chromosomes and Inheritance

ESSENTIAL

?

🔑 **How Are Chromosomes, Genes, and Inheritance Related?**
SC.7.L.16.1, SC.7.N.1.5, SC.7.N.1.6

🔑 **What Happens During Meiosis?**
SC.7.L.16.3

🔑 **How Do Sexual and Asexual Reproduction Compare?**
SC.7.L.16.3, LA.7.2.2.3

my planet diary

Chromosome Sleuth

Finding answers about how chromosomes relate to disease is one job of genetic technologists. These scientists analyze chromosomes from cells. The analysis may pinpoint genetic information that can cause disease or other health problems. In their work, genetic technologists use microscopes, computer-imaging photography, and lab skills. They report data that are used in research and in treating patients affected by genetic diseases.

CAREER

Communicate Answer these questions. Then discuss Question 2 with a partner.

1. Describe a method that genetic technologists use to pursue a scientific explanation.

_____

_____

_____

_____

2. If you were a genetic technologist, what would you like to research?

_____

_____

_____

SC.7.N.1.5

▶ PLANET DIARY Go to **Planet Diary** to learn more about genetic technologists.

Lab zone® Do the Inquiry Warm-Up
Which Chromosome Is Which?

Vocabulary
- meiosis

Skills
- ↻ Reading: Relate Cause and Effect
- △ Inquiry: Design Experiments

How Are Chromosomes, Genes, and Inheritance Related?

Mendel's work showed that genes exist. (Remember that he called them "factors.") But scientists in the early twentieth century did not know what structures in cells contained genes. The search for the answer was something like a mystery story. The story could be called "The Clue in the Grasshopper's Cells."

At the start of the 1900s, Walter Sutton, an American geneticist, studied the cells of grasshoppers. He wanted to understand how sex cells (sperm and eggs) form. Sutton focused on how the chromosomes moved within cells during the formation of sperm and eggs. He hypothesized that chromosomes are the key to learning how offspring have traits similar to those of their parents.

apply it!

△ **Design Experiments** Different types of organisms have different numbers of chromosomes, and some organisms are easier to study than others. Suppose you are a scientist studying chromosomes and you have to pick an organism from those shown below to do your work. Which one would you pick and why?

_____

_____

_____

_____

_____

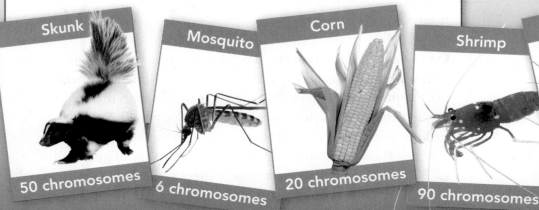

Skunk — 50 chromosomes

Mosquito — 6 chromosomes

Corn — 20 chromosomes

Shrimp — 90 chromosomes

Grasshopper — 24 chromosomes

Chromosomes and Inheritance Sutton needed evidence to support his hypothesis. Look at **Figure 1** to see how he found this evidence in grasshopper cells. To his surprise, he discovered that grasshopper sex cells have exactly half the number of chromosomes found in grasshopper body cells.

Chromosome Pairs Sutton observed what happened when a sperm cell and an egg cell joined. The fertilized egg that formed had 24 chromosomes. It had the same number of chromosomes as each parent. These 24 chromosomes existed as 12 pairs. One chromosome in each pair came from the male parent. The other chromosome came from the female parent.

FIGURE 1 ······························
Paired Up
Sutton studied grasshopper cells through a microscope. He concluded that genes are carried on chromosomes.

 Relate Text and Visuals
Answer the questions in the spaces provided.

❶ Body Cell

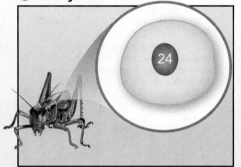

Each grasshopper body cell has 24 chromosomes.

❷ Sex Cells

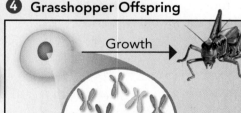

Sutton found that grasshopper sex cells each have 12 chromosomes.

1. How does the number of chromosomes in grasshopper sex cells compare to the number in body cells?

_____

_____

_____

_____

❸ Fertilization

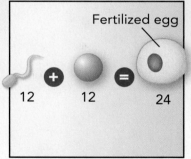

The fertilized egg cell has 24 chromosomes.

❹ Grasshopper Offspring

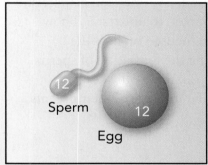

The 24 chromosomes exist as 12 pairs.

2. How is the inheritance of chromosomes similar to what you know about alleles?

_____

_____

_____

_____

Genes on Chromosomes Recall that alleles are different forms of a gene. Because of Mendel's work, Sutton knew that alleles exist in pairs in an organism. One allele comes from the female parent. The other allele comes from the male parent. Sutton realized that paired alleles are carried on paired chromosomes. His idea is now known as the chromosome theory of inheritance.

🔑 **According to the chromosome theory of inheritance, genes pass from parents to their offspring on chromosomes.**

A Lineup of Genes

The body cells of humans contain 46 chromosomes that form 23 pairs. Chromosomes are made up of many genes joined together like beads on a string. Although you have only 23 pairs of chromosomes, your body cells each contain between 20,000 and 25,000 genes. Genes control traits.

Figure 2 shows a pair of chromosomes from an organism. One chromosome is from the female parent. The other chromosome is from the male parent. Notice that each chromosome has the same genes. The genes are lined up in the same order on both chromosomes. However, the alleles for some of the genes are not identical. For example, one chromosome has allele *A,* and the other chromosome has allele *a.* As you can see, this organism is heterozygous for some traits and homozygous for others.

Relate Cause and Effect
Suppose gene A on the left chromosome is damaged and no longer functions. What form of the trait would show? Why?

_____

_____

_____

_____

_____

FIGURE 2 ·····················
A Pair of Chromosomes
Chromosomes in a pair may have different alleles for some genes and the same alleles for others.

Interpret Diagrams For each pair of alleles, tell whether the organism is homozygous or heterozygous. The first two answers are shown.

Gene

Chromosome pair

Heterozygous

Homozygous

_____

_____

_____

_____

_____

Do the Quick Lab *Chromosomes and Inheritance.*

Assess Your Understanding

1a. Describe When two grasshopper sex cells join, the chromosome number in the new cell is (half/double) the number in the sex cells.
SC.7.L.16.1

b. Summarize Describe the arrangement of genes on a pair of chromosomes.

_____

_____

_____
SC.7.L.16.1

c. Relate Evidence and Explanation How do Sutton's observations support the chromosome theory of inheritance?

_____

_____

_____

_____
SC.7.L.16.1, SC.7.N.1.6

got it? ···

○ **I get it!** Now I know that genes are passed from parents to offspring _____

_____

○ **I need extra help with** _____

Go to MY SCIENCE ⓢ COACH *online for help with this subject.*
SC.7.L.16.1

 **FLORIDA** NGSSS

SC.7.L.16.3 Compare and contrast the general processes of sexual reproduction requiring meiosis and asexual reproduction requiring mitosis.

What Happens During Meiosis?

How do sex cells end up with half the number of chromosomes as body cells? The answer to this question is a form of cell division called meiosis. **Meiosis** (my OH sis) is the process by which the number of chromosomes is reduced by half as sex cells form. You can trace the events of meiosis in **Figure 3.** Here, the parent cell has four chromosomes arranged in two pairs. 🔑 **During meiosis, the chromosome pairs separate into two different cells. The sex cells that form later have only half as many chromosomes as the other cells in the organism.**

FIGURE 3 ···

Meiosis

During meiosis, a cell produces sex cells with half the number of chromosomes.

✎ **Interpret Diagrams Fill in the missing terms in the spaces provided, and complete the diagram.**

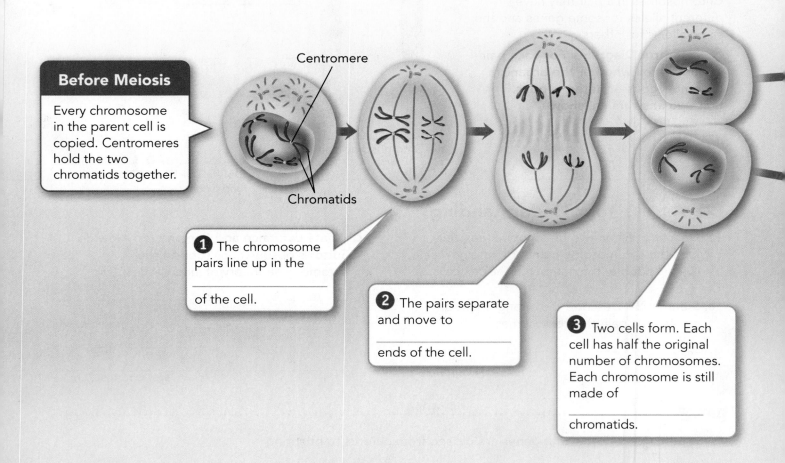

Before Meiosis

Every chromosome in the parent cell is copied. Centromeres hold the two chromatids together.

Centromere

Chromatids

1 The chromosome pairs line up in the
_____
of the cell.

2 The pairs separate and move to
_____
ends of the cell.

3 Two cells form. Each cell has half the original number of chromosomes. Each chromosome is still made of
_____
chromatids.

During meiosis, a cell divides into two cells. Then each of these cells divides again, forming a total of four cells. The chromosomes duplicate only before the first cell division.

Each of the four sex cells shown below receives two chromosomes—one chromosome from each pair in the original cell. When two sex cells join at fertilization, the new cell that forms has the full number of chromosomes. In this case, the number is four. The organism that grows from this cell got two of its chromosomes from one parent and two from the other parent.

did you know?

Researchers at Florida State University have found evidence that a single protein may control how chromosomes separate during meiosis. They are trying to figure out whether taking action during meiosis can prevent the development of some genetic disorders.

5 The centromeres split, and the _____ separate. They become single chromosomes and move to opposite ends of the cell.

4 In each cell, the _____ move to the center.

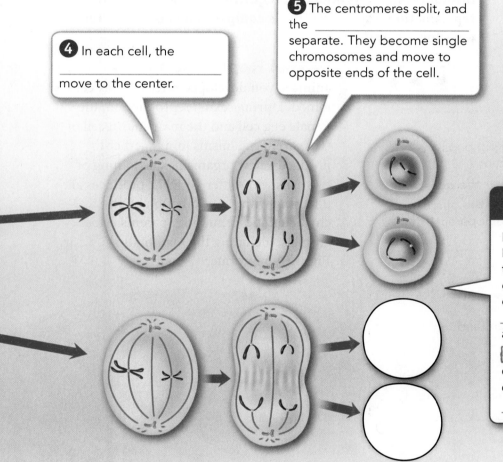

After Meiosis

Four sex cells are produced. Each cell has_____ the number of chromosomes of the_____ cell. Each sex cell has only _____ chromosome from an original pair.

[CHALLENGE] How many chromosomes are in each cell in Step 3?

_____

Lab® zone Do the Quick Lab *Modeling Meiosis.*

🔑 **Assess Your Understanding**

got it? ....

O **I get it!** Now I know that during meiosis, the number of chromosomes_____

_____

O **I need extra help with** _____

SC.7.L.16.3 Compare and contrast the general processes of sexual reproduction requiring meiosis and asexual reproduction requiring mitosis.

LA.7.2.2.3 The student will organize information to show understanding or relationships among facts, ideas, and events (e.g., representing main ideas within the text through comparing and contrasting).

How Do Sexual and Asexual Reproduction Compare?

You now know that sexual reproduction through meiosis starts with the joining of two sex cells. As a result, offspring receive chromosomes (and DNA, or genetic material) from both sexes. Recall that some organisms can reproduce asexually. In many of these organisms, asexual reproduction takes place through mitosis. During mitosis, a parent cell divides into two new cells. No new genetic material is introduced during mitosis. **DNA transfer through sexual reproduction requiring meiosis and asexual reproduction requiring mitosis equip organisms in different ways for survival.**

FIGURE 4 ···

Sexual Reproduction

These wolf cubs and guinea pig pups are products of sexual reproduction.

✎ **Use the photos to answer the questions.**

1. **Interpret Photos** How do the offspring in each photo differ from their parent?

_____

_____

_____

2. **Explain** Why do the parent and the offspring look different?

_____

_____

_____

_____

Sexual Reproduction Like many animals, you developed after two sex cells joined. During sexual reproduction, the female egg cell and the male sperm cell of two parent organisms join together to produce a new organism. The joining of two cells with different DNA produces an offspring with a combination of physical characteristics from both parents. Most animals, including the mammals shown in **Figure 4**, reproduce sexually.

Asexual Reproduction

During asexual reproduction, one parent produces a new organism identical to itself. This new organism receives an exact copy of the parent's DNA. Some animals, including sponges, jellyfish, and worms, reproduce asexually. The hydra, shown in **Figure 5**, reproduces asexually through budding. In budding, a new animal grows out of the parent and breaks off. Some animals reproduce asexually by dividing in two.

Comparing Asexual and Sexual Reproduction

Both sexual and asexual reproduction offer survival advantages and disadvantages. An advantage of asexual reproduction is that one parent can quickly produce many identical offspring. But a major disadvantage is that offspring have the same DNA as the parent. The offspring have no variation from the parent and may not survive changes in the environment. In contrast, sexual reproduction has the advantage of producing offspring with new combinations of DNA. These offspring may have characteristics that help them survive under unfavorable conditions. However, a disadvantage of sexual reproduction is that it requires finding a mate, and the development of offspring takes a longer time.

FIGURE 5 ·····················
A Chip off the Old Block
Budding is the most common form of asexual reproduction for this hydra, a type of cnidarian.

✎ **Relate Text to Visuals** How does this photo show asexual reproduction?

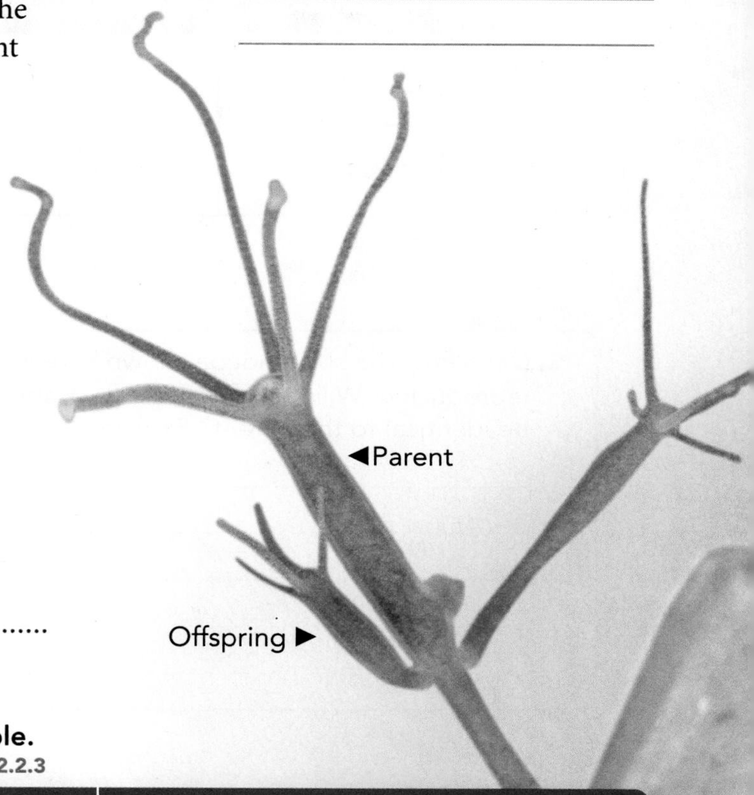

_____

_____

_____

_____

_____

◀Parent

Offspring ▶

FIGURE 6 ·····························
Asexual and Sexual Reproduction
Compare and Contrast Write an advantage and a disadvantage of each type of reproduction in the table.
LA.7.2.2.3

	Asexual Reproduction	Sexual Reproduction
Advantage		
Disadvantage		

Same or *Different?*

Why don't offspring always look like their parents?

FIGURE 7 ···

> **ART IN MOTION** Offspring don't always look like their parents. The type of reproduction and genes determine why this is so.

✎ **Review** Fill in the table to review the two types of reproduction. Then complete the tasks that go with each photo.

Type of Reproduction	Number of Parents	Mitosis or Meiosis	Offspring DNA Compared to Parent(s)	How Offspring Looks Compared to Parent(s)
Asexual				
Sexual				

1. **Describe** The soil amoeba shown here is reproducing. Will the offspring of the amoeba be identical to the parent? Explain.

_____

_____

_____

_____

_____

Soil amoeba reproducing

2. Predict In rabbits, the allele for black fur (*B*) is dominant over the allele for white fur (*b*). Is it possible for the two rabbits shown below to produce a white offspring? Draw a Punnett square to justify your answer.

_____

_____

3. Interpret Tables Suppose both of the rabbits have the genotype *Bb*. What is the probability that an offspring will have white fur? What is the probability that it will have black fur?

_____

_____

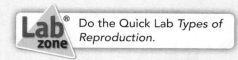 Do the Quick Lab *Types of Reproduction.*

🔑 Assess Your Understanding

2a. Define (Sexual/Asexual) reproduction involves the joining of sperm and egg.
SC.7.L.16.3

b. Compare and Contrast The offspring of (sexual/asexual) reproduction have a better chance of surviving changes in the environment than the offspring of (sexual/asexual) reproduction.
SC.7.L.16.3

c. [CHALLENGE] In rare cases, female sharks born in captivity that have never been exposed to male sharks have become pregant. Is this an example of asexual or sexual reproduction?

_____

_____

_____

_____
SC.7.L.16.3

d. ANSWER THE ESSENTIAL ? Why don't offspring always look like their parents?

_____

_____

_____

_____

_____

_____
SC.7.L.16.1, SC.7.L.16.2, SC.7.L.16.3

got it? ....

○ **I get it!** Now I know that organisms are equipped for survival in different ways as a result of_____

_____

_____

○ **I need extra help with** _____

Go to **MY SCIENCE COACH** online for help with this subject.
SC.7.L.16.3

10 Study Guide

Offspring inherit different forms of _____ called alleles from each parent. The physical appearance of the offspring depends on its combination of alleles, or _____.

LESSON 1 The Genetic Code

SC.7.L.16.1

🔑 The order of the nitrogen bases along a gene forms a genetic code that specifies what type of protein will be produced.

🔑 Because of the way the nitrogen bases pair up, the order of the bases in each new DNA strand matches the order in the original DNA strand.

Vocabulary
- nitrogen bases
- DNA replication

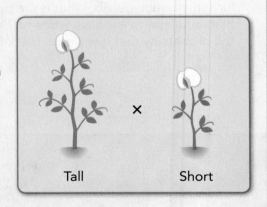

LESSON 2 What Is Heredity?

SC.7.L.16.1, SC.7.N.2.1

🔑 In all of his crosses, Mendel found that only one form of the trait appeared in the F_1 generation. However, in the F_2 generation, the "lost" form of the trait always reappeared in about one fourth of the plants.

🔑 An organism's traits are controlled by the alleles it inherits from its parents. Some alleles are dominant, while other alleles are recessive.

Vocabulary
- heredity • genetics • fertilization • purebred
- allele • dominant allele • recessive allele • hybrid

Tall   ×   Short

LESSON 3 Probability and Heredity

SC.7.L.16.2

🔑 In a genetic cross, the combination of alleles that parents can pass to an offspring is based on probability.

🔑 An organism's phenotype is its physical appearance, or visible traits. An organism's genotype is its genetic makeup, or alleles.

Vocabulary
- probability • Punnett square • pedigree
- phenotype • genotype • homozygous
- heterozygous

LESSON 4 Chromosomes and Inheritance

SC.7.L.16.1, SC.7.L.16.3, SC.7.N.1.5, SC.7.N.1.6

🔑 Genes pass from parents to their offspring on chromosomes. Meiosis produces sex cells that have half as many chromosomes as body cells.

🔑 DNA transfer through sexual reproduction requiring meiosis and asexual reproduction requiring mitosis equip organisms in different ways for survival.

Vocabulary
- meiosis

Review and Assessment

LESSON 1 The Genetic Code

1. DNA has four bases: A, C, G, and T. The base A always pairs with _____, and C always pairs with _____.

  a. A, C   **b.** C, G

  c. C, T   **d.** T, G

                                SC.7.L.16.1

2. The section of DNA within a chromosome that codes for a specific protein is called a(n)

  _____

                                SC.7.L.16.1

3. Draw Conclusions How does the pairing of the nitrogen bases in a DNA molecule make sure that a replicated strand is exactly the same as the original strand?

  _____

  _____

  _____

  _____

                                SC.7.L.16.1

LESSON 2 What Is Heredity?

4. Different forms of a gene are called

  a. alleles.   **b.** hybrids.

  c. genotypes.   **d.** chromosomes.

                                SC.7.L.16.1

5. _____ is the scientific study of heredity.

                                SC.7.L.16.1

6. Explain Mendel crossed two pea plants: one with green pods and one with yellow pods. The F_1 generation all had green pods. What color pods did the F_2 generation have? Explain your answer.

  _____

  _____

  _____

  _____

            SC.7.L.16.2, SC.7.N.2.1

LESSON 3 Probability and Heredity

7. Which of the following represents a heterozygous genotype?

  a. YY   **b.** yy

  c. $Y^H Y^H$ **d.** Yy

                                SC.7.L.16.2

8. An organism's _____ is the way its genotype is expressed.

                                SC.7.L.16.2

9. Make Models Fill in the Punnett square below to show a cross between two guinea pigs that are heterozygous for coat color. *B* is for black coat color, and *b* is for white coat color.

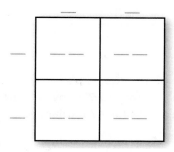

                                SC.7.L.16.2

10. Interpret Tables What is the probability that an offspring from the cross above has each of the following genotypes?

  BB _____

  Bb _____

  bb _____

                                SC.7.L.16.2

11. Apply Concepts What kind of cross might tell you if a black guinea pig is *BB* or *Bb*? Why?

  _____

  _____

  _____

                                SC.7.L.16.2

12. math! A garden has 80 pea plants. Of this total, 20 plants have short stems and 60 plants have tall stems. What percentage of the plants have short stems? What percentage have tall stems?

                                SC.7.L.16.2

LESSON 4 Chromosomes and Inheritance

13. Genes are carried from parents to offspring on structures called

   a. alleles.   **b.** chromosomes.

   c. phenotypes.   **d.** genotypes.

                                    SC.7.L.16.1

14. The process of _____ results in the formation of sex cells.

                                      SC.7.L.16.3

15. Summarize What did Walter Sutton discover about the relationship between allelles and chromosomes?

_____

_____

                                      SC.7.L.16.3

16. Calculate If an organism's body cells have 12 chromosomes, how many chromosomes will the sex cells have? Explain your answer.

_____

_____

_____

_____

                                      SC.7.L.16.3

17. Sequence What happens before meiosis?

_____

_____

                                      SC.7.L.16.3

18. Apply Concepts Use the events of meiosis to explain why a sex cell normally does not receive both chromosomes from a pair.

_____

_____

_____

                                      SC.7.L.16.3

19. **Write About It** Consider the following statement: *Organisms that reproduce asexually are at a higher risk of extinction than organisms that reproduce sexually.* Do you agree or disagree? Explain your answer.
                     SC.7.L.16.3

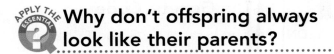

APPLY THE ESSENTIAL **Why don't offspring always look like their parents?**

20. In dogs, the allele for short hair (*A*) is dominant over the allele for long hair (*a*). Two short-haired dogs are the parents of a litter of eight puppies. Six puppies have short hair, and two have long hair. Draw two possible Punnett squares for a cross between two short-haired dogs. Circle the Punnet square that shows the correct cross for this litter. Then explain why this Punnet square shows the genotypes of the parents.

_____

_____

_____

_____

_____

_____

                         SC.7.L.16.1, SC.7.L.16.2

Florida Benchmarks Review

Circle the letter of the best answer.

1 The Punnett square below shows a cross between two pea plants, each with round seeds. What is the missing genotype in the empty square?

	R	R
R	RR	
r	Rr	Rr

A rr
B rR
C Rr
D RR

SC.7.L.16.2

2 Gregor Mendel's discoveries formed the foundation of

A meiosis.
B genetics.
C probability.
D the genetic code.

SC.7.L.16.1, SC.7.N.2.1

3 When DNA replicates, the new strand is _____ the original strand.

A similar to
B larger than
C different from
D identical to

SC.7.L.16.1

4 For a particular plant, leaf texture is either fuzzy or smooth. A purebred fuzzy plant is crossed with a purebred smooth plant. All offspring are smooth. Which sentence best describes the alleles for this trait?

A Fuzzy is dominant over smooth.
B Smooth is dominant over fuzzy.
C Both of the alleles are dominant.
D Both of the alleles are recessive.

SC.7.L.16.1

5 During _____, a cell divides to form two cells that have sets of chromosomes that are complete and identical to each other and to the parent cell.

A meiosis
B mitosis
C DNA replication
D fertilization

SC.7.L.16.3

6 One of the cells shown below is a parent cell about to undergo meiosis. Another cell is in the process of meiosis. A third cell is a sex cell that results from meiosis. Which answer lists the cells in the correct order from the start of meiosis to the end of meiosis?

F.  **G.** **H.**

A H, F, G   B H, G, F
C F, G, H   D G, F, H

HOW CAN SCIENTISTS IDENTIFY HUMAN REMAINS?

How can genetic information be used?

These forensic scientists are putting together the skeletons of war victims. They can determine the age, sex, height, and ancestry of each body by examining bones. But that does not identify who the person was. Other scientists work to determine the identities of the victims.

Develop Hypotheses How do you think a scientist might figure out a person's identity from bones?

_____

_____

_____

_____

_____

_____

▷ **UNTAMED SCIENCE** Watch the **Untamed Science** video to learn more about genetic technology.

Human Genetics and Genetic Technology

FLORIDA Next Generation Sunshine State Standards

Big Idea 2: SC.7.N.2.1
Big Idea 16: SC.7.L.16.1, SC.7.L.16.2, SC.7.L.16.3,
SC.7.L.16.4

Language Arts: LA.7.4.2.2, LA.7.2.2.3
Mathematics: MA.6.A.3.6
Health: HE.6.C.1.4

Check Your Understanding

1. Background Read the paragraph below and then answer the question.

Abdul has a white mouse named Pug. Both of Pug's parents had black fur, but they each had one **allele** for white fur and one allele for black fur. Because the **dominant allele** is for black fur, there was only a 25 percent **probability** that Pug would have white fur.

An **allele** is a different form of a gene.

The trait determined by a **dominant allele** always shows up in an organism if the allele is present.

Probability is a number that describes how likely it is that an event will occur.

• What is the probability that Pug's parents would have an offspring with black fur? _____

> **MY READING WEB** If you had trouble completing the question above, visit **My Reading Web** and type in *Human Genetics and Genetic Technology*.

Vocabulary Skill

High-Use Academic Words High-use academic words are words that are used frequently in classrooms. Look for the words below as you read this chapter.

Word	Definition	Example
normal	*adj.* usual; typical, expected	It is *normal* to feel nervous about going to a new school.
resistant	*adj.* capable of preventing something from happening	The fabric stays clean easily because it is *resistant* to stains.

LA.7.1.6.1

2. Quick Check Choose the word that best completes each sentence.

• Some bacteria are _____ to common antibiotic medicines, so they are not killed by them.

• A _____ body temperature in a human is about 37°C.

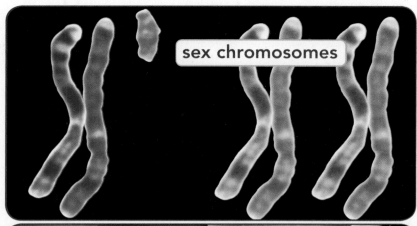

sex chromosomes

genetic disorder

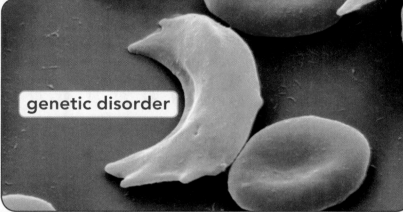

clone

genetic engineering

Chapter Preview

LESSON 1
- sex chromosomes
- sex-linked gene
- carrier
- ↻ Relate Cause and Effect
- △ Infer

LESSON 2
- genetic disorder
- pedigree
- karyotype
- ↻ Outline
- △ Make Models

LESSON 3
- clone
- genetic engineering
- gene therapy
- selective breeding
- hybridization
- inbreeding
- biotechnology
- ↻ Ask Questions
- △ Draw Conclusions

LESSON 4
- genome
- ethics
- ↻ Summarize
- △ Communicate

> VOCAB FLASH CARDS For extra help with vocabulary, visit **Vocab Flash Cards** and type in *Human Genetics and Genetic Technology.*

Human Inheritance

UNLOCK THE ESSENTIAL ?

🔑 **What Are Some Patterns of Human Inheritance?**
SC.7.L.16.1

🔑 **What Are the Functions of the Sex Chromosomes?**
SC.7.L.16.2, SC.7.L.16.3

my planeT DiaRY *for Florida*

BLOG

Posted by: Julian

Location: Rockledge, Florida

I have noticed that there are a lot of physical traits that run in my family. It seems like poor eyesight is common. Both sets of my grandparents have poor eyesight and wear glasses. Both of my parents have poor vision and here I am, yes, I too have to wear glasses. Genetics rules.

Write your answer below.
What characteristics do you have that resemble those of your relatives?

_____

_____

_____

_____

_____

▷ **PLANET DIARY** Go to **Planet Diary** to learn more about human inheritance.

 Lab zone ® Do the Inquiry Warm-Up *How Tall Is Tall?*

FLORIDA NGSSS

SC.7.L.16.1 Understand and explain that every organism requires a set of instructions that specifies its traits, that this hereditary information (DNA) contains genes located in the chromosomes of each cell, and that heredity is the passage of these instructions from one generation to another.

What Are Some Patterns of Human Inheritance?

Look at the other students in your classroom. Some people have curly hair; others have straight hair. Some people are tall, some are short, and many others are in between. You'll probably see eyes of many different colors, ranging from pale blue to dark brown. The different traits you see are determined by a variety of inheritance patterns. 🔑 **Some human traits are controlled by single genes with two alleles, and others by single genes with multiple alleles. Still other traits are controlled by many genes that act together.**

Vocabulary
- sex chromosomes • sex-linked gene • carrier

Skills
⟳ Reading: Relate Cause and Effect
△ Inquiry: Infer

Single Genes With Two Alleles

A number of human traits, such as a dimpled chin or a widow's peak, are controlled by a single gene with either a dominant or a recessive allele. These traits have two distinctly different physical appearances, or phenotypes.

Single Genes With Multiple Alleles

Some human traits are controlled by a single gene that has more than two alleles. Such a gene is said to have multiple alleles—three or more forms of a gene that code for a single trait. Even though a gene may have multiple alleles, a person can carry only two of those alleles. This is because chromosomes exist in pairs. Each chromosome in a pair carries only one allele for each gene. Recall that an organism's genetic makeup is its genotype. The physical characteristics that result are called the organism's phenotype.

Human blood type is controlled by a gene with multiple alleles. There are four main blood types—A, B, AB, and O. Three alleles control the inheritance of blood types. The allele for blood type A is written as I^A. The allele for blood type B is written as I^B. The allele for blood type A and the allele for blood type B are codominant. This means that both alleles for the gene are expressed equally. A person who inherits an I^A allele from one parent and an I^B allele from the other parent will have type AB blood. The allele for blood type O—written as i—is recessive. **Figure 1** shows the different allele combinations that result in each blood type.

FIGURE 1 ·······································
Inheritance of Blood Type
The table below shows which combinations of alleles result in each human blood type.

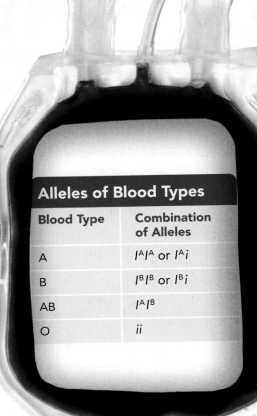

Alleles of Blood Types	
Blood Type	**Combination of Alleles**
A	$I^A I^A$ or $I^A i$
B	$I^B I^B$ or $I^B i$
AB	$I^A I^B$
O	ii

apply it!

Use what you have learned about blood types and **Figure 1** to answer the following questions.

❶ **Interpret Tables** Genotypes are listed in the (left/right) column of the table, while phenotypes are on the (left/right).

❷ △**Infer** Why are there more genotypes than phenotypes for blood types?

_____

_____

_____

_____

423

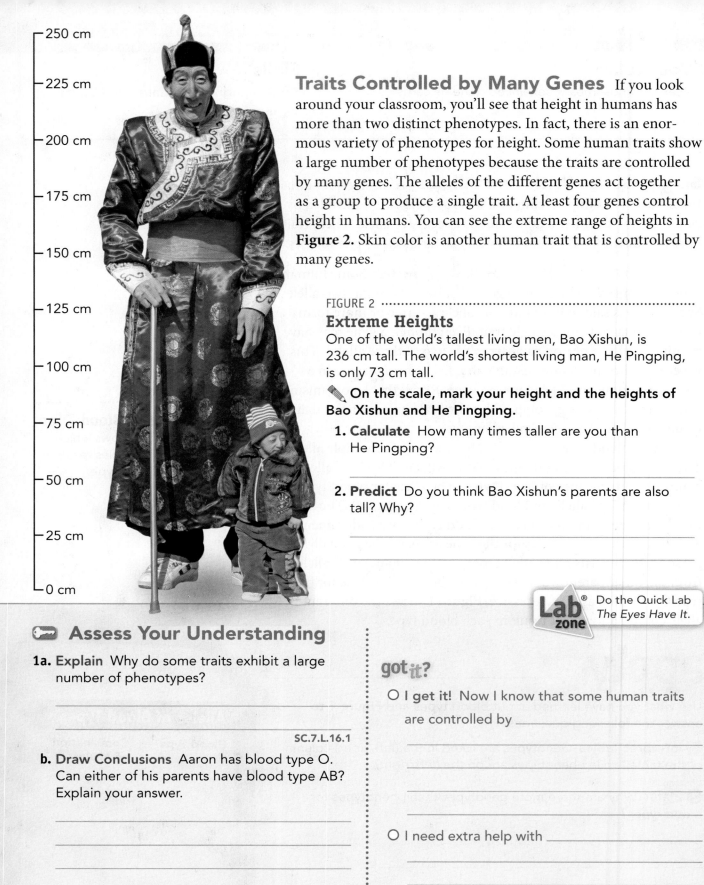

Traits Controlled by Many Genes

If you look around your classroom, you'll see that height in humans has more than two distinct phenotypes. In fact, there is an enormous variety of phenotypes for height. Some human traits show a large number of phenotypes because the traits are controlled by many genes. The alleles of the different genes act together as a group to produce a single trait. At least four genes control height in humans. You can see the extreme range of heights in **Figure 2**. Skin color is another human trait that is controlled by many genes.

FIGURE 2 ···

Extreme Heights

One of the world's tallest living men, Bao Xishun, is 236 cm tall. The world's shortest living man, He Pingping, is only 73 cm tall.

✎ **On the scale, mark your height and the heights of Bao Xishun and He Pingping.**

1. **Calculate** How many times taller are you than He Pingping?

_____

2. **Predict** Do you think Bao Xishun's parents are also tall? Why?

_____

_____

Lab zone ® Do the Quick Lab
The Eyes Have It.

🔑 Assess Your Understanding

1a. Explain Why do some traits exhibit a large number of phenotypes?

_____

_____

SC.7.L.16.1

b. Draw Conclusions Aaron has blood type O. Can either of his parents have blood type AB? Explain your answer.

_____

_____

_____

_____

_____

SC.7.L.16.1

got it?

O **I get it!** Now I know that some human traits are controlled by _____

_____

_____

_____

O **I need extra help with** _____

_____

Go to MY SCIENCE ⑤ COACH *online for help with this subject.*

SC.7.L.16.1

What Are the Functions of the Sex Chromosomes?

The body cells of humans contain 23 chromosome pairs, or 46 chromosomes. The **sex chromosomes** are one of the 23 pairs of chromosomes in each body cell. **The sex chromosomes carry genes that determine a person's gender as being either male or female. They also carry genes that determine other traits.**

Girl or Boy?
The sex chromosomes are the only chromosome pair that do not always match. Girls have two sex chromosomes that match. The two chromosomes are called X chromosomes. Boys have two sex chromosomes that do not match. They have an X chromosome and a Y chromosome. The Y chromosome is much smaller than the X chromosome. To show the size difference, the sex chromosomes in **Figure 3** have been stained and magnified.

Sex Chromosomes and Fertilization
When egg cells and sperm cells form, what happens to the sex chromosomes? Since both of a female's sex chromosomes are X chromosomes, all eggs carry one X chromosome. Males, however, have two different sex chromosomes. Therefore, half of a male's sperm cells carry an X chromosome, while half carry a Y chromosome.

When a sperm cell with an X chromosome fertilizes an egg, the egg has two X chromosomes. The fertilized egg will develop into a girl. When a sperm with a Y chromosome fertilizes an egg, the egg has one X chromosome and one Y chromosome. The fertilized egg will develop into a boy.

FIGURE 3 ·······································

Male or Female?
The father's chromosome determines the sex of his child.

✎ **Using the genotypes given for the mother and father, complete the Punnett square to show the possible genotypes and phenotypes of their child.**

1. **Determine** What is the probability that the child will be a girl? A boy?

   _____

   _____

2. **Interpret Diagrams** What sex will the child be if a sperm with a Y chromosome fertilizes an egg? _____

FLORIDA NGSSS

SC.7.L.16.2 Determine the probabilities for genotype and phenotype combinations using Punnett Squares and pedigrees.

SC.7.L.16.3 Compare and contrast the general processes of sexual reproduction requiring meiosis and asexual reproduction requiring mitosis.

X Chromosome

Y Chromosome

X Chromosomes

425

⟳ Relate Cause and Effect
Underline the cause of
sex-linked traits in males and
circle the effect of the traits.

Sex-Linked Genes The genes for some human traits are
carried on the sex chromosomes. Genes found on the X and Y
chromosomes are often called **sex-linked genes** because their
alleles are passed from parent to child on a sex chromosome. Traits
controlled by sex-linked genes are called sex-linked traits. One
sex-linked trait is red-green colorblindness. A person with this trait
cannot see the difference between red and green. Normal vision is
dominant, while colorblindness is recessive.

FIGURE 4 ··························
⟩ VIRTUAL LAB X and Y Chromosomes
The human X chromosome
is larger and carries more
genes than the human
Y chromosome.

Y Chromosome

Recall that a Y chromosome is smaller
than an X chromosome. Females have two
X chromosomes, but males have one
X chromosome and one Y chromosome.
These chromosomes have different genes.

X Chromosome

Most of the genes on the X chromosome
are not on the Y chromosome. So an
allele on an X chromosome may have no
corresponding allele on a Y chromosome.

Like other genes, sex-linked genes can have dominant and
recessive alleles. In females, a dominant allele on an X chromosome
will mask a recessive allele on the other X chromosome. But in
males, there is usually no matching allele on the Y chromosome to
mask the allele on the X chromosome. As a result, any allele on the
X chromosome—even a recessive allele—will produce the trait in
a male who inherits it. This means that males are more likely than
females to express a sex-linked trait that is controlled by a recessive
allele. Individuals with colorblindness may have difficulty seeing
the numbers in **Figure 5.** Test your vision below.

FIGURE 5 ··································
Colorblindness
Most colorblind individuals have
difficulty seeing red and green.

✎ Communicate Working with a
partner, look at the circles. Write the
number you see in the space below
each circle.

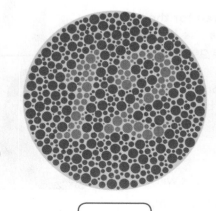

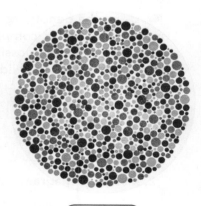

Inheritance of Colorblindness Colorblindness is a trait controlled by a recessive allele on the X chromosome. Many more males than females have red-green colorblindness. You can understand why this is the case by examining the Punnett square in **Figure 6.** Both parents have normal color vision. Notice that the mother carries the dominant allele for normal vision (X^C) and the recessive allele for colorblindness (X^c). A **carrier** is a person who has one recessive allele for a trait and one dominant allele. A carrier of a trait controlled by a recessive allele does not express the trait. However, the carrier can pass the recessive allele on to his or her offspring. In the case of sex-linked traits, only females can be carriers because they are the only ones who can carry two alleles for the trait.

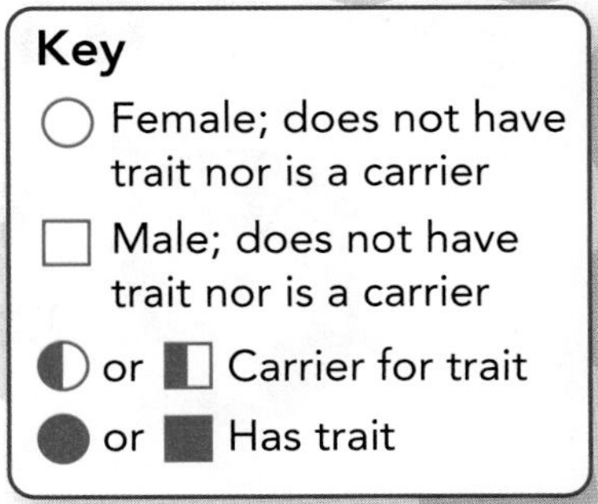

Key
- ○ Female; does not have trait nor is a carrier
- ☐ Male; does not have trait nor is a carrier
- ◑ or ◪ Carrier for trait
- ● or ■ Has trait

Father
normal vision

☐

FIGURE 6 ·····················
Colorblindness Punnett Square
Red-green colorblindness is a sex-linked trait.

✎ **Using the parents' information and the key, complete the Punnett square.**

1. **Identify** Complete the Punnett square by filling in the child's genotype, sex, and phenotype. For each child, draw the correct shape, and color it in to match the key.

2. **Calculate** What is the probability that this couple will have a colorblind child?

   _____

3. **Apply Concepts** What allele combination would a daughter need to inherit to be colorblind?

   _____

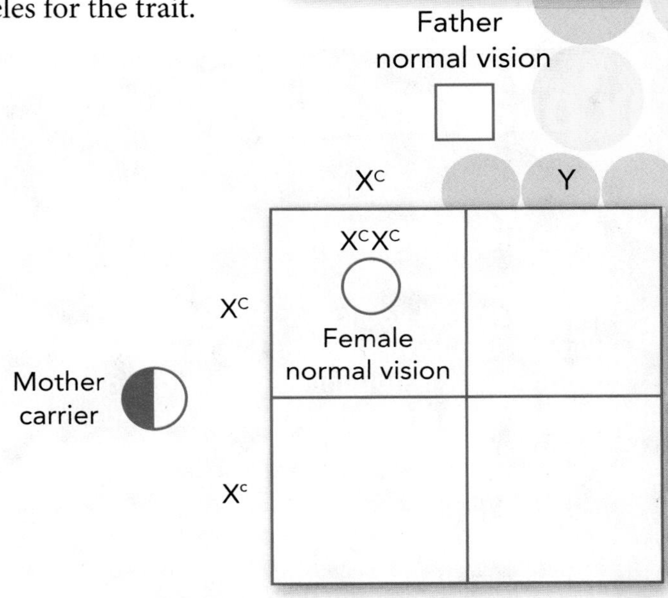

X^C Y

	$X^C X^C$ ○ Female normal vision	
X^C		
X^c		

Mother carrier ◑

🔑 Assess Your Understanding

2a. Review What is the sex of a person who is a carrier for colorblindness? _____

SC.7.L.16.2, SC.7.L.16.3

b. CHALLENGE Mary and her mother are both colorblind. Is Mary's father colorblind, too? How do you know?

_____

_____

_____

_____

SC.7.L.16.2

got it?

○ **I get it!** Now I know that the functions of the sex chromosomes are _____

_____

_____

○ **I need extra help with** _____

_____

Go to **my science** 🔊 **coach** *online for help with this subject.*

SC.7.L.16.2, SC.7.L.16.3

Human Genetic Disorders

UNLOCK THE ESSENTIAL

🔑 **How Are Genetic Disorders Inherited in Humans?**
SC.7.L.16.2, LA.7.4.2.2, HE.6.C.1.4

🔑 **How Are Genetic Disorders Traced, Diagnosed, and Treated?**
SC.7.L.16.2

my planeT DiARY

Doggie Diagnosis

Maybe you have a dog or know someone who does. Did you know that dogs and humans can have some of the same health problems? It is not uncommon for dogs to have cancer, diabetes, allergies, epilepsy, and eye diseases. Scientists are studying the genes and genetic mutations that cause diseases in dogs in the hopes of better understanding human diseases. Most diseases in dogs are caused by a mutation on one gene. In humans, the mutations can be on multiple genes. The genes that cause diseases in dogs are much easier to find than those in humans. So far, scientists are looking into the genes that cause blindness, cancer, and spinal cord disorders in dogs.

German shepherds can have a form of cancer similar to breast cancer in humans.

Dachshunds and humans can both suffer from blindness.

DISCOVERY

Communicate Discuss the questions with a classmate. Then write your answers.

1. Why are scientists studying dog genes to understand human diseases?

_____

_____

_____

_____

2. In what other ways could studying dog diseases be beneficial?

_____

_____

_____

_____

_____

_____

▶ **PLANET DIARY** Go to **Planet Diary** to learn more about human genetic disorders.

Golden retrievers can have cancer that affects the blood vessels.

Lab zone® Do the Inquiry Warm-Up *How Many Chromosomes?*

Vocabulary
- genetic disorder
- pedigree
- karyotype

Skills
- Reading: Outline
- Inquiry: Make Models

How Are Genetic Disorders Inherited in Humans?

Many of the athletes who compete in the Special Olympics have disabilities that result from genetic disorders. A **genetic disorder** is an abnormal condition that a person inherits through genes or chromosomes. 🔑 **Some genetic disorders are caused by mutations in the DNA of genes. Other disorders are caused by changes in the overall structure or number of chromosomes.** In this lesson, you will learn about some common genetic disorders.

Cystic Fibrosis Cystic fibrosis is a genetic disorder in which the body produces abnormally thick mucus in the lungs and intestines. The thick mucus fills the lungs, making it hard for the affected person to breathe. Cystic fibrosis occurs when two mutated alleles are inherited, one from each parent. The mutation causes three bases to be removed from a DNA molecule.

Sickle-Cell Disease Sickle-cell disease is caused by a mutation that affects hemoglobin. Hemoglobin is a protein in red blood cells that carries oxygen. The red blood cells of people with the disease have a sickle, or crescent, shape. Sickle-shaped red blood cells cannot carry as much oxygen as normal cells and also clog blood vessels. The allele for the sickle-cell trait (*S*) is codominant with the normal allele (*A*). A person with one normal allele and one sickle-cell allele (*AS*) will produce both normal hemoglobin and abnormal hemoglobin. This person usually does not have symptoms of the disease. He or she has enough normal hemoglobin to carry oxygen to cells. A person with two sickle-cell alleles (*SS*) will have the disease.

FLORIDA NGSSS

SC.7.L.16.2 Determine the probabilities for genotype and phenotype combinations using Punnett Squares and pedigrees.

LA.7.4.2.2 The student will record information related to a topic.

HE.6.C.1.4 Recognize how heredity can affect personal health.

FIGURE 1 ······························
Sickle-Cell Disease
In a person with sickle-cell disease, red blood cells can become sickle-shaped instead of round.

✎ **Determine** A man has sickle-cell disease. His wife does not have the disease, but is heterozygous for the sickle-cell trait. Use the parents' information to fill in the Punnett square. What is the probability that their child will have sickle-cell disease?

Outline After you read this section, make an outline on a separate sheet of paper that includes the different types of genetic disorders. Use the red headings to help you organize your outline. **LA.7.4.2.2**

Hemophilia Hemophilia is a genetic disorder in which a person's blood clots very slowly or not at all. People with the disorder do not produce enough of one of the proteins needed for normal blood clotting. The danger of internal bleeding from small bumps and bruises is very high. Hemophilia is caused by a recessive allele on the X chromosome. Because hemophilia is a sex-linked disorder, it occurs more frequently in males than in females.

Down Syndrome People with Down syndrome have an extra copy of chromosome 21 in every cell. A person with Down syndrome has three copies of chromosome 21 instead of two. Down syndrome most often occurs when chromosomes fail to separate properly during meiosis, when sex cells (egg and sperm) form. People with Down syndrome have some degree of mental retardation. Heart defects are also common, but can be treated.

FIGURE 2

INTERACTIVE ART **Hemophilia**

Hemophilia occurs more often in males than in females.

Cross a carrier female, X^HX^h, with a healthy male, X^HY, and fill in the Punnett square.

1. **Calculate** What percentage of the offspring
   would be normal? ______
   would be carriers? ______
   would have hemophilia? ______
2. CHALLENGE To have a daughter with hemophilia, the father must have the disorder (X^hY) and the mother must have one of two genotypes. What are they?
   ______

	___	___
___	___	___
___	___	___

Lab zone® Do the Quick Lab *What Went Wrong?*

Assess Your Understanding

1a. Explain Which of the two major causes of genetic disorders is responsible for Down syndrome?

______

______

SC.7.L.16.2, HE.6.C.1.4

b. Infer Why is hemophilia more common in males?

______

______

______

SC.7.L.16.2, HE.6.C.1.4

got it?

O **I get it!** Now I know that the two major causes of genetic disorders are ______

______

O I need extra help with ______

Go to **MY SCIENCE COACH** *online for help with this subject.* SC.7.L.16.4, HE.6.C.1.4

How Are Genetic Disorders Traced, Diagnosed, and Treated?

FLORIDA NGSSS

SC.7.L.16.2 Determine the probabilities for genotype and phenotype combinations using Punnett Squares and pedigrees.

Years ago, only Punnett squares were used to predict whether a child might have a genetic disorder. 🔑 **Today, doctors use tools such as pedigrees, karyotypes, and genetic testing to trace and diagnose genetic disorders. People with genetic disorders are helped through medical care, education, and job training.**

Pedigrees Suppose that you are interested in tracing the occurrence of a trait through several generations of a family. What would you do? A **pedigree** is a chart or "family tree" that tracks which members of a family have a particular trait. The trait in a pedigree can be an ordinary trait, such as eye color, or a genetic disorder. The pedigree shown below is for albinism, a condition in which a person's skin, hair, and eyes lack normal coloring.

apply it!

This pedigree shows the inheritance of the allele for albinism in three generations of a family.

❶ Interpret Diagrams Circle the symbol in the pedigree that represents an albino male.

Key
- ○ Female; does not have trait nor is a carrier
- □ Male; does not have trait nor is a carrier
- ◑ or ◧ Carrier for trait
- ● or ■ Has trait

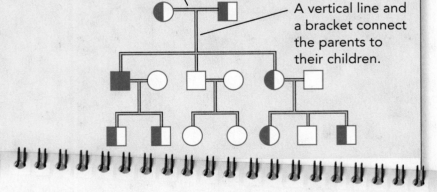

A horizontal line connecting a male and a female represents a marriage.

A vertical line and a bracket connect the parents to their children.

❷ Make Models Using what you have learned about pedigrees and pedigree symbols, construct a possible two-generation pedigree for sickle-cell disease, starting with parents who are both carriers, AS × AS.

431

Karyotypes To detect a chromosomal disorder such as Down syndrome, doctors examine karyotypes. A **karyotype** (KA ree uh typ) is a picture of all the chromosomes in a person's cell. Look at **Figure 3.** As you can see, the chromosomes in a karyotype are arranged in pairs. A karyotype can reveal whether a person has the correct number of chromosomes in his or her cells.

FIGURE 3 ···

Karyotypes

Look at the karyotypes below. One is a normal karyotype and the other is an abnormal karyotype.

✎ **Working with a classmate, compare the two karyotypes.**

1. **Interpret Photos** What numbered set of chromosomes are the most different between the karyotypes? _____

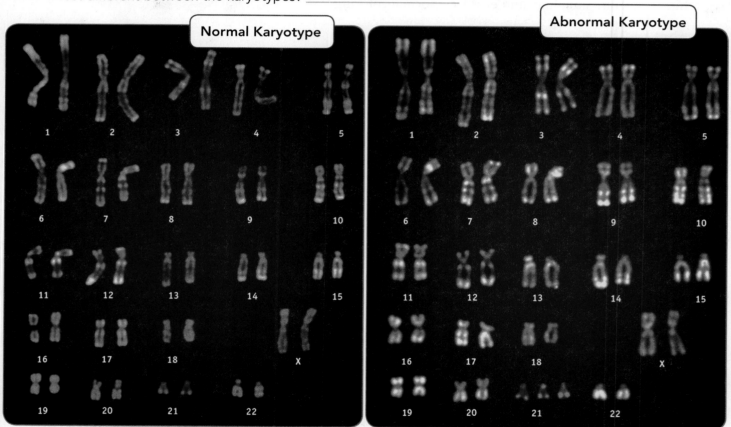

2. **Draw Conclusions** What can you conclude about the individual with the abnormal karyotype? Use evidence to support your answer.

_____

_____

_____

_____

Genetic Counseling

A couple that has a family history of a genetic disorder may turn to a genetic counselor for advice. Genetic counselors help couples understand their chances of having a child with a particular genetic disorder. Genetic counselors also help couples prepare for having children with a disorder. Karyotypes, pedigree charts, and Punnett squares assist genetic counselors in their work.

With advances in technology, new tests have been developed to screen for genetic disorders. Genetic tests examine genes, DNA, enzymes, and proteins to see if an individual has a genetic disorder or carries a gene for a genetic disorder. Whether or not the person develops the disease can also depend on many other genetic factors, environmental conditions, and lifestyle.

Dealing With Genetic Disorders

People with genetic disorders face serious challenges, but they can be helped. Medical treatments help people with the symptoms of some disorders. For example, physical therapy helps remove mucus from the lungs of people with cystic fibrosis. People with sickle-cell disease take folic acid, a vitamin, to help their bodies manufacture red blood cells. Because of education and job training programs, adults with Down syndrome can find work in banks, restaurants, and other places. Most genetic disorders do not prevent people from living active, productive lives.

did you know?

Malaria is an infectious disease that is transmitted to people when they are bitten by an infected mosquito. However, people who have the gene that causes sickle-cell disease are less likely to develop malaria. While most cases of malaria originate overseas, a few cases have originated from Florida mosquitoes.

FIGURE 4

Genetic Disorders

These athletes have Down syndrome, a genetic disorder.

✎ **List** **Name two types of programs that benefit individuals with Down syndrome.**

_____

_____

_____

Lab zone Do the Quick Lab Family Puzzle.

🔑 Assess Your Understanding

got it? ....

○ I get it! Now I know that genetic disorders are traced, diagnosed, and treated by _____

_____

○ I need extra help with _____

Go to MY SCIENCE 🔵 COACH *online for help with this subject.*

SC.7.L.16.2

Advances in Genetics

🔑 **How Can Organisms Be Produced With Desired Traits?**
SC.7.L.16.4, MA.6.A.3.6

🔑 **What Is the Impact of Biotechnology?**
SC.7.L.16.4

MY PLANET DIARY

FUN FACT

Zorses, Zonies, and Zedonks

Most people can tell the difference between a zebra and a horse. But would you be able to tell the difference among a zorse, a zony, and a zedonk? All three types of animals are zebroids, or zebra hybrids. These animals result when a zebra mates with a horse, a pony, or a donkey. Zebroids do not usually occur in nature. They generally result when people cross them on purpose. People may have first crossed zebras and horses in an effort to develop disease-resistant transportation animals for use in Africa. Zebras are resistant to African sleeping sickness. It was hoped that zorses, the offspring of zebras and horses, would have this resistance.

Communicate Discuss these questions with a classmate. Write your answers below.

1. Why may zebras and horses have been first crossed by people?

_____

_____

2. If zebras and horses do not usually mate in nature, should people intentionally cross them? Why or why not?

_____

_____

_____

_____

▶ **PLANET DIARY** Go to **Planet Diary** to learn more about advances in genetics.

 Lab zone® Do the Inquiry Warm-Up *What Do Fingerprints Reveal?*

Vocabulary
- clone • genetic engineering • gene therapy
- selective breeding • hybridization • inbreeding
- biotechnology

Skills
↻ Reading: Ask Questions
△ Inquiry: Draw Conclusions

How Can Organisms Be Produced With Desired Traits?

Unless you are an identical twin, your DNA is different from everyone else's. Because of advances in genetics, DNA evidence can show many things, such as family relationships or the ability to produce organisms with desirable traits. 🔑 **Cloning, genetic engineering, and artificial selection are three different methods for developing organisms with desired traits.**

Cloning For some organisms, such as the dog shown in **Figure 1,** a technique called cloning can be used to produce off-spring with desired traits. A **clone** is an organism that has exactly the same genes as the organism from which it was produced. It isn't hard to clone some kinds of plants, such as African violets. Just cut a stem from one plant and put the stem in soil. Water it, and soon you will have a whole new plant. The new plant is genetically identical to the plant from which the stem was cut.

Genetic Engineering Geneticists have developed another powerful technique for producing organisms with desired traits. In this process, called **genetic engineering,** genes from one organism are transferred into the DNA of another organism. Genetic engineering can produce medicines and improve food crops.

FLORIDA NGSSS

SC.7.L.16.4 Recognize and explore the impact of biotechnology (cloning, genetic engineering, artificial selection) on the individual, society and the environment.

MA.6.A.3.6 Construct and analyze tables, graphs, and equations to describe linear functions and other simple relations.

FIGURE 1 ···

Cloning
This puppy, Lancelot Encore, is thought to be the first commercially cloned puppy in the United States. His owners paid $155,000 to have him cloned in South Korea.

✎ **Make Judgments** Would you pay $155,000 to clone a pet? Why or why not?

_____

_____

_____

_____

FIGURE 2 ....

Genetic Engineering

Scientists use genetic engineering to create bacterial cells that produce important human proteins such as insulin.

✏️ **Relate Text and Visuals** How does a human insulin gene become part of a bacterium's plasmid?

_____

_____

_____

_____

_____

_____

_____

❶ Small rings of DNA, or plasmids, can be found in some bacterial cells.

❷ Scientists remove the plasmid. An enzyme cuts open the plasmid and removes the human insulin gene from its chromosome.

❸ The human insulin gene attaches to the open ends of the plasmid to form a closed ring.

❹ Some bacterial cells take up the plasmids that have the insulin gene.

❺ When the cells reproduce, the new cells will contain copies of the "engineered" plasmid. The foreign gene directs the cells to produce human insulin.

Genetic Engineering in Bacteria One type of bacterium is genetically engineered to produce a human protein called insulin. Many people with diabetes need insulin injections. Bacteria have a single DNA molecule in the cytoplasm. Some bacterial cells also contain small circular pieces of DNA called plasmids. You can see how scientists insert the DNA for the human insulin gene into the plasmid of a bacterium in **Figure 2.** Once the gene is inserted into the plasmid, the bacterial cell and all of its offspring will contain this human gene. As a result, the bacteria produce the protein that the human gene codes for—in this case, insulin. Because bacteria can reproduce quickly, large amounts of insulin can be produced in a short time.

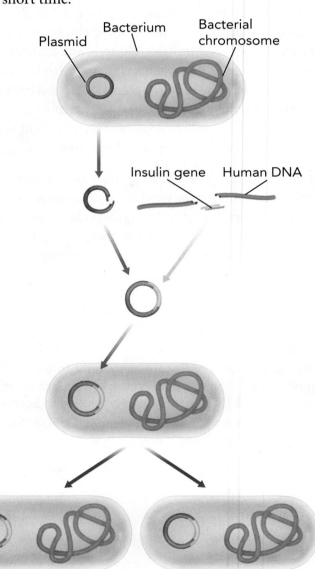

Genetic Engineering in Other Organisms

Scientists can also use genetic engineering techniques to insert genes into animals. For example, human genes can be inserted into the cells of cows. The cows then produce milk containing the human protein coded by the gene. Scientists have used this technique to produce the blood-clotting protein needed by people with hemophilia.

Genes have also been inserted into the cells of plants, such as tomatoes and rice. Some of the genes enable the plants to survive in cold temperatures or in poor soil. Other genetically engineered crops can resist insect pests or contain more nutrients.

Gene Therapy Someday it may be possible to use genetic engineering to correct some genetic disorders in humans. This process, called gene therapy, will involve inserting copies of a gene directly into a person's cells. For example, doctors may be able to treat hemophilia by replacing the defective allele on the X chromosome. The inserted gene would provide the body with the correct instructions to clot blood normally.

Concerns About Genetic Engineering

Some people are concerned about the long-term effects of genetic engineering. For example, some people think that genetically engineered crops may not be entirely safe. People fear that these crops may harm the environment or cause health problems in humans. To address such concerns, scientists are studying the effects of genetic engineering.

FIGURE 3 ·······························

▶ **ART IN MOTION** **Glow Cats**
A fluorescent protein was added to the cells of the cat below. This protein allows the cat to glow red when exposed to ultraviolet light. The cat above lacks this protein.

✏ Identify a Need Describe a problem that could be solved by genetic engineering in plants or animals.

_____

_____

_____

_____

_____

Artificial Selection

The process of artificially selecting organisms with desired traits to be parents of the next generation is called **selective breeding.** Thousands of years ago, in what is now Mexico, the food that we call corn was developed in this way. Every year, farmers saved seeds from the healthiest plants that produced the best food. In the spring, they planted only those seeds. This process was repeated over and over. In time, farmers developed plants that produced better corn. People have used selective breeding with many types of plants and animals. Two techniques for selective breeding are hybridization and inbreeding.

Hybridization

In **hybridization** (hy brid ih ZAY shun), breeders cross two genetically different individuals. Recall that a hybrid organism has two different alleles for a trait. The hybrid organism that results is bred to have the best traits from both parents. For example, a farmer might cross corn that produces many kernels with corn that is resistant to disease. The farmer is hoping to produce a hybrid corn plant with both of the desired traits. Roses and other types of flowers are also commonly crossed.

apply it!

Since the late eighteenth century, gardeners and plant breeders have used hybridization to develop roses with certain characteristics.

❶ Observe Look at each rose below. One characteristic for each flower is given to you. List any other observable characteristics you see.

❷ Draw Conclusions Based on the characteristics of the two roses, draw with colored pencils or describe what you think the hybrid offspring will look like. Name the flower and list its characteristics.

Parent A

fragrant

_____

_____

Parent B

survives cold temperatures

_____

_____

Hybrid name:_____

_____

_____

_____

Inbreeding The technique of **inbreeding** involves crossing two individuals that have similar desirable characteristics. Suppose a male and a female golden retriever are both friendly and have the same coloring. Their offspring will probably also have those qualities. Inbreeding produces organisms that are genetically very similar. When inbred organisms are mated, the chance of their offspring inheriting two recessive alleles increases. This can lead to genetic disorders. For example, inherited hip problems are common in golden retrievers and other types of inbred dogs.

do the math!

Changing Rice Production

This data table shows how worldwide rice production changed between 1965 and 2005. New hybrid varieties of rice plants are one factor that has affected the amount of rice produced.

1 Graph Plot the data from the table and draw a line graph.

2 Interpret Data What is the approximate difference between rice production in 1965 and 2005? _____

3 CHALLENGE What other factors might help account for the difference in rice production between 1965 and 2005?

_____

_____

MA.6.A.3.6

Year	Yield
1965	2.05
1970	2.36
1975	2.5
1980	2.75
1985	3.23
1990	3.54
1995	3.69
2000	3.91
2005	4.08

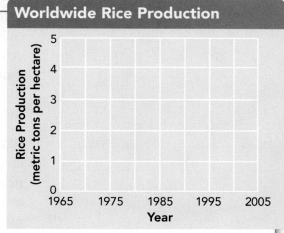

Worldwide Rice Production

Rice Production (metric tons per hectare) vs. Year

Do the Quick Lab
Selective Breeding.

🔑 Assess Your Understanding

1a. Identify The technique of crossing two individuals with similar characteristics is (inbreeding/hybridization).

SC.7.L.16.4

b. Explain Why are identical twins not clones according to the text definition?

_____

_____

SC.7.L.16.4

got it? ··

○ **I get it!** Now I know that the three ways of producing organisms with desired traits are _____

_____

○ **I need extra help with** _____

Go to **MY SCIENCE** 🅢 **COACH** *online for help with this subject.*

SC.7.L.16.4

FLORIDA NGSSS

SC.7.L.16.4 Recognize and explore the impact of biotechnology (cloning, genetic engineering, artificial selection) on the individual, society and the environment.

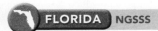

What Is the Impact of Biotechnology?

When scientists change or alter the genetic makeup of an organism, they are using biotechnology. **Biotechnology** is the application of a technological process, invention, or method to living organisms. Inbreeding, hybridization, cloning, and genetic engineering are all examples of biotechnology. **Individuals, society, and the environment can all benefit from biotechnology. But, just like all new technologies, biotechnology can also pose some risks.**

Ask Questions How would society be different without the development of biotechnology?

____

____

____

____

____

____

Impacts on Individuals Biotechnology allows scientists to learn about and develop treatments for human diseases. Genetically engineered animals could produce drugs or proteins that could be useful in medicine. DNA testing can be used to predict an individual's chances of developing certain inheritable diseases. With this knowledge, a person can adjust his or her lifestyle to counteract the effects of the diseases.

Impacts on Society The biotechnology industry has created many new jobs, especially in the medical and agricultural fields. Some biotechnological medical work could result in cheaper medicine. Genetically engineered plants can taste better and have more nutrients, but some fear that they can cause health problems in humans. Some plants are resistant to herbicides, chemicals that kill weeds. Other plants are insect resistant and don't need insecticide. Plants that have these resistances reduce the chance of chemicals getting into the food supply, where they could make people sick. Some genetically engineered crops grow faster and produce larger harvests. This reduces the amount of land needed to grow crops. It also helps to conserve soil and water. As a result, food prices could be lowered.

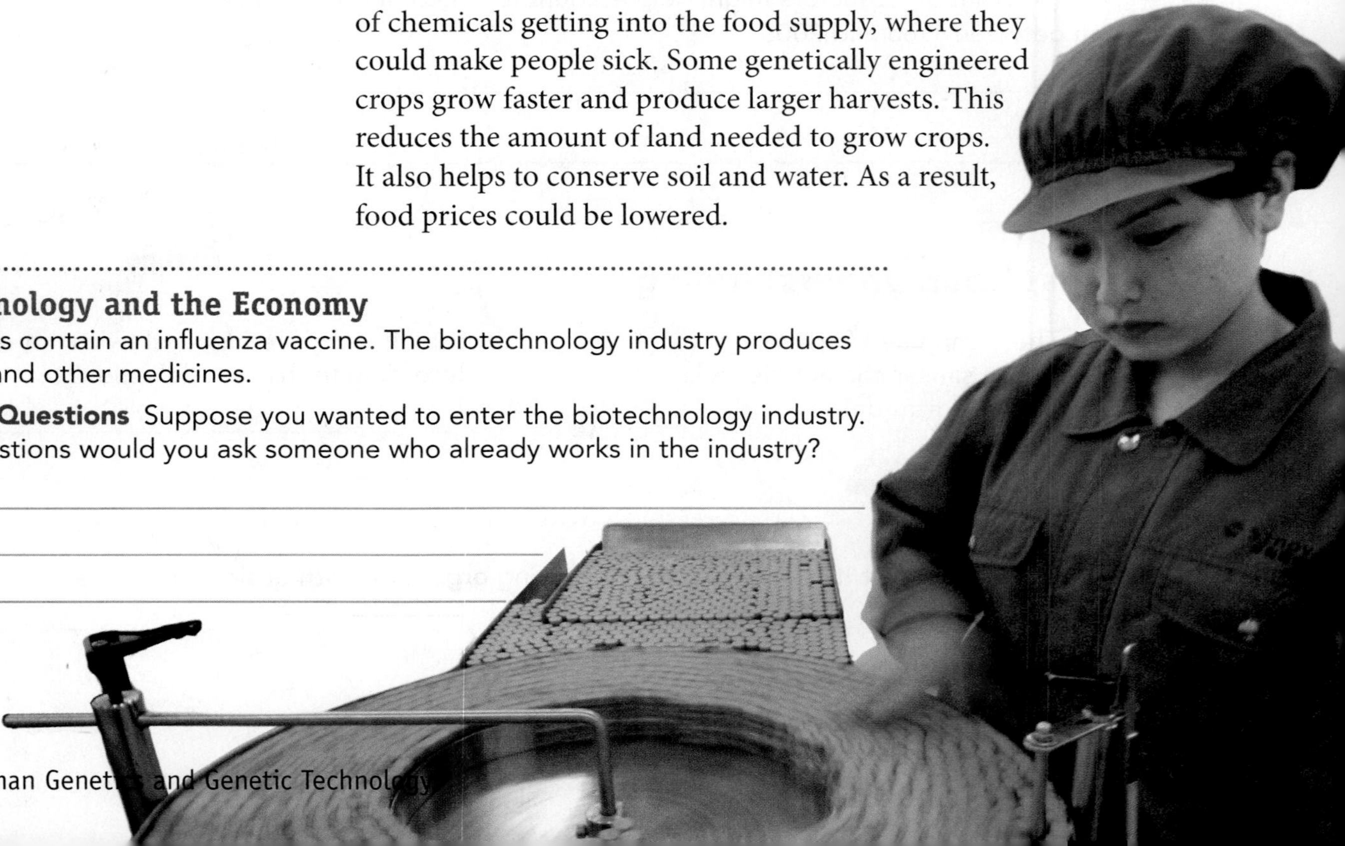

FIGURE 4

Biotechnology and the Economy

These vials contain an influenza vaccine. The biotechnology industry produces vaccines and other medicines.

Pose Questions Suppose you wanted to enter the biotechnology industry. What questions would you ask someone who already works in the industry?

____

____

____

Impacts on the Environment Many of these agricultural advancements also impact the environment. Genetically engineered, insect-resistant plants could harm beneficial insects. Such plants could affect the number and types of living organisms found on Earth. Some people think that genetically engineered plants could also harm the environment. However, some of the crops need less land, water, and pesticides. As a result, farmers can conserve resources and reduce the chemicals that get released into the environment. Scientists continue to study the effects of genetic engineering to determine its overall impact on the environment.

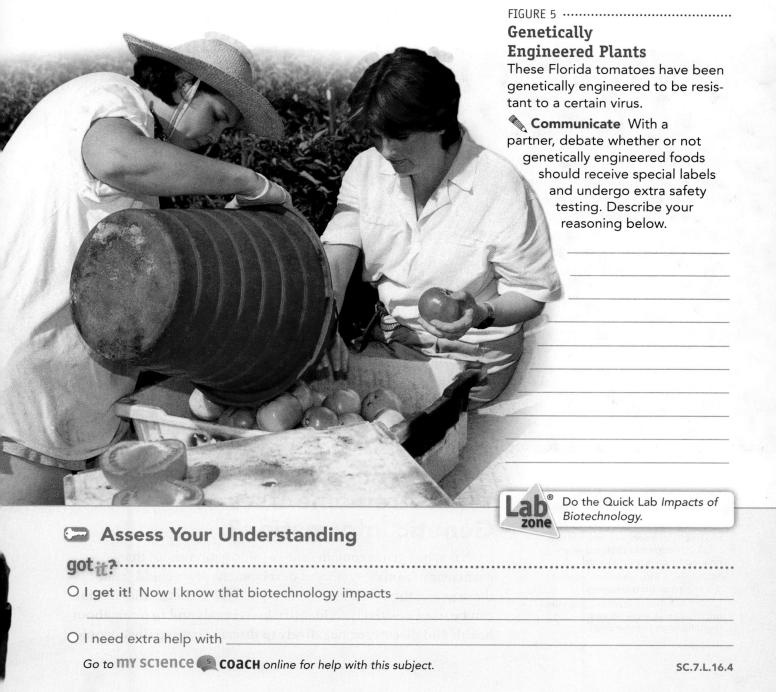

FIGURE 5 ·······························

Genetically Engineered Plants

These Florida tomatoes have been genetically engineered to be resistant to a certain virus.

✎ **Communicate** With a partner, debate whether or not genetically engineered foods should receive special labels and undergo extra safety testing. Describe your reasoning below.

_____

_____

_____

_____

_____

_____

_____

_____

_____

Lab zone ® Do the Quick Lab *Impacts of Biotechnology.*

🔑 **Assess Your Understanding**

got it? ·······································

O **I get it!** Now I know that biotechnology impacts _____

_____

O **I need extra help with** _____

Go to **my science COACH** *online for help with this subject.*

SC.7.L.16.4

Using Genetic Information

UNLOCK THE
ESSENTIAL
?

🗝 **What Are Some Uses of Genetic Information?**
SC.7.N.2.1, SC.7.L.16.4, LA.7.2.2.3

my planet diary

TECHNOLOGY

Freedom Fighters

DNA technology saves lives, and not just through medicine. Since 1992, hundreds of innocent people have been freed from prison—some from death row—thanks to DNA testing. The Innocence Project is an organization that uses DNA testing to free prisoners who were wrongfully convicted. First, a sample of DNA is obtained from evidence saved from the crime scene. Then, a sample is taken from the prisoner. Laboratory procedures allow scientists to compare the two samples. If the prisoner's DNA is different from the DNA at the crime scene, the evidence may help free the prisoner.

Infer If the DNA from the crime scene matches the DNA from the prisoner, what might that suggest?

_____

_____

_____

_____

_____

_____

▷ **PLANET DIARY** Go to **Planet Diary** to learn more about using genetic information.

Labzone
Do the Inquiry Warm-Up
Using Genetic Information.

What Are Some Uses of Genetic Information?

Each person's genes contain unique information about that particular person's growth and development. If we could "read" those genes, think of all we could learn! 🗝 **Genetic information can be used positively to identify individuals and to learn about health and disease, or negatively to discriminate against people.**

Vocabulary
- genome   - ethics

Skills
Reading: Summarize
Inquiry: Communicate

Human Genome Project Imagine trying to crack a code that is six billion letters long. That's exactly what scientists working on the Human Genome Project did. An organism's full set of DNA is called its **genome.** The main goal of the Human Genome Project was to identify the DNA sequence of the entire human genome. In 2003, the project was completed. Scientists continue to research the functions of the tens of thousands of human genes.

DNA Fingerprinting DNA technology used in the Human Genome Project can also identify people and show whether people are related. DNA from a person's cells is broken down into small pieces, or fragments. Selected fragments are used to produce a pattern called a DNA fingerprint. Except for identical twins, no two people have exactly the same DNA fingerprint.

Genetic "fingerprints" can tie a person to the scene of a crime or prevent the wrong person from going to jail. They also can be used to identify skeletal remains. Today, soldiers and sailors give blood and saliva samples so their DNA fingerprints can be saved. DNA records can be used to identify the bodies of unknown soldiers or civilians.

apply it!

DNA fingerprints are stored in national DNA databases such as the Combined DNA Index System (CODIS). Databases contain the genetic information from crime scenes, convicted offenders, and missing persons. Law enforcement uses these databases to see if the DNA they have collected matches a known sample.

Communicate Discuss the following statement with a partner. Identify the pros and cons related to the statement.
Each citizen of the United States should have his or her DNA fingerprint added to the national databases.

Pros: _____

_____

Cons: _____

_____

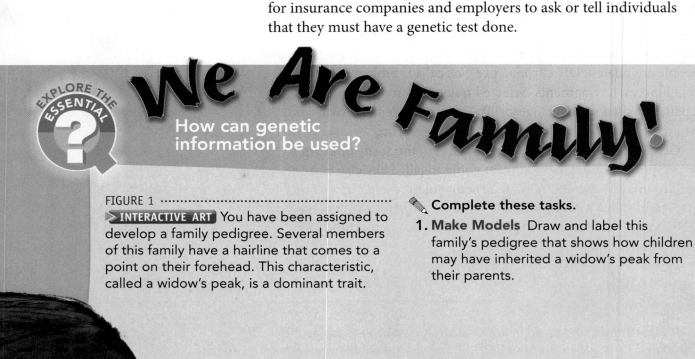

Summarize What is the main purpose of the Genetic Information Nondiscrimination Act? **LA.7.2.2.3**

Genetic Discrimination As it becomes easier to obtain genetic information, there are concerns about who can access that information. There are concerns about how it can be used, too. For example, soldiers provide the government with a DNA sample for identification. It could be possible for the government to use their DNA in other ways such as in criminal cases or paternity suits. **Ethics** is the study of principles about what is right and wrong, fair and unfair. Using genetic information in an ethical way means using it in a way that is fair and just.

The Genetic Information Nondiscrimination Act (GINA) was signed into law in 2008. This act makes it illegal for health insurance companies and employers to discriminate against individuals based on genetic information. It also makes it illegal for insurance companies and employers to ask or tell individuals that they must have a genetic test done.

EXPLORE THE ESSENTIAL ?

We Are Family!

How can genetic information be used?

FIGURE 1

> **INTERACTIVE ART** You have been assigned to develop a family pedigree. Several members of this family have a hairline that comes to a point on their forehead. This characteristic, called a widow's peak, is a dominant trait.

Complete these tasks.

1. **Make Models** Draw and label this family's pedigree that shows how children may have inherited a widow's peak from their parents.

Genetic Privacy Doctors are expected to protect patients' privacy by not revealing their medical information. Patients' medical records may include information such as their medical history and their family's medical history. This information could indicate if a patient is at risk for developing a disease or mental illness. Details about a person's lifestyle may also be included in medical records. Doctors may record if a person drinks alcohol, smokes, or participates in sports that are dangerous.

If a patient has a genetic condition, the patient's relatives are likely at risk, too. Should other family members have the right to know? Or should a patient's medical records be kept private?

2. **⟳ Summarize** What tools and techniques would you use if you wanted to know what your chances were of inheriting a genetic disease from a family member?

_____
_____
_____
_____
_____

3. **Evaluate the Impact on Society** If you learn that you have inherited a particular trait or genetic disease, who would you want to know? For each group of people listed, mark whether or not you think they should have the right to access your personal genetic information. Then explain why in the space below.

Immediate family members   Yes / No

_____
_____
_____

Your principal and teachers   Yes / No

_____
_____
_____

Do the Quick Lab
Extraction in Action.

🗝 Assess Your Understanding

1a. Define What is a genome?

_____
_____

SC.7.L.16.4

b. [CHALLENGE] Do you think it is ethical for doctors to share a patient's medical records? Explain.

_____
_____
_____
_____
_____
_____

SC.7.L.16.4

c. ANSWER THE ESSENTIAL ? How can genetic information be used?

_____
_____
_____
_____
_____
_____

SC.7.N.2.1, SC.7.L.16.4

got it? ·····························

○ **I get it!** Now I know that there are positive and negative ways of using genetic information such as _____

_____
_____

○ **I need extra help with** _____

Go to MY SCIENCE ⓢ COACH *online for help with this subject.*

SC.7.L.16.4

11 Study Guide

Genetic information can be used to _____,

_____, and _____.

LESSON 1 Human Inheritance

SC.7.L.16.1, SC.7.L.16.2, SC7L16.3

🔑 Some human traits are controlled by single genes with two alleles, and others by single genes with multiple alleles. Still other traits are controlled by many genes that act together.

🔑 The sex chromosomes carry genes that determine whether a person is male or female. They also carry genes that determine other traits.

Vocabulary
- sex chromosomes
- sex-linked gene
- carrier

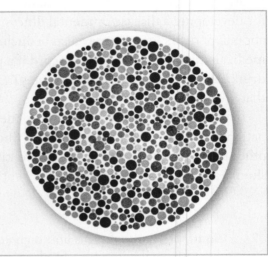

LESSON 2 Human Genetic Disorders

SC.7.L.16.2

🔑 Some genetic disorders are caused by mutations in the DNA of genes. Other disorders are caused by changes in the overall structure or number of chromosomes.

🔑 Today, doctors use tools such as pedigrees, karyotypes, and genetic testing to help trace and diagnose genetic disorders. People with genetic disorders are helped through medical care, education, and job training.

Vocabulary
- genetic disorder
- pedigree
- karyotype

LESSON 3 Advances in Genetics

SC.7.L.16.4

🔑 Cloning, genetic engineering, and artificial selection are three methods for developing organisms with desired traits.

🔑 Individuals, society, and the environment can all benefit from biotechnology. However, biotechnology also poses risks.

Vocabulary
- clone
- genetic engineering
- gene therapy
- selective breeding
- hybridization
- inbreeding
- biotechnology

LESSON 4 Using Genetic Information

SC.7.N.2.1, SC.7.L.16.4

🔑 Genetic information can be used positively to identify individuals and to learn about health and disease, or negatively to discriminate against people.

Vocabulary
- genome
- ethics

Review and Assessment

LESSON 1 Human Inheritance

1. Which human trait is controlled by a single gene with multiple alleles?

   a. height   **b.** dimples

   c. skin color   **d.** blood type

                      SC.7.L.16.1

2. Colorblindness is more common in males than in females because it is carried on the X chromosome, which means it is a _____

              SC.7.L.16.2, SC.7.L.16.3

3. Compare and Contrast Describe the main differences between the inheritance patterns for a dimpled chin and for height.

_____

_____

_____

_____

_____

                      SC.7.L.16.1

4. Interpret Data Complete the Punnett square below to show the possible genotypes for the offspring of a colorblind mother and a father with normal vision. Circle the genotypes that would produce colorblind offspring.

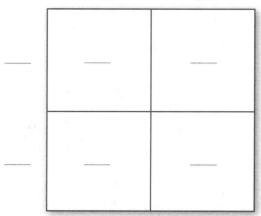

            SC7.L.16.2, SC.7.L.16.3

LESSON 2 Human Genetic Disorders

5. Which of the following would most likely be used to diagnose Down syndrome?

   a. a pedigree   **b.** a karyotype

   c. a Punnett square   **d.** a blood-clotting test

                      SC.7.L.16.2

6. Cystic fibrosis and hemophilia are two examples of _____

                      SC.7.L.12.2

7. Make Generalizations What information is shown by a karyotype?

_____

_____

                      SC.7.L.16.2

8. Relate Cause and Effect How does the cause of cystic fibrosis differ from the cause of Down syndrome?

_____

_____

_____

_____

_____

                      SC.7.L.16.2

9. Interpret Diagrams The pedigree chart below shows the inheritance of sickle-cell disease. Circle all the individuals on the chart who have the disease. Draw a square around individuals who are carriers.

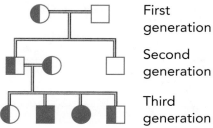

First generation

Second generation

Third generation

Key

◐ or ▨ Carrier of sickle-cell disease

● or ■ Person with sickle-cell disease

                      SC.7.L.16.2

LESSON 3 Advances in Genetics

10. An organism that has the same genes as the organism that produced it is called a

   a. clone.   **b.** hybrid.

   c. genome.   **d.** pedigree.

SC.7.L.16.4

11. Inbreeding and hybridization are two different

types of _____

SC.7.L.16.4

12. **Write About It** Suppose that you are giving a presentation about genetic engineering to a group of people who are not familiar with the topic. Write a short speech that includes a definition of genetic engineering, a description of how it is used, and an explanation of some of the concerns about its use.

SC.7.L.16.4

LESSON 4 Using Genetic Information

13. Genetic fingerprinting is a tool that is used in

   a. gene therapy.   **b.** selective breeding.

   c. cloning.   **d.** identification.

SC.7.L.16.4

14. An organism's _____ is its full set of DNA.

SC.7.L.16.4

15. **Apply Concepts** Around the globe, people are discussing the ethical use of genetic information. Why is this a concern?

_____

_____

_____

_____

_____

_____

_____

SC.7.L.16.4

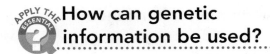

How can genetic information be used?

16. Genetic information can be applied in healthcare, agriculture, forensics, and many other fields. Using at least three vocabulary terms from this chapter, describe a situation in which genetic information such as this karyotype could have either a positive or negative impact on your daily life. Explain your reasoning.

_____

_____

_____

_____

_____

_____

_____

_____

_____

_____

_____

_____

_____

SC.7.L.16.1, SC.7.L.16.4

Florida Benchmarks Review

Circle the letter of the best answer.

1 This Punnett square shows the possible genotypes for the offspring of a colorblind father and a mother who is a carrier. If this couple has a daughter, what is the probability that she will be colorblind?

	X^c	Y
X^c	X^cX^c	X^cY
X^c	X^cX^c	X^cY

A 0 percent **B** 25 percent

C 50 percent **D** 100 percent

SC.7.L.16.2, SC.7.L.16.3

2 Inserting a human gene into a bacterial plasmid is an example of

A inbreeding.

B selective breeding.

C DNA fingerprinting.

D genetic engineering.

SC.7.L.16.4

3 What was the main goal of the Human Genome Project?

A to clone a human

B to identify the sequence of the human genome

C to protect the genetic privacy of individuals

D to collect the genetic fingerprints of all humans

SC.7.L.16.4

4 Which of the following is a selective breeding technique?

A cloning **B** forensics

C inbreeding **D** gene therapy

SC.7.L.16.4

5 How is human blood type inherited?

A through a sex-linked gene

B through a single gene with multiple alleles

C through many genes, which produce many possible combinations of genes and alleles

D through a single gene with two alleles, one that is dominant and one that is recessive

SC.7.L.16.1, SC.7.L.16.2

6 Sasha's mother has sickle-cell disease. Her father does not have the disease and is not a carrier. Sasha has one brother and one sister. Which answer below best describes the genotypes of Sasha and her siblings? The key is for reference.

Key

◯ Female; does not have trait nor is a carrier

▢ Male; does not have trait nor is a carrier

◐ or ◧ Carrier for trait

● or ■ Has trait

A All three children are carriers.

B All three children have sickle-cell disease.

C Sasha and her sister have sickle-cell disease, while their brother is a carrier.

D Sasha and her sister are carriers, while their brother is not.

SC.7.L.16.1, SC.7.L.16.2, SC.7.L.16.3

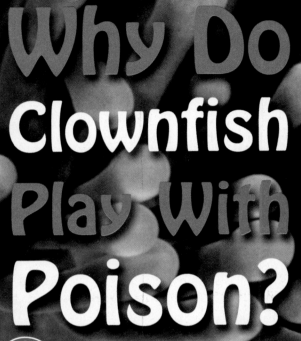

Why Do Clownfish Play With Poison?

How do living things affect one another?

Clownfish live among the poisonous and stinging tentacles of sea anemones to avoid being eaten by larger fish. Amazingly, the clownfish do not get stung! This is because mucus protects the skin of the fish.

Develop Hypotheses **How might a sea anemone benefit from having clownfish around?**

_____

_____

_____

_____

_____

_____

> UNTAMED SCIENCE Watch the **Untamed Science** video to learn more about interactions between organisms.

Populations and Communities

FLORIDA | Next Generation Sunshine State Standards

Big Idea 3: SC.7.N.3.2
Big Idea 17: SC.7.L.17.1, SC.7.L.17.2, SC.7.L.17.3

Language Arts: LA.7.2.2.3, LA.7.4.2.2
Mathematics: MA.6.A.3.6

12 Getting Started

Check Your Understanding

1. **Background** Read the paragraph below and then answer the question.

Raquel planted a garden in a sunny area near her home. First, she loosened the **soil,** so the plant roots could easily grow. If days passed with no **precipitation,** she watered the plants. That was all she had to do—the rest of what the plants needed came from the **atmosphere!**

Soil is made up of rock fragments, water, air, and decaying plant and animal matter.

Rain, hail, sleet, and snow are all types of **precipitation.**

Earth's **atmosphere** contains oxygen, carbon dioxide, nitrogen, and other gases.

• How do soil, precipitation, and the atmosphere help a plant grow?

_____

_____

_____

> MY READING WEB If you had trouble completing the question above, visit **My Reading Web** and type in *Populations and Communities.*

Vocabulary Skill

Latin Word Origins Some key terms in this chapter contain word parts with Latin origins. The table below lists two of the Latin words that key terms come from.

Latin Word	Meaning of Latin Word	Example
aptare	to fit	adaptation, *n.* a characteristic that allows an organism to live successfully in its environment
migrare	to move	immigration, *n.* movement into a population

LA.7.1.6.7

2. **Quick Check** The terms *immigration* and *emigration* both come from the Latin word *migrare*. Circle the meaning of *migrare* in the table above.

organism

immigration

adaptation

predation

Chapter Preview

LESSON 1

- organism • habitat
- biotic factor • abiotic factor
- species • population
- community • ecosystem
- ecology

↻ Compare and Contrast
△ Draw Conclusions

LESSON 2

- producer • consumer
- herbivore • carnivore
- omnivore • scavenger
- decomposer • food chain
- food web • energy pyramid

↻ Identify Supporting Evidence
△ Classify

LESSON 3 ·

- natural selection • adaptation
- niche • competition • predation
- predator • prey • symbiosis
- mutualism • commensalism
- parasitism • parasite • host

↻ Relate Text and Visuals
△ Predict

LESSON 4

- birth rate • death rate
- immigration • emigration
- population density
- limiting factor
- carrying capacity

↻ Relate Cause and Effect
△ Infer

> VOCAB FLASH CARDS For extra help with vocabulary, visit **Vocab Flash Cards** and type in *Populations and Communities.*

Living Things and the Environment

EXPLORE THE ESSENTIAL ❓

🔑 **What Does an Organism Get From Its Environment?**
SC.7.L.17.1, SC.7.L.17.2, SC.7.L.17.3

🔑 **What Are the Two Parts of an Organism's Habitat?**
SC.7.L.17.1, SC.7.L.17.2, SC.7.L.17.3, LA.7.4.2.2

🔑 **How Is an Ecosystem Organized?**
SC.7.L.17.1, SC.7.L.17.2, SC.7.L.17.3

MY PLANET DIARY

DISCOVERY

Love Song

The gray, golden brown, and Goodman's mouse lemurs are some of the world's smallest primates. These three lemurs look similar. Looking so similar makes it difficult for the lemurs to find members of their own kind or species during mating season. However, it seems that the lemurs can identify their own species by song. Scientists recorded the mating calls of the three species of lemurs. They discovered that the lemurs reacted more to the calls from their own species. This allows the lemurs to pick the right mate, even at night.

Communicate **Answer these questions. Discuss your answers with a partner.**

1. If you were looking for your sneakers among several pairs that looked just like yours, what characteristics would make it easier for you to find them?

_____

_____

2. What do you think would happen if a lemur mated with a different kind of lemur?

_____

_____

▷ **PLANET DIARY** Go to **Planet Diary** to learn more about habitats.

Goodman's mouse lemur

Golden brown mouse lemur

Gray mouse lemur

Lab zone® Do the Inquiry Warm-Up *What's in the Scene?*

Vocabulary
- organism • habitat • biotic factor • abiotic factor
- species • population • community • ecosystem
- ecology

Skills
⟳ Reading: Compare and Contrast
△ Inquiry: Draw Conclusions

What Does an Organism Get From Its Environment?

FLORIDA NGSSS

SC.7.L.17.1 Explain the relationships among producers, consumers, and decomposers in a food web.
SC.7.L.17.2 Compare and contrast the relationships among organisms.
SC.7.L.17.3 Describe and investigate various limiting factors in ecosystems.

In a forest, you might see ferns growing in the damp soil and woodpeckers building nests in tree trunks. It might even feel cool and shady, as if there isn't much sun breaking through the treetops. But don't be fooled—the sun is the main energy source in this living system. The sun's energy is transferred between organisms, such as when an animal eats a plant. This is one of the many ways in which living things interact with their environment and depend on it for survival.

A woodpecker is one type of **organism,** or living thing. 🔑 **An organism gets food, water, shelter, and other things it needs to live, grow, and reproduce from its environment.** An environment that provides the things a specific organism needs to live, grow, and reproduce is called its **habitat.** Organisms live in different habitats because they have different requirements for survival and reproduction. A prairie dog, like the one shown in **Figure 1,** obtains the food and shelter it needs from a prairie habitat. It could not survive on this rocky ocean shore.

FIGURE 1 ·······················
What's Wrong With This Picture?
✎ List **Give three reasons why this prairie dog would not survive in this habitat.**

_____
_____
_____
_____

Lab ® Do the Quick Lab
zone *Organisms and Their Habitats.*

🔑 Assess Your Understanding

got it? ···

○ **I get it!** Now I know that an organism's environment provides _____

_____

○ **I need extra help with** _____

Go to **my science** ⓢ **coach** *online for help with this subject.*   SC.7.L.17.1, SC.7.L.17.2, SC.7.L.17.3

FLORIDA NGSSS

SC.7.L.17.1 Explain the relationships among producers, consumers, and decomposers in a food web.

SC.7.L.17.2 Compare and contrast the relationships among organisms.

SC.7.L.17.3 Describe and investigate various limiting factors in ecosystems.

Compare and Contrast
In the paragraphs at the right, circle how biotic and abiotic factors are similar and underline how they are different.

What Are the Two Parts of an Organism's Habitat?

To meet its needs, a prairie dog must interact with more than just the other prairie dogs around it. **An organism interacts with both the living and nonliving parts of its habitat.**

Biotic Factors What living things can you see in the prairie dog's habitat shown in **Figure 2**? The parts of a habitat that are living, or once living, and interact with an organism are called **biotic factors** (by AHT ik). The plants that provide seeds and berries are biotic factors. The ferrets and eagles that hunt the prairie dog are also biotic factors. Worms and bacteria are biotic factors that live in the soil underneath the prairie grass. Prairie dog scat, owl pellets, and decomposing plant matter are also biotic factors.

Abiotic Factors Not all of the factors that organisms interact with are living. **Abiotic factors** (ay by AHT ik) are the nonliving parts of an organism's habitat. These factors, as shown in **Figure 2,** include sunlight, soil, temperature, oxygen, and water.

FIGURE 2 ·······················

Factors in a Prairie Habitat
A prairie dog interacts with many biotic and abiotic factors in the prairie habitat.

Relate Text and Visuals **Add another biotic factor to the picture. For each abiotic factor, draw a line from the text box to an example in the picture.**

Sunlight Because sunlight is needed for plants to make their own food, it is an important abiotic factor for most living things.

Soil Soil consists of varying amounts of rock fragments, nutrients, air, water, and the decaying remains of living things. The soil in an area influences the kinds of plants and animals that can live and grow there.

Temperature The temperatures that are typical in an area determine the types of organisms that can live there.

Oxygen Most living things require oxygen to carry out their life processes. Organisms on land obtain oxygen from air. Aquatic organisms obtain oxygen that is dissolved in the water around them.

Water All living things require water to carry out their life processes. Plants and algae need water along with sunlight and carbon dioxide to make their own food. Other living things depend on plants and algae for food.

apply it!

Brine shrimp eggs are used in Florida, and across the world, to feed small fish in hatcheries. Salt is an abiotic factor in their environment. To see how the amount of salt affects the hatching of brine shrimp eggs, varying amounts of salt were added to four 500-mL beakers.

1 Observe In which beaker(s) did the eggs hatch? _____

2 Infer The manipulated variable was

_____

3 CHALLENGE Beaker _____ was the control.

4 Draw Conclusions What can you conclude about the amount of salt in the shrimps' natural habitat?

_____

_____

_____

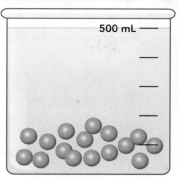

Beaker A
500 mL spring water

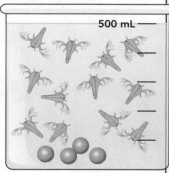

Beaker B
500 mL spring water
+ 2.5 g salt

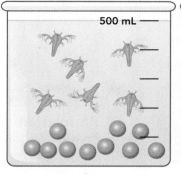

Beaker C
500 mL spring water
+ 7.5 g salt

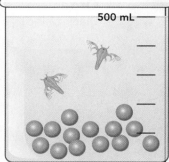

Beaker D
500 mL spring water
+ 15 g salt

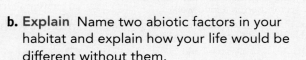
Lab zone — Do the Lab Investigation *World in a Bottle.*

🔑 Assess Your Understanding

1a. Interpret Diagrams List two biotic and two abiotic factors in **Figure 2**.

_____

_____

_____

_____

SC.7.L.17.1, SC.7.L.17.2, SC.7.L.17.3

b. Explain Name two abiotic factors in your habitat and explain how your life would be different without them.

_____

_____

_____

_____

SC.7.L.17.1, SC.7.L.17.2, SC.7.L.17.3

got it? ....

○ **I get it!** Now I know that the two parts of an organism's habitat are _____

_____

○ **I need extra help with** _____

Go to MY SCIENCE **COACH** *online for help with this subject.*   SC.7.L.17.1, SC.7.L.17.2, SC.7.L.17.3

FIGURE 3 ·······················

> REAL-WORLD INQUIRY **Levels of an Ecosystem**
In this figure, the smallest level of organization is
the organism. The largest is the entire ecosystem.

Organism
Black-tailed
prairie dog

Population
Prairie dog town

Community
All the living things that
interact on the prairie

FLORIDA NGSSS

SC.7.L.17.1 Explain the relationships
among producers, consumers, and
decomposers in a food web.

SC.7.L.17.2 Compare and contrast
the relationships among organisms.

SC.7.L.17.3 Describe and investigate
various limiting factors in ecosystems.

LA.7.4.2.2 The student will record
information related to a topic,
including visual aids to organize
and record information.

How Is an Ecosystem Organized?

Most organisms do not live all alone in their habitat. Instead,
organisms live together in populations and communities that
interact with abiotic factors in their ecosystems.

Organisms Black-tailed prairie dogs that live in prairie dog
towns on the Nebraska plains are all members of one species.
A **species** (SPEE sheez) is a group of organisms that can mate with
each other and produce offspring that can also mate and reproduce.

Populations All the members of one species living in a
particular area are referred to as a **population.** The prairie dogs in
the Nebraska town are one example of a population.

Communities A particular area contains more than one
species of organism. The prairie, for instance, includes prairie dogs,
hawks, snakes, and grasses. All the different populations that live
together in an area make up a **community.**

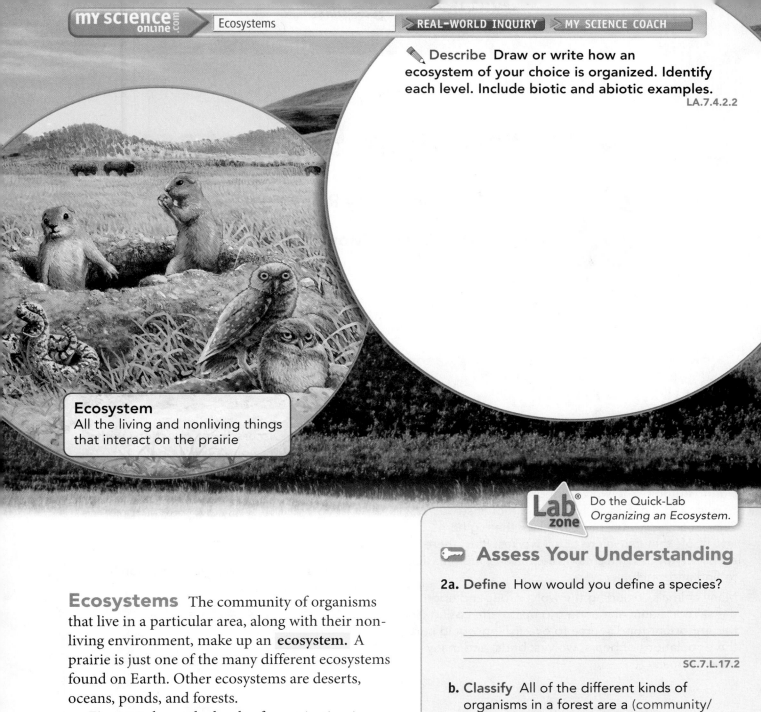

✎ **Describe** Draw or write how an ecosystem of your choice is organized. Identify each level. Include biotic and abiotic examples.

LA.7.4.2.2

Ecosystem
All the living and nonliving things that interact on the prairie

Ecosystems The community of organisms that live in a particular area, along with their non-living environment, make up an **ecosystem.** A prairie is just one of the many different ecosystems found on Earth. Other ecosystems are deserts, oceans, ponds, and forests.

Figure 3 shows the levels of organization in a prairie ecosystem. **The smallest level of organization is a single organism, which belongs to a population that includes other members of its species. The population belongs to a community of different species. The community and abiotic factors together form an ecosystem.**

Because the populations in an ecosystem interact with one another, any change affects all the different populations that live there. The study of how organisms interact with each other and with their environment is called **ecology.**

Lab ® Do the Quick-Lab
zone *Organizing an Ecosystem.*

⚷ **Assess Your Understanding**

2a. Define How would you define a species?

_____

_____

_____

SC.7.L.17.2

b. Classify All of the different kinds of organisms in a forest are a (community/ population).

SC.7.L.17.2

got it? ···································

○ **I get it!** Now I know that ecosystems are

organized into _____

_____

○ **I need extra help with**_____

Go to **my science** ⓢ **coach** *online for help with this subject.*   SC.7.L.17.2

459

2 Energy Flow in Ecosystems

🔑 **What Are the Energy Roles in an Ecosystem?**
SC.7.N.3.2, SC.7.L.17.1, LA.7.4.2.2

🔑 **How Does Energy Move Through an Ecosystem?**
SC.7.N.3.2, SC.7.L.17.1

my pLaneT DiaRY

I'll Have the Fish

Scientists have noticed something fishy going on with the wolves in British Columbia, Canada. During autumn, the wolves ignore their typical food of deer and moose and feast on salmon instead. Salmon are very nutritious and lack the big horns and hoofs that can injure or kill wolves. Plus, there are plenty of fish in a small area, making them easier to find and catch.

Many animals, including the wolves, depend upon the salmon's annual mating trip upstream. Losing this important food source to overfishing would hurt the populations of bears, wolves, birds, and many other animals.

DISCOVERY

Communicate Discuss these questions with a classmate. Write your answers below.

1. What are two reasons the wolves may eat fish in autumn instead of deer or moose?

_____

_____

2. What effect could overfishing salmon have on an ecosystem?

_____

_____

_____

_____

> **PLANET DIARY** Go to **Planet Diary** to learn more about food webs.

 Lab zone Do the Inquiry Warm-Up *Where Did Your Dinner Come From?*

Vocabulary
- producer • consumer • herbivore • carnivore
- omnivore • scavenger • decomposer • food chain
- food web • energy pyramid

Skills
↻ Reading: Identify Supporting Evidence
△ Inquiry: Classify

What Are the Energy Roles in an Ecosystem?

Do you play an instrument in your school band? If so, you know that each instrument has a role in a piece of music. Similar to instruments in a band, each organism has a role in the movement of energy through its ecosystem.

An organism's energy role is determined by how it obtains food and how it interacts with other organisms. 🔑 **Each of the organisms in an ecosystem fills the energy role of producer, consumer, or decomposer.**

Producers Energy enters most ecosystems as sunlight. Some organisms, like the plants and algae shown in **Figure 1,** and some types of bacteria, capture the energy of sunlight and store it as food energy. These organisms use the sun's energy to turn water and carbon dioxide into food molecules in a process called photosynthesis.

An organism that can make its own food is a **producer.** Producers are the source of all the food in an ecosystem. In a few ecosystems, producers obtain energy from a source other than sunlight. One such ecosystem is found in rocks deep beneath the ground. Certain bacteria in this ecosystem produce their own food using the energy in hydrogen sulfide, a gas that is present in their environment.

FLORIDA NGSSS

SC.7.N.3.2 Identify the benefits and limitations of the use of scientific models.

SC.7.L.17.1 Explain and illustrate roles of and relationships among producers, consumers, and decomposers in the process of energy transfer in a food web.

LA.7.4.2.2 The student will record information related to a topic.

FIGURE 1 ·······························
Producers
Producers are organisms that can make their own food.

✏️ **Identify** Complete the shopping list below to identify the producers that are part of your diet.

○ wheat
○ corn
○ banana
○
○
○
○
○
○
○

LA.7.4.2.2

Tape grass and water milfoil

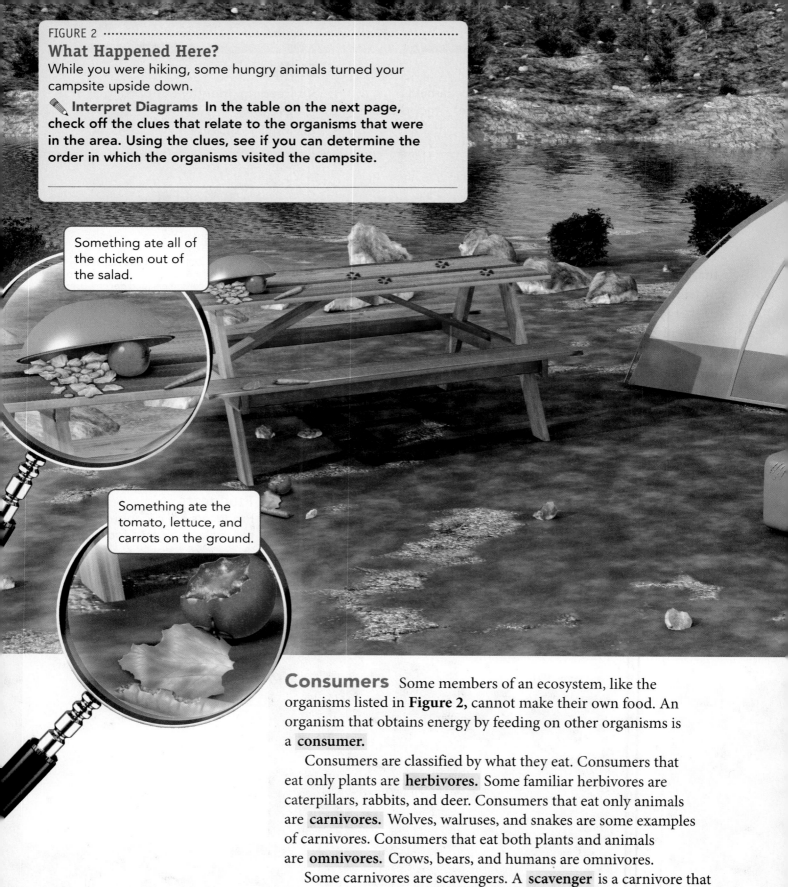

FIGURE 2 ·······················

What Happened Here?
While you were hiking, some hungry animals turned your campsite upside down.

✎ **Interpret Diagrams** In the table on the next page, check off the clues that relate to the organisms that were in the area. Using the clues, see if you can determine the order in which the organisms visited the campsite.

Something ate all of the chicken out of the salad.

Something ate the tomato, lettuce, and carrots on the ground.

Consumers Some members of an ecosystem, like the organisms listed in **Figure 2,** cannot make their own food. An organism that obtains energy by feeding on other organisms is a **consumer.**

Consumers are classified by what they eat. Consumers that eat only plants are **herbivores.** Some familiar herbivores are caterpillars, rabbits, and deer. Consumers that eat only animals are **carnivores.** Wolves, walruses, and snakes are some examples of carnivores. Consumers that eat both plants and animals are **omnivores.** Crows, bears, and humans are omnivores.

Some carnivores are scavengers. A **scavenger** is a carnivore that feeds on the bodies of dead organisms. Scavengers include catfish and vultures.

Clues	Bear	Mold	Rabbit	Wolf
Can easily reach the table top				
Grows on food and breaks it down				
Small enough to enter and exit tent				
Gets energy from meat				
Strong enough to open cooler				
Not a picky eater				
Gets energy from plants				

Something ate the apples and beef jerky from inside the tent.

Something ate strawberries, even some of the moldy ones.

Decomposers If an ecosystem had only producers and consumers, the raw materials of life, such as carbon and nitrogen, would stay locked up in wastes and the bodies of dead organisms. However, there are organisms in ecosystems that prevent this from happening. **Decomposers** break down wastes and dead organisms and return the raw materials to the ecosystem.

You can think of decomposers as nature's recyclers. While obtaining energy for their own needs, decomposers return simple molecules to the environment. These molecules can be used again by other organisms. Mushrooms, bacteria, and mold are common decomposers.

Lab zone® Do the Quick Lab *Observing Decomposition.*

🔑 Assess Your Understanding

1a. Describe An organism's energy role is determined by how it obtains

_____ and how it _____

with other organisms.

SC.7.L.17.1

b. Explain What is the main source of energy for all three energy roles? Why?

_____

_____

_____

_____

_____

_____

_____

SC.7.L.17.1

got it? ....

○ **I get it!** Now I know that the energy roles in

an ecosystem are _____

_____

_____

○ **I need extra help with** _____

_____

Go to **MY SCIENCE** ⑤ **COACH** *online for help with this subject.*

SC.7.L.17.1

463

SC.7.N.3.2 Identify the benefits and limitations of the use of scientific models.

SC.7.L.17.1 Explain and illustrate roles of and relationships among producers, consumers, and decomposers in the process of energy transfer in a food web.

How Does Energy Move Through an Ecosystem?

As you have read, energy enters most ecosystems as sunlight and is converted into food by producers. This energy is transferred to the organisms that eat the producers, and then to other organisms that feed on the consumers. 🔑 **Energy moves through an ecosystem when one organism eats another.** This movement of energy can be shown as food chains, food webs, and energy pyramids.

Food Chains One way to show how energy moves in an ecosystem is with a food chain. A **food chain** is a series of events in which one organism eats another and obtains energy. You can follow one example of a food chain in **Figure 3.**

Food Webs A food chain shows only one possible path along which energy can move through an ecosystem. Most producers and consumers are part of many food chains. A more realistic way to show the flow of energy through an ecosystem is with a food web. As shown in **Figure 4,** a **food web** consists of many overlapping food chains in an ecosystem.

Organisms may play more than one role in an ecosystem. Look at the crayfish in **Figure 4.** A crayfish is an omnivore that is a first-level consumer when it eats plants. But when a crayfish eats a snail, it is a second-level consumer.

Just as food chains overlap and connect, food webs interconnect as well. A gull might eat a fish at the ocean, but it might also eat a mouse in a field. The gull, then, is part of two food webs—an ocean food web and a land food web. All the world's food webs interconnect in what can be thought of as a global food web.

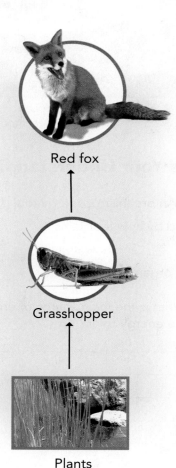

FIGURE 3 ·········

Food Chain

In this food chain, you can see how energy moves from plants, to a grasshopper, to the fox. The arrows show how energy moves up the food chain, from one organism to the next.

apply it!

🔺**Classify** Using what you have learned about food chains, draw or describe a food chain from your local ecosystem. Show at least three organisms in your food chain. Name each organism and label it as a producer, consumer, or decomposer.

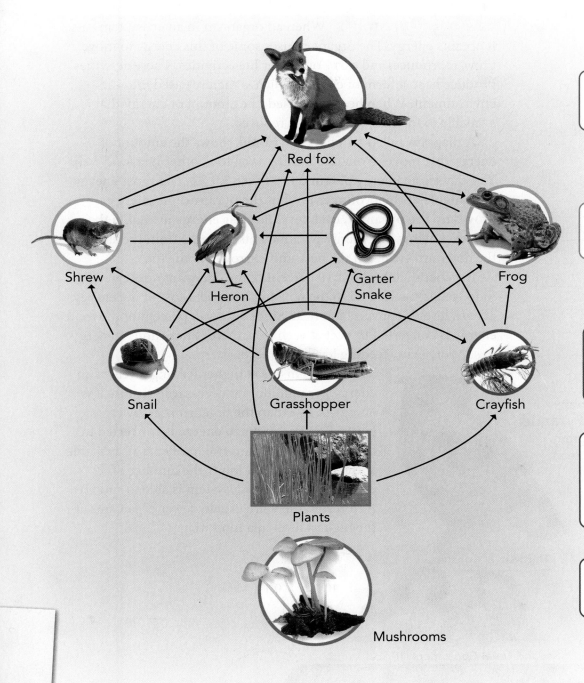

Third-level consumers eat the second-level consumers.

Second-level consumers eat the first-level consumers.

First-level consumers are organisms that feed directly on the producers.

Producers form the base of the food web. The first organism in a food chain is always a producer.

Decomposers consume the wastes and remains of other organisms.

FIGURE 4 ·····································

› INTERACTIVE ART **Food Web**
A food web consists of many interconnected food chains.

✎ **Complete the tasks.**

1. **Interpret Diagrams** Pick two organisms from the food web. Draw arrows connecting them to the decomposers.

2. **Relate Text and Visuals** How can the fox be both a second-level and third-level consumer?

_____
_____
_____
_____
_____
_____

🔁 Identify Supporting Evidence

Look at the energy pyramid. Why is a pyramid the best shape to show how energy moves through an ecosystem?

_____

_____

_____

_____

_____

_____

_____

FIGURE 5 ·······························

▶ VIRTUAL LAB **Energy Pyramid**

This energy pyramid diagram shows the energy available at each level of a food web and how it is calculated. Energy is measured in kilocalories, or kcal.

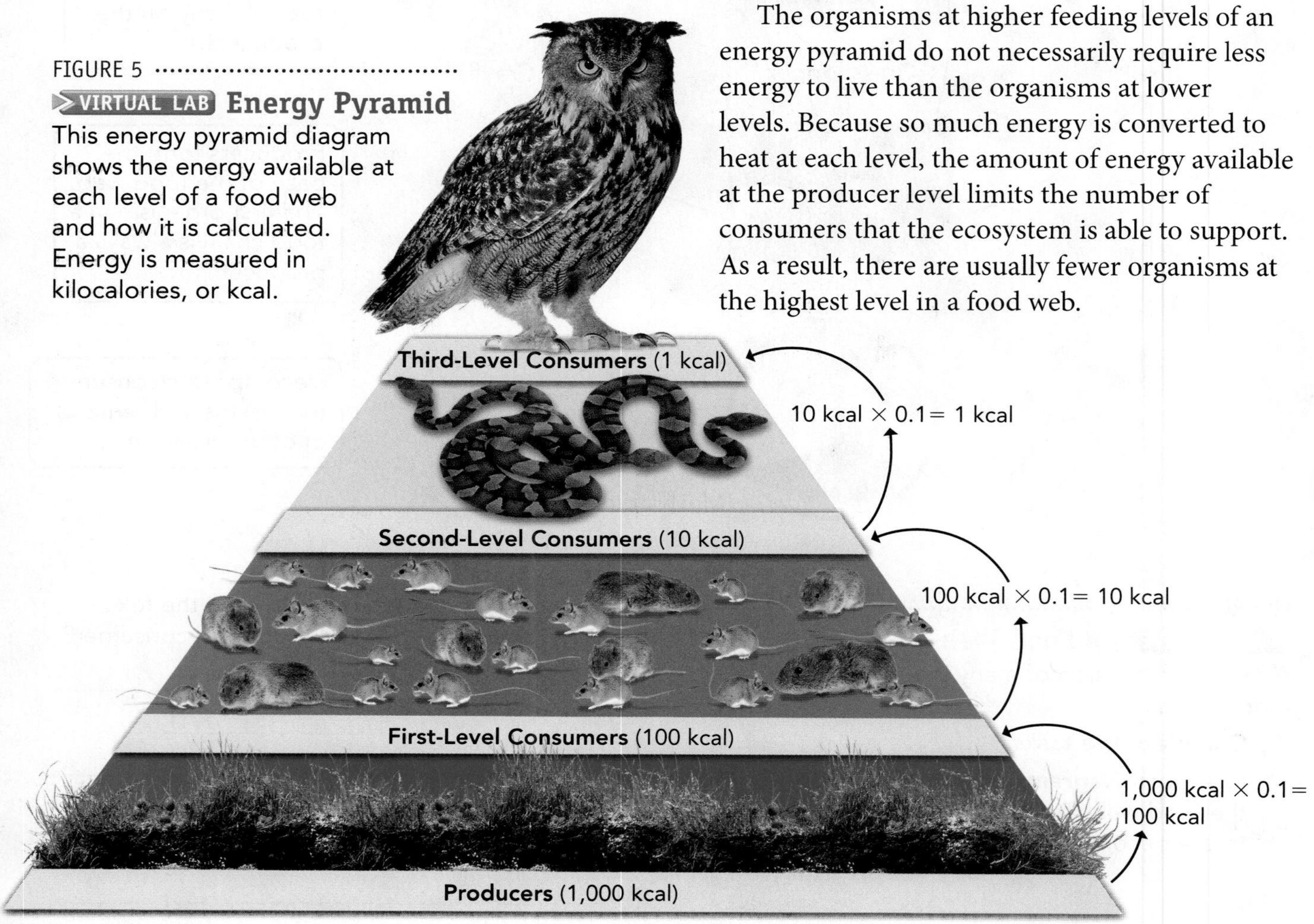

Energy Pyramids When an organism in an ecosystem eats, it obtains energy. The organism uses some of this energy to move, grow, reproduce, and carry out other life activities. These activities produce heat, a form of energy, which is then released into the environment. When heat is released, the amount of energy that is available to the next consumer is reduced.

A diagram called an **energy pyramid** shows the amount of energy that moves from one feeding level to another in a food web. You can see an energy pyramid in **Figure 5.** 🔑 **The most energy is available at the producer level of the pyramid. As energy moves up the pyramid, each level has less energy available than the level below.** An energy pyramid gets its name from the shape of the diagram—wider at the base and narrower at the top.

In general, only about 10 percent of the energy at one level of a food web is transferred to the next higher level. Most of the energy at each level is converted to heat. Since about 90 percent of the food energy is converted to heat at each step, there is not enough energy to support many feeding levels in an ecosystem.

The organisms at higher feeding levels of an energy pyramid do not necessarily require less energy to live than the organisms at lower levels. Because so much energy is converted to heat at each level, the amount of energy available at the producer level limits the number of consumers that the ecosystem is able to support. As a result, there are usually fewer organisms at the highest level in a food web.

Third-Level Consumers (1 kcal)

10 kcal × 0.1 = 1 kcal

Second-Level Consumers (10 kcal)

100 kcal × 0.1 = 10 kcal

First-Level Consumers (100 kcal)

1,000 kcal × 0.1 = 100 kcal

Producers (1,000 kcal)

do the math!

Energy Pyramids

Suppose that the producers at the base of an energy pyramid contain 330,000 kilocalories.

Calculate Using **Figure 5** as a guide, label how much energy would be available at each level of the pyramid based on the questions below.

1 If mice ate all of the plants, how much energy would be available to them as first-level consumers?

2 If all of the mice were eaten by snakes, how much energy would the snakes receive?

3 If all of the snakes were eaten by the owl, how much energy would the owl receive?

4 CHALLENGE About how much energy would the owl use for its life processes or lose as heat? _____

5 CHALLENGE How much energy would be stored in the owl's body? _____

MA.7.A.1.5

Third-Level Consumers
_____

Second-Level Consumers
_____

First-Level Consumers
_____

330,000 kcal
Producers

 Do the Lab Investigation
Ecosystem Food Chains.

Assess Your Understanding

2a. Define A food (web/chain) is a series of events in which one organism eats another and obtains energy. A food (web/chain) consists of many overlapping food (webs/chains).

SC.7.L.17.1

b. Compare and Contrast Why is a food web a more realistic way of portraying an ecosystem than a food chain?

_____

_____

_____

SC.7.N.3.2, SC.7.L.17.1

c. Relate Cause and Effect Why are there usually fewer organisms at the top of an energy pyramid?

_____

_____

_____

_____

_____

_____

_____

SC.7.L.17.1

got it?

○ **I get it!** Now I know that energy moves through an ecosystem when_____

_____

○ **I need extra help with** _____

Go to MY SCIENCE ˢ COACH online for help with this subject.

SC.7.L.17.1

Interactions Among Living Things

UNLOCK THE ESSENTIAL

🔑 **How Do Adaptations Help an Organism Survive?**
SC.7.L.17.2

🔑 **What Are Competition and Predation?**
SC.7.L.17.2, MA.6.A.3.6

🔑 **What Are the Three Types of Symbiosis?**
SC.7.L.17.2, LA.7.2.2.3

MY PLANET DiARY

Predator Power

What predator can close its jaws the fastest? You might think it is a lion or a shark, but you would be wrong. It is the trap-jaw ant that has the fastest strike in the animal kingdom. The trap-jaw ant closes its mouth around its prey in 0.13 milliseconds at speeds of 35 to 64 meters per second! The force created when its jaw snaps shut also helps the ant escape danger by either jumping up to 8.3 centimeters high or 39.6 centimeters sideways.

A trap-jaw ant stalks its prey.

FUN FACT

Communicate Answer the questions below. Discuss your answers with a partner.

1. How does the trap-jaw ant's adaptation help it avoid becoming the prey of another organism?

_____

_____

_____

2. What are some adaptations that other predators have to capture prey?

_____

_____

▶ **PLANET DIARY** Go to **Planet Diary** to learn more about predators.

 Lab zone® Do the Inquiry Warm-Up *Can You Hide a Butterfly?*

FLORIDA NGSSS

SC.7.L.17.2 Compare and contrast the relationships among organisms such as mutualism, predation, parasitism, competition, and commensalism.

How Do Adaptations Help an Organism Survive?

As day breaks, a sound comes from a nest tucked in the branch of a saguaro cactus. Two young red-tailed hawks are preparing to fly. Farther down the stem, a tiny elf owl peeks out of its nest in a small hole. A rattlesnake slithers around the base of the saguaro, looking for breakfast. Spying a shrew, the snake strikes it with needlelike fangs. The shrew dies instantly.

Vocabulary

- natural selection • adaptation • niche • competition
- predation • predator • prey • symbiosis • mutualism
- commensalism • parasitism • parasite • host

Skills

↻ Reading: Relate Text and Visuals

△ Inquiry: Predict

Figure 1 shows some of the many organisms that live in, on, and around the saguaro cactus. Each organism has unique characteristics that affect the individual's ability to survive and reproduce in its environment.

Natural Selection A characteristic that makes an individual better suited to a specific environment may eventually become common in that species through a process called **natural selection.** Natural selection works like this: Individuals whose unique characteristics are well-suited for an environment tend to survive and produce more offspring. Offspring that inherit these characteristics also live to reproduce. In this way, natural selection results in **adaptations,** the behaviors and physical characteristics that allow organisms to live successfully in their environments. For example, the arctic hare has fur that turns from gray to white in the winter, which helps camouflage the hare against the snow.

Individuals with characteristics poorly suited to a particular environment are less likely to survive and reproduce. Over time, poorly suited characteristics may disappear from the species. If a species cannot adapt to changes in its environment, the entire species can disappear from Earth and become extinct.

Red-tailed hawk

Purple martin

Flycatcher

Woodpecker

Elf owl

Saguaro cactus

Wasps

Gila monster

Rattlesnake

Scorpion

Roadrunner

FIGURE 1 ·······························

Saguaro Community

✎ Describe Circle two examples of how organisms interact in this scene. Describe each one.

_____

_____

_____

_____

_____

Niche The organisms in the saguaro community have adaptations that result in specific roles. The role of an organism in its habitat is called its **niche.** A niche includes what type of food the organism eats, how it obtains this food, and what other organisms eat it. A niche also includes when and how the organism reproduces and the physical conditions it requires to survive. Some organisms, like the birds in **Figure 2,** share the same habitat but have very specific niches that allow them to live together. 🔑 **Every organism has a variety of adaptations that are suited to its specific living conditions and help it survive.**

apply it!

Organisms occupy many niches in an environment like the one in this picture.

1 **Identify** List two abiotic factors in the picture.

_____

2 **Interpret Diagrams** Describe the niche of the squirrel in the picture.

_____

_____

3 **Make Generalizations** What adaptations might the squirrel have that make it able to live in this environment?

_____

_____

Lab ® Do the Quick Lab
zone *Adaptations for Survival.*

🔑 **Assess Your Understanding**

1a. Define Adaptations are the _____ and _____ characteristics that allow organisms to live successfully in their environments.

SC.7.L.17.2

b. Explain How are a snake's sharp fangs an adaptation that help it survive in the saguaro community?

_____

_____

SC.7.L.17.2

got it? ●

○ I get it! Now I know that adaptations are_____

_____

○ I need extra help with _____

Go to MY SCIENCE 🄢 COACH *online for help with this subject.*

SC.7.L.17.2

What Are Competition and Predation?

During a typical day in the saguaro community, a range of interactions takes place among organisms. 🔑 **Two major types of interactions among organisms are competition and predation.**

Competition Different species can share the same habitat and food requirements. For example, the flycatcher and the elf owl both live on the saguaro and eat insects. However, these two species do not occupy exactly the same niche. The flycatcher is active during the day, while the owl is active mostly at night. If two species occupy the same niche, one of the species might eventually die off. The reason for this is competition. The struggle between organisms to survive as they attempt to use the same limited resources is called **competition.** For example, weeds in a garden compete with vegetable crops for soil nutrients, water, and sunlight.

In any ecosystem, there are limited amounts of food, water, and shelter. Organisms that share the same habitat often have adaptations that enable them to reduce competition. For example, the three species of warblers in **Figure 2** specialize in feeding only in a certain part of the spruce tree.

FLORIDA NGSSS

SC.7.L.17.2 Compare and contrast the relationships among organisms such as mutualism, predation, parasitism, competition, and commensalism.
MA.6.A.3.6 Construct and analyze tables, graphs, and equations.

Cape May Warbler
This species feeds at the tips of branches near the top of the tree.

Bay-Breasted Warbler
This species feeds in the middle part of the tree.

Yellow-Rumped Warbler
This species feeds in the lower part of the tree and at the bases of the middle branches.

FIGURE 2 ·····························
Niche and Competition
✏️ Each of these warbler species occupies a very specific location in its habitat. By feeding on insects in different areas of the tree, the birds avoid competing for food and are able to live together.

1. **Predict** What could happen if these warbler species fed in the same location on the tree?

_____

_____

_____

_____

2. **List** For what resources do the tree and the grass compete?

_____

_____

_____

_____

_____

471

FIGURE 3 ·····························

Predation
This tiger shark and this albatross are involved in a predator-prey interaction.

✎ **Interpret Photos**
Label the predator and the prey in the photo.

Predation

Predation In **Figure 3,** a tiger shark bursts through the water to seize an albatross in its powerful jaws. An interaction in which one organism kills another for food or nutrients is called **predation.** The organism that does the killing is the **predator.** The organism that is killed is the **prey.** Even though they do not kill their prey, organisms like cows and giraffes are also considered predators because they eat plants.

Predation can have a major effect on a prey population size. Recall that when the death rate exceeds the birth rate in a population, the population size can decrease. So, if there are too many predators in an area, the result is often a decrease in the size of the prey population. But a decrease in the number of prey results in less food for their predators. Without adequate food, the predator population can decline. Generally, populations of predators and their prey rise and fall in related cycles.

FIGURE 4 ··································

Predator Adaptations
A jellyfish's tentacles contain a poisonous substance that paralyzes tiny water animals. The sundew is a plant that is covered with sticky bulbs on stalks. When a fly lands on a bulb, it remains snared in the sticky goo while the plant digests it.

✎ Make Models Imagine an ideal predator to prey upon a porcupine. Draw or describe your predator below and label its adaptations.

Predator Adaptations Predators, such as those in **Figure 4,** have adaptations that help them catch and kill their prey. A cheetah can run very fast for a short time, enabling it to catch its prey. Some predators, such as owls and bats, have adaptations that enable them to hunt at night when their prey, small mammals and insects, are active.

Prey Adaptations How do organisms avoid being killed by effective predators? The smelly spray of a skunk and the sharp quills of a porcupine help keep predators at a distance. As you can see in **Figure 5,** organisms have many kinds of adaptations that help them avoid becoming prey.

Warning Coloring Like many brightly colored animals, this frog is poisonous. Its bright blue and yellow colors warn predators not to eat it.

False Coloring Predators may be confused by a false eyespot and attack the wrong end of the fish. This allows the fish to swim safely away in the opposite direction.

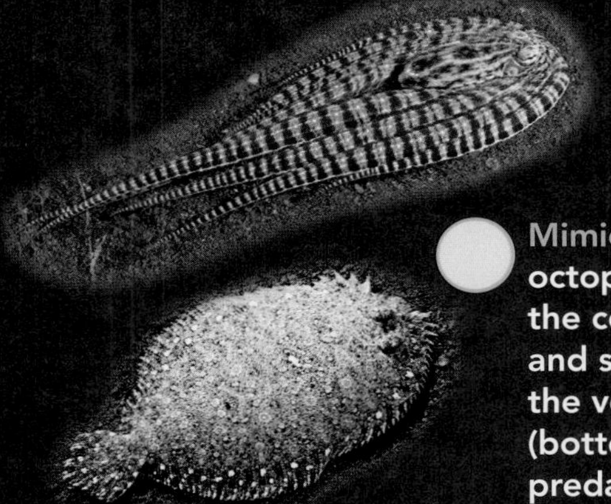

Mimicry The mimic octopus (top) imitates the coloring, shape, and swimming style of the venomous sole fish (bottom) to discourage predators.

Protective Covering Have you ever seen a pinecone with a face? This is a pangolin, a small African mammal. When threatened, the pangolin protects itself by rolling up into a scaly ball.

Camouflage Is it a leaf? Actually, it's a walking leaf insect. But if you were a predator, you might be fooled into looking elsewhere for a meal.

FIGURE 5 ···
> INTERACTIVE ART Defense Strategies
Organisms display a wide range of adaptations that help them avoid becoming prey. **✎ Communicate** In a group, rate each prey adaptation from 1 (best) to 5 (worst) in the circles. Explain your best choice.

_____

_____

_____

Predator–Prey Interactions

On Isle Royale, an island in Lake Superior, the populations of wolves (the predator) and moose (the prey) rise and fall in cycles. Use the graph to answer the questions.

1 Read Graphs What variable is plotted on the x-axis? What two variables are plotted on the y-axis?

_____

2 Interpret Data How did the moose population change between 2002 and 2007? What happened to the wolf population from 2003 through 2006?

_____
_____
_____

3 Draw Conclusions How might the change in moose population have led to the change in the wolf population?

_____
_____
_____

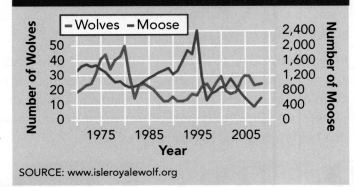

Wolf and Moose Populations on Isle Royale

SOURCE: www.isleroyalewolf.org

4 Explain What adaptations does a wolf have that makes it a successful predator?

_____
_____

5 Predict How might disease in the wolf population one year affect the moose population the next year?

_____
_____
_____

MA.6.A.3.6, MA.7.A.1.5

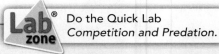
Do the Quick Lab
Competition and Predation.

🔑 Assess Your Understanding

2a. Review Two main ways in which organisms

interact are _____

and _____

SC.7.L.17.2

b. Describe Give an example of competition. Explain your answer.

_____
_____

SC.7.L.17.2

c. Apply Concepts Owls often prey on mice. What adaptations do you think the mice have that help them avoid becoming prey?

_____
_____
_____
_____

SC.7.L.17.2

got it? ....

○ I get it! Now I know that competition and predation_____
_____

○ I need extra help with _____

Go to **MY SCIENCE COACH** online for help with this subject.

SC.7.L.17.2

What Are the Three Types of Symbiosis?

In addition to competition and predation, symbiosis is a third type of interaction among organisms. **Symbiosis** (sim bee OH sis) is any relationship in which two species live closely together and at least one of the species benefits. 🔑 **The three main types of symbiotic relationships are mutualism, commensalism, and parasitism.**

Mutualism   In some relationships, two species may depend on one another. This is true for some species of acacia trees and stinging ants in South America. The stinging ants nest only in the acacia tree, whose thorns discourage the ants' predators. The tree also provides the ants' only food. The ants, in turn, attack other animals that approach the tree and clear competing plants away from the base of the tree. This relationship is an example of mutualism. A relationship in which both species benefit is called **mutualism** (MYOO choo uh liz um). Other examples of mutualism can be seen in **Figure 6.**

FLORIDA NGSSS

SC.7.L.17.2 Compare and contrast the relationships among organisms such as mutualism, predation, parasitism, competition, and commensalism.

LA.7.2.2.3 The student will organize information to show understanding.

FIGURE 6 ·······································
Mutualism
✎ An oxpecker rides and snacks aboard an impala. The oxpecker eat ticks living on the impala's ears. This interaction is an example of mutualism because both organisms benefit.

1. Infer How does the oxpecker benefit?

2. Infer How does the impala benefit?

3. CHALLENGE Explain how the relationship between the hummingbird and the flower is an example of mutualism.

Commensalism Have you ever seen a bird build a nest in a tree? The bird gets a place to live while the tree is unharmed. This relationship is an example of commensalism. **Commensalism** (kuh MEN suh liz um) is a relationship in which one species benefits and the other species is neither helped nor harmed. In nature, commensalism is not very common because two species are usually either helped or harmed a little by any interaction.

Parasitism Many family pets get treated with medication to prevent tick and flea bites. Without treatment, pets can suffer from severe health problems as a result of these bites. A relationship that involves one organism living with, on, or inside another organism and harming it is called **parasitism** (PA ruh sit iz um). The organism that benefits is called a **parasite.** The organism it lives on or in is called a **host.** The parasite is usually smaller than the host. In a parasitic relationship, the parasite benefits while the host is harmed. Unlike a predator, a parasite does not usually kill the organism it feeds on. If the host dies, the parasite could lose its source of food or shelter.

Some parasites, like fleas and ticks, have adaptations that enable them to attach to their host and feed on its blood. Other examples of parasitism are shown in **Figure 7.**

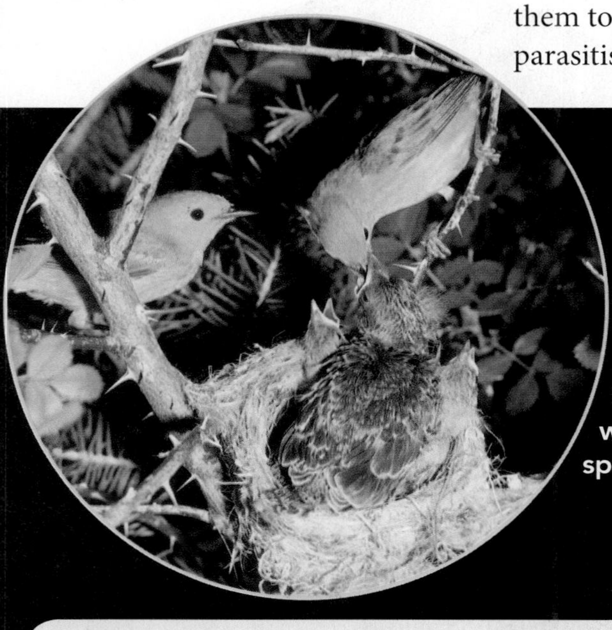

Relate Text and Visuals List the names of the parasites and the hosts in **Figure 7.**

LA.7.2.2.3

Parasites	Hosts

A parasitic cowbird laid its eggs in a yellow warbler's nest. The cowbird chick is outcompeting the warbler chicks for space and food.

Fish lice feed on the blood and other internal fluids of fish.

Dwarf mistletoe is a small parasitic flowering plant that grows into the bark of trees to obtain water and nutrients.

FIGURE 7

Parasitism

There are many examples of parasitic relationships. Besides fleas, ticks, and tapeworms, some plants and birds are parasites. **Explain** Why doesn't a parasite usually kill its host?

_____

_____

_____

Relationships Among Organisms

How do living things affect one another?

FIGURE 8 ···

Each photograph represents a different type of symbiosis.

✎ **Classify** Identify the type of relationship in each photo. Explain how each interaction helps the plant or animal satisfy a basic need.

Interaction 1: A remora fish attaches itself to the underside of a shark without harming the shark and eats leftover bits of food from the shark's meals.

① Interaction 1

_____

_____

_____

_____

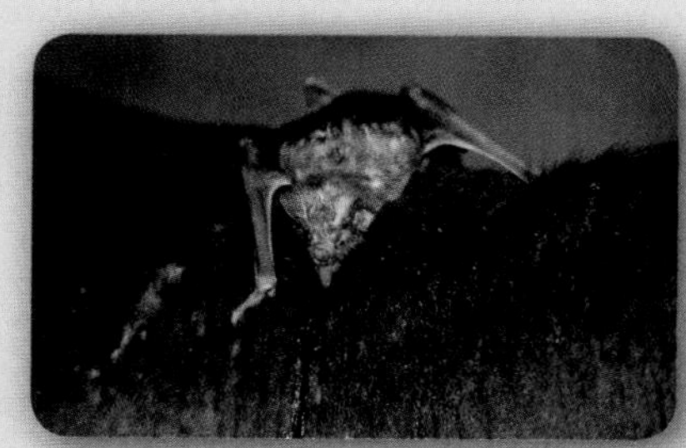

Interaction 2: A vampire bat drinks the blood of horses.

② Interaction 2

_____

_____

_____

Interaction 3: A bee pollinates a flower.

③ Interaction 3

_____

_____

_____

_____

_____

Lab zone® Do the Quick Lab *Type of Symbiosis.*

🔑 Assess Your Understanding

3a. Compare and Contrast Identify two types of interactions among organisms and then compare and contrast them.

_____

_____

_____

_____

SC.7.L.17.2

b. **ANSWER THE ESSENTIAL ?** How do living things affect one another?

_____

_____

_____

_____

_____

SC.7.L.17.2

got it? ···

○ **I get it!** Now I know that the three types of symbiosis differ in _____

_____

○ **I need extra help with** _____

Go to **MY SCIENCE COACH** *online for help with this subject.*

SC.7.L.17.2

EXPLORE THE ESSENTIAL ?

🔑 **How Do Populations Change in Size?**
SC.7.L.17.3

🔑 **What Factors Limit Population Growth?**
SC.7.L.17.3, LA.7.2.2.3

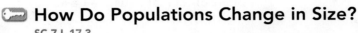

my planet Diary

Prairie Dog Picker-Upper

Did you know that vacuum cleaners do more than just clean carpets? Across the Great Plains, farmers are using specially designed vacuum cleaners to help them remove black-tailed prairie dogs from the farm land. Prairie dogs can eat crops, cause soil erosion, and endanger cattle and farm machinery. The prairie dog vacuum uses a 4-in. plastic hose to suck prairie dogs out of the ground at 483 km/h! The prairie dogs end up in a padded tank, usually unharmed. They are then relocated or donated to the U.S. Fish and Wildlife Service to be fed to endangered eagles, hawks, and black-footed ferrets.

Prairie dogs

TECHNOLOGY

Communicate Discuss these questions with a group of classmates. Write your answers below.

1. If all of the prairie dogs were removed, how do you think the prairie ecosystem would be affected?

_____

_____

_____

2. Should prairie dogs be used as food for endangered species? Explain.

_____

_____

_____

▶ PLANET DIARY   Go to **Planet Diary** to learn more about populations.

Lab zone® Do the Inquiry Warm-Up *Populations.*

SC.7.L.17.3 Describe and investigate various limiting factors in the local ecosystem and their impact on native populations, including food, shelter, water, space, disease, parasitism, predation, and nesting sites.

How Do Populations Change in Size?

Ecologists are scientists who study biotic and abiotic factors of an ecosystem and the interactions between them. Some ecologists study populations and monitor the sizes of populations over time. 🔑 **Populations can change in size when new members join the population or when members leave the population.**

Vocabulary
- birth rate • death rate • immigration
- emigration • population density
- limiting factor • carrying capacity

Skills
↩ Reading: Relate Cause and Effect
△ Inquiry: Infer

Births and Deaths The most common way in which new individuals join a population is by being born into it. The **birth rate** of a population is the number of births in a specific population in a certain time period. For example, suppose that a population of 100 cottontail rabbits produces 1,750 young in a year. The birth rate in this population would be 1,750 rabbits per year.

The main way that individuals leave a population is by dying. The **death rate** is the number of deaths in a specific population in a certain time period. If 1,200 rabbits die in a year in the population, the death rate would be 1,200 rabbits per year.

do the math!

Depending on the size and age of the female, an American alligator can lay between 10 and 50 eggs per year.

1. **Graph** Using the data table and colored pencils, create a double bar graph showing alligator births and deaths for four years.
2. Label the *x*-axis and *y*-axis.
3. Write a title for the graph.
4. Fill in the graph using the colors shown.
5. **Develop Hypotheses** What factors might explain the number of births and deaths in Year 3?

_____
_____
_____
_____
_____
_____
_____

Data Table

Year	Births	Deaths
1	32	8
2	28	13
3	47	21
4	33	16

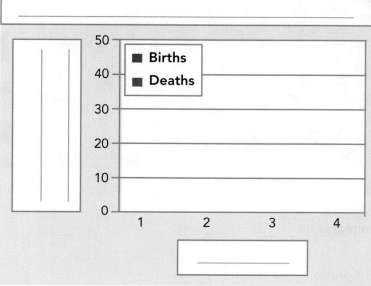

■ Births
■ Deaths

MA.7.S.6.2

The Population Statement
When the birth rate in a population is greater than the death rate, the population will generally increase. This can be written as a mathematical statement using the "is greater than" sign:

If birth rate > death rate, population size increases.

However, if the death rate in a population is greater than the birth rate, the population size will generally decrease. This can also be written as a mathematical statement:

If death rate > birth rate, population size decreases.

Immigration and Emigration
The size of a population also can change when individuals move into or out of the population. **Immigration** (im ih GRAY shun) means moving into a population. **Emigration** (em ih GRAY shun) means leaving a population. For instance, if food is scarce, some members of an antelope herd may wander off in search of better grassland. If they become permanently separated from the original herd, they will no longer be part of that population.

Vocabulary Latin Word Origins
Both the terms *immigration* ("moving into a population") and *emigration* ("moving out of a population") come from the Latin word *migrare* ("to move"). What do you think the prefixes *im–* and *e–* mean?

FIGURE 1
Immigration
White-tailed deer can be found across Florida, from the Panhandle to the Keys. The availability of food, water, and space affects the size of the deer population.

✎ **Apply Concepts** Describe two examples of how immigration and emigration may happen in your classroom.

Immigration:

Emigration:

Graphing Changes in Population Changes in a population's size can be displayed on a line graph. **Figure 2** shows a graph of the changes in a rabbit population. The vertical axis identifies the number of rabbits in the population, while the horizontal axis shows time. The graph represents the size of the rabbit population over a ten-year period.

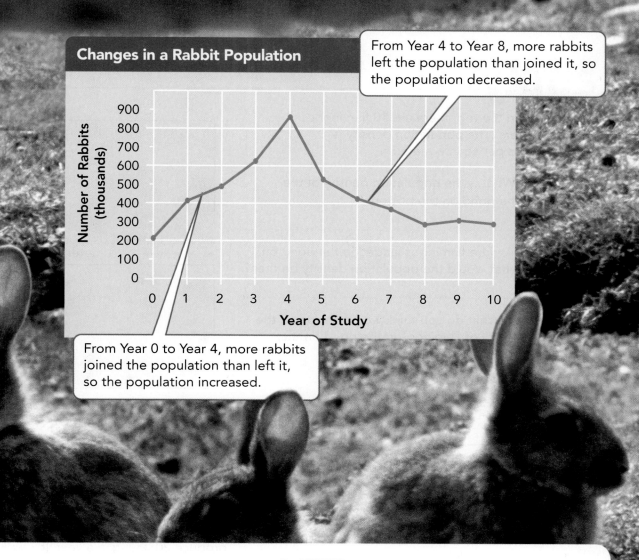

Changes in a Rabbit Population

From Year 4 to Year 8, more rabbits left the population than joined it, so the population decreased.

From Year 0 to Year 4, more rabbits joined the population than left it, so the population increased.

FIGURE 2 ·····

▶ INTERACTIVE ART **Changes in a Rabbit Population**

✎ This graph shows how the size of a rabbit population changed over ten years.

1. **Interpret Data** In Year _____, the rabbit population reached its highest point.

2. **Read Graphs** What was the size of the rabbit population in that year? _____

3. CHALLENGE How do you think the rabbit population affected the fox population over the same ten-year period? Explain your reasoning.

_____

_____

_____

_____

_____

_____

Population Density Sometimes an ecologist needs to know more than just the total size of a population. In many situations, it is helpful to know the **population density** —the number of individuals in an area of a specific size. Population density can be written as an equation:

$$\text{Population density} = \frac{\text{Number of individuals}}{\text{Unit area}}$$

For example, suppose you counted 20 butterflies in a garden measuring 10 square meters. The population density would be 20 butterflies per 10 square meters, or 2 butterflies per square meter.

apply it!

In the pond on the top, there are 10 flamingos in 8 square meters. The population density is 1.25 flamingos per square meter.

1 Calculate What is the population density of the flamingos in the pond on the bottom?

_____

2 Infer If 14 more flamingos landed in the pond on the bottom, what would the population density be then?

_____

3 CHALLENGE What do you think would happen if the population density of flamingos in the pond on the bottom became too great?

_____

_____

_____

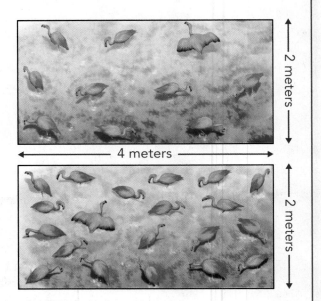
2 meters

4 meters

2 meters

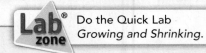
Do the Quick Lab
Growing and Shrinking.

🔑 Assess Your Understanding

1a. **Review** Two ways to join a population are

_____ and _____.

Two ways to leave a population are _____

and _____.

SC.7.L.17.3

b. **Calculate** Suppose a population of 8 wolves produce 20 young in a year. If 7 wolves die, how many wolves remain? (Assume no wolves have moved into or out of the population for other reasons.)

_____

SC.7.L.17.3

got it? ....

○ **I get it!** Now I know that population size changes due to _____

_____

○ **I need extra help with** _____

Go to MY SCIENCE 🄢 COACH *online for help with this subject.*

SC.7.L.17.3

What Factors Limit Population Growth?

When the living conditions in an area are good, a population will generally grow. But eventually an environmental factor will halt population growth. A **limiting factor** is an environmental factor that causes a population to stop growing or decrease. 🔑 **Some limiting factors are food, shelter, water, space, disease, parasitism, predation, and nesting sites.**

Food Organisms don't just need food, they need enough food to survive. Suppose a giraffe must eat 10 kilograms of leaves daily to survive. The trees in an area can provide 100 kilograms of leaves a day while remaining healthy. Five giraffes could live easily here because they would need 50 kilograms of food a day. But 15 giraffes could not survive—there would not be enough food. No matter how much shelter or water is available, the population would not grow much larger than 10 giraffes. The largest population that an area can support is called its **carrying capacity**. The size of a population can vary, but usually stays near the area's carrying capacity.

Shelter Think of ways that humans use shelter, such as for protection from storms. Other organisms also rely on different types of shelter for protection and survival. For example, without a place to hide or hibernate, young black bears can be run out of an area or killed by adults. Also, adult black bears that have a difficult time finding shelter may die or lose their young, affecting the overall population.

Water The quantity and quality of water in an area can mean the difference between life and death for living things. For example, periods of drought can decrease the amount of water in a stream. Low stream flow can limit fish reproduction, reducing the population size. Likewise, poor water quality can limit a population by threatening its health. Look at **Figure 3**.

FLORIDA NGSSS

SC.7.L.17.3 Describe and investigate various limiting factors in the local ecosystem

LA.7.2.2.3 The student will organize information to show understanding.

✏️

🔄 **Relate Cause and Effect** As you read, identify four factors that can limit populations, and fill in the graphic organizer below.

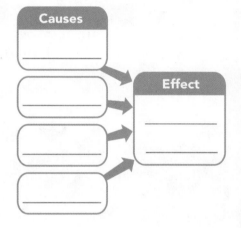

Causes

Effect

FIGURE 3 ·······················🌀

Identifying Limiting Factors

✏️ Describe **What factor may be limiting the population of these laughing gulls in Florida? Explain.**

_____

_____

_____

_____

_____

483

Space
You may think that space only affects animal populations. But the amount of space available determines whether a
plant can obtain the sunlight, water, and soil nutrients it needs.
Many pine seedlings sprout each year in forests. But the roots of
seedlings that are too close together run out of space. Branches
from large trees may block sunlight the seedlings need. Some of
the seedlings die, limiting the size of the pine population. Look
at **Figure 4** to see how space also affects Florida wildflowers.

Disease
Disease is a limiting factor, especially in densely
populated areas. During warm, rainy periods, some crops, such
as tomatoes, can develop a disease called early blight. This
disease causes a plant's leaves to rot and fall off, killing the plant.
Early blight can infect close-growing plants, causing the disease
to spread. This limits the size of the plant population.

Predation and Parasitism
When a large number of
predators, such as lions, live in an area, predation can be a limiting factor. As predators succesfully catch and consume their
prey, the predator population may increase. However, the prey
population decreases. Parasites have a similar effect on
population size. The chestnut lamprey is a parasite that attaches
itself to its host, a fish called yellow perch. The lamprey feeds off
the perch's bodily fluids, eventually killing it. This benefits the
lamprey, but it reduces the perch population.

Nesting Sites
The availability of nesting sites limits populations in much the same way as space. Gannets are seabirds that
come to land only to nest on rocky shores. But the nesting shores
get very crowded. If a pair doesn't find room to nest, they won't
be able to add any offspring to the gannet population. So the
availability of a nesting site on the shore is a limiting factor
for gannets.

FIGURE 4 ···
Space as a Limiting Factor
If no more black-eyed susans (the yellow wildflowers)
can grow in this Florida field, the field has reached its
carrying capacity for these flowers.

✎ Identify **Name three factors that may limit this
plant population.**

_____

_____

_____

apply it!

Florida panthers live only in southern Florida. The panthers are carnivores, primarily hunting white-tailed deer and smaller mammals. They are territorial animals and often kill other panthers that enter their territories. A male panther needs up to 650 square kilometers of land, while females need between 180 and 500 square kilometers. When people build homes and businesses in the panthers' habitat, the habitat becomes frag-mented, or broken up. At the same time, when people drain swamps to build, the plant life changes. Deer may not have enough to eat, and the prey available to the panthers also decreases. Today, fewer than 100 Florida panthers remain in the wild.

✏ **Communicate** Write a letter to the editor that describes how food and space may be limiting factors for the Florida panther. Add a headline to your letter.

LA.7.2.2.3

_____

_____

_____

_____

_____

_____

_____

_____

_____

Lab zone® Do the Quick Lab
Elbow Room.

🔑 Assess Your Understanding

2a. Summarize When there is parasitism or disease in an area, or there is not enough _____, _____, or _____, a population can (begin/stop) growing in size.

SC.7.L.17.3

b. Relate Cause and Effect Choose a limiting factor and describe the factor's effect on population growth.

_____

_____

_____

SC.7.L.17.3

got it? ....

O I get it! Now I know that populations can be limited when _____

_____

O I need extra help with _____

Go to **MY SCIENCE** 🅢 **COACH** *online for help with this subject.*

SC.7.L.17.3

12 Study Guide

Living things interact in many ways, including competition and _____, as well as through symbiotic relationships such as mutualism, commensalism, and _____.

LESSON 1 Living Things and the Environment SC.7.L.17.1, SC.7.L.17.2, SC.7.L.17.3

🔑 An organism gets the things it needs to live, grow, and reproduce from its environment.

🔑 Biotic and abiotic factors make up a habitat.

🔑 The levels of organization in an ecosystem are organism, population, and community.

Vocabulary
- organism • habitat • biotic factor
- abiotic factor • species • population
- community • ecosystem • ecology

LESSON 2 Energy Flow in Ecosystems SC.7.N.3.2, SC.7.L.17.1

🔑 Each organism in an ecosystem is a producer, consumer, or decomposer.

🔑 Energy moves through an ecosystem when one organism eats another.

🔑 As energy moves up the pyramid, each level has less energy available than the level below.

Vocabulary
- producer • consumer • herbivore • carnivore
- omnivore • scavenger • decomposer
- food chain • food web • energy pyramid

LESSON 3 Interactions Among Living Things SC.7.L.17.2

🔑 Every organism has a variety of adaptations that are suited to its specific living conditions and help it survive.

🔑 Two major types of interactions among organisms are competition and predation.

🔑 The three main types of symbiotic relationships are mutualism, commensalism, and parasitism.

Vocabulary
- natural selection • adaptation • niche • competition
- predation • predator • prey • symbiosis • mutualism
- commensalism • parasitism • parasite • host

LESSON 4 Populations SC.7.L.17.3

🔑 Populations can change in size when new members join the population or when members leave the population.

🔑 Some limiting factors for populations are food, shelter, water, space, disease, parasitism, predation, and nesting sites.

Vocabulary
- birth rate • death rate • immigration
- emigration • population density
- limiting factor • carrying capacity

Review and Assessment

LESSON 1 Living Things and the Environment

1. A prairie dog, a hawk, and a snake are all members of the same

    a. niche.   **b.** community.

    c. species.   **d.** population.

           SC.7.L.17.1, SC.7.L.17.2, SC.7.L.17.3

2. Grass is an example of a(n) _____ factor in a habitat.

           SC.7.L.17.1, SC.7.L.17.2, SC.7.L.17.3

3. Sequence Put these levels in order from the smallest to the largest: population, organism, ecosystem, community.

_____

_____

           SC.7.L.17.1, SC.7.L.17.2, SC.7.L.17.3

4. Apply Concepts Name two biotic and two abiotic factors you might find in a forest ecosystem.

_____

_____

           SC.7.L.17.1, SC.7.L.17.2, SC.7.L.17.3

5. Draw Conclusions In 1815, Mount Tambora, a volcano in Indonesia, erupted. So much volcanic ash and dust filled the atmosphere that 1816 is referred to as the "Year Without a Summer." How might a volcanic eruption affect the abiotic factors in an organism's habitat?

_____

_____

_____

_____

_____

           SC.7.L.17.1, SC.7.L.17.2, SC.7.L.17.3

6. Write About It Write at least one paragraph describing your habitat. Describe how you get the food, water, and shelter you need from your habitat. How does this habitat meet your needs in ways that another would not?

           SC.7.L.17.1, SC.7.L.17.2, SC.7.L.17.3

LESSON 2 Energy Flow in Ecosystems

7. A diagram that shows how much energy is available at each feeding level in an ecosystem is a(n)

    a. food web.   **b.** food chain.

    c. water cycle.   **d.** energy pyramid.

                     SC.7.L.17.1

8. A(n) _____ is a consumer that eats only plants.

                     SC.7.L.17.1

9. Interpret Diagrams Which organisms in the illustration are producers? Consumers?

_____

_____

_____

_____

_____

_____

_____

_____

                     SC.7.L.17.1

10. Compare and Contrast How are food chains and food webs different?

_____

_____

_____

_____

           SC.7.N.3.2, SC.7.L.17.1

11. Write About It Think about your own food web. Name the producers and consumers that make up your diet.

_____

_____

_____

_____

_____

           SC.7.L.17.1

487

LESSON 3 Interactions Among Living Things

12. In which type of interaction do both species benefit?

   a. predation   **b.** mutualism

   c. commensalism   **d.** parasitism

                    SC.7.L.17.2

13. A parasite lives on or inside its _____.

                    SC.7.L.17.2

14. Relate Cause and Effect Name two prey adaptations. How does each adaptation protect the organism?

_____

_____

_____

_____

_____

                    SC.7.L.17.2

15. Make Generalizations Competition for resources in an area is usually more intense within a single species than between two different species. Suggest an explanation for this observation.

_____

_____

_____

_____

_____

_____

                    SC.7.L.17.2

16. **Write About It** Some scientists think that the relationship between clownfish and sea anemones is an example of commensalism. Other scientists think that the relationship is mutualism. If this relationship is actually mutualism, how might both the clownfish and sea anemone benefit?

                    SC.7.L.17.2

LESSON 4 Populations

17. All of the following are limiting factors for populations except

   a. space.   **b.** food.

   c. nesting sites.   **d.** time.

                    SC.7.E.17.3

18. _____ occurs when individuals leave a population.

                    SC.7.E.17.3

19. Apply Concepts Your city wants to build a new neighborhood near the town forest. They've asked you to examine the density of the deer population there. Explain why population density would be important to study.

_____

_____

_____

_____

                    SC.7.E.17.3

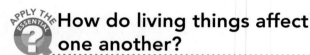

How do living things affect one another?

20. Humans interact with their environment on a daily basis. These interactions can have both positive and negative effects. Using at least four vocabulary terms from this chapter, describe a human interaction and the effect it has on the environment.

_____

_____

_____

_____

_____

_____

_____

_____

_____

                    SC.7.E.17.3

Florida Benchmarks Review

Circle the letter of the best answer.

1 At which level of this energy pyramid is the *least* energy available?

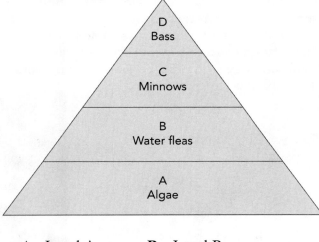

D
Bass

C
Minnows

B
Water fleas

A
Algae

A Level A		**B** Level B	
C Level C		**D** Level D	

SC.7.L.17.1

2 In general, which of the following is a true statement about population size?

A If birth rate < death rate, population size increases.

B If death rate < birth rate, population size decreases.

C If birth rate > death rate, population size increases.

D If death rate > birth rate, population size increases.

SC.7.L.17.3

3 Ecosystems have different levels of organization. A group of similar organisms makes up a

_____, which, along with other types

of organisms, makes up a(n)_____.

A species, population

B habitat, ecosystem

C population, community

D population, habitat

SC.7.L.17.2

4 Three different bird species all live in the same trees in an area, but competition between the birds rarely occurs. Which of the following is a likely explanation for this lack of competition?

A The three species occupy different niches.

B The three species eat the same food.

C The three species have a limited supply of food.

D The three species live in the same part of the trees.

SC.7.L.17.2

5 Symbiotic relationships include mutualism, commensalism, and parasitism. Which of the following is a commensal relationship?

A a bird pollinating a flower

B a mosquito biting a dog

C a hawk eating a mouse

D a bird building a nest in a tree

SC.7.L.17.2

6 Which pair of terms could apply to the same organism?

A carnivore and producer

B consumer and carnivore

C scavenger and herbivore

D producer and omnivore

SC.7.L.17.1

7 How does a limiting factor affect a population?

A It causes a population to grow.

B It causes a population to stop growing.

C It improves an area's carrying capacity.

D It improves living conditions.

SC.7.L.17.3

Science and Society

Fruit That Won't Freeze?

I scream, you scream, we all scream for...fish genes? When the temperature drops below freezing, fish and other animals and insects do something interesting...they don't freeze! The genes of these organisms contain antifreezing proteins, or AFPs, that help prevent the development of ice crystals inside of cells. Fish AFPs have been used in the medical field and in ice cream manufacturing. Some ice cream makers use AFPs to keep ice crystals small.

In 2010, Florida farmers lost strawberry crops to frost damage.

Freezing temperatures threaten Florida crops, that can be damaged when temperatures fall. Plants make AFPs, but the AFPs of animals work at colder temperatures than those of plants. So what if these plants could become more frost-tolerant? In the 1990s, researchers tried inserting a fish gene for AFP into strawberries and other crops. Although the genes were expressed in the plants, the proteins did not provide much, if any, protection from freezing. Still, scientists continue to work to improve frost tolerance of crop plants.

Research It Use reference materials to research what Florida farmers currently do to help their crops tolerate cold temperatures. Write a letter to the farmers explaining how scientific understanding of other organisms' frost tolerance methods might help their crops.

FLORIDA NGSSS

SC.7.N.1.5 Describe the methods used in the pursuit of a scientific explanation.

SC.7.L.16.4 Recognize and explore the impact of biotechnology on the environment.

LA.7.4.2.2 The student will record information related to a topic and list sources of information.

WALKING WHALES?

If you could visit Earth 50 million years ago, you would see many amazing sights. One of the strangest might have been the ancestor of modern whales—walking on land!

For years, scientists have thought that whales evolved from land-dwelling mammals. About 50 million years ago, the ancestors of modern whales had four legs and were similar to large dogs. Over time whales evolved to become the giant marine mammals we see today. However, scientists have had difficulty finding fossils that show how this dramatic change occurred. These missing links could reveal how whales lost their legs.

Now, several new discoveries are helping scientists fill in the blanks. A fossil whale skeleton discovered in Washington State has a pelvis with large cuplike sockets. These sockets likely held short legs that enabled the whale to move on land. Other whale fossils, found in Alabama, include large hind limbs that probably helped the animals swim. Researchers have also discovered the gene mutation that may be responsible for whales losing their legs about 35 million years ago.

Design It Find out more about the evolutionary history of whales. How is a whale flipper similar to a bat wing and a human hand? Design a poster that shows the evolutionary history of whales.

 FLORIDA NGSSS

SC.7.N.1.3 Distinguish between an experiment and other forms of scientific investigation.

SC.7.L.15.1 Recognize that fossil evidence is consistent with the theory of evolution.

SC.7.L.15.2 Explore the theory of evolution and how genetic variation and environmental factors contribute to it.

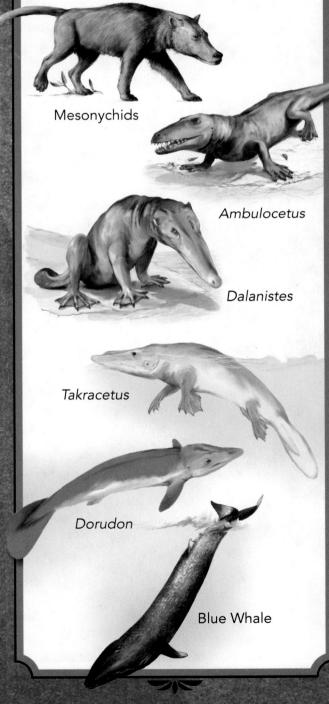

Over 50 million years, whales evolved from a species of doglike land mammals to the aquatic giants we know today.

Mesonychids

Ambulocetus

Dalanistes

Takracetus

Dorudon

Blue Whale

These nine-banded armadillo pups have a tough, scaly skin that acts like armor and helps to protect them from predators.

Summarizing

Life Science

In this Life Science unit, you learned about the diversity of living things. And you learned how the theory of evolution by natural selection explains diversity and change over time. You also learned how genetic information controls the traits of organisms and is passed from generation to generation. Lastly, you learned how living things interact with one another and their environment.

How is DNA important to these young armadillos?

_____

_____

_____

_____

_____

_____

_____

In what way do these animals interact with their environment?

_____

_____

_____

_____

_____

_____

_____

_____

As you study this unit, look for answers to these questions.

How do these plants use the SUNLIGHT?

How is water RECYCLED through the environment?

These American lotus plants in Florida's
Lake Okeechobee soak up sunlight.

Introducing

Life Science

 Florida Big Idea 18

Matter and Energy Transformations

A. Living things all share basic needs for life.

B. Living organisms acquire the energy they need for life processes through various metabolic pathways (photosynthesis and cellular respiration).

C. Matter and energy are recycled through cycles such as the carbon cycle.

❓ How do energy and matter move through ecosystems?

WHERE DOES FOOD COME FROM?

How do energy and matter move through ecosystems?

Flying around hunting for food, this barn owl spots a mouse for dinner. But what did the mouse eat? Perhaps it nibbled on seeds or a caterpillar. Then you might ask, where did the seeds and caterpillar get their food?

△ Develop Hypotheses **Where do living things get their food?**

_____

_____

_____

_____

_____

_____

▷ **UNTAMED SCIENCE** Watch the **Untamed Science** video to learn more about ecosystems and biomes.

Energy, Matter, and Living Things

FLORIDA — Next Generation Sunshine State Standards

Big Idea 2: SC.8.N.2.1, SC.8.N.2.2
Big Idea 18: SC.8.L.18.1, SC.8.L.18.2,
SC.8.L.18.3, SC.8.L.18.4

Language Arts: LA.8.2.2.3
Mathematics: MA.8.A.3.6

Check Your Understanding

1. Background Read the paragraph below and then answer the question.

> In science class, we looked at both plant and animal cells under the microscope. I could see the **nucleus** in many cells. In plant cells, we could see green-colored **chloroplasts.** Both plant and animal cells have **mitochondria,** but they were too small for us to see with the microscopes that we had.

> The **nucleus** is the organelle that acts as the cell's control center and directs the cell's activities.
> **Chloroplasts** are organelles that capture energy from sunlight and use it to produce food for the cell.
> **Mitochondria** are organelles that convert energy in food to energy the cell can use to carry out its functions.

- Circle the names of the organelles found only in plant cells. Underline the organelles found in both plant and animal cells.

    nucleus   mitochondria   chloroplasts

> ▷ MY READING WEB If you had trouble answering the question above, visit **My Reading Web** and type in *Energy, Matter, and Living Things.*

Vocabulary Skill

Greek Word Origins The table below shows the English word parts that have Greek origins. Learning the word parts can help you understand some of the vocabulary in this chapter.

Prefix	Meaning	Example
auto-	self	**autotroph**, *n.* an organism that makes its own food; producer
hetero-	other, different	**heterotroph**, *n.* an organism that cannot make its own food; a consumer

LA.8.1.6.11

2. Quick Check The word part *-troph* comes from the Greek word *trophe,* which means "food." Circle the word part in two places in the chart above. How does the Greek word relate to the meaning of these terms?

_____

_____

heterotroph

fermentation

precipitation

nitrogen fixation

Chapter Preview

LESSON 1
- ecosystem
- photosynthesis
- autotroph
- heterotroph
- chlorophyll

🔁 **Summarize**
△ Classify

LESSON 2
- cellular respiration
- fermentation

🔁 **Relate Text and Visuals**
△ Control Variables

LESSON 3
- evaporation
- condensation
- precipitation
- carbon cycle
- nitrogen fixation

🔁 **Sequence**
△ Infer

 ▷ **VOCAB FLASH CARDS** For extra help with vocabulary, visit **Vocab Flash Cards** and type in *Energy, Matter, and Living Things.*

1 Photosynthesis

How Do Living Things Get Energy From the Sun?
SC.8.L.18.1, SC.8.N.2.1

What Happens During Photosynthesis?
SC.8.L.18.1, LA.8.2.2.3

my planet Diary

MISCONCEPTION

When Is Food Not Food?

Misconception: Some people think that the plant food they give to house and garden plants is food for the plants. It isn't.

Plants make their own food—in the form of sugars—using water, carbon dioxide, and sunlight. So what is the "food" that people add to plants? It's fertilizer. Fertilizer is a mixture of minerals, such as potassium, calcium, and phosphorus. It helps plants grow but doesn't supply them with energy as food does. Farmers add fertilizer to soil to grow better quality crops. People do the same to grow bigger and healthier plants at home.

Communicate Write your answers to the questions below. Then discuss Question 2 with a partner.

1. What is "plant food"?

_____

_____

2. Why do you think people may feed their houseplants more often than farmers fertilize crops?

_____

_____

> PLANET DIARY Go to **Planet Diary** to learn more about photosynthesis.

SC.8.N.2.1

Lab zone® Do the Inquiry Warm-Up *Where Does the Energy Come From?*

Vocabulary
- ecosystem
- autotroph
- chlorophyll
- photosynthesis
- heterotroph

Skills
↻ Reading: Summarize
△ Inquiry: Classify

How Do Living Things Get Energy From the Sun?

FLORIDA NGSSS

SC.8.L.18.1 Describe and investigate the process of photosynthesis, such as the roles of light, carbon dioxide, water, and chlorophyll; production of food; release of oxygen.

SC.8.N.2.1 Distinguish between scientific and pseudoscientific ideas.

On a plain in Africa, a herd of zebras peacefully eats grass. But watch out! A group of lions is about to attack the herd. The lions will kill one of the zebras and eat it.

Both the zebras and the lion you see in **Figure 1** use the food they eat to obtain energy. Every living thing needs energy. All cells need energy to carry out their functions, such as making proteins and transporting substances into and out of the cell. Like the raw materials used within a cell, energy used by living things comes from their environment. Zebra meat supplies the lion's cells with energy. Similarly, grass provides the zebra's cells with energy. But where does the energy in the grass come from? Plants and certain other organisms, such as algae and some bacteria, obtain their energy in a different way. These organisms use the energy in sunlight to make their own food.

FIGURE 1 ·············

An Energy Chain
All living things need energy.

✎ **Interpret Photos** In the boxes, write the direct source of energy for each organism. Which organism shown does not depend on another organism for food?

_____

_____

501

apply it!

A spider catches and eats a caterpillar that depends on plant leaves for food.

1 **Sequence** Draw a diagram of your own that tracks how the sun's energy gets to the spider.

2 **Classify** In your diagram, label each organism as a heterotroph or an autotroph.

The Sun as an Energy Source

The sun is the source of energy in most ecosystems. Recall that an **ecosystem** is a community of organisms that live in a particular area, along with their nonliving environment. The process by which a cell captures energy in sunlight and uses it to make food is called **photosynthesis** (foh toh SIN thuh sis). The term *photosynthesis* comes from the Greek words *photos*, which means "light," and *syntithenai*, which means "putting together."

🔑 **Nearly all living things obtain energy either directly or indirectly from the energy of sunlight that is captured during photosynthesis.** Grass obtains energy directly from sunlight because grass makes its own food during photosynthesis. The zebra and lion both obtain the sun's energy indirectly. When the zebra eats grass, it gets energy from the sun that has been stored in the grass. Similarly, the lion obtains energy stored in the zebra.

Producers and Consumers

Plants make their own food through the process of photosynthesis. An organism that makes its own food is called a producer, or an **autotroph** (AWT oh trohf). An organism that cannot make its own food is called a consumer, or a **heterotroph** (HET ur oh trohf). Many heterotrophs, such as the zebra and the lion, obtain food by eating other organisms. Some heterotrophs, such as fungi, absorb their food from dead or decaying organisms. This type of heterotroph is called a *decomposer*.

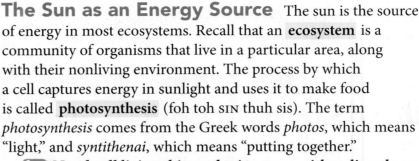

Lab zone® Do the Quick Lab *Energy From the Sun.*

🔑 Assess Your Understanding

1a. Identify An organism that makes its own food is a(n) (autotroph/heterotroph).

SC.8.L.18.1

b. Explain Why do living things need energy?

_____

SC.8.L.18.1

c. Apply Concepts Give an example of how energy from the sun gets into your cells.

_____

_____

_____

SC.8.L.18.1

got it? ....

○ **I get it!** Now I know that living things get energy directly from the sun by _____

or indirectly by _____

○ **I need extra help with** _____

Go to MY SCIENCE ⑤ COACH online for help with this subject.

SC.8.L.18.1

What Happens During Photosynthesis?

You've just read that plants make their own food. So how do they do that? **During photosynthesis, plants and some other organisms absorb energy from the sun and use the energy to convert carbon dioxide and water into sugars and oxygen.** You can think of photosynthesis as taking place in two stages. First, plants capture the sun's energy. Second, plants produce sugars.

Stage 1: Capturing the Sun's Energy

In the first stage of photosynthesis, energy from sunlight is captured. In plants, this process occurs mostly in the leaves. Recall that chloroplasts are green organelles inside plant cells. The green color comes from pigments, colored chemical compounds that absorb light. The main pigment for photosynthesis in chloroplasts is **chlorophyll**.

Chlorophyll functions something like the solar cells in a solar-powered calculator. Solar cells capture the energy in light and convert it to a form that powers the calculator. Similarly, chlorophyll captures light energy and converts it to a form that is used in the second stage of photosynthesis.

During Stage 1, water in the chloroplasts is split into hydrogen and oxygen, as shown in **Figure 2.** The oxygen is given off as a waste product. The hydrogen is used in Stage 2.

FLORIDA NGSSS

SC.8.L.18.1 Describe and investigate the process of photosynthesis, such as the roles of light, carbon dioxide, water, and chlorophyll; production of food; release of oxygen.

LA.8.2.2.3 The student will organize information to show understanding or relationships among facts, ideas, and events (e.g., representing main ideas within the text through charting and summarizing).

Vocabulary Greek Word Origins The Greek word part *chloros-* means "pale green." Circle two words in the text that begin with this word part. Which word means "a green compound that absorbs light"?

⚪ Chloroplast
⚪ Chlorophyll

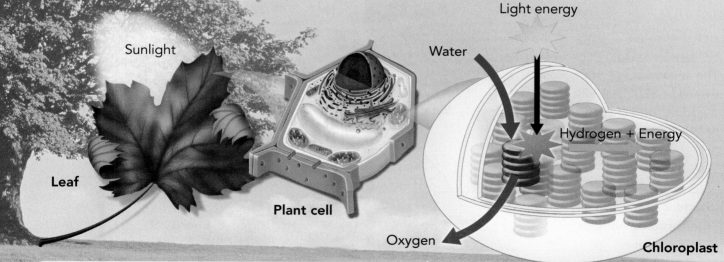

Light energy

Sunlight

Water

Hydrogen + Energy

Leaf

Plant cell

Oxygen

Chloroplast

FIGURE 2

First Stage of Photosynthesis
You might say the first stage of photosynthesis powers the "energy engine" of the living world.

✎ **Make Generalizations** What do you think this sentence means?

_____

_____

Summarize Complete the flowchart to show the process of photosynthesis.

Photosynthesis

Sunlight strikes leaf.

↓

_____ _____ _____

↓

_____ _____ _____ _____

LA.8.2.2.3

Stage 2: Using Energy to Make Food

In the second stage of photosynthesis, cells produce sugars. As shown in **Figure 3**, cells use hydrogen (H) that came from the splitting of water in Stage 1. Cells also use carbon dioxide (CO_2) from the air. Carbon dioxide enters the plant through small openings on the undersides of the leaves and moves into the chloroplasts.

Powered by the energy captured in Stage 1, hydrogen and carbon dioxide undergo a series of reactions that result in sugars. One important sugar produced is glucose. It has the chemical formula $C_6H_{12}O_6$. You may know that sugars are a type of carbohydrate. Cells can use the energy in glucose to carry out vital cell functions.

The other product of photosynthesis is oxygen gas (O_2). Recall that oxygen forms during the first stage when water molecules are split apart. Oxygen gas exits a leaf through the openings on its underside. Almost all the oxygen in Earth's atmosphere is produced by living things through the process of photosynthesis.

FIGURE 3 ···

> INTERACTIVE ART Producing Food
The second stage of photosynthesis makes food for a plant.

Identify Fill in the missing terms in the spaces provided.

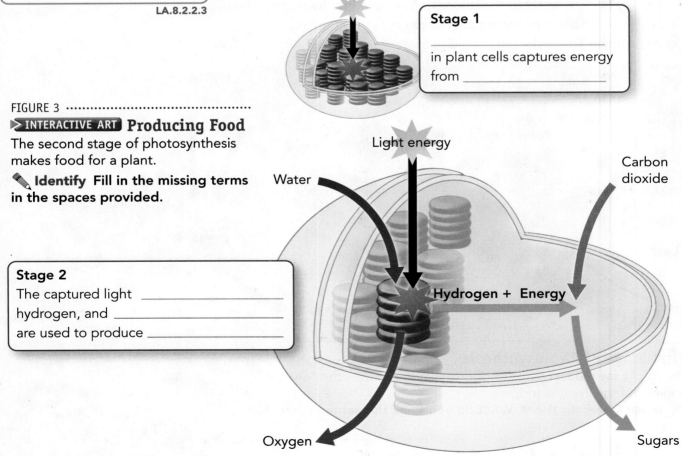

Stage 1
_____
in plant cells captures energy
from _____

Light energy

Water

Carbon dioxide

Hydrogen + Energy

Stage 2
The captured light _____
hydrogen, and _____
are used to produce _____

Oxygen

Sugars

The Photosynthesis Equation

The Photosynthesis Equation The events of photosynthesis that lead to the production of glucose can be summed up by the following chemical equation:

$$\text{light energy} + \underset{\text{carbon dioxide}}{6\,CO_2} + \underset{\text{water}}{6\,H_2O} \longrightarrow \underset{\text{glucose}}{C_6H_{12}O_6} + \underset{\text{oxygen}}{6\,O_2}$$

Notice that six molecules of carbon dioxide and six molecules of water are on the left side of the equation. These compounds are raw materials. One molecule of glucose and six molecules of oxygen are on the right side. These compounds are products. An arrow, meaning "yields," points from the raw materials to the products. Energy is not a raw material, but it is written on the left side of the equation to show that it is used in the reaction.

What happens to the sugars produced in photosynthesis? Plant cells use some of the sugars for food. The cells break down these molecules in a process that releases energy. This energy can then be used to carry out the plant's functions, such as growing and making seeds. Some sugar molecules are made into other compounds, such as cellulose for cell walls. Other sugar molecules may be stored in the plant's cells for later use. When you eat food from plants, such as potatoes or carrots, you are eating the plant's stored energy.

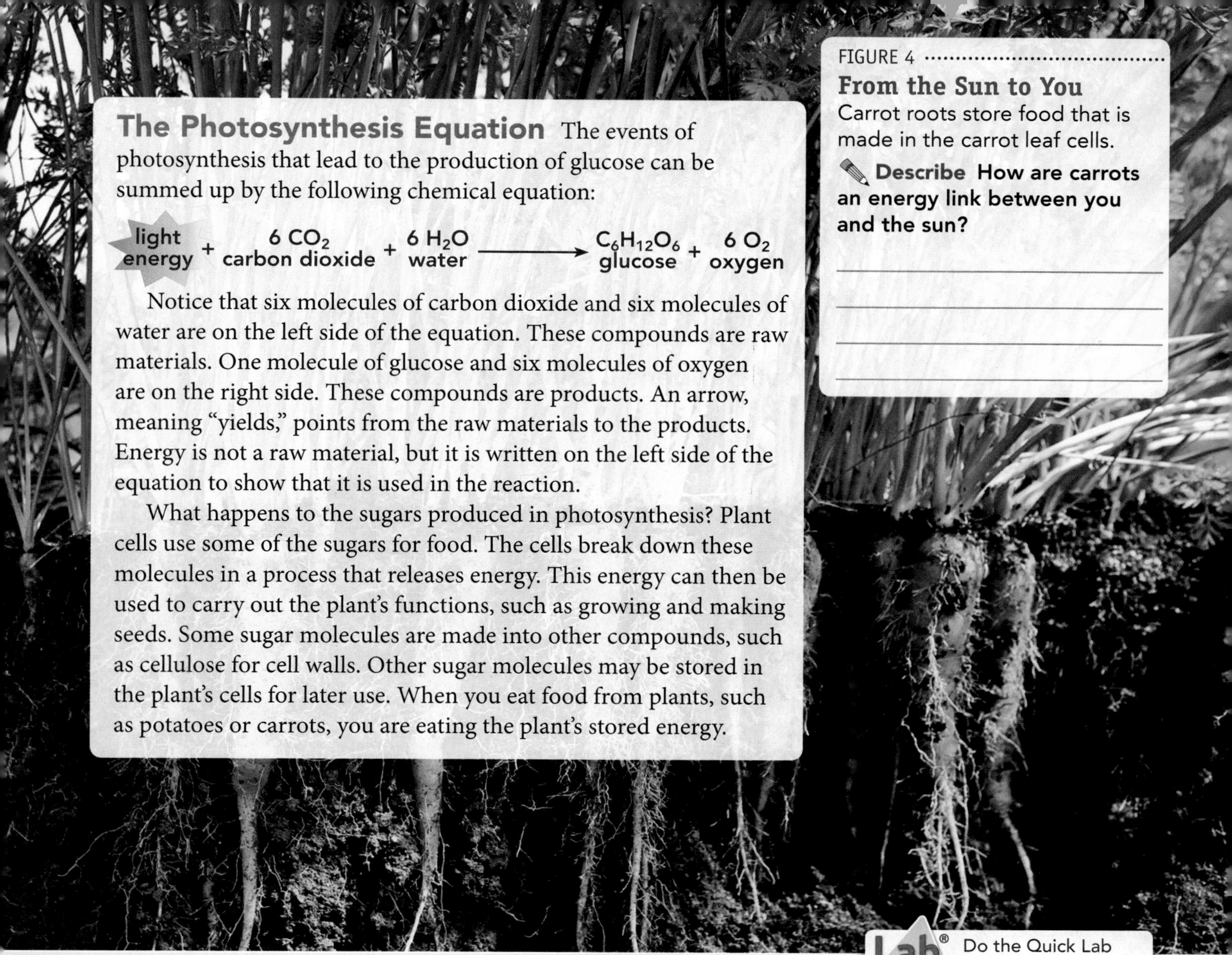

Lab zone® Do the Quick Lab *Looking at Pigments.*

FIGURE 4

From the Sun to You

Carrot roots store food that is made in the carrot leaf cells.

✎ **Describe** How are carrots an energy link between you and the sun?

_____

_____

_____

_____

⚷ Assess Your Understanding

2a. Name Circle two products of photosynthesis.
glucose/carbon dioxide/oxygen/chlorophyll

SC.8.L.18.1

b. Interpret Diagrams Refer to **Figure 3** on the facing page. Where does the hydrogen that is used in Stage 2 of photosynthesis come from?

_____

_____

SC.8.L.18.1

c. CHALLENGE Would you expect a plant to produce more oxygen on a sunny day or a cloudy day? Explain your answer.

_____

_____

_____

_____

SC.8.L.18.1

got it? ....

○ **I get it!** Now I know that during photosynthesis _____

_____

○ **I need extra help with** _____

Go to MY SCIENCE 🗪 COACH *online for help with this subject.*

SC.8.L.18.1

Cellular Respiration

UNLOCK THE ESSENTIAL ?

🔑 **What Happens During Cellular Respiration?**
SC.8.L.18.2, LA.8.2.2.3

🔑 **What Happens During Fermentation?**
SC.8.L.18.2

my planet Diary

FUN FACTS

Going to Extremes

You may not know it, but there are organisms living in rocks deep below Earth's surface. Other organisms hang out in steaming hot lakes, like Grand Prismatic Spring in Yellowstone National Park, shown here. The water in this lake can be as hot as 86°C! Still other organisms nestle inside nuclear waste. All of these organisms are extremophiles, microorganisms that thrive in extreme habitats. These life forms can get energy in strange ways. Some make food from ocean minerals. Others break down compounds in radioactive rocks!

Pose Questions Write a question about something else you would like to learn about extremophiles.

_____

_____

_____

_____

▷ PLANET DIARY Go to **Planet Diary** to learn more about extremophiles.

Do the Inquiry Warm-Up
Cellular Respiration.

FLORIDA NGSSS

SC.8.L.18.2 Describe and investigate how cellular respiration breaks down food to provide energy and releases carbon dioxide.

LA.8.2.2.3 The student will organize information to show understanding or relationships among facts, ideas, and events (e.g., representing main ideas within the text through mapping).

What Happens During Cellular Respiration?

You and your friend have been hiking all morning. You look for a flat rock to sit on, so you can eat the lunch you packed. The steepest part of the trail is ahead. You'll need a lot of energy to get to the top of the mountain! That energy will come from food.

Vocabulary
- cellular respiration
- fermentation

Skills
- ↻ **Reading:** Relate Text and Visuals
- △ **Inquiry:** Control Variables

What Is Cellular Respiration? After you eat a meal, your body breaks down the food and releases the sugars in the food. The most common sugar in foods is glucose ($C_6H_{12}O_6$). **Cellular respiration** is the process by which cells obtain energy from glucose. 🔑 **During cellular respiration, cells break down glucose and other molecules from food in the presence of oxygen, releasing energy.** Because living things need a constant supply of energy, the cells of nearly all living things carry out cellular respiration continuously.

Storing and Releasing Energy Imagine you have money in a savings account. If you want to buy something, you withdraw some money. Your body stores and uses energy in a similar way, as shown in **Figure 1.** When you eat a meal, you add to your body's energy savings account by storing glucose. When cells need energy, they "withdraw" it by breaking down glucose through cellular respiration.

Breathing and Respiration You may have already heard of the word *respiration*. It can mean "breathing"—or moving air in and out of your lungs. Breathing brings oxygen into your lungs, which is then carried to cells for cellular respiration. Breathing also removes the waste products of cellular respiration from your body.

FIGURE 1 ·····························

Getting Energy
Your body runs on the energy it gets from food.

✎ **Complete each task.**

1. **Infer** Color in the last three energy scales to show how the hiker's energy changes.

2. **CHALLENGE** How do you think the hiker's breathing rate changes as she climbs?

_____

_____

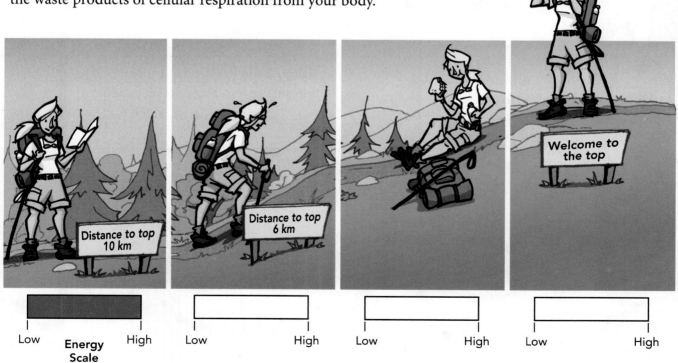

Distance to top 10 km

Distance to top 6 km

Welcome to the top

Low — Energy Scale — High

Low — High

Low — High

Low — High

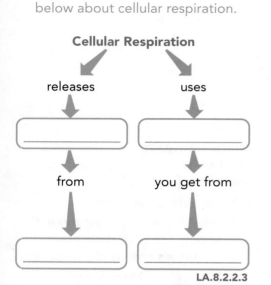

Cellular Respiration

releases   uses

from   you get from

LA.8.2.2.3

The Two Stages of Cellular Respiration Like photosynthesis, cellular respiration is a two-stage process. See **Figure 2.** The first stage occurs in the cytoplasm of a cell. There, molecules of glucose are broken down into smaller molecules. Oxygen is not involved in this stage, and only a small amount of energy is released.

The second stage takes place in the mitochondria. There, the small molecules are broken down even more. This change requires oxygen and releases a great deal of energy that the cell can use for all its activities. No wonder mitochondria are sometimes called the "powerhouses" of the cell!

The Cellular Respiration Equation Although respiration occurs in a series of complex steps, the overall process can be summarized in the following equation:

$$\underset{\text{glucose}}{C_6H_{12}O_6} + \underset{\text{oxygen}}{6\,O_2} \longrightarrow \underset{\text{carbon dioxide}}{6\,CO_2} + \underset{\text{water}}{6\,H_2O} + \text{energy}$$

Notice that the raw materials for cellular respiration are glucose and oxygen. Animals get glucose from the foods they consume. Plants and other organisms that carry out photosynthesis are able to produce their own glucose. The oxygen needed for cellular respiration is in the air or water surrounding the organism.

FIGURE 2 ⋯⋯⋯⋯⋯⋯⋯⋯⋯⋯⋯⋯⋯⋯⋯⋯⋯⋯

▶ **INTERACTIVE ART** **Releasing Energy**
Cellular respiration takes place in two stages.
✏️ **Identify** Fill in the missing terms in the spaces provided.

Stage 1 In the cytoplasm, _____ is broken down into smaller molecules, releasing a small amount of _____

Stage 2 In the _____, the smaller molecules react producing _____ ,water, and large amounts of _____

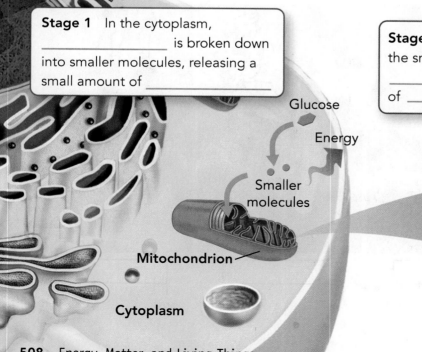

Glucose

Energy

Smaller molecules

Mitochondrion

Cytoplasm

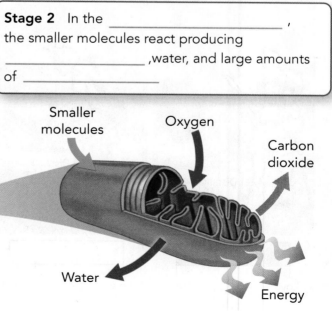

Smaller molecules

Oxygen

Carbon dioxide

Water

Energy

Comparing Two Energy Processes

If you think the equation for cellular respiration is the opposite of the one for photosynthesis, you're right! Photosynthesis and cellular respiration can be thought of as opposite processes. Together, these two processes form a cycle that keeps the levels of oxygen and carbon dioxide fairly constant in Earth's atmosphere. As you can see from **Figure 3,** living things cycle both gases over and over again.

Photosynthesis

FIGURE 3 ·······································

Opposite Processes

Producers carry out photosynthesis, but producers and consumers both carry out cellular respiration.

✎ **Name** Use the word bank to fill in the missing terms. Words can be used more than once.

+   +

Word Bank	
Oxygen	Energy
Carbon dioxide	Glucose
Water	

Cellular Respiration

 Do the Lab Investigation
Exhaling Carbon Dioxide.

🔑 Assess Your Understanding

1a. Describe Why do organisms need to carry out the process of respiration?

_____

_____

_____

SC.8.L.18.2

b. Relate Cause and Effect Why does cellular respiration add carbon dioxide to the atmosphere, but photosynthesis does not?

_____

_____

_____

SC.8.L.18.2

got it? ···

○ **I get it!** Now I know that during cellular respiration, cells _____

_____

○ **I need extra help with** _____

     Go to MY SCIENCE ⓢ COACH *online for help with this subject.*   SC.8.L.18.2

FLORIDA NGSSS

SC.8.L.18.2 Describe and investigate how cellular respiration breaks down food to provide energy and releases carbon dioxide.

What Happens During Fermentation?

Some organisms can live in the presence or absence of oxygen. If not enough oxygen is present to carry out cellular respiration, these organisms switch to another process. **Fermentation** is an energy-releasing process that does not require oxygen. 🔑 **During fermentation, cells release energy from food without using oxygen.** One drawback to fermentation is that it releases far less energy than cellular respiration does.

Alcoholic Fermentation
Did you know that when you eat a slice of bread, you are eating a product of fermentation? Alcoholic fermentation occurs in yeast and other single-celled organisms. This type of fermentation produces alcohol, carbon dioxide, and a small amount of energy. These products are important to bakers and brewers. Carbon dioxide produced by yeast creates gas pockets in bread dough, causing it to rise. Carbon dioxide is also the source of bubbles in alcoholic drinks such as beer and sparkling wine.

Lactic Acid Fermentation
Think of a time when you ran as fast and as long as you could. Your leg muscles were pushing hard against the ground, and you were breathing quickly. But, no matter how quickly you breathed, your muscle cells used up the oxygen faster than it could be replaced. Because your cells lacked oxygen, fermentation occurred. Your muscle cells got energy, but they did so by breaking down glucose without using oxygen. One product of this type of fermentation is a compound known as lactic acid. When lactic acid builds up, you feel a painful sensation in your muscles. Your muscles feel weak and sore. Later, when your cells get more oxygen, the lactic acid breaks down and the pain goes away.

apply it!

A ball of bread dough mixed with yeast is left in a bowl at room temperature. As time passes, the dough increases in size.

1 Compare and Contrast How does fermentation that causes dough to rise differ from fermentation in muscles?

_____

_____

_____

_____

_____

2 Control Variables How would you show that yeast was responsible for making the dough rise?

_____

_____

_____

_____

_____

FIGURE 4 ⋯⋯⋯⋯⋯⋯⋯⋯⋯⋯⋯⋯⋯⋯⋯⋯⋯

> ART IN MOTION **Energy for Life**
Energy processes in living things include photosynthesis, cellular respiration, and fermentation.

 Review Circle the correct answers and complete the sentences in the spaces provided.

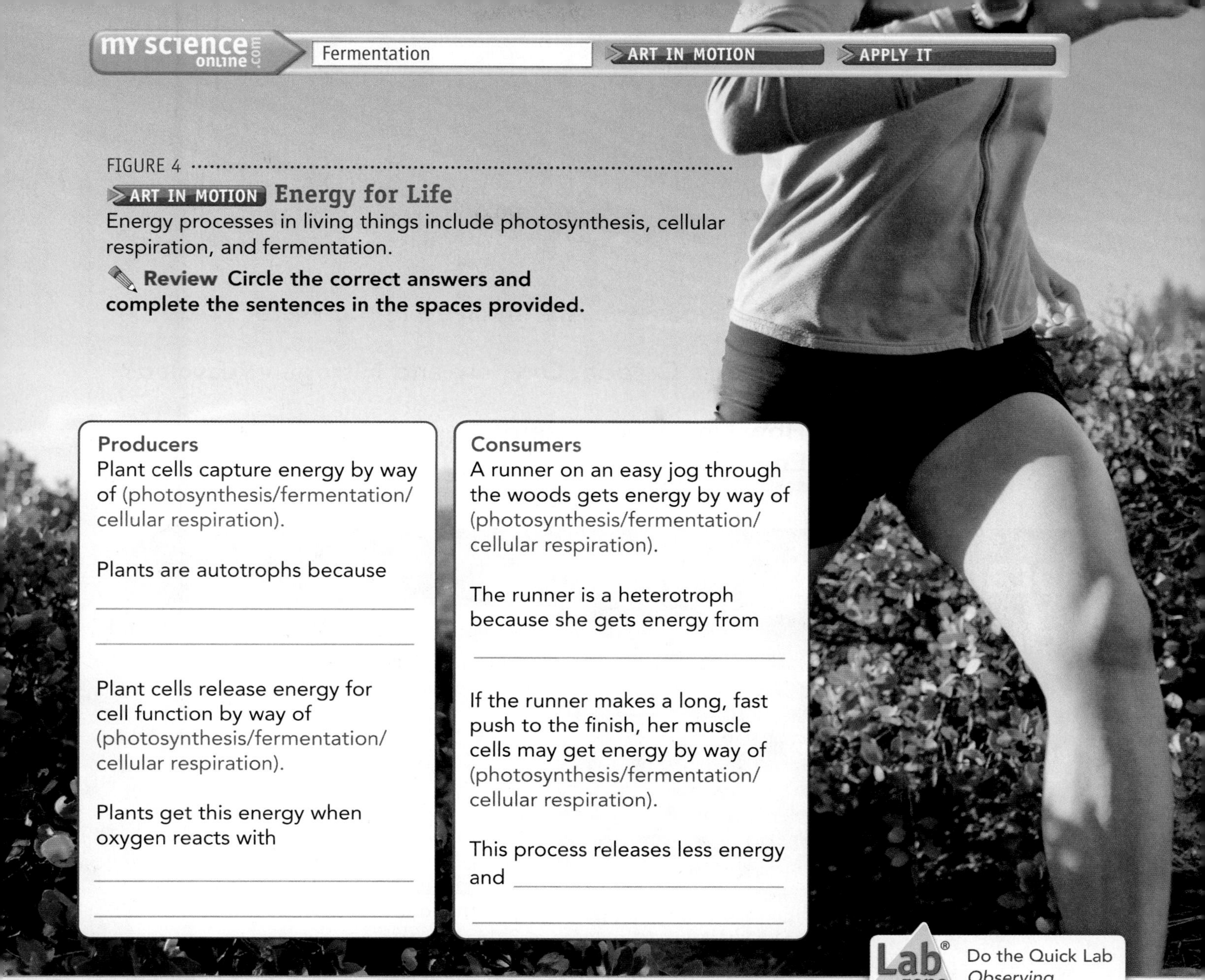

Producers
Plant cells capture energy by way of (photosynthesis/fermentation/cellular respiration).

Plants are autotrophs because

_____

_____

Plant cells release energy for cell function by way of (photosynthesis/fermentation/cellular respiration).

Plants get this energy when oxygen reacts with

_____

_____

Consumers
A runner on an easy jog through the woods gets energy by way of (photosynthesis/fermentation/cellular respiration).

The runner is a heterotroph because she gets energy from

_____

If the runner makes a long, fast push to the finish, her muscle cells may get energy by way of (photosynthesis/fermentation/cellular respiration).

This process releases less energy and _____

_____

 Lab zone Do the Quick Lab *Observing Fermentation.*

Assess Your Understanding

2a. Identify The process in which cells obtain energy without using oxygen is called

_____

SC.8.L.18.2

b. Infer How would athletes be affected if this process could not take place?

_____

_____

_____

_____

SC.8.L.18.2

got it?

○ **I get it!** Now I know fermentation is a way for cells to _____

_____

_____

○ I need extra help with _____

_____

Go to my science COACH *online for help with this subject.*

SC.8.L.18.2

511

Cycles of Matter

UNLOCK THE ESSENTIAL ?

🔑 **What Processes Are Involved in the Water Cycle?**
SC.8.L.18.3

🔑 **How Are Carbon, Oxygen, and Nitrogen Recycled?**
SC.8.L.18.3, SC.8.N.4.2

🔑 **How Do Living Systems Conserve Matter and Energy?**
SC.8.L.18.4, SC.8.N.2.2, MA.6.A.3.6, LA.8.2.2.3

MY PLANET DIARY

Canaries and Coal

Have you ever stopped to listen to a bird sing? If you were a coal miner in the early 1900s, your life may have depended on it! Sometimes miners stumbled upon pockets of carbon monoxide, a toxic, odorless gas that makes it difficult for the body to get enough oxygen. Without fresh air circulating in the mineshafts, the miners would fall asleep and eventually die. To prevent this disaster from happening, canaries were used to monitor the air quality. A singing canary indicated that all was well. If the canary stopped singing and died, the miners knew to leave the mine right away.

DISASTER

Answer the question below.
Do you think it was ethical, or fair, to use canaries this way? Explain.

_____
_____
_____
_____

▶ **PLANET DIARY** Go to **Planet Diary** to learn more about cycles of matter.

Lab® zone Do the Inquiry Warm-Up *Are You Part of a Cycle?*

FLORIDA NGSSS

SC.8.L.18.3 Construct a scientific model of the carbon cycle to show how matter and energy are continuously transferred within and between organisms and their physical environment.

What Processes Are Involved in the Water Cycle?

Recall that energy moves through an ecosystem as organisms eat other organisms. But how does matter move through an ecosystem? Matter in an ecosystem includes water, carbon, oxygen, nitrogen, and many other substances. Recycling is important for ecosystems because matter is limited. In this lesson, you will learn about some of the cycles of matter.

Water is essential for life. The water cycle is the continuous process by which water moves from Earth's surface to the atmosphere and back. 🔑 **The processes of evaporation, condensation, and precipitation make up the water cycle.**

Vocabulary
- evaporation • condensation
- precipitation • carbon cycle
- nitrogen fixation

Skills
↻ Reading: Sequence
△ Inquiry: Infer

Evaporation
How does water from the ground get into the air? The process by which molecules of liquid water absorb energy and change to a gas is called **evaporation.** The energy for evaporation comes from the heat of the sun. In the water cycle, liquid water evaporates from oceans, lakes, and other sources and forms water vapor, a gas, in the atmosphere. Smaller amounts of water also evaporate from living things. Plants release water vapor from their leaves. You release liquid water in your wastes and water vapor when you exhale.

Condensation
As water vapor rises higher in the atmosphere, it cools down. The cooled vapor then turns back into tiny drops of liquid water. The process by which a gas changes to a liquid is called **condensation.** The water droplets collect around dust particles and form clouds.

Precipitation
As more water vapor condenses, the drops of water in the clouds grow larger. Eventually the heavy drops fall to Earth as **precipitation**—rain, snow, sleet, or hail. Precipitation may fall into oceans, lakes, or rivers. The precipitation that falls on land may soak into the soil and become groundwater, or run off the land, flowing back into a river or ocean.

FIGURE 1 ·····················
> **INTERACTIVE ART** Water Cycle
In the water cycle, water moves continuously from Earth's surface to the atmosphere and back.

✎ **Identify** As you read, label the three processes of the water cycle in the diagram.

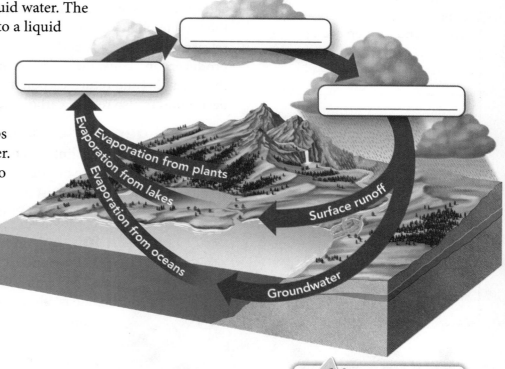

Evaporation from plants
Evaporation from lakes
Evaporation from oceans
Surface runoff
Groundwater

Lab zone ® Do the Quick Lab *Following Water.*

🗨 Assess Your Understanding

got it? ·····················

○ **I get it!** Now I know that the processes of the water cycle are _____

_____

○ **I need extra help with** _____

Go to **my science** COACH online for help with this subject.

SC.8.L.18.3

apply it!

The processes by which carbon and oxygen are recycled are linked.

△ **Infer** On the lines below, describe how you think a cow eating grass is part of both the carbon and oxygen cycles.

_____

_____

_____

_____

_____

_____

_____

How Are Carbon, Oxygen, and Nitrogen Recycled?

Carbon, oxygen, and nitrogen are also necessary for life. Carbon and nitrogen are essential building blocks in the bodies of living things. For example, carbon and nitrogen are major components of the proteins that build muscles. Also, most organisms use oxygen for their life processes. 🔑 **In ecosystems, producers, consumers, and decomposers all play roles in recycling carbon, oxygen, and nitrogen.**

The Carbon Cycle The **carbon cycle** is the process by which carbon moves within and between organisms and their physical environment. Most producers take in carbon dioxide gas from the air during photosynthesis. They use carbon from the carbon dioxide to make food—carbon-containing molecules such as sugars and starches. As consumers eat producers, they take in the carbon-containing food molecules. Consumers then break down the food to obtain energy. As the food is broken down, consumers release carbon dioxide and water into the environment. When producers and consumers die, decomposers break down their remains and return carbon molecules to the soil. Some decomposers also release carbon dioxide into the air.

The Oxygen Cycle The processes by which carbon and oxygen are recycled are linked. Look at **Figure 2.** Like carbon, oxygen cycles through ecosystems. Producers release oxygen as a result of photosynthesis. Most organisms take in oxygen from the air or water and use it to carry out their life processes.

Human Impact Human activities also affect the levels of carbon and oxygen in the atmosphere. When humans burn oil and other plant-based fuels, carbon dioxide is released into the atmosphere. Carbon dioxide levels can also rise when humans clear forests for lumber, fuel, and farmland. Increasing levels of carbon dioxide are a major factor in global warming. When trees are removed from the ecosystem, there are fewer producers to absorb carbon dioxide. There is an even greater effect if trees are burned down to clear a forest. When trees are burned down, additional carbon dioxide is released during the burning process.

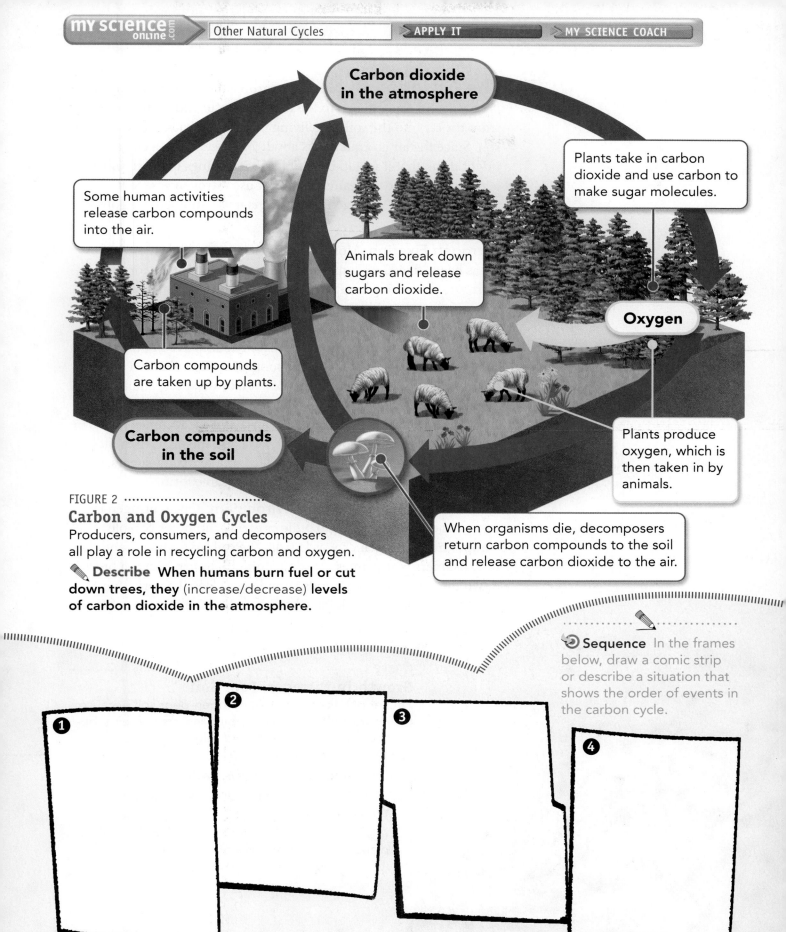

Carbon dioxide in the atmosphere

Some human activities release carbon compounds into the air.

Plants take in carbon dioxide and use carbon to make sugar molecules.

Animals break down sugars and release carbon dioxide.

Oxygen

Carbon compounds are taken up by plants.

Carbon compounds in the soil

Plants produce oxygen, which is then taken in by animals.

FIGURE 2

Carbon and Oxygen Cycles
Producers, consumers, and decomposers all play a role in recycling carbon and oxygen.

✎ **Describe** When humans burn fuel or cut down trees, they (increase/decrease) levels of carbon dioxide in the atmosphere.

When organisms die, decomposers return carbon compounds to the soil and release carbon dioxide to the air.

✎ **Sequence** In the frames below, draw a comic strip or describe a situation that shows the order of events in the carbon cycle.

❶

❷

❸

❹

The Nitrogen Cycle

Like carbon and oxygen, nitrogen is recycled in ecosystems. In the nitrogen cycle, nitrogen moves from the air into the soil, into living things, and back into the air or soil. Since the air around you is about 78 percent nitrogen gas, you might think that it would be easy for living things to obtain nitrogen. However, most organisms cannot use nitrogen gas. Nitrogen gas is called "free" nitrogen because it is not combined with other kinds of atoms.

Nitrogen Fixation Most organisms can use nitrogen only after it has been "fixed," or combined with other elements to form nitrogen-containing compounds. The process of changing free nitrogen into a usable form of nitrogen, as shown in **Figure 4,** is called **nitrogen fixation.** Most nitrogen fixation is performed by certain kinds of bacteria. Some of these bacteria live in bumps called nodules (NAHJ oolz) on the roots of certain plants. These plants, known as legumes, include clover, beans, peas, alfalfa, peanuts, and some trees.

The relationship between the bacteria and the legumes is an example of mutualism. Both the bacteria and the plants benefit from this relationship: The bacteria feed on the plants' sugars, and the plants are supplied with nitrogen in a usable form.

Return of Nitrogen to the Environment Once nitrogen is fixed, producers can use it to build proteins and other complex compounds. Nitrogen can cycle from the soil to producers and then to consumers many times. At some point, however, bacteria break down the nitrogen compounds completely. These bacteria then release free nitrogen back into the air, causing the cycle to continue.

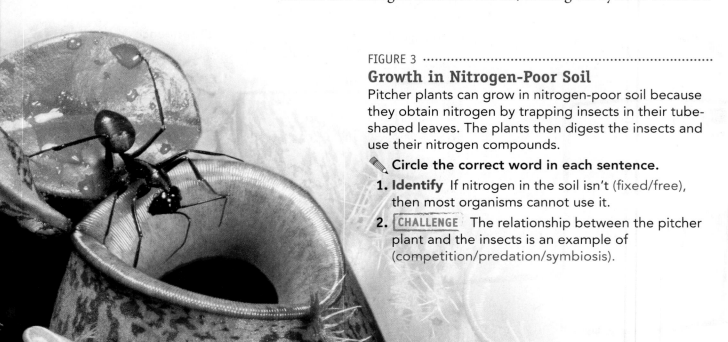

FIGURE 3

Growth in Nitrogen-Poor Soil

Pitcher plants can grow in nitrogen-poor soil because they obtain nitrogen by trapping insects in their tube-shaped leaves. The plants then digest the insects and use their nitrogen compounds.

✎ **Circle the correct word in each sentence.**

1. **Identify** If nitrogen in the soil isn't (fixed/free), then most organisms cannot use it.

2. [CHALLENGE] The relationship between the pitcher plant and the insects is an example of (competition/predation/symbiosis).

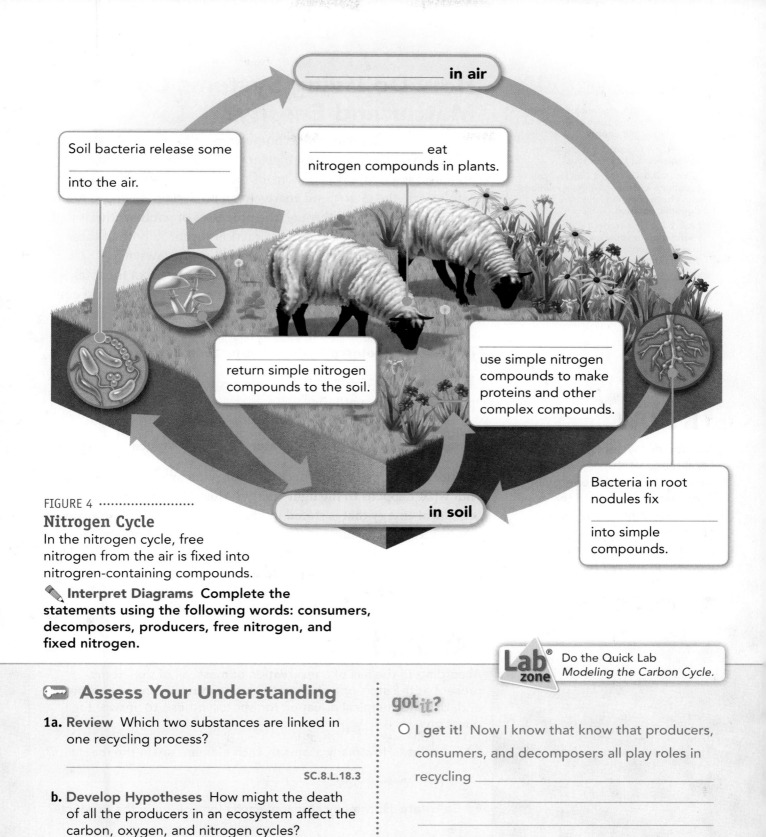

_____ in air

Soil bacteria release some _____ into the air.

_____ eat nitrogen compounds in plants.

return simple nitrogen compounds to the soil.

use simple nitrogen compounds to make proteins and other complex compounds.

_____ in soil

Bacteria in root nodules fix _____ into simple compounds.

FIGURE 4 ....

Nitrogen Cycle

In the nitrogen cycle, free nitrogen from the air is fixed into nitrogren-containing compounds.

✎ **Interpret Diagrams** Complete the statements using the following words: consumers, decomposers, producers, free nitrogen, and fixed nitrogen.

Lab® zone — Do the Quick Lab _Modeling the Carbon Cycle._

🗝 Assess Your Understanding

1a. Review Which two substances are linked in one recycling process?

_____

SC.8.L.18.3

b. Develop Hypotheses How might the death of all the producers in an ecosystem affect the carbon, oxygen, and nitrogen cycles?

_____
_____
_____
_____

SC.8.L.18.3

got it?

○ I get it! Now I know that know that producers, consumers, and decomposers all play roles in recycling _____

_____
_____

○ I need extra help with _____

_Go to_ MY SCIENCE Ⓢ COACH _online for help with this subject._ SC.8.L.18.3

FLORIDA NGSSS

SC.8.L.18.4 Cite evidence that living systems follow the Laws of Conservation of Mass and Energy.

SC.8.N.2.2 Discuss what characterizes science and its methods.

MA.6.A.3.6 Construct and analyze equations to describe simple relations using both common language and algebraic notation.

LA.8.2.2.3 The student will organize information to show understanding (e.g., representing main ideas within the text through summarizing).

How Do Living Systems Conserve Matter and Energy?

A toaster, your bicycle, and a computer are all systems. A system is a group of parts that work together to perform a function. An organism is a living system. One of the functions of a living system is to recycle the matter and energy in an ecosystem. Living systems perform this function through the processes of photosynthesis and respiration. Recall that chemical reactions occur in both of these processes. And all chemical reactions follow the laws of conservation of mass and energy. These laws state that the total amount of matter and energy before a chemical reaction must equal the total amount of matter and energy after the chemical reaction.

🔑 **Living systems conserve matter and energy through the processes of photosynthesis and respiration.**

Photosynthesis The following equation summarizes the process of photosynthesis.

$$\text{light energy} + 6\ CO_2\ (\text{carbon dioxide}) + 6\ H_2O\ (\text{water}) \longrightarrow C_6H_{12}O_6\ (\text{glucose}) + 6\ O_2\ (\text{oxygen})$$

Notice that light energy is necessary for photosynthesis to occur. But what happens to the light energy? Most of it is converted to chemical energy that is stored in the chemical bonds of the sugar molecules. Plants, along with organisms that eat the plants, can later use this energy. Matter is also conserved during photosynthesis. Complete the Do the Math to find out how this is so.

did you know?

Aquatic ecosystems, such as the coral reefs off the coast of Florida, also depend on the energy in sunlight. Algae live within the coral animals that make up the reef. The coral animals benefit from the energy that the algae provide through photosynthesis. In turn, the reef provides a structure on which the algae can grow.

do the math!

According to the law of conservation of mass, all of the atoms present at the start of a chemical reaction must be present at the end. Use the chemical equation for photosynthesis to answer the questions.

❶ **Calculate** How many atoms of each element are in the reactants?

_____

❷ **Calculate** How many atoms of each element are in the products?

_____

❸ **Relate Evidence and Explanation** Explain why the chemical equation for photosynthesis shows conservation of mass.

_____

_____

MA.6.A.3.6, SC.8.N.2.2

Respiration During respiration, the cells in living systems break down chemical bonds and release the energy they contain. The following equation summarizes the process of respiration.

$$\underset{\text{glucose}}{C_6H_{12}O_6} + \underset{\text{oxygen}}{6\,O_2} \longrightarrow \underset{\text{carbon dioxide}}{6\,CO_2} + \underset{\text{water}}{6\,H_2O} + \text{energy}$$

Notice that energy is released in this reaction. An organism, such as the white-tailed deer shown in **Figure 5,** uses this energy to move, grow, reproduce, and carry out other life activities. Notice also that all of the atoms present at the start of the reaction are present at the end. As is true with photosynthesis, matter and energy change forms during respiration, but none of it is destroyed.

Conservation Laws and Earth Systems Recall that Earth is a system made up of the biosphere, geosphere, hydrosphere, and atmosphere. According to the conservation laws, the total amount of matter and energy in the Earth system stays constant. As plants and animals grow, they do not use up matter. Rather, they use energy to transform the raw materials in their environment into living cells. When these organisms die, their matter is returned to the soil, the atmosphere, or other parts of the Earth system. Then the cycle starts again with other organisms.

FIGURE 5 ·······

Conservation in Florida Ecosystems
White-tailed deer are found in many Florida ecosystems.

Infer Imagine that you are a carbon atom in a molecule of carbon dioxide floating in the air of this photo. Describe how you might move through this ecosystem.

Cycles of Matter

ESSENTIAL ?

How do energy and matter move through ecosystems?

FIGURE 6 ···

▶ **REAL-WORLD INQUIRY** Energy and matter are constantly moving through ecosystems.

✏️ **Make Models** Draw and label arrows to represent the following in the figure below: water cycle, carbon cycle, oxygen cycle, nitrogen cycle, and the flow of energy.

🔑 Assess Your Understanding

2a. Summarize In your own words, state the meaning of the conservation of energy.

_____

_____

_____

SC.8.L.18.4, LA.8.2.2.3

b. Apply Concepts Suppose a bug eats a plant. Then a frog eats the bug. Does the frog gain the same amount of energy from eating the bug that the bug gained from eating the plant? Explain why in terms of the law of conservation of energy.

_____

_____

_____

_____

_____

_____

SC.8.L.18.4

c. ANSWER THE ESSENTIAL ❓ How do energy and matter move through ecosystems?

_____

_____

_____

_____

_____

_____

_____

SC.8.L.18.3, SC.8.L.18.4

got it? ∙∙∙∙∙∙∙∙∙∙∙∙∙∙∙∙∙∙∙∙∙∙∙∙∙∙∙∙∙∙∙∙

○ I get it! Now I know that matter and energy are conserved in ecosystems _____

_____

_____

○ I need extra help with _____

Go to MY SCIENCE Ⓢ COACH *online for help with this subject.*   SC.8.L.18.4

Producers,_____, and _____ help to move matter and energy through ecosystems.

LESSON 1 Photosynthesis

SC.8.L.18.1, SC.8.N.2.1

🔑 Nearly all living things obtain energy either directly or indirectly from the energy of sunlight that is captured during photosynthesis.

🔑 During photosynthesis, plants and some other organisms absorb energy from the sun and use the energy to convert carbon dioxide and water into sugars and oxygen.

Vocabulary
- ecosystem
- photosynthesis
- autotroph
- heterotroph
- chlorophyll

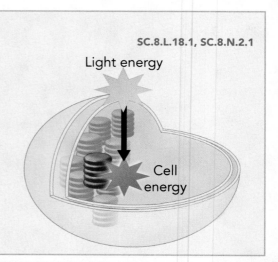

Light energy

Cell energy

LESSON 2 Cellular Respiration

SC.8.L.18.2

🔑 During cellular respiration, cells break down glucose and other molecules from food in the presence of oxygen, releasing energy.

🔑 During fermentation, cells release energy from food without using oxygen.

Vocabulary
- cellular respiration
- fermentation

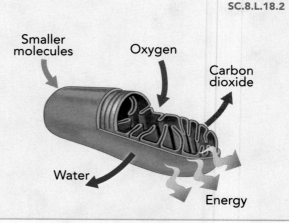

Smaller molecules

Oxygen

Carbon dioxide

Water

Energy

LESSON 3 Cycles of Matter

SC.8.L.18.3, SC.8.L.18.4, SC.8.N.2.2, SC.8.N.4.2

🔑 The processes of evaporation, condensation, and precipitation make up the water cycle.

🔑 In ecosystems, producers, consumers, and decomposers all play roles in recycling carbon, oxygen, and nitrogen.

🔑 Matter and energy are conserved in ecosystems through the processes of photosynthesis and respiration.

Vocabulary
- evaporation
- condensation
- precipitation
- carbon cycle
- nitrogen fixation

Review and Assessment

LESSON 1 Photosynthesis

1. Which of the following organisms are autotrophs?

  a. fungi   **b.** rabbits

  c. humans   **d.** oak trees

                                       SC.8.L.18.1

2. Plants are green because of

_____, the main

photosynthetic pigment in chloroplasts.

                                       SC.8.L.18.1

3. Interpret Diagrams Fill in the missing labels in the diagram below.

                                       SC.8.L.18.1

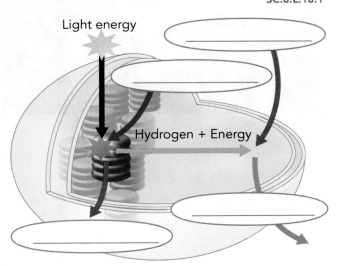

Light energy

Hydrogen + Energy

4. Predict Suppose a volcano threw so much ash into the air that it blocked much of the sunlight. How might this event affect the ability of animals to obtain energy to live?

_____

_____

_____

                                       SC.8.L.18.1

5. **Write About It** How do you get energy? Describe the path of energy from the sun to you, using at least two vocabulary terms you learned in this lesson.

                                       SC.8.L.18.1

LESSON 2 Cellular Respiration

6. In which cell structure does cellular respiration take place?

  a. nucleus   **b.** chloroplast

  c. chlorophyll   **d.** mitochondrion

                                       SC.8.L.18.2

7. _____ is a process that

releases energy in cells without using oxygen.

                                       SC.8.L.18.2

8. What is one common food that is made with the help of fermentation?

_____

                                       SC.8.L.18.2

9. Explain Write a word equation for cellular respiration in cells.

_____

_____

_____

_____

                                       SC.8.L.18.2

10. Summarize In one or two sentences, summarize what happens during each of the two stages of cellular respiration.

_____

_____

_____

_____

_____

_____

_____

_____

                                       SC.8.L.18.2

11. Apply Concepts How is breathing related to cellular respiration?

_____

_____

_____

_____

                                       SC.8.L.18.2

LESSON 3 Cycles of Matter

12. When drops of water in a cloud become heavy enough, they fall to Earth as

    a. permafrost.   **b.** evaporation.

    c. precipitation.   **d.** condensation.

    SC.8.L.18.3

13. Evaporation, condensation, and precipitation are the three main processes in the

    _____

    SC.8.L.18.3

14. **Classify** Which group of organisms is the source of oxygen in the oxygen cycle?

    _____

    _____

    SC.8.L.18.3

15. **Make Generalizations** Describe the roles of producers and consumers in the carbon cycle.

    _____

    _____

    _____

    _____

    _____

    _____

    _____

    SC.8.L.18.3

16. **Draw Conclusions** What would happen if all the nitrogen-fixing bacteria disappeared?

    _____

    _____

    _____

    SC.8.L.18.3

17. **Compare and Contrast** How does the mass of the products of respiration compare with the mass of the reactants? How do you know?

    _____

    _____

    _____

    _____

    SC.8.L.18.4

APPLY THE ESSENTIAL How do energy and matter move through ecosystems?

18. Many acres of the Amazon rain forest have been destroyed to create farmland. Describe how the movement of energy in this area might be affected. How might the carbon and oxygen cycles also be affected?

_____

_____

_____

_____

_____

_____

_____

_____

_____

_____

_____

_____

_____

_____

_____

_____

SC.8.L.18.3, SC.8.N.4.2

Florida Benchmarks Review

Circle the letter of the best answer.

1 Choose the name and cellular process that match the cell structure shown below.

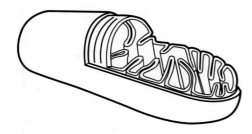

A chloroplast; cellular respiration
B mitochondrion; cellular respiration
C chloroplast; photosynthesis
D mitochondrion; photosynthesis

SC.8.L.18.2

2 What is the source of energy used in photosynthesis?

A glucose
B sunlight
C chlorophyll
D DNA

SC.8.L.18.1

3 Which process produces carbon dioxide?

A photosynthesis
B evaporation
C cellular respiration
D nitrogen fixation

SC.8.L.18.1

4 What is one main difference between fermentation and cellular respiration?

A Fermentation does not require oxygen, while cellular respiration does.
B Fermentation does not release energy, while cellular respiration does.
C Fermentation does not occur in animals, while cellular respiration does.
D Fermentation does not depend on the sun, while cellular respiration does.

SC.8.L.18.2

5 Which two carbon compounds are recycled in the carbon and oxygen cycles?

A carbon dioxide and water
B water and fixed nitrogen
C sugar and water
D carbon dioxide and sugar

SC.8.L.18.3

6 The diagram shows the flow of energy through an ecosystem. Which organisms have the least amount of energy available to them?

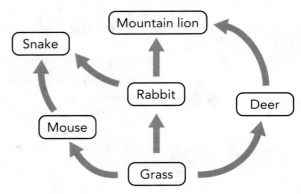

A grass
B mouse, rabbit, and deer
C snake and mountain lion
D grass and mountain lion

SC.8.L.18.4

Florida SCIENCE MATTERS

ARE WE GETTING WARMER?

Explaining Climate Change Most scientists think that an increase in greenhouse gases is warming Earth's climate. The atmosphere contains greenhouse gases, such as carbon dioxide. Greenhouse gases absorb thermal energy radiated from Earth's surface, thus warming the atmosphere. For about 200 years, human activities that release carbon dioxide have been increasing. These activities include burning fossil fuels and cutting down forests. Both fossil fuels and forests are rich in carbon. Look at the graph to see how carbon dioxide in the atmosphere has increased recently.

Earth Systems and the Carbon Cycle
More carbon in the atmosphere affects the carbon cycle. And changes in the carbon cycle affect other Earth systems. For example, as the atmosphere warms, so do the oceans of the hydrosphere. In the cryosphere, glaciers are melting. Melting glaciers are raising sea levels in many parts of the world. Climate change brings warmer temperatures to some regions. Elsewhere, precipitation may increase or decrease.

All these changes affect the biosphere. In many areas, the habitats of plants and animals are changing. Living things that cannot adapt to a new climate may become extinct. Some changes may be beneficial. More carbon dioxide allows plants to carry out photosynthesis at a higher rate. Plants may grow faster and take up more carbon.

Global warming has raised average temperatures in Earth's polar regions. This has caused glaciers to melt and reduced the amount of sea ice during summer. ▲

FLORIDA NGSSS

SC.8.N.1.5 Analyze the methods used to develop a scientific explanation as seen in different fields of science.

SC.8.N.3.2 Explain why theories are modified but rarely discarded.

SC.8.N.4.2 Explain how political, social, and economic concerns can affect science, and vice versa.

SC.8.L.18.3 Construct a scientific model of the carbon cycle to show how matter and energy are continuously transferred.

LA.8.4.2.2 The student will record information related to a topic and attribute sources of information.

Modifying Climate Theory and Models

Most scientists agree on the theory of climate change and its causes. But it is still hard to predict how much warming will occur and where warming will be greatest. To make these predictions, scientists need data on air and water temperatures worldwide. Some of these data are historic weather statistics. Other data are collected by satellites that monitor the atmosphere, ocean, and land surface. Powerful computers use these data in computer models of climate change. Scientists modify their theory and models as they obtain new data on Earth's changing climate.

Climate Science and Decision Making

Around the world, governments are trying to figure out what to do about climate change. Many people think that countries should agree to limit the use of fossils fuels. Others suggest that people should plant more trees to help remove carbon from the atmosphere. Countries on low-lying islands or coastlines are already threatened by rising sea levels. Climate change may cause droughts in areas where people must raise food to feed themselves. By improving their predictions of how much warming may occur, scientists can help governments plan solutions to the problem of climate change.

▼ Direct measurements of carbon dioxide in the atmosphere over many years show how carbon dioxide has been increasing.

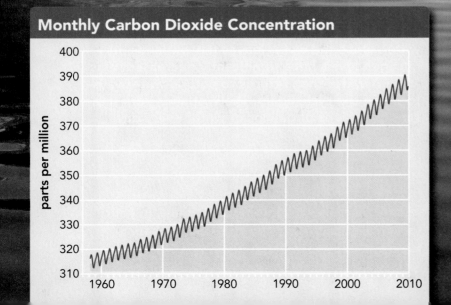

Monthly Carbon Dioxide Concentration

parts per million — y-axis: 310, 320, 330, 340, 350, 360, 370, 380, 390, 400
x-axis: 1960, 1970, 1980, 1990, 2000, 2010

Research It Research a topic related to climate change and write a report about it. How can the science of climate change help decision making in your community and state? Include a list of your information sources.

HARD WORKING Wetlands

Nitrogen is an important nutrient for plants and animals. To help plants grow, nitrogen fertilizers are often added to the soil on farms and in gardens. Plants use much of the nitrogen from the fertilizers, but some of it gets washed away into rivers, streams, lakes, and the ocean.

Although nitrogen is a necessary nutrient, too much nitrogen causes problems in water ecosystems. High levels of nitrogen lead to algae blooms, in which an algae population quickly and dramatically increases. The rapid population explosion causes dissolved oxygen in the water to get used up. Without oxygen, the other plants and animals in the water die off.

To help prevent excess nitrogen from damaging natural water ecosystems, the City of Orlando started the Orlando Easterly Wetlands Park. This wetland habitat was constructed to naturally filter nitrogen out of the water. It works by channeling wastewater containing high levels of nitrogen into the park. As the water moves slowly through the wetlands, plants absorb the nitrogen from the water. Once the water leaves the wetlands, its nitrogen levels have significantly decreased. This "clean" water then returns to natural waterways to begin the cycle again. The Wetlands Park filters tens of millions of gallons of water every day!

▲ The Orlando Easterly Wetlands Park provides a habitat for many wetland organisms, including this purple gallinule.

Research It Find out more about the water quality in your county. Summarize your findings in a visual presentation to your class. Include information about contaminants found in your local water and ways you can help conserve healthy water.

FLORIDA NGSSS

SC.8.N.4.2 Explain how social concerns can affect science, and vice versa.

SC.8.L.18.4 Cite evidence that living systems follow the Laws of Conservation of Mass and Energy.

LA.8.4.2.2 The student will record information related to a topic and attribute sources of information.

Trees: Environmental Factories

FLORIDA NGSSS

SC.8.N.4.1 Explain that science can be used for decision making at the community and other levels.

SC.8.L.18.2 Investigate how cellular respiration breaks down food to provide energy and releases carbon dioxide.

Some of the most important members of your community don't volunteer. They consume huge amounts of water and they make a mess. Despite these drawbacks, these long-standing community members do their share. Who are these individuals? They're trees!

Keeping it clean: Trees remove pollutants from the air. Some researchers have calculated the value of the environmental cleaning services that trees provide. One study valued the air-cleaning service that trees in the Chicago area provide at more than $9 million every year.

Keeping it cool: Trees provide shade and lower air temperature by the process of transpiration. Pollutants, like ozone and smog, form more easily when air temperatures are high, so by keeping the air cool, trees also keep it clean.

Acting locally and globally: Trees help fight global environmental problems such as climate change. Trees remove carbon dioxide from the air and store the carbon as they grow. Experts estimate that urban trees in the United States remove more than 700 million tons of carbon from the air every year.

Helping the local economy: Trees are also good for business. One study found that shoppers spend more money in urban areas where trees are planted than they do in similar areas that don't have trees!

Research It Examine a topographical map of the area where you live. Compare it to an aerial photograph from a library or local archive. Identify areas with a lot of trees, and areas that you think could benefit from more trees. Create a proposal to plant trees in one of the areas you identified. What kinds of trees will you plant? What do those trees need in order to grow well?

Schools, clubs, and civic groups all over the United States volunteer to plant trees in their communities. ▶

These American lotus plants in Florida's Lake Okeechobee soak up sunlight.

Summarizing

Life Science

In this Life Science unit, you learned that living things share a basic need for energy. You learned how living things get energy by way of photosynthesis and cellular respiration. You also learned how matter and energy are conserved and recycled in the environment.

How do these plants use the sunlight?

_____

_____

_____

_____

_____

_____

_____

How is water recycled through the environment?

_____

_____

_____

_____

_____

_____

_____

_____

Research Methods and Sources

How do you begin a research project? Choosing a topic is usually the first step. When you decide on a topic that really catches your interest, you will be ready to start your research. You can get information by using newspapers, magazines, the Internet, and other sources. Once you find sources, you need to evaluate them and make sure the information they contain is accurate.

Choosing Your Topic

Avoid choosing a topic that is too general or covers too much information. Narrowing your choice to a more specific topic will make your research easier.

Narrow your topic by asking yourself questions. Start with these two questions.

✎ Write your answers on a separate paper.

What do I already know about my topic?

What do I want to learn about my topic?

Identify key words related to a topic. Focus on key words in your answers that can help guide your search to narrow your topic. Use your key words and the sources below as a starting point for gathering ideas at the library or on the Internet.

Type of Source	Using the Source
Research Texts	Scan the tables of contents of books about your topic to find specific ideas and more key words for your search.
Library Sources	Look through encyclopedias and atlases to quickly identify important ideas about a topic. Browse the library's online catalog for ideas, too.
Internet Sources	Use a search engine to search your key words. Choose a few interesting Web pages to browse for more information. You can also search online databases and discussion groups.

Revise the questions about your topic. Use the key words you find in your search to make your questions more specific. If you have trouble thinking of a question, use one or more of the five *Ws*: *Who, What, When, Where,* and *Why.*

Evaluating Reliable Sources

The information you find is not always accurate. Some sources may provide information that is out-of-date or contains factual errors. To make sure you can trust the information found in your sources, ask yourself these questions.

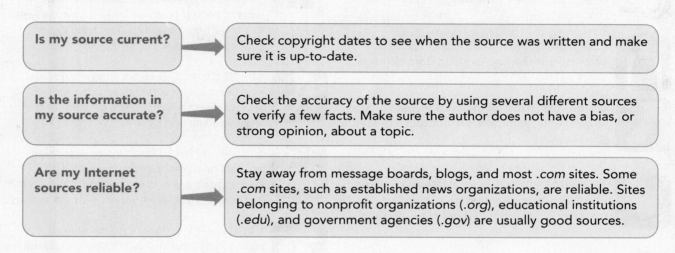

Is my source current?	→	Check copyright dates to see when the source was written and make sure it is up-to-date.
Is the information in my source accurate?	→	Check the accuracy of the source by using several different sources to verify a few facts. Make sure the author does not have a bias, or strong opinion, about a topic.
Are my Internet sources reliable?	→	Stay away from message boards, blogs, and most *.com* sites. Some *.com* sites, such as established news organizations, are reliable. Sites belonging to nonprofit organizations (*.org*), educational institutions (*.edu*), and government agencies (*.gov*) are usually good sources.

✎ **Make Judgments** Decide which source is more reliable for each research topic. Circle it. Then explain your decision.

1. Topic: the types of trees found in Florida's forests

http://www.floridaforests.gov   http://www.inmyforest.com

_____

_____

_____

_____

2. Topic: how global warming has affected Florida's coral reefs

A travel article from 1998   **A scientific article from 2010**

_____

_____

_____

_____

Safety Symbols

These symbols warn of possible dangers in the laboratory and remind you to work carefully.

 Safety Goggles Wear safety goggles to protect your eyes in any activity involving chemicals, flames or heating, or glassware.

 Lab Apron Wear a laboratory apron to protect your skin and clothing from damage.

 Breakage Handle breakable materials, such as glassware, with care. Do not touch broken glassware.

 Heat-Resistant Gloves Use an oven mitt or other hand protection when handling hot materials such as hot plates or hot glassware.

 Plastic Gloves Wear disposable plastic gloves when working with harmful chemicals and organisms. Keep your hands away from your face, and dispose of the gloves according to your teacher's instructions.

 Heating Use a clamp or tongs to pick up hot glassware. Do not touch hot objects with your bare hands.

 Flames Before you work with flames, tie back loose hair and clothing. Follow instructions from your teacher about lighting and extinguishing flames.

 No Flames When using flammable materials, make sure there are no flames, sparks, or other exposed heat sources present.

 Corrosive Chemical Avoid getting acid or other corrosive chemicals on your skin or clothing or in your eyes. Do not inhale the vapors. Wash your hands after the activity.

 Poison Do not let any poisonous chemical come into contact with your skin, and do not inhale its vapors. Wash your hands when you are finished with the activity.

 Fumes Work in a well-ventilated area when harmful vapors may be involved. Avoid inhaling vapors directly. Only test an odor when directed to do so by your teacher, and use a wafting motion to direct the vapor toward your nose.

 Sharp Object Scissors, scalpels, knives, needles, pins, and tacks can cut your skin. Always direct a sharp edge or point away from yourself and others.

 Animal Safety Treat live or preserved animals or animal parts with care to avoid harming the animals or yourself. Wash your hands when you are finished with the activity.

 Plant Safety Handle plants only as directed by your teacher. If you are allergic to certain plants, tell your teacher; do not do an activity involving those plants. Avoid touching harmful plants such as poison ivy. Wash your hands when you are finished with the activity.

 Electric Shock To avoid electric shock, never use electrical equipment around water, or when the equipment is wet or your hands are wet. Be sure cords are untangled and cannot trip anyone. Unplug equipment not in use.

 Physical Safety When an experiment involves physical activity, avoid injuring yourself or others. Alert your teacher if there is any reason you should not participate.

 Disposal Dispose of chemicals and other laboratory materials safely. Follow the instructions from your teacher.

 Hand Washing Wash your hands thoroughly when finished with an activity. Use soap and warm water. Rinse well.

 General Safety Awareness When this symbol appears, follow the instructions provided. When you are asked to develop your own procedure in a lab, have your teacher approve your plan before you go further.

Using a Laboratory Balance

The laboratory balance is an important tool in scientific investigations. You can use a balance to determine the masses of materials that you study or experiment with in the laboratory.

Different kinds of balances are used in the laboratory. One kind of balance is the triple-beam balance. The balance that you may use in your science class is probably similar to the balance illustrated in this Appendix. **To use the balance properly, you should learn the name, location, and function of each part of the balance you are using. What kind of balance do you have in your science class?**

The Triple-Beam Balance

The triple-beam balance is a single-pan balance with three beams calibrated in grams. The back, or 100-gram, beam is divided into ten units of 10 grams each. The middle, or 500-gram, beam is divided into five units of 100 grams each. The front, or 10-gram, beam is divided into ten units of 1 gram each. Each of the units on the front beam is further divided into units of 0.1 gram. What is the largest mass you could find with a triple-beam balance?

The following procedure can be used to find the mass of an object with a triple-beam balance:
1. Place the object on the pan.
2. Move the rider on the middle beam notch by notch until the horizontal pointer on the right drops below zero. Move the rider back one notch.
3. Move the rider on the back beam notch by notch until the pointer again drops below zero. Move the rider back one notch.
4. Slowly slide the rider along the front beam until the pointer stops at the zero point.
5. The mass of the object is equal to the sum of the readings on the three beams.

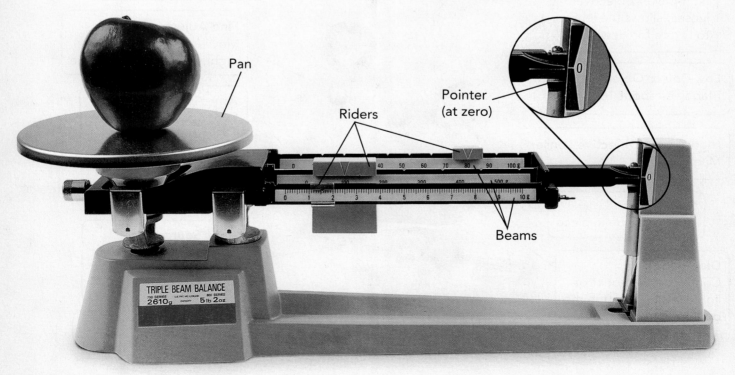

Pan

Riders

Pointer (at zero)

Beams

TRIPLE BEAM BALANCE
700 SERIES   800 SERIES
2610g   CAPACITY   5 lb 2 oz

Using a Microscope

The microscope is an essential tool in the study of life science. It allows you to see things that are too small to be seen with the unaided eye.

You will probably use a compound microscope like the one you see here. The compound microscope has more than one lens that magnifies the object you view.

Typically, a compound microscope has one lens in the eyepiece, the part you look through. The eyepiece lens usually magnifies 10×. Any object you view through this lens would appear 10 times larger than it is.

A compound microscope may contain one or two other lenses called objective lenses. If there are two, they are called the low-power and high-power objective lenses. The low-power objective lens usually magnifies 10×. The high-power objective lens usually magnifies 40×.

To calculate the total magnification with which you are viewing an object, multiply the magnification of the eyepiece lens by the magnification of the objective lens you are using. For example, the eyepiece's magnification of 10× multiplied by the low-power objective's magnification of 10× equals a total magnification of 100×.

Use the photo of the compound microscope to become familiar with the parts of the microscope and their functions.

The Parts of a Microscope

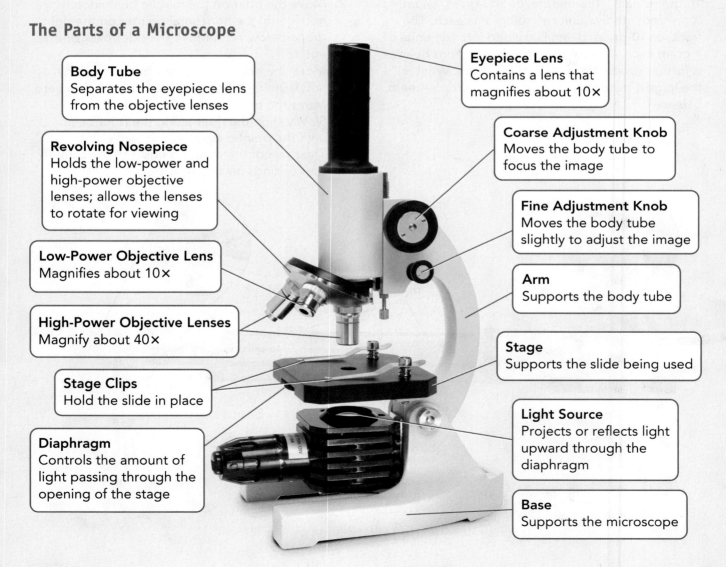

Body Tube
Separates the eyepiece lens from the objective lenses

Revolving Nosepiece
Holds the low-power and high-power objective lenses; allows the lenses to rotate for viewing

Low-Power Objective Lens
Magnifies about 10×

High-Power Objective Lenses
Magnify about 40×

Stage Clips
Hold the slide in place

Diaphragm
Controls the amount of light passing through the opening of the stage

Eyepiece Lens
Contains a lens that magnifies about 10×

Coarse Adjustment Knob
Moves the body tube to focus the image

Fine Adjustment Knob
Moves the body tube slightly to adjust the image

Arm
Supports the body tube

Stage
Supports the slide being used

Light Source
Projects or reflects light upward through the diaphragm

Base
Supports the microscope

Using the Microscope

Use the following procedures when you are working with a microscope.

1. To carry the microscope, grasp the microscope's arm with one hand. Place your other hand under the base.
2. Place the microscope on a table with the arm toward you.
3. Turn the coarse adjustment knob to raise the body tube.
4. Revolve the nosepiece until the low-power objective lens clicks into place.
5. Adjust the diaphragm. While looking through the eyepiece, also adjust the mirror until you see a bright white circle of light. **CAUTION:** *Never use direct sunlight as a light source.*
6. Place a slide on the stage. Center the specimen over the opening on the stage. Use the stage clips to hold the slide in place. **CAUTION:** *Glass slides are fragile.*
7. Look at the stage from the side. Carefully turn the coarse adjustment knob to lower the body tube until the low-power objective almost touches the slide.
8. Looking through the eyepiece, very slowly turn the coarse adjustment knob until the specimen comes into focus.
9. To switch to the high-power objective lens, look at the microscope from the side. Carefully revolve the nosepiece until the high-power objective lens clicks into place. Make sure the lens does not hit the slide.
10. Looking through the eyepiece, turn the fine adjustment knob until the specimen comes into focus.

Making a Wet-Mount Slide

Use the following procedures to make a wet-mount slide of a specimen.

1. Obtain a clean microscope slide and a coverslip. **CAUTION:** *Glass slides and coverslips are fragile.*
2. Place the specimen on the center of the slide. The specimen must be thin enough for light to pass through it.
3. Using a plastic dropper, place a drop of water on the specimen.
4. Gently place one edge of the coverslip against the slide so that it touches the edge of the water drop at a 45° angle. Slowly lower the coverslip over the specimen. If you see air bubbles trapped beneath the coverslip, tap the coverslip gently with the eraser end of a pencil.
5. Remove any excess water at the edge of the coverslip with a paper towel.

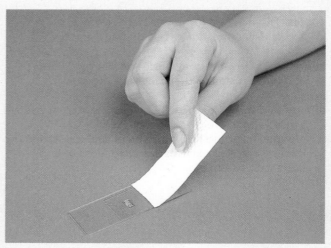

GLOSSARY

A

abiotic factor A nonliving part of an organism's habitat. (456)
factor abiótico La parte sin vida del hábitat de un organismo.

absorption 1. The process by which nutrient molecules pass through the wall of the digestive system into the blood. (151) **2.** The process by which an object takes in, or absorbs, light.
absorción 1. Proceso en el cual las moléculas de nutrientes pasan a la sangre a través de las paredes del sistema digestivo. **2.** Proceso en el cual un objeto recibe, o absorbe, luz.

accuracy How close a measurement is to the true or accepted value. (34)
exactitud Cuán cerca está una medida del valor verdadero o aceptado.

active immunity Immunity that occurs when a person's own immune system produces antibodies in response to the presence of a pathogen. (291)
inmunidad activa Inmunidad que ocurre cuando el sistema inmunológico de una persona produce anticuerpos en respuesta a la presencia de un patógeno.

adaptation An inherited behavior or physical characteristic that helps an organism survive and reproduce in its environment. (365, 469)
adaptación Comportamiento o característica física heredada que ayuda a que un organismo se reproduzca y sobreviva en su medio ambiente.

AIDS (acquired immunodeficiency syndrome) A disease caused by a virus that attacks the immune system. (305)
SIDA (síndrome de inmunodeficiencia adquirida) Enfermedad causada por un virus que ataca el sistema inmunológico.

alleles The different forms of a gene. (395)
alelos Diferentes formas de un gen.

allergen A substance that causes an allergy. (298)
alérgeno Sustancia que causa la alergia.

allergy A disorder in which the immune system is overly sensitive to a foreign substance. (298)
alergia Trastorno fisiológico en el cual el sistema inmunológico es extremadamente sensible a sustancias externas.

alveoli Tiny sacs of lung tissue specialized for the movement of gases between air and blood. (210)
alvéolos Sacos diminutos de tejido pulmonar que se especializan en el intercambio de gases entre el aire y la sangre.

amniotic sac A fluid-filled sac that cushions and protects a developing embryo or fetus in the uterus. (262)
saco amniótico Saco lleno de líquido que acojina y protege al embrión o feto dentro del útero.

anomalous data Data that do not fit with the rest of a data set. (38)
datos anómalos Información que no encaja con los otros datos de un conjunto de datos.

antibiotic A chemical that kills bacteria or slows their growth without harming body cells. (294)
antibiótico Sustancia química que mata las bacterias o disminuye la velocidad de su crecimiento sin dañar las células del cuerpo humano.

antibody A protein produced by a B cell of the immune system that destroys pathogens. (288)
anticuerpo Proteína producida por una célula B del sistema inmunológico que destruye patógenos.

antigen A molecule that the immune system recognizes either as part of the body or as coming from outside the body. (287)
antígeno Molécula que el sistema inmunológico puede reconocer como parte del cuerpo o como un agente extraño.

aorta The largest artery in the body; receives blood from the left ventricle. (201)
aorta La arteria más grande del cuerpo; recibe sangre del ventrículo izquierdo.

artery A blood vessel that carries blood away from the heart. (201)
arteria Vaso sanguíneo que transporta la sangre que sale del corazón.

asexual reproduction A reproductive process that involves only one parent and produces offspring that are genetically identical to the parent. (319)
reproducción asexual Proceso reproductivo que consiste de un solo reproductor y que produce individuos que son genéticamente idénticos al reproductor.

asthma A disease in which the airways in the lungs narrow significantly. (299)
asma Enfermedad en la que las vías respiratorias de los pulmones se estrechan considerablemente.

atom The basic particle from which all elements are made; the smallest particle of an element that has the properties of that element. (99)
átomo Partícula básica de la que todos los elementos están formados; partícula más pequeña de un elemento, que tiene las propiedades de ese elemento.

atrium An upper chamber of the heart that receives blood. (200)
aurícula Cavidad superior del corazón que recibe la sangre.

autotroph An organism that is able to capture energy from sunlight or chemicals and use it to produce its own food. (323, 502)
autótrofo Organismo capaz de capturar y usar la energía solar o de sustancias químicas para producir su propio alimento.

B

B cell A lymphocyte that produces proteins that help destroy pathogens. (288)
célula B Linfocito que produce proteínas que ayudan a destruir patógenos.

binomial nomenclature The classification system in which each organism is given a unique, two-part scientific name indicating its genus and species. (328)
nomenclatura binaria Sistema de clasificación en el que cada organismo tiene un nombre científico específico de dos partes que indica el género y la especie.

biodiversity The total number of different species on Earth, including those on land, in the water, and in the air. (374)
biodiversidad Número total de especies diferentes que habitan la Tierra, incluyendo especies terrestres, marinas y del aire.

biotechnology The application of a technological process, or invention to living organisms. (440)
biotecnología Empleo de seres vivos en un proceso, invento o proceso tecnológico.

biotic factor A living or once living part of an organism's habitat. (456)
factor biótico Parte viva, o que alguna vez tuvo vida, del hábitat de un organismo.

birth rate The number of births per 1,000 individuals for a certain time period. (479)
tasa de natalidad Número de nacimientos por 1.000 individuos durante un período de tiempo determinado.

branching tree diagram A diagram that shows probable evolutionary relationships among organisms and the order in which specific characteristics may have evolved. (339)
árbol ramificado Diagrama que muestra las relaciones evolucionarias probables entre los organismos y el orden en que ciertas características específicas podrían haber evolucionado.

bronchi The passages that direct air into the lungs. (210)
bronquios Conductos que dirigen el aire hacia los pulmones.

C

calorie The amount of energy needed to raise the temperature of one gram of water by 1°C. (189)
caloría Cantidad de energía que se necesita para elevar en 1°C la temperatura de un gramo de agua.

capillary A tiny blood vessel where substances are exchanged between the blood and the body cells. (201)
capilar Vaso sanguíneo diminuto donde se intercambian sustancias entre la sangre y las células del cuerpo.

carcinogen A substance or a factor in the environment that can cause cancer. (301)
carcinógeno Sustancia o factor ambiental que puede causar cáncer.

cardiac muscle Involuntary muscle tissue found only in the heart. (172)
músculo cardiaco Tejido de músculo involuntario, que sólo se encuentra en el corazón.

carnivore A consumer that obtains energy by eating only animals. (462)
carnívoro Consumidor que adquiere su energía al alimentarse de animales solamente.

carrier A person who has one recessive allele and one dominant allele for a trait. (427)
portador Persona que tiene un alelo recesivo y un alelo dominante para un rasgo.

GLOSSARY

carrying capacity The largest population that a particular environment can support. (483)
capacidad de carga Población mayor que un ambiente en particular puede mantener.

cartilage A connective tissue that is more flexible than bone and that protects the ends of bones and keeps them from rubbing together. (168)
cartílago Tejido conector más flexible que el hueso, que protege los extremos de los huesos y evita que se rocen.

cell The basic unit of structure and function in living things. (101, 141)
célula Unidad básica de estructura y función de los seres vivos.

cell cycle The series of events in which a cell grows, prepares for division, and divides to form two daughter cells. (126)
ciclo celular Serie de sucesos en los que una célula crece, se prepara para dividirse y se divide para formar dos células hijas.

cell division A process in which one cell splits into two new cells that are genetically identical to the original cell. (115)
división celular Proceso por el que una célula se divide en dos células que son genéticamente idénticas a la célula original.

cell membrane A thin, flexible barrier that surrounds a cell and controls which substances pass into and out of a cell. (114, 141)
membrana celular Barrera delgada y flexible alrededor de la célula que controla lo que entra y sale de la célula.

cell theory A widely accepted explanation of the relationship between cells and living things. (106)
teoría celular Explicación ampliamente aceptada sobre la relación entre las células y los seres vivos.

cellular respiration The process in which oxygen and glucose undergo a complex series of chemical reactions inside cells, releasing energy. (113, 507)
respiración celular Proceso en el cual el oxígeno y la glucosa pasan por una serie compleja de reacciones químicas dentro de las células y así liberan energía.

cell wall A rigid supporting layer that surrounds the cells of plants and some other organisms. (117)
pared celular Capa fuerte de apoyo alrededor de las células de las plantas y algunos otros organismos.

central nervous system The division of the nervous system consisting of the brain and spinal cord. (237)
sistema nervioso central División del sistema nervioso formada por el cerebro y la médula espinal.

chlorophyll A green photosynthetic pigment found in the chloroplasts of plants, algae, and some bacteria. (503)
clorofila Pigmento verde fotosintético de los cloroplastos de las plantas, algas y algunas bacterias.

chloroplast An organelle in the cells of plants and some other organisms that captures energy from sunlight and changes it to an energy form that cells can use in making food. (123)
cloroplasto Orgánulo de las células vegetales y otros organismos que absorbe energía de la luz solar y la convierte en una forma de energía que las células pueden usar para producir alimentos.

chromosome A threadlike structure within a cell's nucleus that contains DNA that is passed from one generation to the next. (126)
cromosoma Estructura filamentosa en el núcleo celular que contiene el ADN que se transmite de una generación a la siguiente.

cilia Tiny, hairlike projections on the outside of cells that move in a wavelike manner. (210)
cilios Estructuras diminutas parecidas a pelos, ubicadas en el exterior de las células y que ondulan.

circulatory system An organ system that transports needed materials to cells and removes wastes. (198)
sistema circulatorio Sistema de órganos que transporta los materiales que la célula necesita y elimina los desechos.

classification The process of grouping things based on their similarities. (327)
clasificación Proceso de agrupar cosas según sus semejanzas.

classifying The process of grouping together items that are alike in some way. (10)
clasificar Proceso de agrupar objetos con algún tipo de semejanza.

clone An organism that is genetically identical to the organism from which it was produced. (435)
clon Organismo genéticamente idéntico al organismo del que proviene.

commensalism A type of symbiosis between two species in which one species benefits and the other species is neither helped nor harmed. (476)
comensalismo Tipo de relación simbiótica entre dos especies en la cual una especie se beneficia y la otra especie ni se beneficia ni sufre daño.

community All the different populations that live together in a particular area. (458)
comunidad Todas las poblaciones distintas que habitan en un área específica.

compact bone Hard and dense, but not solid, bone tissue that is beneath the outer membrane of a bone. (167)
hueso compacto Tejido de hueso denso y duro, pero no sólido, que se encuentra debajo de la membrana externa de un hueso.

competition The struggle between organisms to survive as they attempt to use the same limited resources in the same place at the same time. (471)
competencia Lucha por la supervivencia entre organismos que se alimentan de los mismos recursos limitados en el mismo lugar y al mismo tiempo.

compound A substance made of two or more elements chemically combined in a specific ratio, or proportion. (100)
compuesto Sustancia formada por dos o más elementos combinados químicamente en una razón o proporción específica.

condensation The change of state from a gas to a liquid. (513)
condensación Cambio del estado gaseoso al estado líquido.

connective tissue A body tissue that provides support for the body and connects all its parts. (142)
tejido conector Tejido del cuerpo que mantiene la estructura del cuerpo y une todas sus partes.

consumer An organism that obtains energy by feeding on other organisms. (462)
consumidor Organismo que obtiene energía al alimentarse de otros organismos.

controlled experiment An experiment in which only one variable is manipulated at a time. (50)
experimento controlado Experimento en el cual sólo se manipula una variable a la vez.

controversy A public disagreement between groups with different views. (69)
controversia Desacuerdo público entre grupos con diferentes opiniones.

convergent evolution The process by which unrelated organisms evolve similar characteristics. (341)
evolución convergente Proceso por el cual organismos no relacionados exhiben una evolución de características similares.

cultural bias An outlook influenced by the beliefs, social forms, and traits of a group. (17)
prejuicio cultural Opinión influenciada por las creencias, costumbres sociales y características de un grupo.

cytokinesis The final stage of the cell cycle, in which the cell's cytoplasm divides, distributing the organelles into each of the two new daughter cells. (130)
citocinesis Última etapa del ciclo celular en la que se divide el citoplasma y se reparten los orgánulos entre las dos células hijas nuevas.

cytoplasm The thick fluid region of a cell located inside the cell membrane (in prokaryotes) or between the cell membrane and nucleus (in eukaryotes). (119, 141)
citoplasma Región celular de líquido espeso ubicada dentro de la membrana celular (en las procariotas) o entre la membrana celular y el núcleo (en las eucariotas).

D

data Facts, figures, and other evidence gathered through observations. (51)
dato Hechos, cifras u otra evidencia reunida por medio de observaciones.

death rate The number of deaths per 1,000 individuals for a certain time period. (479)
tasa de mortalidad Número de muertes per 1.000 individuos durante un período de tiempo determinado.

decomposer An organism that gets energy by breaking down wastes and dead organisms, and returns raw materials to the soil and water. (463)
descomponedor Organismo que obtiene energía al descomponer desechos y organismos muertos y que devuelve la materia resultante al suelo y al agua.

deductive reasoning A way to explain things by starting with a general idea and then applying the idea to a specific observation. (19)
razonamiento deductivo Manera de explicar las cosas en la que se aplica una idea general a una observación específica.

GLOSSARY

density The measurement of how much mass of a substance is contained in a given volume. (28)
densidad Medida de la masa de una sustancia que tiene un volumen dado.

dependent variable The factor that changes as a result of changes to the independent variable in an experiment; also called responding variable. (12)
variable dependiente Factor que cambia a causa de los cambios de la variable independiente de un experimento; también se denomina variable de respuesta.

dermis The inner layer of the skin. (179)
dermis Capa más interna de la piel.

development The process of change that occurs during an organism's life to produce a more complex organism. (319)
desarrollo Proceso de cambio que ocurre durante la vida de un organismo, mediante el cual se crea un organismo más complejo.

diabetes A condition in which the pancreas fails to produce enough insulin or the body's cells cannot use it properly. (300)
diabetes Condición en la que el páncreas no puede producir suficiente insulina o las células del cuerpo no la pueden usar correctamente.

diaphragm A large, dome-shaped muscle located at the base of the lungs that helps with breathing. (212)
diafragma Músculo grande y redondo situado en la base de los pulmones que ayuda a la respiración.

diffusion The process by which molecules move from an area of higher concentration to an area of lower concentration. (114)
difusión Proceso en el que las moléculas se mueven de un área de mayor concentración a otra de menor concentración.

DNA Deoxyribonucleic acid; the genetic material that carries information about an organism and is passed from parent to offspring. (100)
ADN Ácido desoxirribonucleico; material genético que lleva información sobre un organismo y que se transmite de padres a hijos.

DNA replication Before a cell divides, the process in which DNA copies itself. (390)
replicación del ADN Proceso en el que el ADN se duplica, antes de que la célula se divide.

dominant allele An allele whose trait always shows up in the organism when the allele is present. (395)
alelo dominante Alelo cuyo rasgo siempre se manifiesta en el organismo, cuando el alelo está presente.

duct A tiny tube through which chemicals are released from a gland. (245)
ducto Conducto diminuto por el cual se liberan sustancias químicas de una glándula.

E

ecology The study of how organisms interact with each other and their environment. (459)
ecología Estudio de la forma en que los organismos interactúan entre sí y con su medio ambiente.

ecosystem The community of organisms that live in a particular area, along with their nonliving environment. (459, 502)
ecosistema Comunidad de organismos que viven en un área específica, y el medio ambiente que los rodea.

egg A female sex cell. (253)
óvulo Célula sexual femenina.

element A pure substance that cannot be broken down into other substances by chemical or physical means. (99)
elemento Sustancia que no se puede descomponer en otras sustancias por medios químicos o físicos.

embryo 1. The young organism that develops from a zygote. 2. A developing human during the first eight weeks after fertilization has occurred. (261)
embrión 1. Organismo joven que se desarrolla a partir del cigoto. 2. Un ser humano en desarrollo durante las primeras ocho semanas después de llevarse a cabo la fertilización.

emigration Movement of individuals out of a population's area. (480)
emigración Traslado de individuos fuera del área de una población.

empirical evidence Data and observations that are collected through scientific processes and that explain a particular observation. (66)
evidencia empírica Datos y observaciones que se recopilan a través de procesos científicos y que explican una observación particular.

endangered species A species in danger of becoming extinct in the near future. (376)
especie en peligro de extinción Especie que corre el riesgo de desaparecer en el futuro próximo.

endoplasmic reticulum An organelle that forms a maze of passageways in which proteins and other materials are carried from one part of the cell to another. (119)
retículo endoplasmático Orgánulo que forma un laberinto de conductos que llevan proteínas y otros materiales de una parte de la célula a otra.

energy pyramid A diagram that shows the amount of energy that moves from one feeding level to another in a food web. (466)
pirámide de energía Diagrama que muestra la cantidad de energía que fluye de un nivel de alimentación a otro en una red alimentaria.

enzyme 1. A type of protein that speeds up a chemical reaction in a living thing. (193) **2.** A biological catalyst that lowers the activation energy of reactions in cells.
enzima 1. Tipo de proteína que acelera una reacción química de un ser vivo. **2.** Catalizador biológico que reduce la energía de activación de las reacciones celulares.

epidermis The outer layer of the skin. (179)
epidermis Capa externa de la piel.

epithelial tissue A body tissue that covers the interior and exterior surfaces of the body. (142)
tejido epitelial Tejido del cuerpo que cubre las superficies interiores y exteriores.

esophagus A muscular tube that connects the mouth to the stomach. (194)
esófago Tubo muscular que conecta la boca con el estómago.

estimate An approximation of a number based on reasonable assumptions. (33)
estimación Aproximación de un número basada en conjeturas razonables.

estrogen A hormone produced by the ovaries that controls the development of eggs and adult female characteristics. (256)
estrógeno Hormona producida por los ovarios que controla el desarrollo de los óvulos y de las características femeninas adultas.

ethics 1. The rules that enable people to know right from wrong. (16) **2.** The study of principles about what is right and wrong, fair and unfair. (444)
ética 1. Reglas que le permiten a una persona reconocer lo que es moral y lo que no lo es. **2.** Estudio de los principios de qué es lo bueno y lo malo, lo justo y lo injusto.

eukaryote An organism whose cells contain a nucleus. (336)
eucariota Organismo cuyas células contienen un núcleo.

evaluating Comparing observations and data to reach a conclusion about them. (10)
evaluar Comparar observaciones y datos para llegar a una conclusión.

evaporation The process by which molecules at the surface of a liquid absorb enough energy to change to a gas. (513)
evaporación Proceso mediante el cual las moléculas en la superficie de un líquido absorben suficiente energía para pasar al estado gaseoso.

evolution Change over time; the process by which modern organisms have descended from ancient organisms. (338, 357)
evolución Cambios a través del tiempo; proceso por el cual los organismos modernos se originaron a partir de organismos antiguos.

excretion The process by which wastes are removed from the body. (217)
excreción Proceso por el cual se eliminan los desechos del cuerpo.

experimental bias A mistake in the design of an experiment that makes a particular result more likely. (17)
prejuicio experimental Error en el diseño de un experimento que aumenta la probabilidad de un resultado.

extinction The disappearance of all members of a species from Earth. (376)
extinción Desaparición de la Tierra de todos los miembros de una especie.

GLOSSARY

F

Fallopian tube A passageway for eggs from an ovary to the uterus. (256)
trompa de falopio Pasaje por el que pasan los óvulos de un ovario al útero.

feedback Output that changes a system or allows the system to adjust itself. (78)
retroalimentación Salida que cambia un sistema o permite que éste se ajuste.

fermentation The process by which cells release energy by breaking down food molecules without using oxygen. (510)
fermentación Proceso en el que las células liberan energía al descomponer las moléculas de alimento sin usar oxígeno.

fertilization The process in sexual reproduction in which an egg cell and a sperm cell join to form a new cell. (253, 393)
fertilización Proceso de la reproducción sexual en el que un óvulo y un espermatozoide se unen para formar una nueva célula.

fetus A developing human from the ninth week of development until birth. (261)
feto Humano en desarrollo desde la novena semana de desarrollo hasta el nacimiento.

follicle Structure in the dermis of the skin from which a strand of hair grows. (179)
folículo Estructura en la dermis de la piel de donde crece un pelo.

food chain A series of events in an ecosystem in which organisms transfer energy by eating and by being eaten. (464)
cadena alimentaria Serie de sucesos en un ecosistema por medio de los cuales los organismos transmiten energía al comer o al ser comidos por otros.

food web The pattern of overlapping feeding relationships or food chains among the various organisms in an ecosystem. (464)
red alimentaria Patrón de las relaciones de alimentación intercruzadas o de cadenas alimentarias entre los diferentes organismos de un ecosistema.

G

gene A sequence of DNA that determines a trait and is passed from parent to offspring. (359)
gen Secuencia de ADN que determina un rasgo y que se pasa de los progenitores a los hijos.

gene therapy The process of changing a gene to treat a medical disease or disorder. An absent or faulty gene is replaced by a normal working gene. (437)
terapia genética Proceso que consiste en cambiar un gen para tratar una enfermedad o un trastorno médico. El gen ausente o defectuoso se cambia por un gen con función normal.

genetic disorder An abnormal condition that a person inherits through genes or chromosomes. (429)
desorden genético Condición anormal que hereda una persona a través de los genes o cromosomas.

genetic engineering The transfer of a gene from the DNA of one organism into another organism, in order to produce an organism with desired traits. (435)
ingeniería genética Transferencia de un gen desde el ADN de un organismo a otro, para producir un organismo con los rasgos deseados.

genetics The scientific study of heredity. (393)
genética Ciencia que estudia la herencia.

genome A complete set of genetic information that an organism carries in its DNA. (443)
genoma Toda la información genética que un organismo lleva en su ADN.

genotype An organism's genetic makeup, or allele combinations. (402)
genotipo Composición genética de un organismo, es decir, las combinaciones de los alelos.

genus A classification grouping that consists of a number of similar, closely related species. (328)
género Clase de agrupación que consiste de un número de especies similares y estrechamente relacionadas.

gland An organ that produces and releases chemicals either through ducts or into the bloodstream. (152, 245)
glándula Órgano que produce y libera sustancias químicas por los ductos o al torrente sanguíneo.

Golgi apparatus An organelle in a cell that receives proteins and other newly formed materials from the endoplasmic reticulum, packages them, and distributes them to other parts of the cell. (122)
aparato de Golgi Orgánulo de la célula que recibe, empaqueta y distribuye a otras partes de la célula las proteínas y otros materiales que se forman en el retículo endoplasmático.

graph A picture of information from a data table; shows the relationship between variables. (41)
gráfica Representación visual de la información de una tabla de datos; muestra la relación entre las variables.

—————————— **H** ——————————

habitat An environment that provides the things a specific organism needs to live, grow, and reproduce. (455)
hábitat Medio que provee lo que un organismo específico necesita para vivir, crecer y reproducirse.

heart A hollow, muscular organ that pumps blood throughout an organism's body. (200)
corazón Órgano muscular y hueco que bombea sangre a través del cuerpo de un organismo.

hemoglobin An iron-containing protein that binds chemically to oxygen molecules; makes up most of red blood cells. (204)
hemoglobina Proteína que contiene hierro, y que se enlaza químicamente las moléculas de oxígeno; forma la mayoría de los glóbulos rojos.

herbivore A consumer that obtains energy by eating only plants. (462)
herbívoro Consumidor que obtiene su energía al alimentarse de plantas solamente.

heredity The passing of traits from parents to offspring. (392)
herencia Transmisión de rasgos de padres a hijos.

heterotroph An organism that cannot make its own food and gets food by consuming other living things. (323)
heterótrofo Organismo que no puede producir sus propios alimentos y que se alimenta al consumir otros seres vivos.

heterozygous Having two different alleles for a particular gene. (402)
heterocigoto Que tiene dos alelos distintos para un gen particular.

histamine A chemical that is responsible for the symptoms of an allergy. (298)
histamina Sustancia química responsable de los síntomas de una alergia.

HIV (human immunodeficiency virus) The virus that causes AIDS. (305)
VIH (virus de la inmunodeficiencia humana) Virus que causa el SIDA.

homeostasis The condition in which an organism's internal environment is kept stable in spite of changes in the external environment. (112, 155)
homeostasis Condición en la que el medio interno de un organismo se mantiene estable a pesar de cambios en el medio externo.

homologous structures Structures that are similar in different species and that have been inherited from a common ancestor. (360)
estructuras homólogas Estructuras parecidas de especies distintas y que se han heredado de un antepasado común.

homozygous Having two identical alleles for a particular gene. (402)
homocigoto Que tiene dos alelos idénticos para un gen particular.

hormone 1. A chemical that affects growth and development. 2. The chemical produced by an endocrine gland. (153, 246)
hormona 1. Sustancia química que afecta el crecimiento y el desarrollo. 2. Sustancia química producida por una glándula endocrina.

host An organism that a parasite lives with, in, or on, and provides a source of energy or a suitable environment for the parasite to live. (476)
huésped Organismo en el cual vive un parásito y que le sirve de fuente de energía o de medio ambiente.

hybrid An offspring of crosses that has two different alleles for a trait. (396)
híbrido Descendiente de cruces que tiene dos alelos distintos para un rasgo.

hybridization A selective breeding method that involves crossing different individuals to bring together the best traits from both parents. (438)
hibridación Técnica reproductiva en la que se cruzan individuos distintos para reunir los mejores rasgos de ambos progenitores.

GLOSSARY

hypothalamus A part of the brain that links the nervous system and the endocrine system. (248)
hipotálamo Parte del encéfalo que une el sistema nervioso con el sistema endocrino.

hypothesis A possible explanation for a set of observations or answer to a scientific question; must be testable. (48)
hipótesis Explicación posible de un conjunto de observaciones o respuesta a una pregunta científica; se debe poder poner a prueba.

I

immigration Movement of individuals into a population's area. (480)
inmigración Movimiento de individuos al área de una población.

immune response Part of the body's defense against pathogens in which cells of the immune system react to each kind of pathogen with a defense targeted specifically at that pathogen. (287)
reacción inmunológica Parte de la defensa del cuerpo contra los patógenos, en la que las células del sistema inmunológico reaccionan a cada tipo de patógeno con una defensa específica.

immunity The body's ability to destroy pathogens before they can cause disease. (291)
inmunidad Capacidad del cuerpo para destruir los patógenos antes de que causen enfermedades.

inbreeding A selective breeding method in which two individuals with similar sets of alleles are crossed. (439)
endogamia Técnica reproductiva en la que se cruzan dos individuos con conjuntos de alelos parecidos.

independent variable The one factor that a scientist changes during an experiment; also called manipulated variable. (12)
variable independiente El único factor que un científico altera durante un experimento; también se denomina variable manipulada.

inductive reasoning Using specific observations to make generalizations. (20)
razonamiento inductivo Usar observaciones específicas para hacer generalizaciones.

infectious disease A disease caused by the presence of a living thing in the body that can pass from one organism to another. (277)
enfermedad infecciosa Enfermedad causada por la presencia de un ser vivo en el cuerpo y que puede pasar de un organismo a otro.

inferring The process of making an inference, an interpretation based on observations and prior knowledge. (8)
inferir Proceso de hacer una inferencia; interpretación basada en observaciones y conocimientos previos.

inflammatory response Part of the body's defense against pathogens, in which fluid and white blood cells leak from blood vessels into tissues and destroy pathogens by breaking them down. (285)
reacción inflamatoria Parte de la defensa del cuerpo contra los patógenos en la cual los fluidos y los glóbulos blancos salen de los vasos sanguíneos hacia los tejidos y destruyen los patógenos descomponiéndolos.

input Material, energy, or information that goes into a system. (78)
entrada Material, energía o informacion que se agrega a un sistema.

insulin A hormone produced in the pancreas that enables the body's cells to take in glucose from the blood and use it for energy. (300)
insulina Hormona producida por el páncreas, que permite que las células del cuerpo absorban glucosa de la sangre y la usen como energía.

International System of Units (SI) A system of units used by scientists to measure the properties of matter. (23)
Sistema Internacional de Unidades (SI) Sistema de unidades que los científicos usan para medir las propiedades de la materia.

interphase The first stage of the cell cycle that takes place before cell division occurs, during which a cell grows and makes a copy of its DNA. (126)
interfase Primera etapa del ciclo celular que ocurre antes de la división celular y durante la cual la célula crece y duplica su ADN.

involuntary muscle A muscle that is not under conscious control. (171)
músculo involuntario Músculo que no se puede controlar conscientemente.

J

joint A place in the body where two bones come together. (148, 165)
articulación Parte del cuerpo donde se unen dos huesos.

K

karyotype A picture of all the human chromosomes in a cell grouped together in pairs and arranged in order of decreasing size. (432)
cariotipo Fotografía de todos los cromosomas humanos en una célula agrupados en pares y ordenados de los más grandes a los más pequeños.

kidney A major organ of the excretory system; removes urea and other wastes from the blood. (218)
riñón Órgano principal del sistema excretor que elimina la urea, el exceso de agua y otros materiales de desecho del cuerpo.

L

larynx The voice box; located in the top part of the trachea, underneath the epiglottis. (213)
laringe Caja de la voz; está ubicada en la parte superior de la tráquea debajo de la epiglotis.

ligament Strong connective tissue that holds bones together in movable joints. (165)
ligamentos Tejido conector resistente que une dos huesos en las articulaciones móviles.

limiting factor An environmental factor that causes a population to decrease in size. (483)
factor limitante Factor ambiental que causa la disminución del tamaño de una población.

linear graph A line graph in which the data points yield a straight line. (44)
gráfica lineal Gráfica en la cual los puntos de los datos forman una línea recta.

lung 1. An organ found in air-breathing vertebrates that exchanges oxygen and carbon dioxide with the blood. **2.** In humans, one of two main organs of the respiratory system. (210)
pulmón 1. Órgano de los vertebrados que respiran aire, responsable del intercambio de oxígeno y dióxido de carbono en la sangre. **2.** En los seres humanos, uno de los dos órganos principales del sistema respiratorio.

lymphocyte A white blood cell that distinguishes between each kind of pathogen. (287)
linfocito Glóbulo blanco que distingue cada tipo de patógeno.

lysosome A cell organelle which contains chemicals that break down large food particles into smaller ones and that can be used by the rest of the cell. (123)
lisosoma Orgánulo de una célula, que tiene sustancias químicas que convierten partículas grandes de alimentos en partículas más pequeñas que el resto de la célula puede utilizar.

M

making models The process of creating representations of complex objects or processes. (11)
hacer modelos Proceso de crear representaciones de objetos o procesos complejos.

marrow The soft connective tissue that fills the internal spaces in bone. (167)
médula ósea Tejido conector suave que llena los espacios internos de un hueso.

mass A measure of how much matter is in an object. (25)
masa Medida de cuánta materia hay en un cuerpo.

mean The numerical average of a set of data. (37)
media Promedio numérico de un conjunto de datos.

median The middle number in a set of data. (37)
mediana Número del medio de un conjunto de datos.

meiosis The process that occurs in the formation of sex cells (sperm and egg) by which the number of chromosomes is reduced by half. (408)
meiosis Proceso durante la formación de las células sexuales (espermatozoide y óvulo) por el cual el número de cromosomas se reduce a la mitad.

melanin A pigment that gives the skin its color. (179)
melanina Pigmento que da color a la piel.

meniscus The curved upper surface of a liquid in a column of liquid. (26)
menisco Superficie superior curva de un líquido en una columna de líquido.

menstrual cycle The monthly cycle of changes that occurs in the female reproductive system, during which an egg develops and the uterus prepares for the arrival of a fertilized egg. (258)
ciclo menstrual Ciclo mensual de cambios del sistema reproductor femenino, durante el cual se desarrolla un óvulo y el útero se prepara para la llegada del óvulo fecundado.

menstruation The process in which the thickened lining of the uterus breaks down and blood and tissue then pass out of the female body through the vagina. (258)
menstruación Proceso en el cual el recubrimiento grueso del útero se rompe, y sangre y tejido salen del cuerpo femenino a través de la vagina.

metabolism The combination of chemical reactions through which an organism builds up or breaks down materials. (318)
metabolismo Combinación de reacciones químicas mediante las cuales un organismo compone o descompone la materia.

metric system A system of measurement based on the number 10. (23)
sistema métrico Sistema de medidas basado en el número 10.

microorganism A living thing too small to see without a microscope. (275)
microorganismo Ser vivo que es tan pequeño que sólo es visible a través de un microscopio.

microscope An instrument that makes small objects look larger. (106)
microscopio Instrumento que permite que los objetos pequeños se vean más grandes.

mitochondria Rod-shaped organelles that convert energy in food molecules to energy the cell can use to carry out its functions. (119)
mitocondria Estructura celular con forma de bastón que transforma la energía de las moléculas de alimentos en energía que la célula puede usar para llevar a cabo sus funciones.

mitosis The second stage of the cell cycle during which the cell's nucleus divides into two new nuclei and one set of DNA is distributed into each daughter cell. (127)
mitosis Segunda etapa del ciclo celular, durante la cual se divide el núcleo de la célula en dos núcleos nuevos y el conjunto del ADN se reparte entre cada célula hija.

mode The number that appears most often in a list of numbers. (37)
moda Número que aparece con más frecuencia en una lista de números.

model A representation of a complex object or process, used to help people understand a concept that they cannot observe directly. (77)
modelo Representación de un objeto o proceso complejo que se usa para explicar un concepto que no se puede observar directamente.

molecule A neutral group of two or more atoms held together by covalent bonds. (100)
molécula Grupo neutral de dos o más átomos unidos por medio de enlaces covalentes.

multicellular Consisting of many cells. (101)
multicelular Que se compone de muchas células.

muscle tissue A body tissue that contracts, or shortens, making body parts move. (142)
tejido muscular Tejido del cuerpo que se contrae o encoge, y permite que se muevan las partes del cuerpo.

mutualism A type of symbiosis in which both species benefit from living together. (475)
mutualismo Tipo de relación simbiótica entre dos especies en la cual ambas especies se benefician de su convivencia.

N

natural selection The process by which organisms that are best adapted to their environment are most likely to survive and reproduce. (368, 469)
selección natural Proceso por el que los organismos que se adaptan mejor a su ambiente tienen mayor probabilidad de sobrevivir y reproducirse.

negative feedback A process in which a system is turned off by the condition it produces. (249)
reacción negativa Proceso en el cual un sistema cesa de funcionar debido a la condición que produce.

nephron Small filtering structure found in the kidneys that removes wastes from blood and produces urine. (218)
nefrona Estructura diminuta de filtración ubicada en los riñones, que elimina los desechos de la sangre y produce la orina.

nerve A bundle of nerve fibers. (235)
nervio Conjunto de fibras nerviosas.

nerve impulse The message carried by a neuron. (235)
impulso nervioso Mensaje que una neurona transporta.

nervous tissue A body tissue that carries electrical messages back and forth between the brain and other parts of the body. (142)
tejido nervioso Tejido del cuerpo que transporta impulsos eléctricos entre el cerebro y otras partes del cuerpo.

neuron A cell that carries information through the nervous system. (235)
neurona Célula que transporta información a través del sistema nervioso.

niche How an organism makes its living and interacts with the biotic and abiotic factors in its habitat. (470)
nicho Forma en que un organismo vive e interactúa con los factores bióticos y abióticos de su hábitat.

nitrogen bases Molecules that contain nitrogen and other elements. (387)
bases nitrogenadas Moléculas que contienen nitrógeno y otros elementos.

nitrogen fixation The process of changing free nitrogen gas into nitrogen compounds that plants can absorb and use. (516)
fijación del nitrógeno Proceso que consiste en transformar el gas de nitrógeno libre en compuestos de nitrógeno que las plantas pueden absorber y usar.

noninfectious disease A disease that is not caused by a pathogen. (297)
enfermedad no infecciosa Enfermedad que no es causada por un patógeno.

nonlinear graph A line graph in which the data points do not fall along a straight line. (44)
gráfica no lineal Gráfica lineal en la que los puntos de datos no forman una línea recta.

nucleus 1. In cells, a large oval organelle that contains the cell's genetic material in the form of DNA and controls many of the cell's activities. (118, 141) **2.** The central core of an atom which contains protons and neutrons. **3.** The solid inner core of a comet.
núcleo 1. En las células, orgánulo grande y ovalado que contiene el material genético de la célula en forma de ADN y que controla muchas actividades celulares. **2.** Centro del átomo que contiene los protones y neutrones. **3.** Centro sólido de un cometa.

nutrient 1. A substance such as nitrogen or phosphorus that enables plants and algae to grow. **2.** Substances in food that provide the raw materials and energy needed for an organism to carry out its essential processes. (151)
nutriente 1. Sustancia como el nitrógeno o el fósforo que hace posible que las plantas y algas crezcan. **2.** Sustancias de los alimentos que dan el material y la energía que un organismo necesita para sus funciones vitales.

O

objective Describes the act of decision-making or drawing conclusions based on available evidence. (18)
objetivo Describe el acto de tomar una decisión o llegar a una conclusión basándose en la evidencia disponible.

observing The process of using one or more of your senses to gather information. (7)
observar Proceso de usar uno o más de tus sentidos para reunir información.

omnivore A consumer that obtains energy by eating both plants and animals. (462)
omnívoro Consumidor que adquiere su energía al alimentarse de plantas y animales.

opinion An idea about a situation that is not supported by evidence. (67)
opinión Idea sobre una situación que la evidencia no sustenta.

organ A body structure that is composed of different kinds of tissues that work together. (102, 143)
órgano Estructura del cuerpo compuesta de distintos tipos de tejidos que trabajan conjuntamente.

organelle A tiny cell structure that carries out a specific function within the cell. (118)
orgánulo Estructura celular diminuta que realiza una función específica dentro de la célula.

organ system A group of organs that work together, performing major functions. (102, 144)
sistema de órganos Grupo de órganos que trabajan conjuntamente y realizan funciones importantes.

organism A living thing. (455)
organismo Un ser vivo.

osteoporosis A condition resulting from a loss of minerals in which the body's bones become weak and break easily. (169)
osteoporosis Condición producida por la pérdida de minerales en la que los huesos del cuerpo se vuelven frágiles y se quiebran fácilmente.

output Material, energy, result, or product that comes out of a system. (78)
salida Material, energía, resultado o producto que un sistema produce.

ovary 1. A flower structure that encloses and protects ovules and seeds as they develop. **2.** Organ of the female reproductive system in which eggs and estrogen are produced. (256)
ovario 1. Estructura de la flor que encierra y protege a los óvulos y las semillas durante su desarrollo. **2.** Órgano del sistema reproductivo femenino en el que se producen los óvulos y el estrógeno.

ovulation The process in which a mature egg is released from the ovary into a Fallopian tube. (258)
ovulación Proceso en el cual el óvulo maduro sale del ovario y pasa a las trompas de falopio.

P

parasite An organism that benefits by living with, on, or in a host in a parasitism interaction. (279, 476)
parásito Organismo que vive dentro de o sobre otro organismo y que se alimenta de él.

parasitism A type of symbiosis in which one organism lives with, on, or in a host and harms it. (476)
parasitismo Tipo de relación simbiótica en la cual un organismo vive con o en un huésped y le hace daño.

passive immunity Immunity in which antibodies are given to a person rather than produced within the person's own body. (293)
inmunidad pasiva Inmunidad en la que una persona recibe anticuerpos en vez de producirlos en su propio cuerpo.

pathogen An organism that causes disease. (277)
patógeno Organismo que causa enfermedades.

pedigree A chart that shows the presence or absence of a trait according to the relationships within a family across several generations. (401, 431)
genealogía Diagrama que muestra la presencia o ausencia de un rasgo según las relaciones familiares a través de varias generaciones.

penis The organ through which both semen and urine leave the male body. (255)
pene Órgano por el cual salen del cuerpo masculino tanto el semen como la orina.

percent error A calculation used to determine how accurate, or close to the true value, an experimental value really is. (36)
error porcentual Cálculo usado para determinar cuán exacto, o cercano al valor verdadero, es realmente un valor experimental.

peripheral nervous system The division of the nervous system consisting of all of the nerves located outside the central nervous system. (237)
sistema nervioso periférico División del sistema nervioso formada por todos los nervios ubicados fuera del sistema central nervioso.

peristalsis Waves of smooth muscle contractions that move food through the esophagus toward the stomach. (194)
peristalsis Contracciones progresivas de músculo liso que mueven el alimento por el esófago hacia el estómago.

personal bias An outlook influenced by a person's likes and dislikes. (17)
prejuicio personal Perspectiva influenciada por las preferencias de un individuo.

phagocyte A white blood cell that destroys pathogens by engulfing them and breaking them down. (286)
fagocito Glóbulo blanco que destruye los patógenos envolviéndolos y descomponiéndolos.

pharynx The throat; part of both the respiratory and digestive systems. (210)
faringe Garganta; parte de los sistemas respiratorio y digestivo.

phenotype An organism's physical appearance, or visible traits. (402)
fenotipo Apariencia física, o rasgos visibles, de un organism.

photosynthesis The process by which plants and other autotrophs capture and use light energy to make food from carbon dioxide and water. (113, 502)
fotosíntesis Proceso por el cual las plantas y otros autótrofos absorben la energía de la luz para producir alimentos a partir del dióxido de carbono y el agua.

pituitary gland An endocrine gland that regulates many body activities and controls the actions of several other endocrine glands. (248)
glándula pituitaria Glándula endocrina que regula muchas actividades corporales y controla las acciones de varias otras glándulas endocrinas.

placenta An organ in most pregnant mammals, including humans, that links the mother and the developing embryo and allows for the passage of materials between them. (262)
placenta Órgano de la mayoría de los mamíferos preñados, incluyendo a los seres humanos, que conecta a la madre con el embrión en desarrollo y que permite el intercambio de materiales.

population All the members of one species living in the same area. (458)
población Todos los miembros de una especie que viven en el mismo lugar.

population density The number of individuals in an area of a specific size. (482)
densidad de población Número de individuos en un área de un tamaño específico.

pore An opening through which sweat reaches the surface of the skin. (179)
poros Aberturas a través de las cuales sale el sudor a la superficie de la piel.

precipitation Any form of water that falls from clouds and reaches Earth's surface as rain, snow, sleet, or hail. (513)
precipitación Cualquier forma del agua que cae de las nubes y llega a la superficie de la tierra como lluvia, nieve, aguanieve o granizo.

precision How close a group of measurements are to each other. (34)
precisión Cuán cerca se encuentran un grupo de medidas.

predation An interaction in which one organism kills another for food or nutrients. (472)
depredación Interacción en la cual un organismo mata a otro para alimentarse u obtener nutrientes de él.

predator The organism that does the killing in a predation interaction. (472)
depredador Organismo que mata durante la depredación.

predicting The process of forecasting what will happen in the future based on past experience or evidence. (9)
predecir Proceso de pronosticar lo que va a suceder en el futuro, basándose en evidencia o experiencias previas.

prey An organism that is killed and eaten by another organism in a predation interaction. (472)
presa Organismo que es consumido por otro organismo en el proceso de depredación.

probability A number that describes how likely it is that a particular event will occur. (399)
probabilidad Número que describe cuán probable es que ocurra un suceso.

process A sequence of actions in a system. (78)
proceso Secuencia de acciones en un sistema.

producer An organism that can make its own food. (461)
productor Organismo que puede generar su propio alimento.

prokaryote A unicellular organism that lacks a nucleus and some other cell structures. (335)
procariota Organismo unicelular que carece de un núcleo y otras estructuras celulares.

Punnett square A chart that shows all the possible combinations of alleles that can result from a genetic cross. (400)
cuadrado de Punnett Tabla que muestra derivar de un cruce genético.

purebred An offspring of crosses that has the same form of traits. (393)
raza pura Descendiente de cruces, que tiene los mismos rasgos.

R

range The difference between the greatest value and the least value in a set of data. (37)
rango Diferencia entre el mayor y el menor valor de un conjunto de datos.

recessive allele An allele that is hidden whenever the dominant allele is present. (395)
alelo recesivo Alelo que se no manifiesta cuando el alelo dominante está presente.

GLOSSARY

reflex An automatic response that occurs rapidly and without conscious control. (240)
reflejo Respuesta automática que ocurre rápida e involuntariamente.

repeated trial A repetition of an experiment to gather additional data and determine whether the experiment's results support the hypothesis. (52)
prueba repetida Repetición de un experimento para recopilar datos adicionales y determinar si los resultados de un experimento sustentan la hipótesis.

replication 1. An attempt to repeat a scientist's experiment by a different scientist or group of scientists. (52) **2.** The process by which a cell makes a copy of the DNA in its nucleus before cell division. (126)
replicación 1. Intento por parte de un científico, o grupo de científicos, de repetir el experimento de otro científico. **2.** Proceso en el que la célula copia el ADN de su núcleo antes de la división celular.

response An action or change in behavior that occurs as a result of a stimulus. (152)
respuesta Acción o cambio del comportamiento que ocurre como resultado de un estímulo.

ribosome A small grain-shaped organelle in the cytoplasm of a cell that produces proteins. (118)
ribosoma Orgánulo pequeño con forma de grano en el citoplasma de una célula que produce proteínas.

S
---

scavenger A carnivore that feeds on the bodies of dead or decaying organisms. (462)
carroñero Carnívoro que se alimenta de los restos de organismos muertos o en descomposición.

science A way of learning about the natural world through observations and logical reasoning; leads to a body of knowledge. (7)
ciencia Estudio del mundo natural a través de observaciones y del razonamiento lógico; conduce a un conjunto de conocimientos.

scientific explanation A generalization that makes sense of observations by using logical reasoning. (65)
explicación científica Generalización que usa el razonamiento lógico para darle sentido a las observaciones.

scientific inquiry The ongoing process of discovery in science; the diverse ways in which scientists study the natural world and propose explanations based on evidence they gather. (47)
indagación científica Proceso continuo de descubrimiento en la ciencia; diversidad de métodos con los que los científicos estudian el mundo natural y proponen explicaciones del mismo basadas en la evidencia que reúnen.

scientific law A statement that describes what scientists expect to happen every time under a particular set of conditions. (75)
ley científica Enunciado que describe lo que los científicos esperan que suceda cada vez que se da una serie de condiciones determinadas.

scientific theory A well-tested explanation for a wide range of observations or experimental results. (74, 366)
teoría científica Explicación comprobada de una gran variedad de observaciones o resultados de experimentos.

scrotum An external pouch of skin in which the testes are located. (254)
escroto Bolsa de piel externa en donde se encuentran los testículos.

selective breeding Method of breeding that allows only those organisms with desired traits to produce the next generation. (438)
cruce selectivo Técnica reproductiva por medio de la cual sólo los organismos con rasgos deseados producen la próxima generación.

semen A mixture of sperm and fluids. (255)
semen Mezcla de esperma y fluidos.

sex chromosomes A pair of chromosomes carrying genes that determine whether a person is male or female. (425)
cromosomas sexuales Par de cromosomas portadores de genes que determinan el sexo (masculino o femenino) de una persona.

sex-linked gene A gene that is carried on a sex (X or Y) chromosome. (426)
gen ligado al sexo Gen de un cromosoma sexual (X o Y).

sexual reproduction A reproductive process that involves two parents that combine their genetic material to produce a new organism which differs from both parents. (319)
reproducción sexual Proceso de reproducción que involucra a dos reproductores que combinan su material genético para producir un nuevo organismo que es distinto a los dos reproductores.

shared derived characteristic A characteristic or trait, such as fur, that the common ancestor of a group had and passed on to its descendants. (339)
característica derivada compartida Característica o rasgo, como el pelaje, del ancestro común de un grupo que éste pasa a sus descendientes.

significant figures All the digits in a measurement that have been measured exactly, plus one digit whose value has been estimated. (34)
cifras significativas En una medida, todos los dígitos que se han medido con exactitud, más un dígito cuyo valor se ha estimado.

skeletal muscle A muscle that is attached to the bones of the skeleton and provides the force that moves the bones; also called striated muscle. (147, 172)
músculo esquelético Músculo que está conectado a los huesos del esqueleto y que proporciona la fuerza que mueve los huesos; llamado también músculo estriado.

skeleton 1. The inner framework made up of all the bones of the body. (147, 163) **2.** A framework that shapes and supports an animal, protects its internal organs, and allows it to move in its environment.
esqueleto 1. Estructura interna compuesta de todos los huesos del cuerpo. **2.** Estructura que da forma y soporte a un animal, protege sus órganos internos y le permite moverse en su medio ambiente.

skepticism An attitude of doubt. (16)
escepticismo Actitud de duda.

smooth muscle Involuntary muscle found inside many internal organs of the body. (172)
músculo liso Músculo involuntario que se halla dentro de muchos órganos internos del cuerpo.

species A group of similar organisms that can mate with each other and produce offspring that can also mate and reproduce. (328, 458)
especie Grupo de organismos semejantes que pueden cruzarse y producir descendencia fértil.

sperm A male sex cell. (253)
esperma Célula sexual masculina.

spongy bone Layer of bone tissue that has many small spaces and is found just inside the layer of compact bone. (167)
hueso esponjoso Capa de tejido óseo que tiene muchos orificios pequeños y que se encuentra próxima a la capa de hueso compacto.

spontaneous generation The mistaken idea that living things arise from nonliving sources. (320)
generación espontánea Idea equivocada de que los seres vivos surgen de fuentes inertes.

stimulus Any change or signal in the environment that can make an organism react in some way. (152)
estímulo Cualquier cambio o señal del medio ambiente que puede causar una reacción en un organismo.

stress 1. A force that acts on rock to change its shape or volume. **2.** The reaction of a person's body to potentially threatening, challenging, or disturbing events. (158)
esfuerzo 1. Fuerza que actúa sobre las rocas y que cambia su forma o volumen. **2.** Reacción del cuerpo de un individuo a sucesos como posibles amenazas, desafíos o trastornos.

striated muscle A muscle that appears banded; also called skeletal muscle. (172)
músculo estriado Músculo con forma de franjas; también se llama músculo esquelético.

subjective Describes the influence of personal feelings on a decision or conclusion. (18)
subjetivo Describe la influencia de sentimientos personales sobre una decisión o conclusión.

symbiosis Any relationship in which two species live closely together and that benefits at least one of the species. (475)
simbiosis Cualquier relación en la cual dos especies viven muy cerca y al menos una de ellas se beneficia.

synapse The junction where one neuron can transfer an impulse to the next structure. (236)
sinapsis Confluencia donde una neurona puede transferir un impulso a la siguiente estructura.

system A group of related parts that work together to perform a function or produce a result. (78)
sistema Grupo de partes relacionadas que trabajan conjuntamente para realizar una función o producir un resultado.

GLOSSARY

—————————— **T** ——————————

target cell A cell in the body that recognizes a hormone's chemical structure. (246)
célula destinataria Célula del cuerpo que reconoce la estructura química de una hormona.

taxonomy The scientific study of how living things are classified. (327)
taxonomía Estudio científico de cómo se clasifican los seres vivos.

T cell A lymphocyte that identifies pathogens and distinguishes one pathogen from another. (287)
célula T Linfocito que identifica a los patógenos y distingue un patógeno de otro.

tendon Strong connective tissue that attaches muscle to bone. (172)
tendón Tejido conectivo resistente que une un músculo a un hueso.

testis Organ of the male reproductive system in which sperm and testosterone are produced. (254)
testículo Órgano del sistema reproductor masculino en el que se producen el esperma y la testosterona.

testosterone A hormone produced by the testes that controls the development of sperm and adult male characteristics. (254)
testosterona Hormona producida por los testículos que controla el desarrollo del esperma y las características del hombre adulto.

threatened species A species that could become endangered in the near future. (376)
especie amenazada Especie que puede llegar a estar en peligro de extinción en el futuro próximo.

tissue A group of similar cells that perform a specific function. (102, 142)
tejido Grupo de células semejantes que realizan una función específica.

toxin A poison that can harm an organism. (278)
toxina Veneno que puede dañar un organismo.

trachea The windpipe; a passage through which air moves in the respiratory system. (210)
tráquea Conducto por el cual circula el aire en el sistema respiratorio.

trait A specific characteristic that an organism can pass to its offspring through its genes. (367)
rasgo Característica específica que un organismo puede transmitir a sus descendientes a través de los genes.

tumor A mass of rapidly dividing cells that can damage surrounding tissue. (301)
tumor Masa de células que se dividen rápidamente y que puede dañar los tejidos que la rodean.

—————————— **U** ——————————

umbilical cord A ropelike structure that forms between the embryo or fetus and the placenta. (263)
cordón umbilical Estructura con forma de cuerda que se forma en el útero entre el embrión o feto y la placenta.

unicellular Made of a single cell. (101)
unicelular Compuesto por una sola célula.

urea A chemical that comes from the breakdown of proteins. (217)
urea Sustancia química que resulta de la descomposición de proteínas.

ureter A narrow tube that carries urine from one of the kidneys to the urinary bladder. (218)
uretra Conducto estrecho que lleva la orina desde uno de los riñones a la vejiga urinaria.

urethra A small tube through which urine leaves the body. (218)
uretra Conducto pequeño a través del cual la orina sale del cuerpo.

urinary bladder A sacklike muscular organ that stores urine until it is eliminated from the body. (218)
vejiga urinaria Órgano muscular con forma de saco que almacena la orina hasta que se elimine del cuerpo.

urine A watery fluid produced by the kidneys that contains urea and other wastes. (217)
orina Fluido acuoso producido por los riñones que contiene urea y otros materiales de desecho.

uterus The hollow muscular organ of the female reproductive system in which a fertilized egg develops. (257)
útero Órgano muscular hueco del sistema reproductor femenino en el que se desarrolla un óvulo fertilizado.

V

vaccination The process by which harmless antigens are deliberately introduced into a person's body to produce active immunity; also called immunization. (292)
vacunación Proceso por el cual antígenos inocuos se introducen deliberadamente en el cuerpo de una persona para producir una inmunidad activa; también se le llama inmunización.

vaccine A substance used in a vaccination that consists of pathogens that have been weakened or killed but can still trigger the body to produce chemicals that destroy the pathogens. (292)
vacuna Sustancia que se inyecta en la vacunación; consiste de patógenos débiles o muertos que pueden estimular al cuerpo a producir sustancias químicas que destruyan esos patógenos.

vacuole A sac-like organelle that stores water, food, and other materials. (122)
vacuola Orgánulo en forma de bolsa que almacena agua, alimentos y otros materiales.

vagina A muscular passageway leading to the outside of a female's body; also called the birth canal. (257)
vagina Pasaje muscular que se extiende hasta una abertura del cuerpo de una mujer; también llamada canal de nacimiento.

valve A flap of tissue in the heart or a vein that prevents blood from flowing backward. (201)
válvula Lámina de tejido del corazón o de una vena que impide que la sangre fluya hacia atrás.

variable A factor that can change in an experiment. (12)
variable Factor que puede cambiar en un experimento.

variation Any difference between individuals of the same species. (369)
variación Cualquier diferencia entre individuos de la misma especie.

vein 1. A narrow deposit of a mineral that is sharply different from the surrounding rock. **2.** A blood vessel that carries blood back to the heart. (201)
vena 1. Placa delgada de un mineral que es marcadamente distinto a la roca que lo rodea. **2.** Vaso sanguíneo que transporta la sangre al corazón.

ventricle A lower chamber of the heart that pumps blood out to the lungs or body. (200)
ventrículo Cavidad inferior del corazón que bombea la sangre a los pulmones o el cuerpo.

vertebrae The bones that make up the backbone of an organism. In humans, one of the 26 bones that make up the backbone. (163)
vértebras Huesos que componen la columna de un organismo. En los seres humanos, cada uno de los 26 huesos que componen la columna vertebral.

villi Tiny finger-shaped structures that cover the inner surface of the small intestine and provide a large surface area through which digested food is absorbed. (196)
vellosidades Pequeñas estructuras con forma de dedo que cubren la superficie interna del intestino delgado y proporcionan una superficie amplia a través de la cual se absorbe el alimento digerido.

vocal cords Folds of connective tissue that stretch across the opening of the larynx and produce a person's voice. (213)
cuerdas vocales Pliegues de tejido conector que se extienden a lo largo de la abertura de la laringe y que producen la voz de una persona.

volume The amount of space that matter occupies. (26)
volumen Cantidad de espacio que ocupa la materia.

voluntary muscle A muscle that is under conscious control. (171)
músculo voluntario Músculo que se puede controlar conscientemente.

W

weight A measure of the force of gravity acting on an object. (25)
peso Medida de la fuerza de gravedad que actúa sobre un objeto.

Z

zygote A fertilized egg, produced by the joining of a sperm cell and an egg cell. (253)
cigoto Óvulo fertilizado, producido por la unión de un espermatozoide y un óvulo.

A

Abiotic factors, 456
in ecosystems, 459
Absorption, 151
Accuracy, 34
time measurement, 31
Active immunity, 291
Adaptation, 365, 468, **469**–477
commensalism and parasitism, **476**–477
competition, **471**
finding niches, 470
mutualism, **475**, 477
natural selection, **469**
predation, **472**–474
symbiosis, 475–477
Adrenal gland, 247
AIDS and HIV, 305–307
Alcoholic fermentation, 510
Algae, 461
Alleles, 395–397
of blood type, 423
dominant and recessive, **395**
and genotype, 402
human, 422–424
and probability, 400
and range of phenotypes, 424
symbols for, 396
See also Genetics
Allergen, 298
Allergies, 298
Alveoli, 210, 214–215
Amino acids, 190
Amniotic sac, 262
Animals
classification, 337
cytokinesis in, 130
function of cells in, 124–125
structure of cells in, 117–123
Anomalous data, 38
Antibiotics, 294
Antibodies, 288
Antigens, 287
Aorta, 201
Application of skills
Apply It!, 17–18, 21, 45, 49, 71, 74, 79, 110, 114, 122, 127, 143, 148, 153, 159, 166, 174, 193, 203, 207, 213, 234, 236, 246, 280, 289, 294, 298, 321, 333, 336, 340, 359, 366, 388, 397, 403, 405, 423, 431, 438, 443, 457, 464, 470, 482, 485, 502, 510, 514

Do the Math!, 133, 268, 415, 518
analyze experimental results, 66
analyze graphs, 102, 131
calculate, 28, 36, 196, 217, 263, 329, 399, 467, 518
classify, 329
develop hypotheses, 259, 479
draw conclusions, 102, 301, 305, 474
estimate, 33, 196
explain, 33, 474
graph, 9, 189, 259, 305, 439, 479
infer, 9
interpret data, 9, 131, 305, 370, 377, 439, 474
interpret photos, 33
interpret tables, 263, 301
predict, 28, 51, 377, 474
read graphs, 51, 66, 259, 474
relate evidence and explain, 518
relate evidence and explanation, 66
select and analyze, 370
Science Matters
Abominable Mystery, 88
Are We Getting Warmer?, 526–527
Bones in Space, 346
Colwell's Gift, 347
Fruit That Won't Freeze?, 490
Hard-Working Wetlands, 528
Ready for a Close-Up, 89
Trees: Environmental Factories, 529
Walking Whales?, 491
Apply It! *See* Application of skills
Archaea, 335
Arteries, 201
Artificial selection, 367
Asexual reproduction, 319, 411
Assessment
Assess Your Understanding, 13, 17, 21, 23, 31, 35, 39, 43, 45, 48, 54–55, 65, 67, 71, 73, 75, 77, 79, 83, 103, 105, 107, 111, 115, 123, 125, 131, 145, 148, 151, 153, 161, 164, 166, 169, 173, 175, 179, 191, 197, 203, 207, 211, 215, 219, 223, 234, 240, 243, 248, 251, 257, 259, 261, 263, 265, 277, 281, 284, 289, 293, 295, 300, 303, 306–307, 319, 322, 325, 329, 331, 333, 337, 341, 357, 361, 367, 371, 373, 375, 377, 389, 391, 394, 397,

401, 403, 407, 409, 413, 424, 427, 430, 433, 439, 441, 445, 455, 457, 459, 463, 467, 470, 474, 477, 482, 485, 502, 505, 509, 511, 513, 517, 521
Florida Benchmarks Review, 59, 87, 135, 183, 227, 269, 311, 345, 381, 417, 449, 489, 525
Review and Assessment, 57–58, 85–86, 133–134, 181–182, 267–268, 309–310, 343–344, 379–380, 415–416, 447–448, 487–488, 523–524
Study Guide, 56, 84, 132, 180, 224, 266, 308, 342, 378, 414, 446, 486, 522
Asthma, 296, **299**
Atoms, 99, 103
Atrium (heart), 200–201
Autonomic nervous system, 239
Autotrophs, 323, **502**
Axon, 235–236

B

B cells, 288
Bacteria, 278–279, 516
classification, 335
as decomposers, 463
as food producers, 461
and genetic engineering, 436
Bacterial disease, 294
Balance. *See* Homeostasis
Bias, 17
awareness of, 17
controlling, 50, 89
Big Idea, xxx–1, 92–93, 350–351, 494–495
Binomial nomenclature, 328–329
Biodiversity, 374–375
diversity of species, 363–365
endangered, extinct, and threatened species, 376–377
Biosphere, and conservation of energy, 519
Biotechnology, 440–441, 490
Biotic factors, 456
Birth rate, 479–480
Bladder, 218
Blood
and breathing, 214
composition of, 204–205
plasma, 204–205
platelets, 205
red blood cells, 204
white blood cells, 205
function of, 199

INDEX

Page numbers for key terms are printed in **boldface** type.

INDEX

Page numbers for key terms are printed in **boldface** type.

INDEX

Page numbers for key terms are printed in **boldface** type.

INDEX

Page numbers for key terms are printed in **boldface** type.

ACKNOWLEDGMENTS

Staff Credits

The people who made up the *Interactive Science* team—representing composition services, core design digital and multimedia production services, digital product development, editorial, editorial services, manufacturing, and production—are listed below:

Jan Van Aarsen, Samah Abadir, Ernie Albanese, Chris Anton, Bridget Binstock, Suzanne Biron, Niki Birbilis, MJ Black, Nancy Bolsover, Stacy Boyd, Jim Brady, Katherine Bryant, Michael Burstein, Pradeep Byram, Jessica Chase, Jonathan Cheney, Arthur Ciccone, Allison Cook-Bellistri, Rebecca Cottingham, AnnMarie Coyne, Bob Craton, Chris Deliee, Paul Delsignore, Michael Di Maria, Diane Dougherty, Kristen Ellis, Theresa Eugenio, Amanda Ferguson, Jorgensen Fernandez, Kathryn Fobert, Julia Gecha, Mark Geyer, Steve Gobbell, Paula Gogan-Porter, Jeffrey Gong, Sandra Graff, Robert M. Graham, Adam Groffman, Lynette Haggard, Christian Henry, Karen Holtzman, Susan Hutchinson, Sharon Inglis, Marian Jones, Sumy Joy, Sheila Kanitsch, Courtenay Kelley, Chris Kennedy, Toby Klang, Greg Lam, Russ Lappa, Margaret LaRaia, Ben Leveillee, Thea Limpus, Charles Luey, Dotti Marshall, Kathy Martin, Robyn Matzke, John McClure, Mary Beth McDaniel, Krista McDonald, Tim McDonald, Rich McMahon, Cara McNally, Bernadette McQuilkin, Melinda Medina, Angelina Mendez, Maria Milczarek, Claudi Mimo, Mike Napieralski, Deborah Nicholls, Dave Nichols, William Oppenheimer, Jodi O'Rourke, Ameer Padshah, Lorie Park, Celio Pedrosa, Jonathan Penyack, Linda Zust Reddy, Jennifer Reichlin, Stephen Rider, Charlene Rimsa, Walter Rodriguez, Stephanie Rogers, Marcy Rose, Rashid Ross, Anne Rowsey, Logan Schmidt, Amanda Seldera, Laurel Smith, Nancy Smith, Ted Smykal, Emily Soltanoff, Cindy Strowman, Dee Sunday, Barry Tomack, Elizabeth Tustian, Patricia Valencia, Ana Sofia Villaveces, Stephanie Wallace, Christine Whitney, Brad Wiatr, Heidi Wilson, Heather Wright, Rachel Youdelman.

Photography

All otherwise unacknowledged photos are copyright © 2011 Pearson Education.

Cover, Front and Back
Enrique R. Aguirre/Photolibrary New York.

Front Matter
Page vi palm tree l, Fotomak/Shutterstock; **vi palm tree r,** Albo/Shutterstock; **vi roller coaster,** Jeffrey Greenberg/Photo Researchers, Inc.; **vi Florida Keys,** Thomas Barrat/Shutterstock; **vii coral,** Doug Perrine/Minden Pictures; **vii manatees,** Jeff Mondragon/Alamy; **vi–vii bkgrnd,** Serg64/Shutterstock; **viii,** NASA Human Spaceflight Collection; **ix,** Tom Barrick, Chris Clark/SGHMS/Photo Researchers, Inc.; **x,** Gerry Ellis/Minden Pictures; **xii,** Raga Jose Fuste/AGE Fotostock; **xiii,** AFP/Getty Images; **xiv,** Sayyid Azim/AP Images; **xv,** Chris Newbert/Minden Pictures; **xvi,** Chris Newbert/Minden Pictures; **xvii,** ZSSD/SuperStock; **xviii,** HALEY/SIPA/Newscom; **xix,** Gary Bell/Zefa/Corbis; **xx,** Rolf Nussbaumer/Minden Pictures; **xxi laptop,** iStockphoto; **xxi TV,** Shutterstock; **xxiii laptop,** iStockphoto; **xxv girl in lab,** JupiterImages/Getty Images; **xxviii,** laptop.

Unit 1 Big Idea Opener
Pages xxx–1, Ron Thompson/St. Petersburg Times/Zuma Press.

Chapter 1
Pages 2–3 spread, NASA Human Spaceflight Collection; **3 t,** Michael Nichols/National Geographic Image Collection; **5 m1,** Ken Seet/Corbis; **5 m2 ball,** Chiyacat/Dreamstime; **5 m2 water,** Jon Helgason/iStockphoto; **6,** Michael Nichols/National Geographic Image Collection; **7,** Karl Ammann/Nature Picture Library; **8 t,** Anup Shah/Nature Picture Library; **8 b,** Manoj Shah/The Image Bank/Getty Images; **9,** Christoph Becker/Nature Picture Library; **10,** Kennan Ward/Corbis; **11,** Rainer Raffalski/Alamy; **12 inset,** GK Hart/Vikki Hart/Stone/Getty Images; **12 spread,** GK Hart/Vikki Hart/Stone/Getty Images; **13 inset,** Ken Karp/Digital Light Source/Photolibrary New York; **14 bkgrnd,** Jennifer Borton/iStockphoto; **14 slinky,** Sarah Holmstrom/iStockhphoto; **15 bl dolphin,** David Fleetman/Nature Picture Library; **15 r tooth,** Mark A. Schneider/Photo Reseachers, Inc.; **15 tl rainbow,** Karen Bleier/AFP/Getty Images; **16,** Photo Network/Alamy; **18 t,** Ken Seet/Corbis; **18–19 water spread,** Jon Helgason/iStockphoto; **19 t,** Duncan Walker/iStockphoto; **19 b,** MBI/Alamy; **20–21 spread,** Stephen Dorey-Commercial/Alamy; **21 ant with leaf,** Redmond Durrell/Alamy; **22 ostrich egg,** Philip Dowell/Dorling Kindersley; **22 nest,** Shattil & Rozinski/Nature Picture Library; **22 ostrich,** Digital Vision/Alamy; **22 inset,** Anthony Mercieca/Photo Researchers, Inc.; **24,** Richard Haynes; **25,** Richard Haynes; **27 tr,** Joe Traver/Time & Life Pictures/Getty Images; **28 beach ball,** Chiyacat/Dreamstime; **28 bkgrnd,** Britvich/Dreamstime; **28 bowling ball,** Terex/Dreamstime; **29,** Ingots/Image Source Pink/JupiterImages; **32 l,** Simon Kwong/Reuters/Corbis; **32–33 bkgrnd,** Michael S. Yamashita/Corbis; **33 inset,** Kevin Fleming/Corbis; **35,** Robert Manella/Comstock/Corbis; **36,** Comstock Images/JupiterUnlimited; **37,** Barry Mansell/Minden Pictures; **38–39 spread,** Chris Johnson/Alamy; **39 t,** NASA/Corbis; **40 b,** Superclic/Alamy; **40 t,** Digital Vision/Alamy; **42,** Katherine Feng/Minden Pictures; **43,** Eric Baccega/Nature Picture Library; **44,** Image100 /SuperStock; **46 b,** *Galileo Demonstrating the Law of Gravity of the Free Fall.* Detail of *The Trial of Galileo* (ca. 1839), Giuseppe Bezzuoli. Fresco. Museum of Physics and Natural History (Museo di Fisica e Storia Naturale), Florence, Italy; **47,** Andy Sands/Nature Picture Library; **48,** Richard Haynes; **49 t,** Idamini/Alamy; **50 b,** Richard Haynes; **51,** Idamini/Alamy; **52,** Idamini/Alamy; **53 t,** U.S. Department of Energy Human Genome Program; **54 hand-crumpled paper,** D. Hurst/Alamy; **54 flat paper,** Don Carstens/Brand X Pictures/JupiterImages; **55,** Franck Robichon/EPA/Corbis, **58,** Image100/Corbis.

Chapter 2
Pages 60–61 spread, Tom Barrick, Chris Clark/SGHMS/Photo Researchers, Inc.; **63 b,** Harris Shiffman/Shutterstock; **63 m1,** George Silk/Time & Life Pictures/Getty Images; **63 m2,** Photodisc/Getty Images; **63 t,** Michael Rondou/St.Petersburg Times/Zuma Press; **64,** Richard J. Ferro/Zuma Press; **65,** Michael Rondou/St.Petersburg Times/Zuma Press; **66,** Brzostowska/Shutterstock; **67,** Bay Area News Group/Zuma Press; **68 b,** James L. Amos/Photo Researchers, Inc.;

ACKNOWLEDGMENTS

68 t, Ralph Lee Hopkins/National Geographic Stock; **69 bkgrnd,** Ekaterina Pokrovskaya/Shutterstock; **70 bkgrnd,** Galen Rowell/Corbis; **70 bkgrnd two eggs,** George Silk/Time & Life Pictures/Getty Images; **71,** Stacy Gold/ National Geographic/Getty Images; **72 bkgrnd,** Viorika Prikhodko/iStockphoto; **72 l,** Bettmann/Corbis; **73,** Solar and Heliospheric Observatory Collection/NASA; **74 l,** M. I. Walker / Photo Researchers, Inc.; **74 r,** Perennou Nuridsany/ Photo Researchers, Inc.; **74 l,** M. I. Walker/Photo Researchers, Inc.; **74 tl,** Perennou Nuridsany/Photo Researchers, Inc.; **75,** Photodisc/Getty Images; **76,** Joseph Sohm/Visions of America/Corbis; **78 l,** PhotoStock-Israel/Alamy; **78 r,** Bryan Whitney/Photonica/Getty Images; **79 inset,** Harris Shiffman/ Shutterstock; **79 bkgrnd,** Kevin Foy/Alamy; **80–81 spread,** Stephen Frink; Collection/Alamy; **82 bkgrnd,** James Balog/ Aurora Photos; **83,** Shelley Mays/The Tennessean/AP Images; **84 b,** Shelley Mays/The Tennessean/AP Images; **84 m,** George Silk/Time & Life Pictures/Getty Images; **84 t,** Richard J. Ferro/ Zuma Press.

Unit 1 Feature
Page 88 bkgrnd, Daniel Vega/AGE Fotostock; **88 t,** Topic Photo Agency/AGE Fotostock; **88 m1,** Howard Rice/Dorling Kindersley; **88 m2,** Marianne Venegoni/Shutterstock; **88 b,** USDA; **89,** Tiago Estima/iStockphoto.

Unit 1 Big Idea Review
Pages 90–91, Ron Thompson/St. Petersburg Times/Zuma Press.

Unit 2 Big Idea Opener
Pages 92–93, Gary Corbett/AGE Fotostock/Photolibrary New York.

Chapter 3
Pages 94–95 spread, Solvin Zankl/Nature Picture Library; **97 b,** Biodisc/Visuals Unlimited/Alamy; **97 m1,** Perennou Nuridsany/Photo Researchers, Inc.; **97 t,** Dr. David Scott/ Phototake; **98,** Photo by Ed Swinden/Courtesy of the University of Manchester; **99,** E. R. Degginger/Photo Researchers, Inc.; **100 t,** Creatas/Photolibrary New York; **101 br,** Dr. David Scott/Phototake; **101 bl,** Biophoto Associates/Photo Researchers Inc.; **101 tl,** Profs. P. Motta and S. Correr/Science Photo Library/Photo Researchers, Inc.; **101 tr,** Phototake; **102,** Cordelia Molloy/Photo Researchers, Inc.; **104,** Biophoto Associates/Photo Researchers, Inc.; **105 b,** Nils-Johan Norenlind/AGE Fotostock; **105 t,** Steve Gschmeissner/Photo Researchers, Inc.; **106 l,** Dr. Cecil H. Fox/ Photo Researchers, Inc.; **106 m1,** Dr. Jeremy Burgess/Photo Researchers, Inc.; **106 m2,** Dave King/Dorling Kindersley, Courtesy of The Science Museum, London; **106 r,** Science Museum Library/Science and Society Picture Library; **107 b,** John Walsh / Photo Researchers, Inc.; **107 l,** M. I. Walker/ Photo Researchers, Inc.; **107 r,** Perennou Nuridsany/Photo Researchers, Inc.; **108 b,** Dorling Kindersley; **108 ml,** Wes Thompson/Corbis; **108 mr,** Millard H. Sharp/Photo Researchers, Inc.; **108 tl,** Paul Taylor/Riser/Getty Images, Inc.; **108 tr,** Bill Beaty/Visuals Unlimited/Getty Images, inc.; **110–111 spread,** A. Syred/Photo Researchers, Inc.; **112,** David M. Phillips/Photo Researchers, Inc.; **113 boy,** Cultura Limited/Superstock; **113 orange tree,** Wendell Metzen/

Index Stock Imagery/Photolibrary New York; **114 t,** Perennou Nuridsany/Photo Researchers, Inc.; **114 b,** Perennou Nuridsany/Photo Researchers, Inc.; **115,** Steve Gschmeissner/ Photo Researchers, Inc.; **116,** Dr. Torsten Wittmann/Photo Researchers, Inc.; **118 l,** Alfred Paskieka/Photo Researchers, Inc.; **118 r,** Bill Longcore/Photo Researchers, Inc.; **119,** CNRI/ Photo Researchers, Inc./Photo Researchers, Inc.; **122,** Photo Researchers, Inc.; **123,** Biophoto Associates/Science Photo Library; **124,** George Grall/National Geographic Image Collection; **125 br,** Eric Bean/Getty Images; **125 l,** Helmut Gritscher/Peter Arnold Inc.; **125 tr,** Suzi Eszterhas/Minden Pictures; **128 b,** Ed Rescheke/Peter Arnold, Inc.; **128 m,** Ed Rescheke/Peter Arnold, Inc; **128 t,** Ed Rescheke/Peter Arnold, Inc.; **129 b,** Ed Reschke/Peter Arnold, Inc.; **129 m,** Ed Reschke/Peter Arnold, Inc.; **129 t,** Ed Rescheke/Peter Arnold, Inc.; **130 b,** Biodisc/Visuals Unlimited/Alamy; **130 t,** Dr. Gopal Murti/Photo Researchers, Inc.; **132,** Paul Taylor/Riser/Getty Images, Inc.; **134,** Dorling Kindersley.

Chapter 4
Pages 136 b, Comstock Select/Corbis; **139 m1,** Innerspace Imaging/Photo Researchers, Inc.; **139 m2,** Ed Reschke/Peter Arnold, Inc.; **140,** iStockphoto; **141 bkgrnd,** Dr. Gopal Murti/ Photo Researchers, Inc.; **142 bl,** Manfred Kage/Peter Arnold, Inc.; **142 br,** Biophoto Associates/Photo Researchers, Inc.; **142 tl,** ISM/Phototake; **142 tr,** Innerspace Imaging/Photo Researchers, Inc.; **142–143 spread,** Dorling Kindersley; **146,** Lebedinski Vladislav/Shutterstock; **147 boy,** Claro Cortes IV/ Reuters/Corbis; **147 octopus,** Jeff Rotman/Nature Picture Library; **148,** Juice Images/Photolibrary New York; **150–151 spread,** Stephen Frink/Photolibrary New York; **152,** David McCarthy/Photo Researchers, Inc.; **153,** iStockphoto; **154,** O. Burriel/Photo Researchers, Inc.; **155,** Mike Chew/Corbis; **156–157 spread,** Duomo TIPS/Photolibrary New York; **158 t inset,** Mike Kemp/AGE Fotostock; **158–159 bkgrnd,** Michael Meisl/Photolibrary New York; **159 tl inset,** John Henley/ Corbis; **159 tr inset,** SuperStock; **160–161 spread,** Michael Wong/Photolibrary New York; **162 l,** Thinkstock/PunchStock; **162 m,** Nick Caloyanis/National Geographic Stock; **162 r,** Copyright © 2008 Bone Clones; **163,** Steve Gorton/Dorling Kindersley; **165,** Corbis/AGE Fotostock; **168 b,** Moodboard/ Corbis; **168 t,** JGI/Blend Images/Getty Images; **169 l,** Steve Gschmeissner/Photo Researchers, Inc.; **169 r,** Scott Camazine/ Phototake; **170 bkgrnd,** Dan Galic/Alamy; **172 bl,** Eric Grave/ Photo Researchers, Inc.; **172 br,** Ed Reschke/Peter Arnold, Inc.; **172 tr,** Astrid & Hans-Frieder/Photo Researchers, Inc.; **173,** Image Source/AGE Fotostock; **175,** Roger Ressmeyer/ NASA/Corbis; **176,** Mauritius/SuperStock; **176 b,** Custom Medical Stock Photo; **177,** Tom Carter/Alamy; **178 l,** Alloy Photography/Veer; **178 m,** David Vintiner/zefa/Corbis; **178 r,** Comstock Select/Corbis; **180 r,** Alloy Photography/Veer; **180 l,** John Henley/Corbis; **182,** Martin Lee/Mediablitz Images Limited (UK)/Alamy.

Chapter 5
Pages 184–185 spread, Raga Jose Fuste/AGE Fotostock; **188,** BlueMoon Stock/Alamy; **189,** Jupiter Images/Polka Dot/ Alamy; **190 b,** Angelo Cavalli/zefa/Corbis; **190 bkgrnd,** Zing/ Shutterstock; **191 t inset,** Michael Rosenfeld/FoodPix/Getty Images; **198 m,** Sheila Terry/Photo Researchers, Inc.; **198–199 spread,** Zephyr/Photo Researchers, Inc.; **203,** Tim Ridley/

Dorling Kindersley; **206,** Photodisc/Alamy; **208 b,** Eddy Gray/ Photo Researchers, Inc.; **208 t,** BananaStock/JupiterImages; **213,** Anne Ackermann/Digital Vision/Getty Images; **216,** Roger Ressmeyer/Corbis; **217,** David Young-Wolff/PhotoEdit, Inc.; **220 l,** Fotosearch; **220 m,** Steve Skjold/Alamy; **220 r,** Anderson Ross/Digital Vision/Getty Images; **221,** Pete Saloutos/Corbis; **224 b,** Pete Saloutos/Corbis.

Chapter 6
Pages 228–229 spread, AFP/Getty Images; **231 b,** Dopamine/Photo Researchers, Inc.; **233,** Larry Dale Gordon/ Getty Images; **234 b,** Mile Powell/Allsport Concepts/Getty Images; **234 t,** Cre8tive Studios/Alamy; **236,** TBD; **238,** Gregor Schuster/Getty Images; **240,** Richard Haynes; **242,** Rebecca Hale/National Geographic Stock; **243,** Comstock/ Corbis; **243 l,** Michael Nemeth/Getty Images; **244,** Ben Blankenburg/Corbis/JupiterImages; **245,** Sandy Huffacker/ Stringer/Getty Images News; **246,** Tom Sanders/Aurora/Getty Images; **246 lock,** Adrian Brockwell/Alamy; **250–251 spread,** Matt Lange/Southcreek Global/Zuma Press; **251,** Sean Justice/ Photonica/Getty Images; **252 l,** Keystone/Stringer/Hulton Archive/Getty Images; **252 r,** Adrian Arbib/Corbis; **254–255 t spread,** Gary Cornhouse/Digital Vision/Alamy; **259 bkgrnd,** Steve Teague/Alamy; **260,** Michelle Del Guercio/The Medical File/Peter Arnold Inc.; **261,** Dopamine/Photo Researchers, Inc.; **263** Don Farrall/Photodisc/Getty Images; **264,** BSIP/ Photolibrary New York; **265 l,** Big Cheese Photo LLC/Alamy; **265 r,** Tony Freeman/PhotoEdit, Inc.

Chapter 7
Pages 270–271 spread, AP Photo/Sayyid Azim; **273 b,** Frank Krahmer/Corbis; **273 m1,** Stem Jems/Photo Researchers, Inc.; **273 m2,** D. Hurst/Alamy; **273 t,** J. Cavallini/Custom Medical Stock Photo, Inc.; **275,** Andrew Brookes/Corbis; **276 l,** Bettmann/Corbis; **276 r,** Jochen Sands/Digital Vision/Getty Images; **278 l,** Dr. Hans Gelderblom/Visuals Unlimited/Getty Images; **278 r,** J. Cavallini/Custom Medical Stock Photo, Inc.; **279 b,** Dennis Kunkel Microscopy, Inc/Phototake; **279 t,** SPL/Photo Researchers, Inc.; **280,** Jose Pedro Fernandes/ Alamy; **281 bkgrnd,** Bruce Heinemann/Getty Images; **281 finger,** Karen Kasmauski/Corbis; **281 tick,** Peter Arnold, Inc/Alamy; **283,** Science Pictures Ltd./Photo Researchers, Inc.; **285,** Stockbyte/Getty Images; **287 tr,** Stem Jems/ Photo Researchers, Inc.; **290 virus,** Alfred Pasieka/Photo Researchers, Inc.; **291,** Digital Vision/Getty Images; **292,** D. Hurst/Alamy; **293,** Stockbyte/Getty Images; **294 bottles,** Ramona Heim/Shutterstock; **294 cough drops,** Reggie Lavoie/Shutterstock; **294 tissue,** Diana Rich/Shutterstock; **294 tl,** MedicalRF/Getty Images; **295,** Stephen Sweet/Alamy; **296 t,** Judith Collins/Alamy; **297 boy,** Marcus Marter/South Bend Tribune/AP Images; **297 x–ray,** Simon Fraser/Photo Researchers, Inc.; **298 bkgrnd,** Crystal Cartier Photography/ Brad X Pictures/Jupiter Images; **298 inset,** Chris Rout/Alamy; **300,** David Kelly Crow/PhotoEdit, Inc.; **301,** Eye of Science/ Photo Researchers, Inc.; **302 inset,** Scott Camazine/Alamy; **302 r,** Michael Keller/Corbis; **303,** Jose Luis Pelaez Inc./Blend Images/Getty Images; **304 b,** Hisham Ibrahim/Photov/Alamy; **304 ribbon,** Digital Vision/Alamy; **305,** Alex Segre/Alamy; **306,** NIBSC/Photo Researchers, Inc.; **308 b,** Digital Vision/ Alamy; **308 t,** Dennis Kunkel Microscopy, Inc./Phototake.

Chapter 8
Pages 312–313 manatee, Chris Newbert/Minden Pictures; **313 hyrax,** Gerry Ellis/Minden Pictures; **315 m1,** Bennett/ Animals Animals/Earth Scenes; **315 m2,** Eye of Science/ Photo Researchers, Inc.; **315 t,** Mau Horng/Shutterstock; **316,** George Steinmetz/Corbis; **317 b,** Kjell Sandved/Photolibrary New York; **317 m,** Mau Horng/Shutterstock; **317 r,** Matt Meadows/Peter Arnold; **317 tl,** Paroli Galperti/Photolibrary New York; **318,** Science Photo Library/Photolibrary New York; **318 l,** Biophoto Associates/Photo Researchers, Inc.; **318 r,** Kerstin Hinze/Nature Picture Library; **319 bl,** David Tipling/ NPL/Minden Pictures; **319 ml,** Ingo Arndt/Nature Picture Library; **319 mr,** Ingo Arndt/Nature Picture Library; **319 t,** John Kaprielian/Photo Researchers, Inc.; **320 b,** Dan Duchars/ Photolibrary New York; **320 t inset,** Jürgen and Christine Sohns/Photolibrary New York; **321,** Breck P. Kent/Animals Animals/Earth Scenes; **322,** Anup Shah/NPL/Minden Pictures; **324 b,** Jose Fuste Raga/AGE Fotostock/Photolibrary New York; **324 t,** Pichugin Dmitry/Shutterstock; **325,** Barry Mansell/ Nature Picture Library; **326,** Chip Clark; **327,** Ilian Animal/ Alamy; **328 bl,** Eric Isselée/Shutterstock; **328 br,** Rod Williams/ Nature Picture Library; **328 t,** Darren Bennett/Animals Animals/Earth Scenes; **329,** Alan Gleichman/Shutterstock; **330,** FloridaStock/Shutterstock; **332,** Visuals Unlimited/ Corbis; **333 bl,** Hemera Technologies/Jupiter Unlimited; **333 bm,** Kim Taylor/Nature Picture Library; **333 br,** Joseph Calev/Shutterstock; **333 tl,** Armando Frazao/iStockphoto; **333 tm,** WizData, Inc./Shutterstock; **333 tr,** Eric Isselée/ Shutterstock; **334,** Michael Durham/Minden Pictures; **335 b,** Visuals Unlimited/Getty Images; **335 t bacteria,** SciMAT/Photo Researchers, Inc.; **336 l inset,** Dennis Kunkel; **336 r inset,** Eye of Science/Photo Researchers, Inc.; **336–337 bkgrnd,** Niels Kooyman/Foto Natura/Minden Pictures; **307 inset,** Otto Plantema/Foto Natura/Minden Pictures; **338,** Dave Watts/ Nature Picture Library; **340 b,** Tim Laman/Nature Picture Library; **340 t,** Photo courtesy of Research in Review, Florida State University: U. Treesucon, David Redfield Expedition. Used by permission; **340–341 bkgrnd,** Frans Lanting/Corbis; **341 camera,** Jasmina007/Shutterstock; **341 lemur,** Nick Garbutt/Nature Picture Library; **342 b,** Dennis Kunkel; **342 m,** Alan Gleichman/Shutterstock; **342 t,** Biophoto Associates/ Photo Researchers, Inc.; **344,** Virgin Galactic.

Unit 2 Feature
Page 346 tl, AVAVA/Shutterstock; **346 bl,** Claudio Bertoloni/ Shutterstock; **346 bkgrnd,** Orla/Shutterstock; **347,** Adrian Arbib/Alamy.

Unit 2 Big Idea Review
Pages 348–349, Gary Corbett/AGE Fotostock/Photolibrary New York.

Unit 3 Big Idea Opener
Pages 350–351, Heidi & Hans-Juergen Koch/Minden Pictures.

Chapter 9
Pages 352–353 spread, Chris Newbert/Minden Pictures; **355 t,** Sinclair Stammers/Photo Researchers, Inc.; **355 m2,** Jono Gaza/Shutterstock; **355 b,** Dr. Thomas C. Emmel, Department of Zoology, University of Florida/U.S. Fish and Wildlife Service; **355 m1 l,** PetStock Boys/Alamy; **355 m1 r,**

ACKNOWLEDGMENTS

Derrell Fowler Photography; **356 bl,** Gordon Wiltsie/National Geographic Stock; **356 br,** Model by Tyler Keillor/Photo courtesy of University of Chicago; **357 r,** Reimar Gaertner/AGE Fotostock; **357 l,** Better Stock/Shutterstock; **358 b,** Florida Museum of Natural History/Erika H. Simons; **358 t,** Nathan Allred/Alamy; **359 inset,** Sinclair Stammers/Photo Researchers, Inc.; **359 bkgrnd,** Klaus Guldbrandsen/SPL/Photo Researchers, Inc.; **360 l,** Winfried Wisniewski/Zefa/Corbis; **360 m,** Pacific Stock/SuperStock; **360 r,** SuperStock; **362 inset,** The Gallery Collection/Corbis; **362 bl,** Dorling Kindersley; **362–363 bkgrnd,** Andreas Gross/Westend 61/Alamy; **363 tl inset,** Ingo Arndt/Minden Pictures; **363 tr inset,** Enzo & Paolo Ragazzini/Corbis; **363 bl inset,** Nigel Reed/QED Images/Alamy; **363 br inset;** Wardene Weisser/Bruce Coleman Inc./Alamy; **363 t,** Tui De Roy/Minden Pictures; **364 bl,** Stuart Westmorland/Science Faction; **364 br,** Joe McDonald/Corbis; **366 l,** GK Hart/Vikki Hart/Getty Images; **366 m,** Steve Shott/Dorling Kindersley; **366 r,** Dorling Kindersley; **367 l,** Georgette Douwma/Nature Picture Library; **367 m,** PetStock Boys/Alamy; **367 r,** Derrell Fowler Photography; **370,** Mitsuaki Iwago/Minden Pictures; **371 bkgrnd,** © 2007 Maury Hatfield. All Rights Reserved.; **372 t,** 2007 Gerald McCormack/Cook Islands Biodiversity Database, Version 2007.2 Cook Islands Natural Heritage Trust, Rarotonga; **372 b,** John T. Rotenberry/University of California at Riverside; **373 l,** Thomas & Pat Leeson/Photo Researchers, Inc.; **373 r,** Thomas & Pat Leeson/Photo Researchers, Inc.; **373 bkgrnd,** Momatiuk-Eastcott/Corbis; **374,** Clearviewstock/Shutterstock; **374,** Jono Gaza/Shutterstock; **376 t,** Dr. Thomas C. Emmel, Department of Zoology, University of Florida/U.S Fish and Wildlife Service; **376 b,** 2007 James D. Watt/Image Quest Marine; **377,** Jonathan G./Shutterstock; **378 t,** Reimar Gaertner/AGE Fotostock; **378 br,** Thomas & Pat Leeson/Photo Researchers, Inc.; **378 bl,** Thomas & Pat Leeson/Photo Researchers, Inc.; **378 m,** Joe McDonald/Corbis; **380,** S.Borisov/Shutterstock.

Chapter 10

Pages 382–383 spread, ZSSD/SuperStock; **385 m2,** Timothy Large/iStockphoto; **386 bkgrnd,** Omikron/Photo Researchers, Inc.; **386 inset,** Science Source/Photo Researchers, Inc.; **386–387 t,** Shattil & Rozinski/Nature Picture Library; **387 chromosome,** Andrew Syred/Photo Researchers, Inc.; **388 chromosome,** Andrew Syred/Photo Researchers; **388 diamond,** Mark Evans/iStockphoto; **391 dna strand,** Dr. Gopal Murti/Science Photo Library/Photo Researchers, Inc.; **392 inset,** Bettmann/Corbis; **392 peas,** Wally Eberhart/Getty Images; **394 bkgrnd,** Andrea Jones/Alamy; **397 bkgrnd,** Monika Gniot/Shutterstock; **397 l inset,** Herman Eisenbeiss/Photo Researchers, Inc.; **397 r inset,** WildPictures/Alamy; **398 bkgrnd,** National Oceanic and Atmospheric Administration (NOAA); **398 inset,** J. Pat Carter/AP Images; **399,** Brand X/Jupiter Images; **400–401 bkgrnd,** Monika Gniot/Shutterstock; **402–403 bkgrnd,** Agg/Dreamstime; **403 l,** Timothy Large/iStockphoto; **403 r,** Jomann/Dreamstime; **404 l,** Phototake NYC; **404 r,** Phototake NYC; **405 corn,** Cathleen Clapper/iStockphoto; **405 grasshopper,** Proxyminder/iStockphoto; **405 mosquito,** Frank Greenaway/Dorling Kindersley; **405 shrimp,** Jane Burton/Dorling Kindersley; **405 skunk,** Eric Isselée/iStockphoto; **405 t,** © 2009 Robbin Moran; **410 l,** Paul Bricknell/Dorling Kindersley; **410 r,** Konrad Wothe/Minden Pictures; **412 inset,** Biophoto Associates/Photo Researchers, Inc.; **412–413 bkgrnd,** Miguel Salmeron/Getty Images; **413 inset,** Isifa Image Service S.R.O./Alamy.

Chapter 11

Pages 418–419 spread, HALEY/SIPA/Newscom; **443 b,** Yonhap Choi Byung-kil/AP Images; **421 m1,** Oliver Meckes & Nicole Ottawa/Photo Researchers, Inc.; **421 m2,** Splashnews/Newscom; **421 tl,** Addenbrookes Hospital/Photo Researchers, Inc.; **421 tr,** Addenbrookes Hospital/Photo Researchers, Inc.; **423,** Timothey Kosachev/iStockphoto; **424,** China Daily China Daily Information Corp-CDIC/Reuters; **425 x and y chromosomes,** Addenbrookes Hospital/SPL/Photo Researchers, Inc.; **425 x chromosomes,** Addenbrookes Hospital/Photo Researchers, Inc.; **426 bl,** Michael Newman/PhotoEdit, Inc.; **426 br,** Jupiterimages/Brand X/Alamy; **428 l,** Paul Cotney/iStockphoto; **428 m,** John Long/iStockphoto; **428 r,** Lisa Svara/iStockphoto; **429,** Oliver Meckes & Nicole Ottawa/Photo Researchers, Inc.; **431,** Nancy Hamilton/Photo Researchers, Inc.; **432 l,** Dennis Kunkel/Phototake NYC; **432 r,** Dennis Kunkel/Phototake NYC; **433 b,** Tomas Ovalle/The Fresno Bee/AP Images; **433 t,** iStockphoto; **434,** Yonhap/Choi Byung-kil/AP Images; **434 bkgrnd,** Anke van Wyk/Shutterstock; **434 inset,** Udo Richter/AFP/Getty Images; **435,** Splashnews/Newscom; **440,** Jason Lee/Reuters; **441,** Thomas Wright/University of Florida/AP Images; **442,** PeJo/Shu/Shutterstock; **442–443 bkgrnd spread,** Andrey Prokhorov/iStockphoto; **443 scientist,** Laura Doss/Photolibrary New York; **444 dna sequence bkgrnd,** David Fairfield/Getty Images; **444 silhouette,** Kenneth C. Zirkel/iStockphoto; **446 m,** Tomas Ovalle/The Fresno Bee/AP Images; **446 t,** Jupiterimages/Brand X/Alamy; **446 br,** Andrey Prokhorov/iStockphoto; **446 bl,** Splashnews/Newscom; **448,** Dennis Kunkel/Phototake.

Chapter 12

Pages 450–451 spread, Gary Bell/Zefa/Corbis; **453 b,** Imagebroker/Alamy; **453 m1,** Photodisc/Getty Images; **453 m2,** age Fotostock/SuperStock; **454 bl,** Jörn Köhler; **454 br,** Wildlife/A.Visage/Peter Arnold; **454 tr,** Frans Lanting/Corbis; **455 prairie dog,** Jim Brandenburg/Minden Pictures; **455 seascape,** Bruno Morandi/Robert Harding World; **458–459 bkgrnd,** S.J. Krasemann/Peter Arnold; **460,** Ian McAllister/Photolibrary New York; **461,** Jerome Wexler /Photo Researchers, Inc.; **461 inset,** Edward Kinsman/Photo Researchers, Inc.; **464 b,** Peter Blottman/iStockphoto; **464 m,** Jerry Young/Dorling Kindersley; **464 t,** Dorling Kindersley; **465 crayfish,** Frank Greenaway/Dorling Kindersley/Courtesy of the Natural History Museum, London; **465 frog,** Geoff Brightling/Dorling Kindersley; **465 garter snake,** Jerry Young/Dorling Kindersley; **465 grasshopper,** Jerry Young/Dorling Kindersley; **465 heron,** Judy Foldetta/iStockphoto; **465 mushrooms,** Neil Fletcher/Dorling Kindersley; **465 plants,** Peter Blottman/iStockphoto; **465 red fox,** Dorling Kindersley; **465 shrew,** Rollin Verlinde/Dorling Kindersley; **465 snail,** Nicholas Homrich/iStockphoto; **466 grass,** Kim Taylor and Jane Burton/Dorling Kindersley; **466 large mouse l,** Frank Greenaway/Dorling Kindersley; **466 large mouse r,** Frank Greenaway/Dorling Kindersley; **466 mid-sized mouse,** Frank Greenaway/Dorling Kindersley; **466 owl,** Eric Isselée/iStockphoto; **466 smallest mouse,** Frank Greenaway/Dorling Kindersley; **466 snake,** Dave King/Dorling Kindersley; **468 inset,** Alex Wild; **471 bl,** Michael P. Gadomski/Photo Researchers, Inc.;

471 b, Jim Zipp/Photo Researchers Inc.; **471 m,** Jim Zipp/
Photo Researchers, Inc.; **471 t,** Tom Vezo/Minden Pictures;
472 bl, Hiroya Minakuchi/Minden Pictures; **472 bm,**
Imagebroker/Alamy; **472 flies,** Sándor F. Szabó/iStockphoto;
472 tr, Bill Curtsinger/National Geographic Stock; **473 br,**
Nature's Images/Photo Researchers, Inc.; **473 mimic octopus,**
Ethan Daniels/Alamy; **473 mr,** AGE Fotostock/SuperStock;
473 sole fish, Fabrice Bettex/Alamy; **473 t r,** Michael D. Kern/
Nature Picture Library; **473 tl,** Jeff Hunter/Getty Images;
475 l, Manoj Shah/Animals Animals/Earth Scenes; **475 r,**
Michael Fogden/Animals Animals/Earth Scenes; **476 br,**
USGA; **476 tl,** Jeff Foott/Gettty Images; **476 tr,** Anthony
Bannister/Animals Animals/Earth Scenes; **477 b,** Dietmar
Nill/Nature Picture Library; **477 tl,** Norbert Wu/ Minden
Pictures; **477 tr,** Jim Clare/NPL/Minden Pictures; **478,** Shattil
& Rozinski/Nature Picture Library; **479,** Chris Johns/National
Geographic Stock; **480,** Photodisc/Getty Images; **481,** Kim
Taylor/Nature Picture Library; **483,** Blickwinkel/Alamy; **484
inset,** Tim Mannakee/Grand Tour/Corbis; **484–485 bkgrnd,**
Tim Fitzharris/Minden Pictures/National Geographic Stock;
485 inset, Amy Newman/St. Petersburg Times/Zuma Press;
486 b, Amy Newman/St. Petersburg Times/Zuma Press; **486 t,**
Anthony Bannister/Animals Animals/Earth Scene.

Unit 3 Feature
Page 490 bkgrnd, Chris O'Meara/AP Images; **490 l,** E. Skylar
Litherland/Sarasota Herald-Tribune/AP Images.

Unit 3 Big Idea Review
Pages 492–493, Heidi & Hans-Juergen Koch/Minden Pictures.

Unit 4 Big Idea Opener
Pages 494–495, Wendell Metzen/Index Stock.

Chapter 13
Pages 496–497 spread, Rolf Nussbaumer/Minden Pictures;
499 m1, Vincenzo Lombardo/Getty Images; **499 t,** AGE
Fotostock/SuperStock; **500,** David Cook/BlueShiftStudios/
Alamy; **501 bkgrnd,** Robbert Koene/Getty Images;
501 l inset, Adrian Bailey/Aurora Photos; **501 r inset,** AGE
Fotostock/SuperStock; **503 bkgrnd,** Rich Iwasaki/Getty
Images; **505,** Yuji Sakai/Getty Images; **506,** Pete Saloutos/
Corbis; **510,** Vincenzo Lombardo/Getty Images; **511,** Noah
Clayton/Getty Images; **512,** Juniors Bildarchiv/Alamy; **514,**
Emma Firth/Dorling Kindersley; **516,** Dr. Paul A. Zahl/Photo
Researchers, Inc.; **518,** Christian Wheatley/Shutterstock;
519, Scott Leslie/Minden Pictures; **522,** Scott Leslie/Minden
Pictures; **524,** Rickey Rogers/Reuters/Photo Researchers, Inc.

Unit 4 Feature
Pages 526–527, Wendell Metzen/Index Stock.

Unit 4 Feature
Page 528 bkgrnd, Carrie Garcia/Alamy; **528 l,** FloridaStock/
Shutterstock.

Unit 4 Big Idea Review
Pages 530–531, Wendell Metzen/Index Stock.

Appendix A
Page 532, Mike Kemp/Getty Images.

this is your book

you can write in it

take note

this space is yours—great for drawing diagrams and making notes

this is your book

you can write in it

this is your book

you can write in it

this is your book

you can write in it